Petroleum geochemistry is an early developed part of organic geochemistry. Much research has been done during the last few years on the composition, physical characteristics and modes of occurrence of crude oil and natural gas. This research was mainly led by oil companies and the American Petroleum Institute. The purpose of this book is to present the modern views on the fundamental aspects of petroleum geochemistry, a subject matter that has not been summarized in book form before. Growing interest in petroleum geochemistry by the petroleum industry, especially by exploration and production departments, as well as by organic geochemists and chemists in general, makes such a presentation most desirable. A number of active research workers, each of them recognized authors in their own fields, have been invited to contribute chapters. Recent and older works are brought together in a proper perspective in these reviews. Important aspects such as petroleum geology, the role of clay minerals in petroleum geochemistry, hydrocarbons and non-hydrocarbon compounds, and asphaltic substances, are thoroughly discussed. The book does not attempt to cover the field completely, but rather emphasizes some of the more significant subjects of petroleum geochemistry. For example, discussions of porphyrins and asphaltenes are among the subjects. The results of the most modern techniques have been summarized and are brought here to the reader's attention.

A great variety of scientists and engineers who are engaged in or otherwise have an interest in the petroleum industry will certainly find this work of great value and interest.

FUNDAMENTAL ASPECTS OF PETROLEUM
GEOCHEMISTRY

FUNDAMENTAL ASPECTS OF PETROLEUM GEOCHEMISTRY

EDITED BY

BARTHOLOMEW NAGY

Department of Chemistry, University of California, San Diego, La Jolla, Calif. (U.S.A.)

AND

UMBERTO COLOMBO

Department of Geochemistry, Istituto di Ricerche "G. Donegani", Montecatini–Edison, Novara (Italy)

ELSEVIER PUBLISHING COMPANY Amsterdam London New York 1967

ELSEVIER PUBLISHING COMPANY
335 JAN VAN GALENSTRAAT, P.O. BOX 211, AMSTERDAM

AMERICAN ELSEVIER PUBLISHING COMPANY, INC.
52 VANDERBILT AVENUE, NEW YORK, N.Y. 10017

ELSEVIER PUBLISHING COMPANY LIMITED
12 B, RIPPLESIDE COMMERCIAL ESTATE
RIPPLEROAD, BARKING, ESSEX

LIBRARY OF CONGRESS CATALOG CARD NUMBER 65-13239
WITH 125 ILLUSTRATIONS AND 75 TABLES

PRINTED IN THE NETHERLANDS

PREFACE

Petroleum geochemistry is an important branch of scientific activity. It is of interest to industrial scientists, particularly those working in the field of oil exploration or exploration research. In addition, petroleum geochemistry is concerned with basic scientific matters. It deals with the chemistry of organic fluids in geological environments and with the related rocks; and it attempts to determine and to explain the processes by which they have developed during geological time.

Because of the economic importance of petroleum a considerable amount of research has been conducted during recent decades on the composition, physical characteristics and modes of occurrence of crude oil and natural gas, mainly by oil companies and the American Petroleum Institute. These investigations, together with similar systematic studies on coal, have led to the development of the broader field of organic geochemistry, the study of all organic matter in rocks. Current interest in organic geochemistry is well shown by the rapidly increasing number of journal articles on subjects ranging from lipids in Precambrian rocks and the nature of kerogen, to organic matter in carbonaceous meteorites. It is probable that without the petroleum and coal research experience acquired over many years, organic geochemistry would not be such an active field of investigation today.

This book has been planned to bring together articles on some of the fundamental aspects of petroleum geochemistry, which is a most important and early phase of organic geochemistry, so that the tasks and difficulties met in organic geochemistry might be more fully appreciated. At the same time the book could serve as a reference volume for industrial scientists. Chapters on some of the major aspects of petroleum geochemistry have been contributed by active and authoritative research workers on this subject.

It is important to recognise the close connection between petroleum, an organic fluid, and inorganic mineral matter. The geology of petroleum is therefore described, and there is also a chapter on clay mineralogy. Other chapters deal separately with petroleum hydrocarbons, non-hydrocarbons, porphyrins, asphaltic material, petroleum–water systems and migration, and finally with the origin and evolution of petroleum. In this manner the reader can get a view of the main aspects of petroleum geochemistry.

Some authors put forward hypotheses regarding the origin of petroleum and include some which are rather controversial. The Editors are of the opinion that the presentation and discussion of the principal hypotheses on the formation of petroleum, even though controversial, are essential features in any volume on petroleum geochemistry. It is hoped that the reader will find the information and ideas summarised in the various chapters useful, and will regard the book, in some respects, as a progress report on a rapidly evolving field of scientific endeavour.

Bartholomew Nagy
University of California, San Diego
La Jolla, California, U.S.A.

Umberto Colombo
Istituto di Ricerche "G. Donegani"
Montecatini–Edison
Novara, Italy

CONTENTS

Contents

Chapter 1

OIL AND GAS ACCUMULATIONS, AND SOME ALLIED DEPOSITS

GEORGE D. HOBSON

Department of Geology, Imperial College of Science and Technology, London (Great Britain)

INTRODUCTION

Information, on which views about the nature and origin of oil fields are based, has been obtained in a variety of ways. Much of it has come from wells drilled in the search for and development of oil fields. These wells have provided rock fragments and in some cases cores, but the volume of rock made available thereby for visual examination and other studies is but a microscopic portion. This is true even for the reservoir rock in which the oil is stored, a rock which has been cored far more frequently than the other rocks penetrated by the wells.

Sometimes the relics of former oil fields are exposed at the surface, and then under favourable circumstances a greater expanse of rock is available for direct study. However, the contents and sometimes the rocks also have almost certainly suffered changes as a result of being at or comparatively near to the surface. On rare occasions mining has been carried out in oil-bearing rocks, or in rocks carrying asphalt as a general impregnation in its pores.

Sedimentary rocks themselves, which are the types of main interest in this connection, have long been studied with respect to their nature and origin, yet knowledge on these features is still incomplete in some cases. A generalized picture of the conditions under which they were formed can, however, often be deduced. Crude oils and allied substances are extremely complex in their make-up, and studying them is difficult because of their nature and complexity. Nevertheless, substantial advances in knowledge have been made, especially in recent years, and these have contributed to a better understanding of the problems of the origin of oil and oil fields. With improved definition of the problems greater progress is being made towards their solution. The solutions will call for team work, with contributions from geologists, chemists, biochemists, physical chemists and physicists. In the past a considerable amount of information which bears on these problems has come as a by-product from the search for and development of oil fields. Furthermore, it has been possible to draw upon the results obtained from investigations not primarily concerned with oil fields. In recent years laboratory studies aimed at solving the problems have been supported by or based on specially planned field investigations making use of wells. This is a valuable development, and shows the importance which the major oil companies attach to solving the problems.

NATURE OF OIL AND GAS ACCUMULATIONS

The existence of oil and gas fields calls for the presence of a rock in which the hydro-carbons can be stored, and from which they can flow at acceptable rates, together with means for retaining the hydrocarbons in that rock until wells are drilled in order to extract the fluids.

The rock in which the oil and gas are stored is the reservoir rock. It must be porous to provide storage space, and comparatively highly permeable to permit fluid flow at reasonable rates. A large proportion, if not all, of the openings in the rock must be interconnected. These openings are of a single type in some reservoir rocks; there may be several types of openings in other reservoir rocks. The common-est openings are the pores between the grains of which the rock is composed. In general the pores are only a small fraction of an inch in width. The other types of openings are cracks, cavities inside fossils, and spaces resulting from solution of the rock or from volumetrically incomplete replacement of parts of the rock. Some of the latter types of openings can be substantially wider than pores; their contribution to the total storage space is, however, not necessarily large, but their influence on the overall permeability is commonly relatively much more important.

Sandstones, grits, limestones and dolomites are by far the most common kinds of reservoir rocks. They are the coarser-grained sedimentary rocks. There are rare cases where the reservoir rock is a shale or an igneous or a metamorphic rock. The shale reservoir rocks are usually described as "fractured", but the relatively large openings may not be simple joints in every instance, although they are un-doubtedly secondary in origin. Similarly, fractures or allied openings are important in enabling igneous and metamorphic rocks to act as reservoir rocks. The pores in sedimentary rocks are primary in origin, having been formed between the grains as they were deposited, although the original openings have commonly been changed in detail as a result of compaction, deposition of cements and sometimes so-called pressure solution of the constituent grains.

The upper seal to the oil and gas accumulation is provided by the cap rock; the lower seal may be partially or wholly provided by water in the reservoir rock, or by the rock adjacent to the reservoir rock. Cap rocks are usually fine grained. They are very low in permeability; but it is obvious that low permeability in itself would not prevent escape of oil and gas. The retention of these fluids depends on the high capillary pressure of the cap rock. This property is involved when a non-wetting fluid (in this case oil or gas) is prevented from entering pores filled with water until a sufficiently large pressure difference is developed which is able to make the cur-vature of the interface so great that the non-wetting fluid can enter the very small pores of the cap rock. The permeability is dependent on the sizes of the pores and the number of pores in unit area, whereas the capillary pressure is determined by the sizes of the pores and the interfacial tension between the water and oil or gas.

The typical cap rocks are clays and shales. Compact limestones, salt and

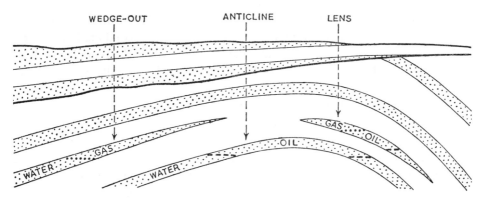

Fig.1. Cross-section showing several types of traps for hydrocarbons. (After HOBSON, 1962b.)

gypsum or anhydrite can also serve as cap rocks. Plastic rather than brittle compact rocks make the best cap rocks, because they are able to flow rather than fracture when the rocks are strongly folded, with the result that oil and gas accumulations are preserved under tectonic conditions which would lead to losses were the cap rock brittle.

Sometimes the oil is prevented from escaping by cement or by the presence of asphaltic material clogging the pores of a reservoir rock which has been exposed by erosion. This asphaltic material is a residue from the oil or in part the result of alteration. Hence its presence under these circumstances implies some earlier loss of oil.

The site where the oil or gas is held is referred to as a trap, and this requires that the under side of the cap rock or of the cap rock in conjunction with any other retaining agent shall be in principle convex upwards, a condition which is satisfied by a wide range of shapes. These range from a slight doming, such as can occur with a flat-lying lens or a very gentle anticline (Fig.1), to strong or even acute arching in sharp anticlines, and the angular forms associated with depositional wedge-outs, bevelling at unconformities, and with faults (Fig.2). The lower

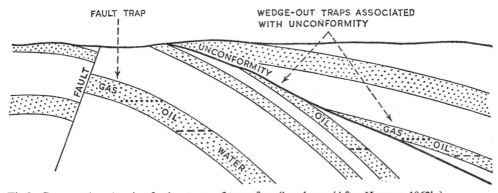

Fig.2. Cross-section showing further types of traps for oil and gas. (After HOBSON, 1962b.)

boundary of the accumulation, as mentioned above, is defined by water, by rock with properties comparable with those of a cap rock, or by a combination of water and suitable rock. When water provides the lower boundary the boundary will be horizontal, provided that the rock is of uniform properties laterally and that there is no flow of the water. If these two conditions are not met the boundary will be inclined; the departure from horizontality usually being small.

The petroleum accumulation is situated in what is locally the highest available part of the reservoir rock, unless there is marked flow of the underlying water. The fluids in the trap are arranged in the order of their densities: free gas, when present, is uppermost as the gas cap; beneath is oil containing dissolved gas; and at the bottom is water. There are also accumulations of gas alone over the water, or of oil with dissolved gas, but no free gas resting on water.

The boundaries between the free gas and oil with dissolved gas, and between the oil and water are not sharp; there are transition zones, the thicknesses of which depend on the sizes of the pores, the densities of the pair of fluids involved and on the interfacial tension between this pair of fluids. Moreover, even in the so-called gas and oil zones the pores contain appreciable amounts of water known as interstitial water. The proportion of interstitial water may be of the order of 20% of the pore space, and is dependent on the sizes and detailed geometry of the openings in the reservoir rock. Much of this water occurs as collars round grain contacts; there will also be very thin films on the grain surfaces; and lastly, pores surrounded by unusually small throats will be full of water. This description would apply in its entirety to a reservoir rock which was preferentially wetted by water, a condition which is believed to exist in many reservoir rocks. There have been suggestions, however, that some reservoir rocks are not preferentially water-wet, although all have been full of water initially. The problem of wettability is difficult, and evidence obtained by KYTE et al. (1961) on cores indicates that the wettability under surface conditions is not necessarily the same as under the higher pressure and temperature which exist in a reservoir rock at depth. For the cores examined they suggested that there may be increased preferential adsorption of crude oil components at low temperatures. The interstitial water content is likely to be lower, although not zero, even if the rock is preferentially oil-wet.

In the oil/water transition zones in moving upwards there is a change from pores fully charged with water to pores in which oil occupies the bulk of the space. In the gas/oil transition zone the change in going upwards is from pores occupied mainly by oil with dissolved gas to pores occupied mainly by free gas.

Individual reservoir rocks vary widely in thickness and extent, and their detailed properties may change both laterally and vertically. Thicknesses range from a few to hundreds of feet, and areas from a fraction of a square mile to hundreds of square miles. The height of petroleum columns ranges from a few tens to thousands of feet in oil and gas fields. The total volume of oil can be as much as 0.1 cubic mile in one field.

The space occupied by an oil or gas accumulation is sometimes a comparatively large proportion of the total pore space in the entire reservoir rock; on the other hand, it is often but a small proportion of that space. Many factors are involved in determining the total amount of oil or gas in a reservoir rock, but a favourably placed small, thin lens of rock is likely to have a higher proportion of its entire pore space occupied by oil or gas than a more extensive, thick reservoir rock.

Oil and gas fields have now been developed down to depths of more than 20,000 ft. Mean pressure gradients may be about 0.43–1.0 p.s.i./ft., and mean temperature gradients 0.0054–0.012 °C/ft. Thus the pressures and temperatures in accumulations vary widely, and it is clear that the current temperatures and pressures in many accumulations are well below the maximum values to which they have been subjected.

Oil and gas fields are almost always in sedimentary rocks, and on the rare occasions when the reservoir rock is an igneous or metamorphic rock, it is always near to sedimentary rocks. The sediments in oilfield areas are usually of marine or marginal marine origin. The age of the reservoir rocks ranges from Precambrian to Pleistocene.

COMPOSITION OF THE FLUIDS

The gas is usually composed mainly of methane. Small amounts of the other low members of the paraffin series occur commonly. However, when there is no associated oil, methane may be the only hydrocarbon. Carbon dioxide, hydrogen sulphide and nitrogen are by no means rare in natural gases; they are usually present in only small proportions, but there are occasional examples in which these non-hydrocarbon gases are the dominant components. Helium may be present in very small amounts, however, it rarely occurs in commercial quantities.

The oil is complex in composition. Carbon and hydrogen are the principal elements (Table I); oxygen, nitrogen and sulphur are subordinate in amount; and a very wide range of metallic elements has been found, in trace amounts usually, although a few, such as vanadium and nickel, are sometimes present in relatively large amounts in the ash from crude oils and allied substances.

The components range widely in boiling point, however, numerous components cannot be distilled at atmospheric pressure without undergoing thermal breakdown. Consequently, some of the compounds found in fractions obtained by distillation were not present in the parent crude oil.

A considerable amount of information has been obtained on the types of compounds present, and a few lengthy investigations have provided information on the individual compounds in the lower-boiling-point fractions. Two hundred and thirty individual hydrocarbons have been separated to date from the Ponca City crude oil, the boiling point range being from −161 °C to 475 °C. It appears that

TABLE I

ELEMENTAL COMPOSITION OF SOME CRUDE OILS, MINERAL WAX, AND ASPHALTIC SUBSTANCES

		Percentage composition					
		C	H	S	N	N+O	O
Crude oils	Mecock, W. Va.	83.6	12.9	0.37			3.6
	Humboldt, Kans.	85.6	12.4	0.76			
	Healdton, Okla.	85.0	12.9	0.6			
	Coalinga, Calif.	86.4	11.7	0.7			
	Beaumont, Texas	85.7	11.0			2.61	
Wax	Ozokerite	84–86	14–16	0–1.5	0–0.5		
Natural asphalts	Athabaska Tar	84.4	11.23	2.73	0.04		
	Bermudez Lake	82.88	10.79	5.87	0.75		
	Trinidad Pitch Lake	80–82	10–11	6–8	0.6–0.8		
	Asphalt from Utah limestone	89.9	9	0		1.1	
	Native asphalt	82	11	2	2–2.5		
Asphaltites	Gilsonite	85–86	8.5–10	0.3–0.5	2–2.8		
	Glance Pitch	80–85	7–12	2–8		0–2	0–2
Asphaltic pyrobitumens	Wurtzilite	79.5–80	10.5–12.3	4–6	1.8–2.2		
	Albertite	83.4–87.2	8.96–13.2	Tr–1.2	0.42–3.1		1.97–2.22

in the lower boiling ranges the hydrocarbons with the simpler structures are more abundant than those which are highly branched. The simpler paraffins (alkanes), naphthenes (cycloalkanes) and aromatics are dominant; the many isomers are present in only small proportions. As the boiling point increases the amounts of polynuclear aromatics and polycycloparaffins rise, whereas the normal and branched-chain paraffins, and monocycloparaffins decrease in abundance. Most of the cycloparaffin or naphthene structures are derivatives of cyclopentane or cyclo-hexane.

The higher-molecular-weight hydrocarbons include molecules consisting of two or more structure units of the same type or different types, with paraffin side-chains. Only very rarely are olefinic-type hydrocarbons present in crude oils, and when present the amounts are small. It is believed that much of the oxygen, nitrogen or sulphur in crude oils is in the heavier molecules, especially the asphaltic fractions. Small amounts of porphyrins have been detected in some crude oils. Naphthenic acids occur in crude oils, especially those with an abundance of naphthenic hydrocarbons.

Although crude oils are complex in composition they are decidedly simpler than was thought to be the case in view of the many possible hydrocarbons. Considerable differences exist in the make-up of crude oils (Table II), yet it has been noted that some compounds are present in fairly constant ratios (Table III).

TABLE II

COMPOSITION OF SOME CRUDE OILS IN TERMS OF THE MAIN HYDROCARBON GROUPS, RESINS AND ASPHALTENES

(After SACHANEN, 1950)

Type of crude	Source	Paraffins (%)	Naphthenes (%)	Aromatics (%)	Resins and asphaltenes (%)
Paraffinic		40	48	10	2
Paraffinic–	Oklahoma City	36	45	14	5
naphthenic	East Texas	33	41	17	9
Naphthenic	Emba–Dossor	12	75	10	3
	Balachany	9	66	19	6
	Bibi Eibat	11	60	19	10
Naphthenic–	Santa Fé	20	45	23	12
aromatic	Borneo	15	35	35	15
Mixed asphaltic	Inglewood	8	42	27	23
	Perm	13	15	40	32
Bermudez asphalt	Bermudez Lake	5	15	20	60

TABLE III

RATIOS OF AMOUNTS OF CERTAIN HYDROCARBONS IN A NUMBER OF CRUDE OILS
(After BAKER, 1962)

Hydrocarbons	Volume ratio of hydrocarbons in crude oils	
	Average for 21 U.S. crudes	Average for 11 non-U.S. crudes
$\dfrac{\text{Methylcyclohexane}}{\text{Cyclohexane}}$	2.13	2.47
$\dfrac{\text{Toluene}}{\text{Benzene}}$	4.27	4.78
$\dfrac{\text{n-Hexane}}{\text{n-Heptane}}$	1.08	1.29

Paraffinic crudes occur in several parts of the U.S.A., but other countries do not produce true paraffinic crudes in any substantial quantity. Naphthenic crudes are rare.

The water associated with gas and oil accumulations is usually saline, and often more saline than sea water. In many cases it appears to be a modified sea water, being relatively deficient in the sulphate ion. BUCKLEY et al. (1958) examined water from drillstem tests in petroliferous horizons in the Gulf Coast area of the U.S.A. and found as much as 14 standard cubic feet of methane per barrel of water. In a sample from the Woodbine sand the ethane-+ fraction was 3.36% of the dissolved gas, and this fraction was 72.8% ethane, 20.8% propane, 5.1% butanes and 1.3% pentanes by volume.

According to KARTSEV et al. (1959) organic anions, chiefly naphthenate, may range 0–500 mg/100 g of oilfield waters. Occasionally there are soaps of aliphatic acids, in much smaller amounts than those of naphthenic acids.

THE ORIGIN OF OIL AND GAS FIELDS

When the arrangement of the gas, oil and water is considered according to density and the occurrence of the hydrocarbons in the highest part of the reservoir which is available locally and sealed, it appears most improbable that the hydrocarbons could have been formed exactly where they now occur. Furthermore, the considerable solubility of the gas in the oil indicates that the total volume occupied by the hydrocarbons must vary with the temperature and pressure, which are controlled by the depth of burial. Slow changes take place in the depth of burial, and depending on circumstances at a given time the depth of burial of some accumulations will be increasing, while it will be decreasing for others. The mobility of oil and gas and their ready response to changes in conditions immediately suggest the possibility that they could have been formed at places other than where they are now found. Once this is admitted then it is apparent that the formation of the hydro-carbons need not have been in the reservoir rock.

The reservoir rock characteristics of igneous and metamorphic rocks, now serving as oil or gas reservoirs, are clearly much younger than the formation of the rocks themselves. Examples of the same rocks without these features show no evidence of oil, although it must be admitted that the more usual reservoir rocks show oil only in certain positions, the traps. (The reservoir rock appreciably down-dip of an oil accumulation is generally described as oil-free. It is not certain whether there is no oil whatsoever, or no readily visible amount of oil. As will be seen later oil and gas have been in some of these rocks. The absence of free gas can readily be explained; bacterial clean-up has been suggested to account for the lack of oil. A rock which produces water and has no visible oil spotting is apt to receive little further consideration.) It is, moreover, difficult to visualise how oil and gas could have been retained in some of these rocks, and also in more usual reservoir rocks at a time when there was no sealing cap rock. In addition the phys-ical conditions believed to have been involved in the formation of igneous and meta-morphic rocks appear to be incompatible with the presence of certain substances found in crude oils.

It is, therefore, necessary to postulate that, at least, the bulk of the oil and gas now in a reservoir rock was formed in or entered that rock only after a cap rock had covered it. Admittedly isolated globules of gas or oil, if appreciably greater in diameter than the throats between the pores in a reservoir rock, would not rise by buoyancy. Isolation of oil globules could not be accepted unless the total volume of oil was a large proportion of the pore space in the reservoir rock. Gas present in a newly deposited reservoir rock would in many instances be at a low pressure, and hence many times more voluminous than the same mass of gas after deep burial of the rock.

Very small amounts of hydrocarbons have been found in a variety of living organisms. The organisms examined belong to the plant and animal kingdoms; some are terrestrial and others marine in habitat. Coals and some oil shales are deposits containing large proportions of organic matter, but reservoir rocks show no evidence of the very large concentrations which would be needed to give in situ the known oil saturations, nor do reservoir rocks exhibit the right environments of deposition for this to happen in general. It is also most doubtful whether com-plete or almost complete destruction of the non-hydrocarbon organic matter could occur to ensure that the hydrocarbons are the main organic components incorpor-ated in the sediments.

A study of oil and gas accumulations reveals no general association with or proximity to coal-bearing strata or oil shales. The shells or other mineral structures of various aquatic organisms occur in abundance in some reservoir rocks, but this does not mean that the organic matter originally associated with these remains was necessarily entombed in the sediments.

A variety of considerations therefore indicate that oil and natural gas appear initially in the sediments in low concentrations, concentrations which are far less than those of commercial accumulations. They or their parent substances at least sometimes, and probably commonly, were not part of the newly-formed reservoir rocks. Thus the idea of a source rock arose.

The basic functions of source rocks, reservoir rocks and cap rocks are well defined from the point of view of oil fields, but this does not preclude the possibility of a dual role, i.e., some reservoir rocks may have served as source rocks; some cap rocks could have served as source rocks to the reservoir rock below, or to reservoir rocks higher in the sequence. The reservoir and cap rocks are obvious for an oil and gas accumulation; the source rock for a particular accumulation is commonly a matter of conjecture. When it is possible to date crude oils with reasonable accuracy some of the arguments about the sources of given oils may be resolved.

Examination of various types of sedimentary rocks has shown that generally the finer-grained the rock the greater the content of organic matter. Seas and other bodies of water in which sediments are laid down have a variety of organisms living in them; in addition, organic matter may be brought in from other sources. Climatic conditions, the depth of water and the supply of nutrients control the kinds of organisms and their abundance. Some organisms are the food of others, and such organic matter as is not eaten, in the conventional sense, is subjected to bacterial attack, which may lead to its extensive breakdown before burial in the sediments, or to varying degrees of breakdown in the upper layers of the sediment. The greatest breakdown is caused by aerobic bacteria. Hence organic matter sedimented in waters containing little or no free oxygen will suffer relatively little or at least slower bacterial attack than that which falls to the bottom in oxygenated waters.

The sedimentation of fine-grained mineral matter and of low-density organic matter takes place only in still water, which because of its stagnancy is low in free oxygen content. Coarse-grained sediments can be deposited from moving water, which will be oxygenated when the depth is not great. Thus there are several reasons why the finer-grained sediments may, under identical circumstances, contain more organic matter than coarse-grained sediments initially.

The organic matter of living organisms is made up mainly of varying proportions of proteins, fats and carbohydrates. These differ in their resistance to breakdown by bacterial action. The organic substances found in the sediments will therefore be the products of bacterial action, together with any substances which have not been attacked by aerobic or anaerobic bacteria; these may include some hydrocarbons formed in living organisms. It is not easy, in the light of present knowledge, to be sure what parts of that organic matter may be capable of giving oil, may be residues from the formation of oil, if it is formed in the sediments, or may have no significance with respect to the formation of oil.

There are many different bacteria, and the organic substances available in newly-formed sediments are complex in composition. The extent of bacterial attack depends on many factors including the nature of the substances, types of bacteria, temperature, pressure, mineral substances in solution and whether "waste" products accumulate. It is well-known that methane, carbon dioxide, and hydrogen sulphide can be formed by bacterial action on certain types of organic matter. Trace amounts of some bacterial substances are hydrocarbons. Very small amounts of ethane, propane, butane and pentane have been reported in the products of certain bacterial actions.

Methane has long been known to be formed from decaying vegetable matter under stagnant conditions. A few years ago EMERY and HOGGAN (1958) examined the gases in marine sediments (the maximum depth in the sediments being about 12 ft., and the maximum age about 15,000 years). Carbon dioxide, methane, ethane, propane, butane, isobutane, ethylene, hexane, isopentane, cyclobutane, cyclopentane, benzene, toluene and xylene were recorded. The total organic matter ranged 15,000–85,000 p.p.m. and the total hydrocarbons measured ranged 48–260 p.p.m. (Table IV). The increase in methane content with increase in depth in the Santa

TABLE IV

AMOUNTS OF HYDROCARBONS AND TOTAL ORGANIC MATTER IN RECENT SEDIMENTS
(After EMERY and HOGGAN, 1958)

Area	Depth in core (inches)	Parts per million		
		Methane	Hydrocarbons	Total organic matter
Santa Monica	2–26	0.02		34,000
Basin: 2980	26–50	0.11		25,000
ft. depth	50–74	0.37		15,000
Santa Carolina	0–8	0.004		85,000
Basin: 4551	8–32	0.006	48	71,000
ft. depth	32–56	0.19	105	63,000
	56–80	0.06	60	50,000
Newport marsh	6–8	0.16		60,000
Seal Beach marsh	6–18	0.047		60,000?
Santa Barbara	4–28	0.4	260	58,000
Basin: 1945	28–52	7.3	210	57,000
ft. depth	52–76	30	180	53,000
	76–100	65	130	52,000
	100–124	89	120	48,000
	124–148	139	150	44,000

TABLE V

RESULTS OF CHROMATOGRAPHIC ANALYSES OF ORGANIC SOLVENT EXTRACTS FROM RECENT SEDIMENTS
(After SMITH, 1954)

Source of samples	Depth below sea floor (ft.)	Chromatographic analysis of extracted organic matter (%)			
		Paraffin–naphthene	Aromatic	Asphaltic	Remaining on alumina
7 miles off	3–4	6.0	1.5	14.0	78.5
Grande Island,	18–22	17.9	2.5	12.1	67.5
Louisiana	102–103	25.0	5.7	10.6	58.7
Pelican Island, near Mississippi delta	20–2314 (mean figures for 10 clay samples)	14.1	6.0	18.5	61.4

TABLE VI

ORGANIC MATTER AND HYDROCARBON CONTENTS OF RECENT SEDIMENTS[1]
(After SMITH, 1954)

Sample	Depth (fathoms)	Percentage of extract			Hydro-carbons (p.p.m.)	Organic extract as % dry sediment
		Paraffin–naphthenes	Arom-atics	O–N–S com-pounds		
Continental shelf south-west of Cape Verde	60	8.2	6.0	11.4	29	0.021
Continental slope off Portuguese Guinea	150	5.6	2.9	10.9	28	0.034
Continental slope off Portuguese Guinea	300	4.4	2.7	9.1	36	0.051
Continental slope west of Cape Verde	460	3.6	2.1	9.6	33	0.057
Mud flat, Orinoco delta	—[2]	5.7	2.2	10.3	25	0.0314
Tidal flat, Orinoco delta	—[2]	3.9	3.7	17.7	59	0.0768
Coast, Orinoco delta		0.2	0.6	5.2	82	1.212

[1] Chromatographic separation on alumina: paraffin–naphthenes eluted by n-heptane; aromatics by benzene; asphaltic or oxygen-, nitrogen-, sulphur-containing compounds by pyridine, acetone and methanol.
[2] Intermittently exposed.

Barbara Basin core is suggestive of methane generation in the sediment. For this core there is a broad parallelism between the trends of the hydrocarbon and organic matter contents, but the observations are not sufficiently numerous to be sure of its significance. It is noteworthy that no hydrogen was present, and this is consistent with its absence in natural gas. Laboratory fermentations commonly give considerable amounts of hydrogen.

Earlier SMITH (1952) examined samples down to as much as 100 ft. below the surface of the sediments at sites in the Gulf of Mexico, and by chromatographic separation obtained paraffin-naphthene, aromatic and asphaltic fractions (Table V, Grande Islands samples). Similar results have been obtained on samples from various marine environments and depths of water (Tables VI and VII). The contents of hydrocarbons varied, but were generally comparable with those of the much older deposits used in some of Smith's studies.

TABLE VII

RESULTS OF CHROMATOGRAPHIC ANALYSES OF ORGANIC SOLVENT EXTRACTS FROM RECENT MARINE DEPOSITS
(After STEVENS et al., 1958)

Location[1]	Depth range (ft.)	Chromatographic analysis (on activated silica)		
		n-heptane fraction[2] (%)	Benzene fraction (%)	Methanol fraction (%)
A	0–7	4.6	18.4	77.0
B	0–8	6.5	15.4	78.1
C	0–5	7.7	10.1	73.2
D	0–7	9.8	12.9	77.3
E	0–10	10.4	14.2	75.4

[1] The depth of water at the locations was 40–55 ft., the sites being 6–28 miles off-shore from Texas and Louisiana.
[2] The n-heptane fraction contains all the paraffins and some of the naphthenes; the methanol fraction contains the so-called asphaltic components.

Investigations on several Recent lake sediments have also shown the presence of hydrocarbons (Tables VIII and IX). The examination of shales from various parts of the geological column has, moreover, revealed the same main groups of hydrocarbons and related substances (Table X).

STEVENS et al. (1958) have noted that the paraffin hydrocarbons in Recent marine muds and soils showed the molecules in the 22–32 carbon atom range to have a predominance of molecules with odd numbers of carbon atoms. In this respect there is a difference from crude oil, and from a shale suggested as being a source rock, which showed no predominance of molecules with odd numbers of carbon atoms. MARTIN et al. (1963) later investigated the distribution of n-paraffins

TABLE VIII

ORGANIC MATTER AND HYDROCARBON CONTENTS OF RECENT LAKE SEDIMENTS[1]
(After JUDSON and MURRAY, 1956)

	Depth of water (ft.)	Depth in sediment (inches)	Sediment	Hydrocarbons (p.p.m.)	Organic matter (%)
Lake Mendota[2]	69	0–10	Black sludge	120	10
	69	10–16	Buff marl	350	10
	69	20–26	Buff marl	225	12
Trout Lake	95	0–9	Olive green gyttja	275	43
	95	9–18	Olive green gyttja	285	46
	95	18–27	Olive green gyttja	270	50

[1] All samples contained paraffin–naphthene and aromatic hydrocarbons.
[2] The waters of Lake Mendota are deficient in dissolved oxygen for much of the year; those of Trout Lake have some oxygen all the year, possibly favouring hydrocarbon destruction.

TABLE IX

ORGANIC MATTER AND HYDROCARBON CONTENTS OF RECENT LAKE DEPOSITS, TOGETHER WITH CHROMATOGRAPHIC ANALYSES OF EXTRACTS
(After SMITH, 1954)

Non-marine sample	Hydrocarbons (p.p.m.)	Organic matter (%)	Chromatographic analysis of extract	
			Paraffin– naphthene (%)	Aromatic (%)
Stony Lake, N.J.[1]	224	11.2	1.4	0.6
Lake Wapalanne, N.J.[1]	105	2.23	1.6	3.1
Mirror Lake, N.J.[1]	52	2.3	1.1	1.1
Marsh sample, N.J.[2]	116	6.81	0.9	0.8
Rancosas Creek, N.J.[2]	90	1.13	4.3	3.7
Hemlock Forest, N.J.	135	3.87	2.2	1.3
Soil, Indiana[3]	31	0.45	2.8	4.0
Peat, Minnesota[4]	986	10.5	3.8	5.6

[1] Near-shore surface mud; 3 ft. or less of water.
[2] Shallow water cover.
[3] 2 ft. below surface.
[4] 66–78 inches below floor of Lake Minnetonka.

TABLE X

ORGANIC EXTRACTS, HYDROCARBONS, AND CHROMATOGRAPHIC ANALYSES OF EXTRACTS FROM SOME
RECENT AND ANCIENT DEPOSITS[1]
(After BONNETT, 1958)

		Percentage of extract			Hydro-carbons (p.p.m.)	Organic extract as % of sediment
		Paraffin–naphthenes	Aromatics	Asphaltic		
Recent	Silt } from Wash	18.7	19.1	25.1	201	0.0503
	Clay }	15.2	—	13.6	36	0.0235
Eocene	London Clay	Not separated				0.0041
Cretaceous	Gault Clay	26.3	10.8	28.8	56	0.0151
Jurassic	Kimmeridge Clay	7.8	12.2	26.7	39	0.0197
	Oxford Clay	9.1	20.5	32.7	156	0.0529
	Middle Lias Clay	12.6	26.2	10.4	68	0.0175
Triassic	Rhaetic Shale	12.3	49.5	15.1	426	0.0689
Carboniferous	Coal Measure Shale (Caerphilly)	5.9	22.9	42.6	67	0.0233
	Coal Measure Shale	9.5	20.8	31.4	39	0.013
	Millstone Grit Shale (grey)	Not separated				0.0034
	Millstone Grit Shale (black)	7.6	19.3	12.7	25	0.0092
	Broxburn Curly Oil Shale	45.7	11.0	12.4	3,290	0.583
	S2 Shale	9.4	29.6	38.2	43	0.011

[1] Chromatographic separation on alumina: paraffin–naphthenes eluted by *n*-heptane; aromatics
by benzene; asphaltic fraction by pyridine and methanol.

in crude oils (Eocene to Ordovician in age) for the carbon numbers from 4 upwards,
and in some cases found a marked dominance of odd numbers in the range from
11 to 19 (two such crudes were from the Ordovician and one from Devonian).
Some crude oils showed slight evidence of odd preference at carbon numbers below 10.

A sample of plankton collected off the east coast of Florida had about 0.4%
(on a dried-weight basis) of liquid and solid hydrocarbons, the normal paraffins
from which showed only a slight odd carbon preference, the odd/even ratio being
1.1. There were no aromatic hydrocarbons in the plankton. On the other hand a
recent mud had infrared spectrograms which suggested that a relatively simple
mixture of aromatic type compounds was present. Ancient clays and shales and
a crude oil had indications of a complex mixture of aromatic hydrocarbons.

Some twenty years ago TRASK and PATNODE (1942) and their collaborators
examined rock and sediment samples from many areas, and among other things

assessed the content of organic matter. In general they found that the finer-grained rocks contained more organic matter than those which were coarse. Areas with sediments rich in organic matter were rare, and the average figure for many samples was about 2.5 % for Recent sediments and about 1.5 % for ancient deposits.

Detailed studies on a few samples showed that "lignin-humus"-type complexes constituted a higher proportion of the organic matter in ancient than in Recent marine sediments, whereas the reverse was true for nitrogenous compounds. (It may be noted that KIDWELL and HUNT (1958) found humic acids to be a major constituent of the acetone-soluble, CS_2-insoluble fraction of the extracts from the very young deposits of the Pedernales area.) A small amount of carbohydrates was present in the Recent sediment, but none in the ancient sediment. The ether extract, which would include oils, fats, pigments and sulphur compounds, was 1 % of the total organic matter in the Recent sediment and 3 % in the ancient sediment.

The $^{13}C/^{12}C$ ratio of the organic carbon in crude oils, in the soluble and total organic matter in Recent and ancient sediments, as well as in various plants and coals has proved to be less than that of a standard carbonate sample. Examination of a moderate number of observations indicates that the ratio is lower for non-marine than for marine crude oils, for marine sediments than for marine organisms, and for non-marine sediments than for non-marine and terrestrial plants. For the few cases studied, the lipids in plants had a lower ratio than the entire plant, and gases in petroliferous areas had relatively much lower ratios than crude oils.

WHITLOCK et al. (1962) have noted that for the small number of ancient sediments examined the isotopic composition of the bulk organic matter agreed closely with that of the associated crude oils. The values for a considerable number of crude oils differed from those of organic matter distinctly derived from marine waters, but in the main had a similar range to values measured for terrestrial organic matter and that arising in fresh water. As a consequence they have suggested the possibility that most crudes are derived from organic matter developed in the latter environments, a hypothesis which, in the case of oils in marine environments, would require substantial amounts of organic matter to be carried in from terrestrial sources. However, study of SILVERMAN and EPSTEIN's (1958) data for marine and non-marine environments suggests that although this hypothesis could explain the values observed for marine crude oils and deposits, it leaves a problem in the case of non-marine crudes and deposits.

Since lipids have a lower ratio than the bulk plant matter, the other main components may also differ in this respect. Should the higher values be associated with the more easily destroyed components, their destruction would leave a residue with a low $^{13}C/^{12}C$ ratio.

A single core of Recent sediment showed the same $^{13}C/^{12}C$ ratio at different levels, but another core had considerable differences in these ratio at different levels. These and other considerations pose the problem of how far the generalisations indicated above are valid. More data, and measurements on fractions of the organic matter in sediments, are needed for a better evaluation of the hypothesis quoted.

A basic problem with respect to source rocks is the condition of any hydrocarbons or allied substances which eventually become the accumulated oil. Are they present as minute free globules having essentially the composition of crude oil, or do they occur adsorbed on mineral matter or organic matter? Or are they in solution in the interstitial water?

Single solvents, mixtures of solvents or a sequence of solvents have been used to extract hydrocarbons from samples of rocks or sediments. Commonly the samples have been dried before submission to solvent extraction. Hot solvent has been employed; cold solvent and ultrasonic vibrations have also been used (McIVER, 1962). It may be wondered whether drying changes the association of the hydrocarbons and mineral matter or solid organic matter. Do the solvents extract material which would not be free to move from the rock under natural conditions with water in the pores? In the case of Recent deposits are the hydrocarbons extracted such as are directly incorporated in crude oil, or do they have to undergo modification before becoming the components found in crude oil? The values of the odd/even ratios of carbon atoms per molecule for certain ranges of hydrocarbons in Recent sediments suggest that if the data are for potential source rocks modifications are necessary. If modifications are necessary do the changes take place in the source rock or in the reservoir rock? Are the hydrocarbons found in ancient sediments of the same kinds as may have been removed from the rock in question to give a crude oil accumulation? Removal of hydrocarbons from Recent sediments, with the odd/even carbon-atom ratios of the material being removed the same as in crude oils, would leave behind a mixture with a higher odd/even ratio than in the original material. This would not be consistent with the value of the ratio reported for the hydrocarbons in ancient deposits.

For various reasons the results of the chromatographic analyses may not be strictly comparable: (1) the original extractions were done under somewhat different conditions or with different solvents; (2) the adsorbents employed differed; (3) there were differences in the solvents used for elution. Hence, deductions drawn from a comparison of the data published by a worker on one series of samples studied over a short period may carry rather more weight than those made when data provided by different workers at different times are compared. It may also be noted that the data on the composition of various types of crude oils shown in Table II, while comparable as between the different crudes, have been determined in a different manner from the results of the examination of organic matter extracted by solvents from sediments reported in the other Tables.

There have been suggestions that hydrocarbons are not formed in source rocks, but rather that they are incorporated in the rocks. Clearly, any hydrocarbon incorporated and persisting might contribute to the eventual crude oil. It seems certain, however, that hydrocarbon gases are formed in some sediments, and it may be wondered to what extent a different situation exists with regard to the heavier hydrocarbons. If any hydrocarbons are generated in the source rock it is difficult to avoid the thought that bacteria play some part in the process. Studies of a series of Recent sediments by DUNTON and HUNT (1962) failed to show any hydrocarbons in the C_4–C_8 range, but rocks of Miocene to Precambrian age all had hydrocarbons in this range. The authors noted that for a given total organic content the amount of hydrocarbons increased with the age of the rock; the oldest sample had the highest proportion of hydrocarbons relative to its organic content. All the ancient samples contained methane, ethane and propane. The work by MARTIN et al. (1963) showed no obvious relationship between the distribution of odd and even carbon numbers and age.

Evidence pointing to changes of organic substances in the sediments is building up. For example, the asphaltic matter in petroleum is, in physical and chemical properties, unlike compounds developed in living matter. The mechanisms and agents involved are not known with certainty, but laboratory studies indicate that the products of the transformation of hydrocarbons, crude oils (COLOMBO et al., 1964) and a fatty acid (JURG and EISMA, 1964), by radioactivity or thermal means, are influenced by the presence of mineral matter and liquid water.

STEVENS et al. (1958) plotted the results of the chromatographic fractionation of 325 crude oils and of the solvent extracts of 60 soils and 20 marine mud samples on a triangular diagram with the *n*-heptane, benzene and methanol fractions as the three apices. The crude oils gave a group of points near the *n*-heptane–benzene side of the triangle, and in the central part, whereas the soils and muds gave points near the methanol apex. The points for soils were more widely spread than for the muds.

In Fig.3 data from SMITH (1954) and ORR and EMERY (1956) for Recent sediments, and from BONNETT (1958) for ancient deposits, have been associated

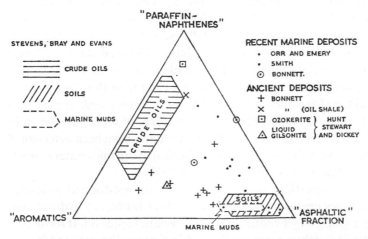

Fig.3. Diagram showing the composition of crude oils and of the organic extracts from various soils, and Recent and ancient sediments. (Based on STEVENS et al., 1958, with additions.)

with those given by STEVENS et al. (1958). The points bridge the gap between the fields shown by the last authors for crude oils and for soils and Recent sediments, but it cannot be stated how far differences in detailed analytical techniques have affected the results. Except for the material from oil shale the analyses invariably show a greater amount of asphaltic material than for the crude oils, and in general the Recent deposits have less aromatics than the ancient deposits.

The above-mentioned oil-shale extract seemingly differs from extracts of the middle and upper Green River oil shales of Uinta County, Utah, examined by HUNT et al. (1954). The latter extracts gave infrared spectra which resembled the spectra for gilsonite, an asphaltite found in the same region. The existence of a difference is comparable with the observations that oil shales on thermal treatment give paraffin-, mixed-, or aromatic-base crude products depending on the location of the shales.

MIGRATION AND ACCUMULATION

There are good grounds for believing that the proportion of hydrocarbons in a source rock is small. Hence the formation of an oil and gas accumulation must involve a phase during which the hydrocarbons move and are eventually segregated in a trap. This is known as the process of migration and accumulation. If, as seems likely on many occasions, the source rock is not the reservoir rock, two stages are involved, namely, movement from the source to the reservoir rock, and movement within the reservoir rock to the site where the accumulation is formed. The first stage has been described as primary migration and the second stage as secondary migration.

Hypotheses on migration mechanisms must depend at present on assumptions about the condition of the hydrocarbons in the source rock. If the hydrocarbons are adsorbed on the minerals or on the organic matter they must be detached before migration can occur. Detachment would appear to involve entry into solution and/or suspension in some manner or their displacement as a separate phase. They may already be in solution, or they may be present as minute free globules. Whatever the condition the hydrocarbons will be associated with a relatively very large proportion of water, especially if the source rock is fine-grained, as in the case of clays, and if they are there before the source rock has had its porosity markedly reduced by the process of compaction which takes place as the rock is progressively buried more deeply. The alternatives exist that the hydrocarbons migrate in solution or in free form. Should migration be in solution there must be a mechanism for release from solution.

Circumstantial evidence suggests that in some cases there has been downward primary migration. The gas and in all probability free oil globules also would be less dense than the water. Consequently the globules would tend to rise by buoyancy. Hence the migration mechanism in such cases cannot be by the movement of the globules in stationary water. Moreover, consideration of the interfacial forces suggests that unless the globules are smaller than the openings they would have to pass in moving through the reservoir rock from one pore to another buoyancy would be inadequate to cause the required distortion of the globules. So upward rise of globules in stationary water is probably also excluded.

Compaction involves contraction of the pore space, fluid being expelled from the rock. Broadly the flow must be upwards, but locally and possibly temporarily there can be downward flow. Evidence for this has been reported by KIDWELL and HUNT (1958). Should the hydrocarbons be in solution they would be carried by the water, and movement by diffusion would also be possible. ROOF and RUTHERFORD (1958) have concluded that for the heavier hydrocarbons particularly, primary migration dominated by a diffusion mechanism would be extremely slow. Indeed, it appears to be too slow to account for many oil accumulations.

Very large volumes of water will be expelled during the compaction of clays, and for a constant rate of loading by deeper burial the rate of flow at a given horizon will diminish as compaction proceeds. It therefore appears that if the hydrocarbons are in solution the rate of entry into the reservoir rock will diminish as burial proceeds. Should compaction cease, owing to cessation of deposition or to uplift and erosion, entry of hydrocarbons by means other than by diffusion would stop. It could be renewed by further burial, although presumably it would not do so until the stresses arising either from burial or from tectonic forces exceeded the stress at which compaction had previously stopped.

Should the hydrocarbons be present as free globules, flowing water in compaction may apply a decidedly greater pressure gradient to the globules than buoyancy alone. Moreover, the mineral grains by pressing on the globules would distort them. These two factors might cause movement of the globules, but the rate of movement would be expected to be much less than the rate of flow (linear velocity) of the water. Hence movement of free globules would be slower and less efficient in a sense than movement of dissolved hydrocarbons.

Distortion of globules means an increase in curvature and an increased rate of going into solution. As a result there would be movement in solution from strongly curved to less strongly curved globules, and the latter would grow at the expense of the former. Diffusion is involved in this process. From the data available ROOF and RUTHERFORD (1958) concluded that diffusion would be a more adequate means of migration for light than for heavy hydrocarbons. The gases are more soluble in water than are the heavier hydrocarbons, and the solubility rises with increase in pressure. However, it falls with rise in temperature. Hence deeper burial, which involves an increase in temperature and pressure, invokes competing effects, with the probability that the pressure effect will be dominant. Although in compaction the water will generally be moving upwards relative to the mineral matter, it is by no means certain that while increase in depth of burial continues the water being expelled by compaction is necessarily moving into zones of lower pressure and temperature. Water could become saturated with gas in solution, and some of this might only be released when the area was subjected to uplift and erosion, with a consequent drop in pressure. Gas released in a reservoir rock could go towards forming an accumulation. Some gas might, however, be released from water in non-reservoir rocks.

In the discussion so far true solution has alone been considered. BAKER (1962) suggested that hydrocarbons were solubilized in soap micelles in water. Experiments showed that when soap micelles were present the hydrocarbon solubilities were decidedly higher than the values for solubility in water without soap. Furthermore, it was shown that the ratio of the solubilities of benzene and toluene, for example, in naphthenate soap solutions was similar to the ratio in which these compounds occur in crude oils (Table III). As a result of these observations Baker has proposed that hydrocarbon migration takes place in micellar solution; that removal of hydrocarbons from a source rock is selective; and that crude oil is formed only when the hydrocarbons are released from solution in the soap micelles.

Laboratory studies have demonstrated that hydrocarbons can be released from the soap micelles by dilution; naphthenic acids have been observed in crude oils and naphthenate ions in oilfield waters. Migration in micellar solution would enable the hydrocarbons to move through the source rock much more easily than can be visualized for free oil globules, so the mechanism offers distinct advantages in the primary migration phase.

Dilution by fresh water cannot be regarded as a common event in oilfield areas, and on such occasions as it happens it might frequently be late in the history of the area. Dilution by mingling with salt water containing less soap can be more readily visualized if the concentration of soap is linked with the organic matter incorporated in the sediments.

A release mechanism which operates when the solution enters or is in a reservoir rock is required. Pressure and temperature changes are therefore improbable as the main factors causing release, for particular values could be reached on occasions in rocks other than reservoir rocks, and then hydrocarbons would be lost as regards oil and gas accumulation unless they were able to migrate in their new state (HOBSON, 1961b). Dilution would be a possibility should the water incorporated in reservoir rocks contain less soap than that in source rocks. An alternative would be some phenomenon linked with differences in the mineralogy of typical source and reservoir rocks. It appears, however, that any thought of reservoir rocks being their own source rocks has to be rejected if migration in solubilized or micellar solution is involved and a release mechanism of either of these two forms is required.

Hypotheses need to be considered quantitatively as well as qualitatively so far as is practicable. The amount of water expelled by compaction per unit area of a clayey rock is dependent on the thickness of the rock and on the load imposed on it. Volumetrically it can be large, but it is obviously limited. The amount entering a reservoir rock depends on the area of contact with the compacting rock. Thus for a given thickness of compacting rock and load, an extensive reservoir rock will receive more compaction fluid than a limited lens of reservoir rock. In the former case the oil accumulation may occupy but a small fraction of the total pore space in that rock; there appear to be some lenses at least in which the oil-bearing part is a substantial fraction of the total space. (This state of affairs raises problems with respect to the hypothesis of oil release by dilution.) If the amount of hydrocarbons transported by unit volume of the compaction fluid is small a large volume must enter per unit area to fill a large proportion of the lens, unless the lens itself is thin.

It is evident that the relevant relationship is of the following form:

$$a \times t \times s = A \times v \times p$$

where a is the area of the accumulation; t is the average thickness of the oil column; s is the mean oil saturation/unit volume of rock; A is the area of source rock contributing oil; v is the average volume of fluid expelled per unit area from the source rock into the reservoir rock (by compaction or other means); and p is the mean ratio of oil to fluid expelled.

The amount of fluid expelled will be a function of the character, thickness, setting and depth of burial of the source rock.

TRASK (1936), when he tried to determine the relationship between the amount of organic matter and the quantity of oil formed at Santa Fe Springs, took note of many of these factors, but some important ones seem to have been overlooked in calculations by others.

Because practically all wells in oilfield areas are drilled in the expectation of obtaining oil or gas it is not always possible to obtain the basic data which may be needed to make certain computations. Thus the extent and the nature of reservoir rocks outside the producing area are sometimes not known. However, there are cases where a lens contains oil and gas and is less extensive than the underlying accumulations. It will then be penetrated by wells and its extent will be closely defined by wells aimed at the deeper objectives. Moreover, the thicknesses of the enclosing beds will be defined. Under such conditions quantitative studies should be of improved accuracy.

If primary migration takes place as free oil or gas droplets then on entering the reservoir rock from the bottom exceedingly small droplets would be able to rise separately by buoyancy if their size is less than that of the pore throats. Larger droplets would stay near the point of entry, and be joined by others, with coalescence. Any oil entering at the top would initially collect there and eventually coalesce with other droplets. In the case of entry at the bottom when the coalesced oil or gas mass was of sufficient height, it would begin to rise by buoyancy, even in the absence of any water flow. Water flow with an upward direction would reduce somewhat the critical height needed. The critical height would depend on the liquid densities, interfacial tension and the sizes of the pores and throats. On reaching the top of the reservoir rock the hydrocarbons would be constrained by any cap rock which had been deposited. Oil or gas which had collected at the top beneath a cap rock which was not horizontal would begin to rise obliquely to the highest available point once the height of the mass had attained a suitable value. It should be noted that hydrocarbon masses may attain sufficient height to rise and then be stopped temporarily by a slight diminution in pore size, such as a fine sand streak within a medium-sized sand; therefore, a conventional cap rock is not necessary. Further growth in height will enable buoyancy to cause renewed rise until an even finer barrier is met. Upward directed water flow will aid the rise.

Should migration be in solution, and should release as crude oil occur at or near the point of entry to the reservoir rock, the subsequent events will be the same as those described above.

SMITH (1952) and KIDWELL and HUNT (1958) observed increased proportions of hydrocarbons in sands as compared with the adjacent clays, suggesting early oil migration.

The rate of accumulation will be slow. Many factors will affect the rate, and it is possible that there may be temporary halts in the movement of the oil and gas to give the first large accumulation. A very thin and non-commercial layer of oil or gas might form at the top of a horizontal reservoir rock. If this were then tilted there would be readjustments due to buoyancy, and a more compact and commercially significant accumulation could then be created at a point where there was a trap.

The accumulation would remain unchanged in size or position only so long as there was no change in conditions. Increase in depth of burial would drive free gas into solution, in oil in particular, reducing the total volume occupied by the hydrocarbons. Erosion, with pressure reduction, would cause marked expansion of the accumulation due to gas evolution from the oil that was saturated with gas. Tilting of the rocks would change the position of an accumulation in the reservoir rock if there was no barrier at the appropriate point caused by wedging out of the reservoir rock or by the presence of cement. Pressure gradients associated with water flow could cause changes in the position of the oil/water contact, or gas/water contact. Oil might be carried out of accumulations where the fluid contacts were at or very close to a spilling plane. Oil might also spill out under a spilling plane as a result of further accretion, or of expansion of the accumulation as a whole on pressure drop, to give an adjacent accumulation or to escape. Some changes in the overall gas content of an accumulation could take place with flowing water via solubility and diffusion effects (HOBSON, 1962a).

When a source rock varies in character vertically it seems possible that oil leaving it early could differ from that leaving it late. The same would be true if slow evolution took place within the source rock, and the effect would be particularly noticeable were there to be a temporary halt in the compaction of a source rock, if, as seems likely, migration is associated with compaction. A further possibility exists if migration takes place with the hydrocarbons in soap micelles. For this mechanism should the pores become too small in the later stages of compaction to allow the passage of the larger micelles, the composition of the hydrocarbons issuing from the source rock would change. Should the source rock change in character laterally oils supplied by different parts could differ. Whether these somewhat different oils ultimately become mingled in a single accumulation would be dependent on the structure and continuity of the reservoir rock.

EVOLUTION AND OTHER CHANGES

Various views have been expressed about the possibility and nature of evolutionary changes in the characteristics of crude oils. There have been suggestions that virgin crude oil is very heavy and asphaltic and that with increase in age and/or depth of burial it breaks down to lighter types of oil. In the Gulf Coast area of the U.S.A., BARTON (1934) assembled data on oil gravities, and it was suggested that there were trends towards lighter oils with increased age or depth. There have been suggestions of ultimate breakdown to give a gas and a solid or semi-solid residue.

A more recent study of Gulf Coast oils by HAEBERLE (1951) led him to conclude that the environment of the oil-forming beds played an important part in determining the specific gravity of the crude oil. Lighter oils were formed in the more marine environments (Table XI). WEEKS (1958), too, has suggested that crude oils increase in lightness basinwards. HUNT (1953), from his studies on Wyoming crude oils, concluded that the major differences were dependent on source materials and environment of deposition. The more naphthenic and aromatic crudes were associated with the more saline environments of deposition, characterized by carbonates and sulphates rather than clastic sediments. For oils formed in clastic sediments the more aromatic and naphthenic types were associated with the higher sand/shale ratios, i.e., near-shore basin positions.

It seems reasonable to expect the environment of deposition to control the organisms living in the water, and to affect the bacterial changes in particular to which the organic matter was subjected on incorporation in the sediments. The chemistry of the environment is likely to be an important factor. Consequently virgin crude oils may well differ, and on this account it becomes difficult to demonstrate that the oils now found have undergone changes, except in special circumstances.

There have also been suggestions of alteration in the course of migration. In western Canada crude oils have nickel and vanadium contents which generally run parallel to variations in sulphur, resins and asphaltenes, and they are con-

TABLE XI

VARIATION OF CRUDE OIL GRAVITIES WITH RESERVOIR DEPTH AND AGE IN THE GULF COAST AREA OF THE U.S.A.[1]
(After HAEBERLE, 1951)

		Depth (1,000 ft.)											
		0–1	1–2	2–3	3–4	4–5	5–6	6–7	7–8	8–9	9–10	10–11	11–12
		Oil gravity (° A.P.I.)											
Miocene				19	23	28	36	39					
Oligocene	Frio			27	32	33	42	45	47	50	53	47	
	Vicksburg			26		37	46	46	47	53	48	50	
Eocene	Jackson	20	24	25	35	48	50	46					
	Yegua	18	28	32	38	46	50	49	51	52	50		
	Cook Mt.			45	44		39		53				
	Mt. Selman	18	18	34	28	41							
	Wilcox	19	18	22	27	39	41	47	48	50	46	53	44
		Shallower water						Deeper water					

[1] The above data are for the southern area which extends from the Mexican border to the northern edges of Calhoun, Wharton, Colorado and Fayette counties.

sidered by HODGSON and BAKER (1959) to be apparently sensitive indicators of crude-oil alteration. They note that adsorption loss (on porous solids) of high-molecular-weight and polar materials would be evident at points remote from the source of the oil; these materials would also be associated at the time of deposition with fine-grained rocks as distinct from near-shore coarse-grained deposits. So far as oil fields are concerned both effects would operate in the same direction, and Hodgson and Baker conclude that the probable direction of movement of oil within oil fields during relocation (defined as the movement and resulting alterations of a developing crude oil) and accumulation is towards "lows" in metal, sulphur, asphaltene and resin contents.

Even if Baker's hypothesis is applicable it seems that there is room for differences in the composition of crude oils, provided that the hydrocarbons available to be taken into micelles are not always present in the same proportions or are not sufficient to saturate the micelles. Perhaps differences in the soaps could also affect the composition of the crude oil.

At first sight it might appear that the ratio of gas to oil in an accumulation would be a guide to original differences or to evolution, and consequently this ratio might be significant. However, detailed consideration shows that so far as individual accumulations are concerned, and especially those in extensive reservoir horizons with more than one trap, a variety of processes can cause the ratios now found in accumulations to differ from the ratio in which gas and oil were formed, or in which they entered or appeared in the reservoir rock initially (HOBSON, 1961b).

Many oil and gas accumulations have had a long and varied history. They are not all now in the place where they were originally trapped, and some may even be in a different reservoir rock. It is probable that all will include oil and gas which have at least gone through a phase of increasing temperature and pressure. Many now exploited will currently be at pressures and temperatures below the maximum values to which they have been subjected. Some may have had more than one peak in their temperature and pressure histories. The consequences of rise in temperature and pressure will depend on the composition and proportions of oil and gas in an accumulation, and on the temperatures and pressures reached. It is by no means certain that a drop in pressure and temperature will always return the oil and gas accumulation to exactly the same conditions as it was in at a given temperature and pressure before passing through the peak values.

Under suitable values of pressure and temperature it is possible for quite heavy molecules to be vaporized, and there are hydrocarbon accumulations (condensate or distillate fields) in which large amounts of heavy hydrocarbons are in the vapour phase. "Black oil rings" have been reported below the vapour-phase material in some areas. In reaching this state the increasing pressure will have caused a reduction in the total space occupied by the hydrocarbon accumulation. When pressure drop occurs there will be expansion and ultimately material will come out of the vapour phase. In non-homogeneous reservoirs in particular it is possible that should the condensing material fail to dissolve all the residual black oil, perched masses of "tar" may later be found in an oil column, or there may be tar-coated sand grains.

Asphalts are visualised as colloidal systems in which asphaltenes are "peptized" in the oily constituents by the resins. Crude oils themselves have some colloi-

TABLE XII

ELEMENTAL COMPOSITION OF A CRUDE OIL, AND OF ASPHALTUM PRECIPITATED FROM IT BY VARIOUS REAGENTS
(After GURWITSCH and MOORE, 1926)

| | Percentage composition | | | |
	C	H	O	C/H
Original oil	86.03	12.7	1.1	6.77
Asphaltum precipitated by 4:3 alcohol–ether	85.73	12.29	1.65	6.97
Asphaltum precipitated by 3:4 alcohol–ether	84.19	12.06		6.98
Asphaltum precipitated by 0.7 sp. gr. benzine	84.44	10.71	3.47	7.87

dal characteristics. In view of the complexity and variety of crude oils, and also the complexity of asphalts, it is, perhaps, not surprising to find differences in behaviour when these substances are subjected to treatment which leads to the formation of precipitates or concentrates. Thus GURWITSCH and MOORE (1926) have shown that the composition of the precipitated asphaltum depends on the nature of the precipitating medium (Table XII). By varying the pressure and temperature under which propane is mixed with residual asphalts it has proved possible to obtain a variety of fractions as precipitates which differ considerably in their characteristics. In the laboratory it has been found that when a large quantity of natural gas is dissolved in some crude oils under pressure there is precipitation of asphaltic matter. This is analogous to the use of light petroleum ether for precipitating asphaltic matter in laboratory studies. Should it be an irreversible process it may be wondered whether it accounts for the specks of hard asphaltic matter found in some oil sands.

Whether the explanations put forward above are reasonable can only be ascertained by considering the geological data and the probable geological history in each instance, for other explanations have legitimately been offered in some cases. In the Oficina area of Venezuela RENZ et al. (1958) have suggested a second incursion of crude oil which enveloped tarry oil or occupied the pores between tarcoated grains. They postulated that the tarry oil resulted from the weathering of a crude oil.

Tarry oil has been noted at oil/water contacts in some fields, and also in some oil reservoirs near faults. Reactions at oil/water contacts, possibly aided or caused by bacteria, have been suggested to explain these occurrences of tarry oil.

The existence of tarry materials, apparently in contact with more normal crude oil, suggests immiscibility, or extremely slow rates of interdiffusion of the components of the two types of oil.

DERIVED DEPOSITS

Asphaltic deposits take a variety of forms, and the properties of the materials in them differ considerably. The amounts of carbon and hydrogen in these asphaltic materials are not unlike those in crude oils, but the quantities of sulphur, nitrogen or oxygen are frequently greater (Table I). There are impregnations in which the asphalt occupies the pores and other openings in a rock in a manner comparable with the oil impregnation in a reservoir rock. Asphalt lakes are known in which the material contains little non-bituminous matter. One of these, the Bermudez lake, is estimated to have had at least $2 \cdot 10^6$ tons of asphalt, a quantity which would indicate derivation from a large, if not a major, oil accumulation. The Trinidad Pitch Lake contains an intimate mixture of asphalt, salt water and mineral matter.

Asphalt veins are found in some regions. Their extents and widths vary widely. Some are reported to have been traced for as much as 30–40 miles; widths up to 33 ft. have been noted; and there are workings going down over 200 ft. Statements have been made that some veins cut through 1,000 ft. or more of strata. Some veins or groups of veins contain very large amounts of asphalt; the Cowboy and Bonanza veins of Utah are estimated to have $16 \cdot 10^6$ tons of asphalt.

Table XIII compares some of the characteristics of a few natural asphalts, asphaltites and asphaltic pyrobitumens. The fusing point, determined under standard conditions, increases broadly in the order of the groups mentioned, whereas the solubility in 88° petroleum naphtha decreases.

Veins of waxy material (ozokerite) have been found and exploited in some areas. Ozokerite veins up to 2 ft. in thickness are known, and the rock adjacent to the veins may be saturated with ozokerite. The rock walls against some gilsonite (asphaltite) veins are said to be impregnated with gilsonite for a distance up to about 2 ft. from the vein, with no clear line of demarcation between impregnated and non-impregnated rock. The gilsonite-impregnated zones are thinner in shales than in sandstones.

High pressures, to a considerable extent of tectonic origin, may precede rupture of the strata in strongly folded areas. Faults can also be formed under tensional conditions. Escape of hydrocarbons to the surface from accumulations may then become possible, giving seeps and the possibility of several additional types of "hydrocarbon" occurrences.

Not all seepages, however, take place from faults, and some result from exposure of the reservoir rock by erosion, while others may be associated with

TABLE XIII

COMPOSITION OF VARIOUS BITUMENS AND NATURAL TARS IN TERMS OF ASPHALTENES, OILY CONSTITUENTS AND ASPHALTIC RESINS
(After ABRAHAM, 1960)

	Fusing point (°F R.B.)	Asphaltenes (%)	Oily constituents (%)	Asphaltic resins (%)	Solubility in 88° petroleum naphtha (%)
Athabaska Tar[1]	63				78.2
Val de Travers[1]	79	19.9	42.2	32.2	
Gard[1]	106.5–136.5	29–36.7	61	8	
Bermudez[2]	145–160	35.3	39.6	14.4	60–75
Trinidad Pitch Lake[2]	164	26.1	31.9	29.4	62–64
Selenitza[2]	253.5	45.2	24.5	18.8	
Gilsonite (Utah)	270–400	32.6			10–60
Albertite	Infusible				0.5–2

[1] Extracted material.
[2] Refined.

joints in the cap rock of an oil accumulation that has been brought near to the surface by uplift and erosion.

At the surface light hydrocarbons will vaporize from the escaping oil. Indeed, some loss of light hydrocarbons probably takes place before the surface is reached. The residual material may also be thickened by oxidation, although much appears to depend on the type of oil. Asphaltic oils give a persistent residue, but it is thought that waxy oils are more readily attacked by bacteria so that there is no marked accumulation of wax at the surface. The persistence even of asphaltic residues near the point of escape must depend among other things on the topography. When there is a depression the escaping oil will accumulate, and undergo inspissation, forming an asphalt lake such as the Bermudez lake in Venezuela.

The escaping oil may mingle with the soil, forming an asphaltic carpet. A further possibility is that it may become mixed with new sediment, a process which is taking place on the foreshore at the mouth of the Guapo River, east of Point Fortin (BARR et al., 1958). There heavy seepage oil is being mixed with beach sand.

There is no reason for seepages always to occur on land. Oil escaping under water in which sediment was being laid down could become mixed with sediment and form new and exceptional deposits. The oil may have become thickened to some extent before actual escape in some cases, and very little sediment may be needed to make the bulk density greater than water. Some spread or carriage of the oil/mineral matter complexes from the point of escape is possible. It seems likely that the material of the Trinidad Pitch Lake, consisting of about 40% bitumen, 31% silty mineral matter, and 29% water intimately mixed, with some gas, was formed in this way, Eventually the emulsion was covered by normal sediments, and may have been distorted and displaced in later folding to give the present inverted flat conical mass.

Even though the Trinidad Pitch Lake may be unique, it is improbable that the mechanism described for the formation of the "emulsion" is also unique. There have been occasional reports of oily clays, without, unfortunately, detailed published accounts of the occurrences. These may well be instances of the incorporation of seepage oil in newly forming sediments, with the proportions of oil, clay and water differing from those of the Pitch Lake material.

It has been suggested that the Athabaska "tar" sands were formed by oil that was escaping into sands in the process of deposition. Cores of the material are said sometimes to have shown bands of tar between sectors of tar-impregnated sand (HUME, 1947). However, doubts have been expressed about the above condition being original, and there is by no means agreement concerning the mode of origin of the Athabaska tar sands. The specific gravity of the "tar" in the Athabaska tar sands is reported to be 1.002–1.027, and the viscosity is stated to range 3,000–400,000 poises at 60°F.

Descriptions of some asphalt and ozokerite veins suggest a change in properties with depth, and also with distance from the margins. Thus there are references to the asphalt obtained at depth having a lower fusing point than the near-surface material; and to "liquid ozokerite" dripping from the walls in some of the deeper ozokerite mines, as well as to "liquid gilsonite" being found at depth in the Bonanza gilsonite mine (HUNT et al., 1954). Asphalt from a grahamite vein in Trinidad was 12.8% soluble in 88° petroleum naphtha at a depth of 100 ft., 15.2% soluble at 140 ft., and 18.5% soluble at 200 ft., but 56% soluble in the centre of the vein at the same depth (ABRAHAM, 1960). Occasionally the near-surface material is suggested as resembling a different type of asphalt from the material in the same vein at depth.

The above observations imply that there is a higher proportion of the more mobile, and presumably more volatile, components of the asphalt complex at depth, and sometimes also in the centre of the vein.

The rheological properties of asphaltic bitumens have been investigated. The experimental materials were residues obtained from the distillation of crude oils, and in some cases the residues had been subjected to other treatments. They may well, therefore, have been submitted to higher temperatures and to other conditions which differ considerably from those met by natural vein materials, which are commonly assumed to be residuals from crude oils. It is not certain how far the properties of the two groups depend on their histories, but the behaviour of the former may, nevertheless, be a guide to the probable behaviour of the latter group.

It may be noted that some asphaltic bitumens showed Newtonian flow behaviour, whereas others had some elasticity and were non-Newtonian. Rise in temperature caused a very marked drop in viscosity, whereas at constant temperatures the viscosity increased with increase in pressure. The rates of change were not constant, even for a single asphalt. Hence the magnitudes of changes depend on the pressure and temperature ranges considered.

As indicated earlier temperature and pressure increase with depth in the earth's crust, and the rates of increase differ somewhat with the geological circumstances. Assuming a surface temperature of 20°C and a temperature of 30°C at a depth of 1,000 ft., together with a pressure gradient of 0.43 p.s.i./ft., the figures in Table XIV were deduced from laboratory data for the viscosities of asphaltic materials (SAAL, 1950).

TABLE XIV

VISCOSITIES OF ASPHALTIC MINERALS (IN POISES)

	0 ft.	1,000 ft.
Residual asphalt from Californian crude oil	$11.5 \cdot 10^6$	$1.05 \cdot 10^6$
Residual asphalt from Venezuelan crude oil	$35.5 \cdot 10^6$	$3.55 \cdot 10^6$

When it is recalled that the amounts of the more liquid components probably increase at depth, and that rise in temperature reduces the viscosity of the micellar fluid, reduces the volume of the micelles by changing adsorption and may alter their structure and cohesion, it appears that despite the pressure effect the mobility of the vein material may be far higher at depth than at the surface.

HUNT et al. (1954) studied the "hydrocarbon" materials in the veins and rocks of the Uinta Basin, Utah, where ozokerite, albertite, gilsonite and wurtzilite are reported to occur. The gilsonites are described as branching downwards *"into a series of veinlets in the rich oil shales"* of the Green River formation. The implications of these observations are that the veins arise from material in the oil shales and are sometimes actually in these rocks. The vein and rock materials examined were apparently from outcrops, and could therefore have suffered inspissation. The condition of the material at the time of injection and the reasons for injection are therefore speculative matters. However, "liquid gilsonite" is stated to occur in sandstones in the south of the basin.

Elsewhere in the Uinta Basin ozokerite is found in fault breccias. This is suggested as having come from lacustrine oil shales in the upper Wasatch. In the overlying basal Green River formation fractured bituminous shales give oil in two fields, and the heavy ends of this oil resemble ozokerite.

The ozokerite, albertite, gilsonite, and wurtzilite of the Uinta Basin were seemingly derived from beds of progressively younger age, and which appear to represent different depositional environments, with greater salinity and a larger hydrogen sulphide content in the waters in which the younger beds were laid down. The lake varied in extent during the Eocene.

Secondary openings such as joints and fractures can be formed only in a rock which has become rigid, and in the case of deeply buried rocks this implies the possession of considerable strength and non-plastic behaviour for the conditions involved. Certainly the comparatively free adjustments normally associated with compaction will no longer be possible at the time at which the openings form. When oil occurs in the "joints" of a shale the question always arises as to where it was accumulated before it entered the joints. If, as inferred earlier, the amount of oil formed is only a very small fraction of the volume of the source rock, and compaction is well advanced at the time when joints form it is difficult to understand how much indigenous oil could enter the joints direct from the source rock. Hence a temporary storage place outside or interbedded with the source rock seems to be required. Similar arguments apply in the cases of asphalt and ozokerite veins. Furthermore, without the existence of such a storage place it is not easy to account for the quite substantial amounts of asphalt localised in some veins.

An obvious problem is the condition of the material immediately prior to its injection into the secondary openings. Was the material highly viscous and in a condition which required only slow loss of a comparatively small amount of a mobile component to give the asphaltic material now found in a vein? Or was there quite mobile material from which asphaltic matter was separated relatively quickly in the vein? How was the material driven into the openings? Pressure energy stored mainly in compressed fluids is presumably the effective agent in causing seepages or flow into wells.

The estimates of HUNT et al. (1954) of the depths of burial afford some guide to the physical conditions to which the materials have been subjected: wurtzilite: 3,100 ft.; gilsonite: 4,000 ft.; albertite: 7,200 ft.; ozokerite: 8,000 ft.

Separation of waxy complexes is well-known in the production of certain types of crude oils. These have been observed not only in wells, but also in pipe lines and in tanks. Loss of gas from solution and cooling may be contributory factors to this separation; they are certainly associated with it. It is a temptation to believe that the flow (engendered by faulting) of waxy crude oil through fissures has led to the formation of the ozokerite deposits.

Apparently the maximum widths and linear extents of ozokerite veins which have been observed are much less than those of asphalt veins, and it may be wondered whether this means differences in the conditions of the materials at the time of injection. Was the asphaltic material in a highly viscous condition at that stage, as distinct from the mobile liquid from which waxy deposits are formed in wells? Earlier reference has been made to means whereby thickened oil and even precipitates can be obtained independent of flow. The mention of "liquid gilsonite" in sands suggests the possibility of a thickened material existing before injection. It is not certain how far this is an original condition, or whether there has been previous loss of more mobile components. Asphaltic limestones and sandstones appear to be instances where oils have lost their lighter components while in the rock pores, with the result that the asphaltic residue is no longer able to flow under the conditions available. There must be a limit to the thickening which can take place without complete loss of mobility, and the development of non-Newtonian behaviour could be a critical factor. More detailed information is required on the chemical composition and physical properties of the asphalts and waxes, and on the geological setting of the deposits, as well as on the geological history of the areas in question, before the various possibilities can be more satisfactorily evaluated.

GEOCHEMICAL PROSPECTING AND SOME OTHER POINTS

Reference has been made to seepages. These are the obvious points of escape of oil and gas. It is likely, however, that there are other points of escape which are less apparent. Indeed, the possibility of there being micro-seeps of one kind or another cannot be excluded. Apart from direct escape via minute cracks, some components might move in aqueous solution and perhaps eventually be released from solution. The escaping material might cause changes in the overlying rocks, and some might be adsorbed on the mineral matter. Concepts of this kind led, many years ago, to the idea of geochemical prospecting for oil and gas as a direct means for locating accumulations.

The subject is extremely difficult. Some of the methods are direct and look for hydrocarbons; others are indirect and search for features which are suggested as being associated with the presence of hydrocarbons underground or with their escape. Methods vary in the type of hydrocarbon or other substance detected by the analyses.

Broadly, hydrocarbons or other closely related organic substances obtained from near-surface rocks, soils, soil gases or waters may be of Recent origin, arising from modern plant and micro-biological activity, or of ancient origin, having been formed when or soon after the rocks in question were deposited, or having moved into them. There could be cases in which the hydrocarbons and other substances are of mixed origin. For various reasons there could be lithological associations with regard to hydrocarbon content—the nature of the solid surface is also important. Clearly, Recent or ancient hydrocarbons which are indigenous (i.e., formed in, or have moved into the rocks at a geologically early date) to the rock or soil sample in no way prove that there is a commercially valuable oil or gas accumulation at depth in the immediate neighbourhood from which the samples were taken. However, circumstances can be visualised under which their pattern of occurrence could indicate the presence of a structure suitable for trapping hydrocarbons, but not necessarily containing an oil or gas accumulation (FREDERICKSON, 1960).

Dating techniques could permit the recognition of samples with hydrocarbons of recent origin.

Should hydrocarbons escaping from an accumulation dissolve in water which is moving parallel to the bedding it is apparent that they might be detected at points which are laterally displaced with respect to the parent accumulation. Diffusion processes would be likely to lead to spreading in the course of escape.

Because of the above features the interpretation of the observations made in geochemical surveys raises many problems. An anomaly may be shown, but its significance with respect to there being an oil or gas accumulation may be debatable (HOBSON, 1961a).

Coals are known to be able to adsorb considerable amounts of methane. The same phenomena may well operate with some components of the disseminated organic matter found in clays and shales, as well as in soils.

When natural gases have unusually large amounts of non-hydrocarbon components, such as some in the Mexican oilfield areas with high proportions of carbon dioxide, the Lacq gas with much hydrogen sulphide, and the gases of the Eocene in the Sui region of West Pakistan with considerable percentages of nitrogen and carbon dioxide (TAINSH et al., 1959), are they of mixed origin? There are cases of high-relief reservoirs, like the Tensleep reservoir at Elk Basin, in which the density of the gas-free oil increases with depth (ESPACH and FRY, 1951). Can these be explained entirely by gravitational segretation, or did denser oil enter the reservoir in the later stages of accumulation? HETHERINGTON and HORAN (1960) noted that density layering has been observed in various fields, and that it is to be expected as a consequence of gravitational separation. Are the high water salinities commonly found in oil reservoir rocks the result of a semi-permeable membrane effect associated with the cap rock? If so soap micelles could probably be held back by similar means. Reservoir rock size, its detailed composition and geologic setting, the micellar solubility of oil and the soap content of oilfield brines, should be considered in elucidating these and other problems. The presence of hydrocarbon accumulations may prevent the operation of some processes in the rocks. Light can be thrown on certain problems by paying special attention to oil and gas accumulations in lenses. In other instances the precise nature of varying sectors of an extensive limestone, and the amount and distribution of secondary carbonates may be relevant.

These are but a few of the numerous additional fascinating points which would merit discussion if space allowed.

CONCLUSION

The foregoing account of oil and gas fields and related deposits is necessarily brief, and also incomplete because of the many problems remaining to be solved. A selection only of the hypotheses concerning various matters has been given. Yet it is hoped that it is sufficient to outline the general picture, and to permit the chapters which follow on more restricted topics to be fitted into place.

Attention has been drawn to some of the unknowns, and it is possible in some cases that the sifting, analysis and synthesis of data already in oil company files could provide answers to certain problems and define others more clearly. Against this background, the application of old and new techniques could be more effective.

REFERENCES

ABRAHAM, H., 1960. *Asphalts and Allied Substances*, 6 ed. Van Nostrand, New York, N.Y., 1: 370 pp.
BAKER, E. G., 1962. Distribution of hydrocarbons in petroleum. *Bull. Am. Assoc. Petrol. Geologists*, 46: 76–84.
BARR, K. W., WAITE, S. T. and WILSON, C. C., 1958. The mode of oil occurrence in the Miocene of southern Trinidad. In: L. G. WEEKS (Editor), *Habitat of Oil*. Am. Assoc. Petrol. Geologists, Tulsa, Okla., pp.533–550.
BARTON, D. C., 1934. Natural history of Gulf Coast crude oil. In: W. E. WRATHER and F. H. LAHEE (Editors), *Problems of Petroleum Geology*. Am. Assoc. Petrol. Geologists, Tulsa, Okla., pp.109–156.

BONNETT, B., 1958. *Organic Matter in Fine-Grained Rocks, and its Relation to the Origin of Petroleum*. Ph. D. Thesis, Univ. London, 155 pp.

BUCKLEY, S. E., HOCOTT, C. R. and TAGGART, M. S., 1958. Distribution of dissolved hydrocarbons in sub-surface waters. In: L. G. WEEKS (Editor), *Habitat of Oil*. Am. Assoc. Petrol. Geologists, Tulsa, Okla., pp.850–882.

COLOMBO, U., DENTI, E. and SIRONI, G., 1964. A geochemical investigation upon the effects of ionizing radiation on hydrocarbons. *J. Inst. Petrol.*, 50: 228–237.

DUNTON, M. L. and HUNT, J. M., 1962. Distribution of low-molecular-weight hydrocarbons in recent and ancient sediments. *Bull. Am. Assoc. Petrol. Geologists*, 46: 2246–2248.

EMERY, K. O. and HOGGAN, D., 1958. Gases in marine sediments. *Bull. Am. Assoc. Petrol. Geologists*, 42: 2174–2188.

ESPACH, R. H. and FRY, J., 1951. Variable characteristics of the oil in the Tensleep sandstone reservoir, Elk Basin field, Wyoming and Montana. *J. Petrol. Technol.*, 192: 75–82.

FREDERICKSON, A. F., 1960. Method of evaluating certain types of geochemical anomalies. *Bull. Am. Assoc. Petrol. Geologists*, 44: 632–635.

GURWITSCH, L. and MOORE, H., 1926. *The Scientific Principles of Petroleum Technology*, 2 ed. Chapman and Hall, London, 470 pp.

HAEBERLE, F. R., 1951. Relationship of hydrocarbon gravities to facies in Gulf Coast. *Bull. Am. Assoc. Petrol. Geologists*, 35: 2238–2248.

HETHERINGTON, G. and HORAN, A. J., 1960. Variations with elevation of Kuwait reservoir fluids. *J. Inst. Petrol.*, 46: 109–114.

HOBSON, G. D., 1961a. The status of geochemical prospecting. *Petroleum (London)*, 24: 255–258.

HOBSON, G. D., 1961b. Problems associated with the migration of oil in "solution". *J. Inst. Petrol.*, 47: 170–173.

HOBSON, G. D., 1962a. Factors affecting oil and gas accumulations. *J. Inst. Petrol.*, 48: 165–168.

HOBSON, G. D., 1962b. The occurrence and origin of oil and gas. In: *Modern Petroleum Technology*, 3 ed. Inst. Petrol., London, pp.1–21.

HODGSON, G. W. and BAKER, B. L., 1959. Geochemical aspects of petroleum migration in Pembina, Redwater, Joffre and Lloydminster oil fields of Alberta and Saskatchewan, Canada. *Bull. Am. Assoc. Petrol. Geologists*, 43: 311–328.

HUME, G. S., 1947. Results and significance of drilling operations in the Athabaska bituminous sands. *Trans. Can. Inst. Mining Met.*, 49: 298–324.

HUNT, J. M., 1953. Composition of crude oil and its relation to stratigraphy in Wyoming. *Bull. Am. Assoc. Petrol. Geologists*, 37: 1837–1872.

HUNT, J. M., STEWART, F. and DICKEY, P. A., 1954. Origin of hydrocarbons in Uinta Basin, Utah. *Bull. Am. Assoc. Petrol. Geologists*, 38: 1671–1698.

JUDSON, S. and MURRAY, R. C., 1956. Modern hydrocarbons in two Wisconsin lakes. *Bull. Am. Assoc. Petrol. Geologists*, 40: 747–750.

JURG, J. W. and EISMA, E., 1964. Petroleum hydrocarbons: generation from fatty acids. *Science*, 144: 1451.

KARTSEV, A. A., TABASARANSKII, Z. A., SUBBOTA, M. I. and MOGILEVSKI, G. A., 1959. *Geochemical Methods of Prospecting for Petroleum and Natural Gas*. Univ. Calif. Press, Los Angeles, Calif., 349 pp.

KIDWELL, A. L. and HUNT, J. M., 1958. Migration of oil in recent sediments of Pedernales, Venezuela. In: L. G. WEEKS (Editor), *Habitat of Oil*. Am. Assoc. Petrol. Geologists, Tulsa, Okla., pp.790–817.

KYTE, J. R., NAUMANN, V. Q. and MATTAX, C. C., 1961. Effect of reservoir environment on water-oil displacements. *J. Petrol. Technol.*, 13: 579–582.

MARTIN, R. L., WINTERS, J. C. and WILLIAMS, J. A., 1963. Composition of crude oils by gas chromatography; geological significance of hydrocarbon distribution. *World Petrol. Congr., Proc., 6th, Frankfurt/Main*, 5: 231–260.

McIVER, R. D., 1962. Ultrasonics—a rapid method for removing soluble organic matter from sediments. *Geochim. Cosmochim. Acta*, 26: 343–345.

ORR, W. L. and EMERY, K. O., 1956. Composition of organic matter in marine sediments; preliminary data on hydrocarbon distribution in basins off southern California. *Bull. Geol. Soc. Am.*, 67: 1247–1257.

RENZ, H. H., ALBERDING, H., DALLMUS, K. F., PATTERSON, J. M., ROBIE, R. H., WEISBORD, N. E. and MASVALL, J., 1958. Eastern Venezuela Basin. In: L. G. WEEKS (Editor), *Habitat of Oil*. Am. Assoc. Petrol. Geologists, Tulsa, Okla., pp.551–600.

ROOF, J. G. and RUTHERFORD, W. M., 1958. Rate of migration of petroleum by proposed mechanisms. *Bull. Am. Assoc. Petrol. Geologists*, 42: 963–980.

SAAL, R. N. J., 1950. Physical properties of asphaltic bitumen. 1. Rheological properties. In: J. PH. PFEIFFER (Editor), *The Properties of Asphaltic Bitumen with Reference to its Technical Applications*. Elsevier, Amsterdam, pp.49–76.

SACHANEN, A. N., 1950. Hydrocarbons in petroleum. In: A. E. DUNSTAN, A. W. NASH, B. T. BROOKS and H. TIZARD (Editors), *The Science of Petroleum*. Oxford Univ. Press, London, 5(1): 55–77.

SILVERMAN, S. R. and WEEKS, S., 1958. Carbon isotopic compositions of petroleums and other sedimentary organic materials. *Bull. Am. Petrol Geologists,* 42: 998–1012.

SMITH, P. V., 1952. Preliminary note on the origin of petroleum. *Bull. Am. Assoc. Petrol. Geologists*, 36: 411–413.

SMITH, P. V., 1954. Studies on the origin of petroleum: occurrence of hydrocarbons in recent sediments. *Bull. Am. Assoc. Petrol. Geologists*, 38: 377–404.

STEVENS, N. P., BRAY, E. E. and EVANS, E. D., 1958. Hydrocarbons in recent sediments of the Gulf of Mexico. In: L. G. WEEKS (Editor), *Habitat of Oil*. Am. Assoc. Petrol. Geologists, Tulsa, Okla., pp.779–789.

TAINSH, H. R., STRINGER, K. V. and AZAD, J., 1959. Major gas fields of West Pakistan. *Bull. Am. Assoc. Petrol. Geologists*, 43: 2675–2700.

TRASK, P. D., 1936. Proportion of organic matter converted into oil in Santa Fé Springs field, California. *Bull. Am. Assoc. Petrol. Geologists*, 20: 245–257.

TRASK, P. D. and PATNODE, H. W., 1942. *Source Beds of Petroleum*. Am. Assoc. Petrol. Geologists, Tulsa, Okla., 566 pp.

WEEKS, L. G., 1958. Habitat of oil and some factors that control it. In: L. G. WEEKS (Editor), *Habitat of Oil*. Am. Assoc. Petrol. Geologists, pp.1–61.

WHITLOCK, D. W., ECKELMANN, W. R., BROECKER, W. S. and ALLSUP, J. R., 1962. Implications of carbon isotopic composition of total organic carbon of some recent sediments and ancient oils. *Bull. Am. Assoc. Petrol. Geologists*, 46: 699–704.

Chapter 2

THE SIGNIFICANCE OF CLAY MINERALS IN SEDIMENTS

CHARLES E. WEAVER

Department of Earth Sciences, Georgia Institute of Technology, Atlanta, Ga. (U.S.A.)

INTRODUCTION

This chapter covers briefly the structure and composition of the major clay mineral types; the distribution and occurrence of clay minerals in sedimentary rocks; and the value of clays to the field of petroleum geology and geochemistry.

Due to the extreme fine-grained nature of the clay minerals, they were little understood and the nature of their crystal structure in considerable doubt until the development of the X-ray diffraction methods in the early thirties. Ross, Hendricks, Kerr, Hofmann, Gruner, Pauling, and Bradley, along with others, established the crystal structure and the inter-relation of the various clay minerals. During the late forties the X-ray diffractometer was made commercially available and since then there has been a continuously increasing study and understanding of the clay minerals.

There has been an intense effort by geologists, mineralogists, and geo-chemists to determine the geologic significance of the clay minerals. The petroleum industry in particular has investigated the clay minerals in the hope they would be used in identifying environments, locating source areas, identifying formations, zoning and correlating, and understanding the origin and migration of hydro-carbons.

The role of clay minerals in the origin and migration of hydrocarbons must be extremely important but, as yet, little is known. Shales (sedimentary rocks composed largely of clay minerals) comprise well over 50% of sedimentary rocks and contain three-fourths of the preserved organic matter. At the time of depo-sition, shales probably contained over three-fourths of the water trapped by sedi-ments. Most of the compaction necessary for fluid migration occurs in shale. Most sandstone and some limestone reservoirs contain clay minerals which affect the implacement and the withdrawal of hydrocarbons.

The organic content of shales ranges from less than 0.1 to greater than 30%. Nearshore Recent sediments (primarily muds) contain an average of 2.5% organic material, open ocean sediments less than 1%, lagoons 1–7%, and Mississippi delta muds 2–3% (TRASK, 1939). These values are similar to those found in ancient shales from equivalent environments. Organic material may occur as discrete particles and laminae, intimately mixed with the clay minerals, or adsorbed from the dissolved state onto inorganic minerals.

There is considerable literature on the presence and distribution of organic material in shales; however, there is relatively little information concerning the effects of clay minerals on organic matter (for review see SMITH and BADER, 1961). GRIM (1953) has suggested that montmorillonite might act as a catalyst in the forming of hydrocarbons. Montmorillonite is known to have a strong affinity for organic compounds (COWAN and WHITE, 1958). WHITEHOUSE and JEFFREY (1953) reported on the removal of organic material from solution by various clay minerals. In a recent study of the removal of organic compounds from solutions by clay minerals, SMITH and BADER (1961) found a differential selection of organics. They also found that montmorillonite had the greatest capacity to associate with the organic compounds, followed by illite, kaolinite, and quartz. Both pH and chlorinity affect the amount of clay-organic association. They concluded: "More than one process is involved when organic compounds are associated with minerals settling through the water column. The magnitude of any one will be controlled by the structure and molecular weight of the compound and the structure and surface areas of the mineral. Thus, a triggering mechanism related to the type mineral and the type compound will cause the formation of a complex clay-organic gel which appears to have both chemical and physical characteristics. It is possible that both a molecular sieve-type process and a catalytic reaction may occur." MILNE and SHOTT (1958) reported montmorillonite muds from the Mobile River, partially complexed with organic material. They believe this association is "modified or partially destroyed in sea water." Expanded and degraded illite and chlorite have a strong affinity for some of the organic compounds found in the Mississippian crude oils of Illinois (SMOOT, 1959).

Clay minerals are present in reservoir sandstones and can complicate the problem of oil recovery. The clay can occur as discrete grains or aggregates and be little affected by fluid movement; however, in many sands clay minerals coat the sand- and silt-size grains. In the small pore channels, relatively slight expansion or movement of the clay minerals can effectively block the movement of hydrocarbons or other fluids. MOORE (1960) reports that only 1–4% of water-sensitive clays may completely plug a formation. In California sands containing less than 5% montmorillonite, the average permeability of rock decreases from 1,600 millidarcys in air to 620 millidarcys in salt water and 120 millidarcys in fresh water (MORRIS et al., 1959).

Expanded clay minerals (montmorillonite, vermiculite, and mixed-layer clays) which are in contact with the formation brine are flocculated and unexpanded. In this condition the clays occupy a minimum volume of pore space. When the cation concentration of the brine is decreased by the injection of fresh water, the clays deflocculate and expand. This can block the smaller channels and decrease permeability to near zero.

Another type of plugging apparently can be caused by the physical movement of thin flakes and books of kaolinite. In some cases kaolinite, and probably other clay minerals, are actually transported into the well bore along with the hydro-carbons.

COMPOSITION AND STRUCTURE

An excellent and detailed discussion on the structure, composition, and identification of the layer silicates was prepared by WARSHAW and ROY (1961).

Most of the clay minerals are hydrous layer lattice silicates. Attapulgite and sepiolite which have chain-type structures will not be discussed as they are relatively scarce in sedimentary rocks. The term "clay" has a connotation of small partical size, generally finer than 2 or 4 μ. Actually, many clay minerals are coarser than 4 μ and many non-clay minerals occur in sizes finer than 2 μ. The clay mineralogist is primarily concerned with the study of layer lattice silicates many of which are extremely fine grained. The great bulk of these fine-grained layer silicates occur in sediments.

The basic structural units in layer silicates are silica layers and brucite or gibbsite layers. The former consist of SiO tetrahedra connected at three corners in the same plane forming a hexagonal network. The tips of the tetrahedrons all point to the same direction. This unit is called the tetrahedral layer. The brucite or gibbsite layer consists of two planes of hydroxyl ions between which lay a plane of magnesium or aluminium ions which is octahedrally coordinated by the hydroxyls. This unit is known as the octahedral layer. These layers are combined so that the oxygens at the tips of the tetrahedrons project into a plane of hydroxyls in the octahedral layer and replace two-thirds of the hydroxyls.

Nearly all of the clay minerals are composed of combinations of these two types of layers. The major subdivision of the layer lattice silicates is based upon the type of combinations of the tetrahedral and octahedral layers. Additional subdivision is based on: (1) whether the octahedral layer contains two cations per half unit cell (dioctahedral) as in gibbsite or three cations per half unit cell (trioctahedral) as in brucite; (2) the manner of stacking of the tetrahedral–octahedral units upon each other; and (3) the amount and type of isomorphous replacement of the cations.

The 1:1 or two-layer clay-mineral group consists of one tetrahedral layer and one octahedral layer. These two layers are approximately 7 Å thick. This two-layer group is divided into kaolin (dioctrahedral) and septechlorite (trioctahedral) families. The kaolin minerals are all pure hydrous aluminum silicates. The different members are characterized by the manner of stacking of the basic 7-Å layers (Table I).

The trioctahedral two-layer minerals are called septechlorites (NELSON and ROY, 1954). The serpentine minerals (chrysotile and antigorite are the most common) which are included in this family consist of a tetrahedral layer and an

TABLE I

STRUCTURAL SCHEMES OF KAOLIN MINERALS
(After WARSHAW and ROY, 1961)

Kaolin minerals	$(Al_4Si_4O_{10}(OH)_8$
Nacrite	6-layer monoclinic
Dickite	2-layer monoclinic
Kaolinite	1-layer triclinic
Kaolinite d (Fireclay)	1-layer monoclinic, b axis disordered
Halloysite	1 layer, a and b disordered
Endellite $Al_4Si_4O_{10}(OH)_8.4H_2O$	1 layer + H_2O

octahedral layer containing largely magnesium with only minor amounts of aluminum. The other minerals in this family have a wide range of variations in composition. Aluminum, iron, manganese, nickel, chromium can substitute for magnesium in the octahedral layer and aluminum, ferric iron, and germanium for silicon in the tetrahedral layer (ROY and ROY, 1954). The septechlorites in normal sediments usually occur mixed with kaolinite and/or chlorite and are difficult to identify.

The three-layer or 2:1 layer lattice silicates consist of two silica tetrahedral layers between which is an octahedral layer. These three layers form a unit approximately 10 Å thick. The oxygens at the tips of the tetrahedrons point in towards the center octahedral layer and substitute for two-thirds of the octahedrally coordinated hydroxyls. The 2:1 clay minerals include the talc, mica, and montmorillonite groups which are by far the most abundant of the clay minerals.

The pure end members of this family are talc, a hydrous magnesium silicate; pyrophyllite, hydrous aluminum silicate; and minnesotaite, a hydrous iron silicate.

The 2:1 structural unit of the micas is similar to that for talc; however, between the 2:1 units is a layer of large cations. These are referred to as interlayer cations. Potassium is the most common, but sodium and calcium also occur. These interlayer cations fit into the hexagonal ring formed by the tetrahedral oxygen ions and bond adjacent 2:1 units. The inter-layer cations balance the charge due to the substitution of cations of lesser charge for some of those of greater charge in the tetrahedral and/or octahedral layer. The basic 2:1 units are stacked together in a variety of combinations: 2M (two-layer monoclinic), 1M (one-layer monoclinic), 1Md (disordered one-layer monoclinic), and 3T (three-layer trigonal). The first three are by far the most common. Muscovite is commonly the 2M type, phlogopite the 1M, and mixed-layer clays 1 Md.

The mica family is subdivided on the basis of whether they are dioctahedral (muscovite type) or trioctahedral (biotite type). The micas are further characterized by the number of silicon ions in the tetrahedral position: tetrasilicic, trisilicic, disilicic, and monosilicic. Aluminum and less commonly ferric iron substitute for the silicon. The micas are further categorized according to the wide range of cations and combination of cations which occur in the octahedral layer. Aluminum (muscovite) and magnesium (phlogopite) are the only two which occur alone in the octahedral layers. Most micas have two or more cations in the octahedral layers. Aluminum, magnesium, and iron occur in practically all combinations in the octahedral layer. Mn, V, Cr, Li, Ti and a variety of other cations can occur in varying amounts. The substitution of a cation of a lower charge for a cation of a higher charge, in both the octahedral (e.g., Mg^{2+} replacing Al^{3+}) and tetrahedral (e.g., Al^{3+} replacing Si^{4+}) layer, give the $2:1$ lattice a net negative charge which is satisfied by the interlayer cations. There is a long list of mica names (FOSTER, 1956; WARSHAW and ROY, 1961) which have been established from the study of coarse-grained minerals. Most of these minerals probably exist in argillaceous sediments but their identification is extremely difficult.

The fine-grained micas belong to the illite family. The dioctahedral illites greatly predominate over the trioctahedral. The most common illite mineral is dioctahedral and has approximately half as much aluminum substituting for silica in the tetrahedral layer ($0.5:3.5$) as does muscovite ($1:3$). Approximately three-fourths of the octahedral cations are aluminum, minor amounts of ferric iron are present, and approximately one-eighth of the cations are divalent (magnesium and ferrous iron). This gives a total negative charge of approximately 0.75 as compared with a value of one for muscovite.

Muscovite: $K(Al_2)(Si_3Al)O_{10}(OH)_2$

Illite: $K_{0.75}(Al_{1.50}Fe_{0.25}^{3+}\ Fe_{0.03}^{2+}\ Mg_{0.22})(Si_{3.50}Al_{0.50})O_{10}(OH)_2$

Although the aluminum illites are variable in composition, the reported variation is smaller than might be expected: tetrahedral aluminum ranges from 0.39 to 0.62, octahedral magnesium from 0.11 to 0.43, and octahedral iron from 0.06 to 0.58.

The dioctahedral iron illite is the mineral glauconite. Glauconite is also used as a rock name and is applied to any aggregate of fine-grained, green-layer lattice minerals. As with the aluminum illites the iron illite layers commonly occur interlayered with montmorillonite-like layers. In glauconites more than half the octahedral positions are filled with iron, the most abundant being ferric iron. The aluminum content of the tetrahedral layer is usually less than that of the aluminum illites and the magnesium content of the octahedral layer greater. HENDRICKS and ROSS (1941) gave the following formula as characteristic of many glauconites:

$(K, Ca/2, Na)_{0.84}(Al_{0.74}Fe_{0.97}^{3+}Fe_{0.19}^{2+}Mg_{0.40})(Si_{3.65}Al_{0.35})O_{10}(OH)_2$

Aluminum in the tetrahedral layer of well-crystallized 1M glauconites range from 0.13 to 0.58 and divalent cations in the octahedral layer from 0.55 to 0.89 (WARSHAW, 1957; BURST, 1958b).

Most aluminum illites have the 2M structure; whereas the glauconites, like the iron-rich micas, have a 1M or a 1Md structure. Most aluminum illites and some glauconites are fairly well crystallized and contain only potassium-bound, non-expanded layers.

There is a great number of clays referred to as the mixed-layer clays. The most abundant mixed-layer clay is composed of randomly intermixed layers of illite, either the aluminum or iron variety, and 2:1 layers which have a weaker lattice charge and contain water layers. The 2:1 weakly-charged layers are usually called montmorillonite and the clay a mixed-layer illite–montmorillonite. The ratio of these two types of layers can vary from more than 9:1 to less than 1:9. Some people call any mixed-layer illite–montmorillonite with a ratio of 7:3 or larger illite. As the spectrum is continuous the terms illite and montmorillonite should be reserved for the end members and any mineral composed of a mixture of the two types of layers should be called a mixed-layer illite–montmorillonite and the ratio of the types of layers reported.

Trioctahedral illites are relatively rare as pure mineral concentrates, but have been reported in Scottish soils (WALKER, 1950). The composition is similar to biotite:

$$K_{0.33}Ca_{0.08}Na_{0.10} (Al_{1.24}Ti_{0.13}Fe_{0.77}^{3+}Mg_{0.81})(Si_{3.30}Al_{0.70}) O_{10}(OH)_2$$

As the interlayer cations are relatively easily leached from biotite, the clay-size minerals are usually mixed-layer biotite–vermiculite (expanded biotite).

The expanded or expandable 2:1 minerals vary widely in chemical composition and in layer lattice charge. These minerals are characterized by the presence of loosely bound cations and layers of water or polar organic molecules between the silicate sheets. The interlayer width is reversibly variable. The interlayer water can be driven off at temperatures between 120° and 200°C. Sodium, calcium, magnesium, and aluminum are the most common naturally occurring interlayer cations.

The dioctahedral variety is by far the most abundant. The layer lattice charge on the expanded clays range from 0.3 to 0.8 per $O_{10}(OH)_2$ units of structure. The low charged (0.3–0.6), expanded minerals are called montmorillonite, mont-morillonids, and smectites, among others. Subdivision of the expanded clay group is still a problem as they are not well understood.

The low charge (0.3–0.5) dioctahedral minerals which have most of their charge originating in the octahedrae are called montmorillonites. A typical formula would be:

$$(Ca, Na)_{0.40}(Al_{1.50}Fe_{0.15}{}^{-0.35}Mg_{0.35}) (Si_{3.95}Al_{0.05}{}^{-0.05}) O_{10} (OH)_2$$

Similar type expanded minerals which have a relatively high tetrahedral charge content, 0.4, are called beidellites. These clays have a total charge of 0.7 or higher. Identical minerals which are known to have been derived by leaching potassium from illite or muscovite are referred to as dioctahedral vermiculite. There is apparently a complete gradation in composition and charge between montmorillonite and beidellites. The ferric iron-rich variety is called nontronite.

Although they are rare in sediments, there is a wide spectrum of trioctahedral expanded clays. The most common in the low-charge range 0.3–0.5 is hectorite, which contains magnesium and lithium in the octahedral layer, and saponite, which has considerable magnesium in the octahedral layer and some aluminum substitution in the tetrahedral layer.

Trioctahedral expanded 2:1 minerals with a lattice charge of 0.6–0.8 are called vermiculites. These minerals are usually coarser grained and have better crystal organization than most expanded clays. The decision as to whether a clay should be called a vermiculite or not is usually based on its ability to adsorb two layers of ethylene glycol and expand to 17 Å. WALKER (1958) has shown that magnesium-based expanded clays with a charge greater than 0.6 will only adsorb one layer of glycerol and expand to 14.3 Å (vermiculite); whereas those with a smaller charge will adsorb two layers and obtain a 17.5 Å thickness (montmorillonite). The present classification of the expanded clays and the illites is not at all satisfactory.

All the non-expanded 2:1 and 2:2 layer lattice silicates can have their interlayer cations removed. Water and organic molecules can then penetrate between these layers to form expanded layer minerals.

Chlorite also occurs as a clay-size mineral. It consists of a 2:1 talc layer plus a brucite layer. This forms a unit 14 Å thick. Most chlorites are trioctahedral, although WEAVER (1959) has reported the presence of dioctahedral chlorite in some bentonite deposits. As substitution can occur both in the 2:1 layers and in the brucite layer, the chlorites have a wide range of composition. The coarser grained chlorites have been analyzed and classified (HEY, 1954) but little is known of the composition of sedimentary chlorites, since they rarely occur as pure minerals. They are usually classed as iron-rich or magnesium-rich chlorites.

There is a large number of clays which are not pure mineral types but consist of interstratified units of different chemical composition (in detail, this may include nearly all the 2:1 layer minerals). These are called mixed-layer clays. The two or possibly three different units can be regularly interstratified *ABABAB* or more commonly randomly interstratified *AABABBABA*.

The most common regularly interstratified clay mineral, corrensite (LIPPMANN, 1954), consists of alternate layers of chlorite and vermiculite or chlorite and montmorillonites.

Mixed-layer illite–montmorillonite is by far the most abundant (in the vicinity of 90%) mixed-layer clay. These two units occur in all possible proportions from 9:1 to 1:9. Many of those with a 9:1 or even 8:2 ratio are called illites or glauconites (according to HOWER, 1961, all glauconites have some interlayered montmorillonite) and those which have ratios of 1:9 and 2:8 are usually called montmorillonite. This practice is not desirable and is definitely misleading. Other random mixed-layer clays are chlorite–montmorillonite, biotite–vermiculite, chlorite–vermiculite, illite–chlorite–montmorillonite. Most commonly, one of the layers is the expanded type and the other is non-expanded.

IDENTIFICATION

The identification of clay minerals by X-ray diffraction is by far the most useful and reliable technique available. The clay fraction (usually less than 2 μ) is separated from the rock, dispersed in water and allowed to settle on a glass slide so that most of the flakes are oriented parallel with the slide. The orientation em-

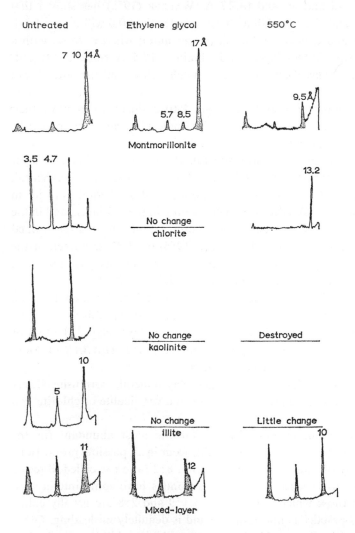

Fig.1. X-ray diffraction patterns representative of the five major clay types.

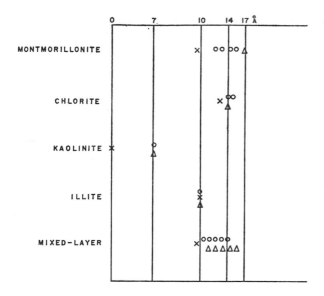

Fig.2. Diagram illustrating the movement of the 001 X-ray diffraction peak when clays are glycolated and heated.

phasizes the (001) series of reflections. These reflections are usually all that are necessary for routine clay-mineral identification. If it is necessary to determine whether a clay is dioctahedral or trioctahedral or 1M, 2M, etc., it is necessary to use unoriented clay samples.

Fig.1 contains X-ray powder-diffraction patterns of five standard clay samples, untreated, treated with ethylene glycol, and heated to 550°C. Most shales contain several clay minerals and it is usually necessary to glycolate (replace the water with ethylene glycol) and heat the shale in order to identify the several components. The position of the peaks for untreated samples is the same as listed in Table I. The method of marking the X-ray peaks of the different clay minerals used in Fig.1 will be used in subsequent figures, that is: stippled = mixed-layer illite–montmorillonite, cross-hatched = montmorillonite, horizontal-lined = kaolinite, open 10 Å = illite, open 7 Å and 14 Å = chlorite. Fig.2 is a schematic diagram illustrating the shifting of the (001) peaks when the clays are subjected to various treatments.

Montmorillonite is one of the most sensitive clay minerals. Untreated, its (001) peak ranges from 12 to 15 Å, depending on whether it contains one or two layers of water; treated with ethylene glycol it expands to 17 Å; and when heated, it collapses to 9.5 Å (as the water or glycol is driven off). Chlorite is unaffected by ethylene glycol; heat, however, will cause the 14 Å peak to move to about 13.8 Å and will destroy all peaks except the 13.8 Å (001) peak (and the weak (005) peak). Kaolinite is unaffected by ethylene glycol and is destroyed at a temperature near 550 °C. Illite is relatively unaffected by either of these treatments. Mixed-layer or intergrown illite–montmorillonite will have peaks which fall at average values somewhere between the peaks of pure illite (10 Å) and pure montmorillonite (12–15 Å). The exact position will depend on the relative amounts of the two

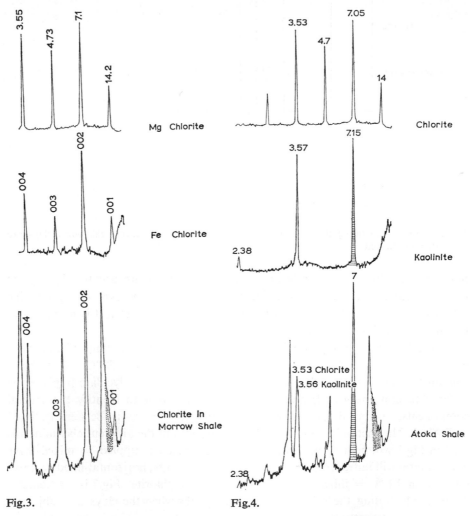

Fig.3.   Fig.4.

Fig.3. X-ray diffractometer patterns of Mg and Fe chlorites and a chloritic shale.

Fig.4. X-ray diffractometer patterns of chlorite, kaolinite, and a shale containing both chlorite and kaolinite.

components. The example in Fig.1 contains 70–80% illite layers and 20–30% montmorillonite layers (7:3). In the mixed-layer ratio, 7:3, 5:5, 1:4, etc., the first number refers to the non-expanded clay; i.e., illite or chlorite, and the second number to the expanded (containing water) clay, i.e., montmorillonite, or vermiculite.

Specific minerals

Chlorite
Fig.3 shows X-ray diffractometer patterns of two chlorites with a regular sequence of the (001) peaks. The variation in the relative heights of (001) peaks of the clay minerals may be caused by variation in the chemical composition as can be seen by comparing the Mg chlorite with the Fe chlorite. Peak-height variations can also be due to structural differences. Fig.3 also shows this same (001) sequence in a shale which contains several other clays.

Chlorite and kaolinite
One of the most difficult distinctions to make is between chlorite and kaolinite. The 14 Å and 4.7 Å peaks of chlorite are usually weak and obscured by other peaks and the 7.1 and 3.5 Å peaks fall in nearly the same position as two of the strong kaolinite peaks (Fig.4). However, when both clays are present, the 3.53 Å (chlorite) and 3.57 Å (kaolinite) peaks are usually slightly offset from one another, and a double peak or broad peak which is less intense than the 7.1 Å peak is obtained (Fig.4). In addition, kaolinite has a 2.38 Å (003) peak which is absent or very weak in chlorite patterns.

Illite
Illite is usually quite easy to identify. Some information on the grain-size and degree of crystallinity can be obtained from the shape of the X-ray peaks. The fine-grained, poorly developed illites, such as the Fithian, have relatively broad peaks, whereas fine-grained muscovites and most illites have a relatively narrow, sharp peak. Fig.5 shows the difference between the Fithian illite, a fine-grained muscovite, and a shale illite. The pattern of the shale illite is quite similar to that of the fine-grained muscovite. The iron content of a mica strongly affects the height of the (002) 5 Å peak, and iron-rich micas or illites, such as biotite or glauconite, have a very low 5 Å peak (Fig.5).

Montmorillonite
Montmorillonite is the most common expanding clay found in shales. From the position of its (001) peak, it is possible to estimate the type of exchangeable cations it contains: 12.4 Å, one layer of water and probably Na^+; 14–15.4 Å, two layers of water and probably Ca^{2+} and/or Mg^{2+}. Although the 14 Å montmorillonite

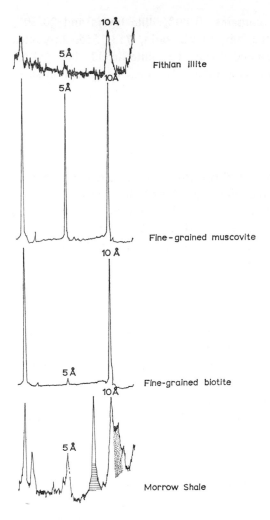

Fithian illite

Fine-grained muscovite

Fine-grained biotite

Morrow Shale

Fig.5. X-ray diffractometer patterns of illite, fine-grained muscovite, fine-grained biotite and an illitic shale.

peak overlaps the 14 Å chlorite peak, it can easily be identified by the fact that it expands to 17 Å when allowed to adsorb sufficient quantities of ethylene glycol.

Mixed-layer clays

Commonly the montmorillonite is intergrown with layers of chlorite (mixed-layer chlorite–montmorillonite). This mixture causes the glycolated sample to produce a broad 14–17 Å X-ray peak. When heated, only the montmorillonite layers collapse to 10 Å, and the resulting X-ray diffraction is a broad 10–14 Å peak. When the intergrown layers have some semblance of regularity, the resulting peaks can be quite narrow. When these latter clays are heated to 500°C, the resulting

X-ray peaks can range between 10.1 and 14 Å depending on the relative proportions of the two types of layers.

Montmorillonite (12–15.4 Å) most commonly occurs intergrown with illite (10 Å) layers (mixed-layer illite–montmorillonite). If the mixture consists of 10 Å layers and 12 Å layers, the position of the resulting X-ray peak will be smaller than 12 Å and the mixture usually can be identified. However, if the mixture is of 10 Å and 15 Å layers, identification is uncertain, particularly if the 15 Å layers predominate. These mixed-layer clays usually can be identified after they have been glycolated. If the peak does not shift completely to 17 Å, some non-montmorillonitic layers are present—either illite or chlorite. If the sample is heated to 550°C and the peak shifts to 9.5–10 Å, the non-expanded layers must be a 10 Å material (usually illite). If the peak does not shift completely to the 10 Å position some chlorite layers are probably present, and the clay is probably an illite–

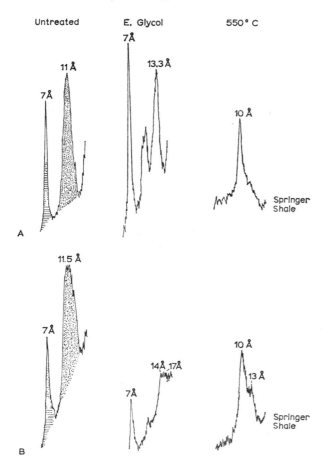

Fig.6. X-ray diffractometer patterns of mixed-layer illite-montmorillonite (A) and mixed-layer illite-chlorite-montmorillonite (B).

chlorite–montmorillonite intergrowth. Fig.6 shows a mixed-layer illite–mont-morillonite (7:3) clay.

It is difficult to accurately calculate the percentage of the various clay minerals in a complex mixture. However, it is possible to standardize the procedure so that reasonable precision can be obtained.

First make an X-ray pattern of the glycolated sample. Heat the same slide at 280–380°C for approximately 1 hour and obtain an X-ray pattern in the 10–7 Å interval. On the heated pattern the 7 Å peak reflects the combined chlorite and kaolinite content. The 10 Å peak represents the combined illite, montmorillonite, and mixed-layer illite–montmorillonite content. Divide the peak-height value obtained for the 7 Å peak by 2.5 to correct for the difference in diffraction ability between the 7 Å and 10 Å peaks. Total the corrected 7 Å value and the 10 Å value and calculate the percentages represented by the two peaks. The 7 Å percentage value represents the combined percentage of kaolinite and chlorite and the 10 Å value represents the combined percentage of illite and expanded clays.

On the glycolated pattern measure the peak height of the 17 Å peak and divide by 4 to correct for differences in diffractive ability. This value and the peak height of the 10 Å peak from the glycolated pattern can be compared to the heated 10 Å peak height and the total percentage of 10 Å material and the percentages of illite and montmorillonite can be calculated. The percentage of mixed-layer illite–montmorillonite is obtained by subtracting the percent illite and montmorillonite from the total 10 Å percentage obtained from the heated pattern. Use the 3.53 chlorite peak height and the 3.57 kaolinite peak height directly to calculate the relative percentages of the two minerals. These values can then be multiplied by the total percent of 7 Å material obtained from the heated sample. The 7 Å heated and glycolated peaks can be compared and the peak-height values of one or the other of the patterns corrected, if necessary.

DISTRIBUTION OF CLAY MINERALS

More than 50% of the minerals in sedimentary rocks are probably clay minerals; more than 95% of all sedimentary rocks contain clay minerals; shales are estimated to comprise somewhere between 50% and 80% (PETTIJOHN, 1949) of the geologic section. Quantitative X-ray analyses of 300 representative non-silty shale samples (SHAW and WEAVER, 1958) indicate that the average shale composition is 30% quartz, 5% feldspar, 4.7% carbonates, 0.5% iron oxides, 1% organic, and 60% clay. Frequency curves, Fig.7, indicate that the distribution of quartz is nearly normal. The clay curve is slightly skewed towards the low clay content values. The feldspar and carbonate curves have long tails extending towards the high-percentage values.

Illite is the most abundant clay mineral (probably greater than 50%), mont-

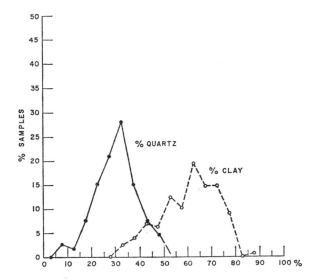

Fig.7. Frequency curves showing the amount of quartz and clay in 300 shale samples.

morillonite and mixed layer illite–montmorillonite next, followed by kaolinite, chlorite, and mixed-layer chlorite–montmorillonite (or vermiculite). Other clay minerals are relatively rare in normal sediments.

Recent

Though there has been a recent flurry of interest in the clay minerals in Recent sediments, there is still relatively little known about them. Fig.8 is a map summarizing the present data on the distribution of clay minerals in Recent marine sediments. To a large extent the ocean clays are similar in composition to the clays in the surrounding soils and sediments from which they are derived.

Only a relatively minor amount of work has been done on deep-sea clays. CORRENS (1937, 1939) found that kaolinite and halloysite are a common constituent of the sediments in the equatorial part of the Atlantic Ocean. He also showed that most of the sediments from the same area contained more than 50% calcium carbonate. As kaolinite presumably is formed only in an acid environment and as the rivers carrying detritus to this area drain tropical lateritic (kaolinitic) soils, there seem little doubt that the Atlantic Ocean kaolinite is land derived and detrital in origin. DIETZ (1941) concluded: "... the clay-mineral distribution on the sea floor is regionally similar to that on land in having a relative abundance of kaolinite and iron oxide in tropical regions and of illite and montmorillonite in temperate and polar regions. This suggests that deep-sea clays are terrestrially derived".

Recent studies (HEEZEN et al., 1960) in the eastern half of the North Atlantic

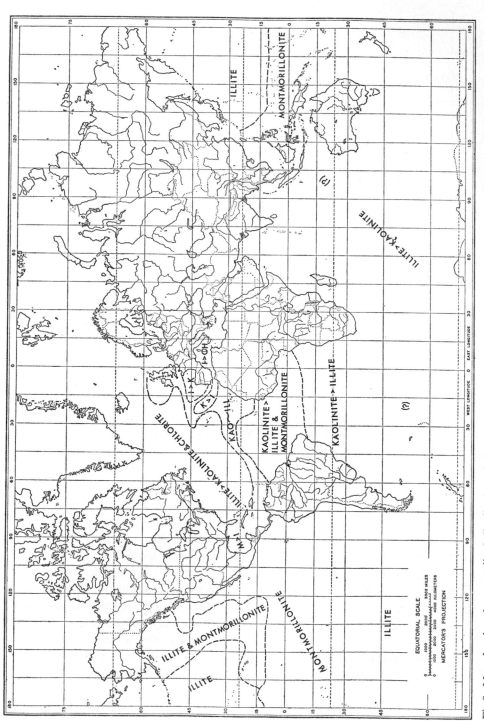

Fig.8. Map showing the generalized distribution of clay minerals in modern marine muds. Data taken from: CORRENS (1939), PINSAK and MURRAY (1959), GRY et al (1959), GRIPPAMA (1960), GROSERY-SZAY (1961a, b) and GORPERG (1963).

show illite is dominant (approximately 60–70%), chlorite is next in abundance, followed by kaolinite and montmorillonite. Off the coast of Brazil montmorillonite and kaolinite are the most abundant clays in the samples they examined. EROSCHEV-SHAK (1961a) reports kaolinite values as high as 80% or more in the equatorial regions of the Atlantic. Scattered samples from the Indian Ocean indicates that illite and kaolinite are predominant (GORBUNOVA, 1960).

In a recent study of Pacific Ocean muds GRIFFIN and GOLDBERG (1963) report that the mid-North Pacific has a high illite content which they believe to be primarily of eolian origin. The North Pacific coastal sediments are enriched in an expanded 2:1 clay which may be stripped illite and chlorite rather than montmorillonite and are considered to have been transported by rivers. Chlorite increases to the north presumably reflecting a northern source. In the South Pacific montmorillonite is the dominant clay mineral. It is closely associated with the zeolite, phillipsite. Griffin and Goldberg believe both minerals are formed from the sub-sea alteration of volcanic materials.

Studies of the off-shore sediments of the Gulf of Mexico by PINSAK and MURRAY (1958) and GRIFFIN (1960) show that montmorillonite is the most abundant clay followed by illite and mixed-layer illite–montmorillonite. Most of these clays were carried into the Gulf by the Mississippi River.

The Recent sediments between the Mississippi delta and Florida have been the most thoroughly studied (JOHNS and GRIM, 1958; MILNE and EARLEY, 1958; GRIFFIN, 1960). Griffin concluded after a detailed study of this area that three major rivers—Mississippi, Mobile, and Apalachicola—supply most of the clay minerals to the northeastern Gulf of Mexico; the Mississippi is carrying abundant montmorillonite which is derived from the bordering soils; the eastern Apalachicola river carries a kaolinite-rich suite obtained from the kaolinite-rich soils of the southern Appalachian Mountains. As these river-borne clays enter saline water, there is a very slight relative increase in the proportion of kaolinite to montmorillonite; that portion of the clay not deposited at the river mouths is distributed by the Gulf currents; in the shallow-water near-shore sediments there is a gradational change from the western montmorillonite facies to the eastern kaolinitic facies; farther off shore the clay suite is dominated by the much more abundant Mississippi clay suite. WEAVER (1960) found that the carbonate muds east of the Florida Reef Tract were composed of illite, chlorite and talc, which were presumably derived from the southern Appalachians. West of the reefs the muds contain a Gulf clay suite (montmorillonite predominant).

MILLOT (1953) reports that the clays transported by the Oued Sebou, Niger, Durance, Meurthe, Mosel, Rhine and Rhône rivers and deposited in the river valleys, estuaries and deltas "contain a replica of the material in the up-stream basins".

Clay-mineral studies of the Mississippi Delta (GRIM and JOHNS, 1954; MILNE and EARLEY, 1958) indicate that there is very little difference between the clay composition of the river-suspended sediment load and that of the delta muds. The data of Grim and Johns indicate that between the river and delta samples there is generally less than 10% difference in the amount of any one clay mineral.

The montmorillonitic Guadalupe Delta (GRIM and JOHNS, 1954) and the kaolinitic Orinoco Delta (DIETZ, 1941) are both similar in composition to the surrounding soils.

The Chesapeake Bay sediments (POWERS, 1954) contain a clay suite (illite, chlorite, kaolinite) similar to that carried by the Susquehanna River (WEAVER, 1958b).

The dominant clay-mineral character of the Recent fluviatile, deltaic, shallow-marine, and deep-marine sediments is apparently controlled by the detrital clay material derived from the land areas. Although the bulk character of the marine clay suite is determined by the source material, considerable local variation in the composition of the shallow clay-mineral suites usually has been attributed to syngenetic alterations of the detrital clay material. Recent studies indicate that in general there is an increase in the relative amount of illite or chlorite, or both, and a decrease in the amount of kaolinite seaward (GRIM et al., 1949; GRIM and JOHNS, 1954; POWERS, 1954; GRIFFIN and INGRAM, 1955). The recent studies of GRIFFIN (1960), and TAGGART and KAISER (1960) indicate that variations in source and the distribution of current can account for many of the near-shore clay-mineral variations.

Chemical analysis of the clay fraction presents data which are commonly difficult to interpret. GRIM and JOHNS (1954) show that the open Gulf clays contain 0.92% more MgO than the deltaic clays (3.37% as opposed to 2.45%); however, the Gulf clays contain 1.98% less CaO than the deltaic clays (1.34% as opposed to 3.32%). Thus, from this data the increase in total magnesium could be accounted for merely by the base exchange of magnesium for calcium.

The increase in K_2O content gulfward is 0.85% (1.51% as opposed to 2.36%). Part of this increase can be accounted for by the adsorption of potassium on the exchange positions of montmorillonite. KELLEY and LIEBIG (1934) found that after leaching montmorillonite with sea water 6.6% of the exchange cations were potassium; however, it is more likely that most of this potassium is adsorbed by stripped or degraded illite. Numerous people who have worked with soils (reviewed by REITEMEIER, 1951, and WEAVER, 1958a) have shown that weathered illites are capable of fixing several percent of potassium between the potassium-deficient illite layers. Samples from the Ouachita Mountains (which supply detritus to the Gulf of Mexico) containing 50–70% of weathered illite (glycolate to 16.6 Å) contain 1.6–1.9% K_2O. When these samples are treated with KOH the expanded illite contracts to 10 Å and fixes 1.9–3.3% additional K_2O. These samples show this same contraction when soaked in sea water for 20–30 days. Samples of sediment from the northern part of the Brazos River (in the area where it drains through Palaeozoic illitic shales) contain an abundance of expanded illite which readily reverts to illite when treated with potassium. Thus, there is little doubt that expanded illites are carried into the Gulf of Mexico and that after reaching the Gulf, they are quite capable of fixing potassium and contracting to 10 Å. These clays are probably present in sufficient abundance to account for much of the increase in K_2O content of the clays seaward.

K–Ar age studies of Recent marine and deltaic muds afford dates ranging from 100 to over 800 million years (HURLEY et al., 1959, 1961). It is apparent that most of the Recent clays are detrital in origin. These studies have not yet shown whether any appreciable amount of potassium is adsorbed by the clays when they are deposited in a marine environment.

Studies of the Recent indicate that, at the most, somewhat less than half the clay minerals is altered to any extent in a normal marine environment. Probably most of this alteration is in the form of cation adsorption or reconstitution of slightly weathered illites and chlorites back to their original form. In some situations different cations than were there originally may be adsorbed (or precipitated) between the detrital clay sheets. This latter process needs more thorough investigation before its significance can be evaluated. In any event there is little if any evidence that the basic detrital lattice is being altered to a measurable extent in Recent marine environments. In the South Pacific and other local areas where there is an abundance of glassy volcanic material montmorillonite can apparently be formed on the sea floor.

Ancient sediments

Fig.9 is an attempt to estimate the relative distribution of the four major clay-mineral groups through the various geologic periods. The expanded clay group includes montmorillonite and mixed-layer clays with expanded layers. Montmorillonite (more than 90% expanded layers) is most abundant in the Tertiary but is relatively common in sediments as old as Upper Mississippian. Mixed-layer illite–montmorillonite comprises most of the expanded clay in pre-Upper Mississippian sediments though chlorite–montmorillonite is relatively abundant in the Lower Ordovician and in the Tertiary of California. Attapulgite and sepiolite are abundant in some Tertiary rocks such as the Florida carbonate (REYNOLDS and GOODELL, 1962) and African carbonate rocks (MILLOT et al., 1961). Chamosite and other varieties of iron-rich clays dominate in some of the sedimentary iron-ore deposits. Talc is relatively common throughout the geologic section, particularly in carbonate rocks, but seldom occurs in abundance.

Fig.9 indicates a significant change in the clay suite that occurs in the Upper Mississippian. Pre-Upper Mississippian sediments are composed largely of illite and chlorite (approximate average is 80% illite and 10% chlorite). Post Lower Mississippian sediments have a more balanced suite and contain considerably more kaolinite and expanded clays.

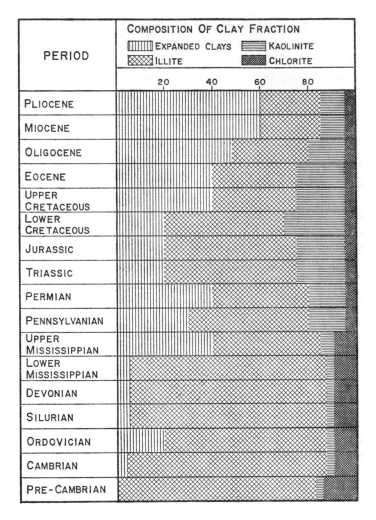

Fig.9. Relative distribution of the four major clay-mineral groups through the geologic periods.

The decrease in montmorillonite in older sediments is in part due to the greater depth of burial to which these rocks have been subjected and their conversion to mixed-layer illite–montmorillonite. Recent experimental work by HAWKINS (1961) shows that the presence of CO_2 favors the formation of illite over other clays. The abundance of carbonate rocks and the high CO_2 content of the ancient seas and atmosphere may have enhanced the formation of illite.

The increase in kaolinite, montmorillonite, and mixed-layer illite–montmorillonite and the added complexity of the clay-mineral suites near the end of the Mississippian roughly coincide with a major change in the tectonic pattern of North America and also with an increase in complexity of heavy-mineral suites

(PETTIJOHN, 1957; W. W. Rubey, personal communication, 1957). In pre-Devonian time, orogenic activity was restricted to long, narrow belts along the borders of the present continent. During Devonian time large areas in the stable interior of the continent were uplifted, and from Mississippian time on, much detrital material was derived from these areas of epeirogenic uplift (EARDLEY, 1951). This regional change in orogenic activity could affect the clay mineralogy in three ways: (1) change the source area from one of predominantly metamorphic rocks to one where igneous and older sedimentary rocks were an increasingly important factor; (2) provide many source areas which were much closer to the site of deposition; (3) increase the area for fresh-water continental deposition. These three factors would tend to increase the kaolinite and montmorillonite content of clay material while reducing the illite and chlorite contribution. The amount of kaolinite would be augmented by the increase in land plants, and by the increase in the amount and preservation of continental and shallow-marine near-shore sediments.

It is also likely that concomitant with the change in the tectonic pattern there was an increase in volcanism. The first major post-Devonian volcanic activity apparently occurred during the Upper Mississippian and may have ushered in the "widespread unrest in early Pennsylvanian" in the south central part of the present continent and other areas (EARDLEY, 1951). The Pennsylvanian sediments are, in general, mixtures of clays derived from the borderland orogenic belts and of older sediments from the interior epeirogenic uplifts.

The Permian, Triassic, and Jurassic were times of excessive volcanism (EARDLEY, 1951), as is suggested by the common occurrence of montmorillonite throughout this section of rocks. Volcanoes were relatively inactive during Early Cretaceous times, but volcanism was apparently rejuvenated with increased vigor in the Late Cretaceous (preceding Laramide orogeny) and resulted in the occurrence of strongly montmorillonitic sediments throughout the United States. Volcanic activity continued unabated throughout the Tertiary. Uplifted igneous and meta-morphic rocks continued to supply illite, chlorite, and kaolinite to the Tertiary basins; but this contribution is probably at least matched by montmorillonite and mixed-layer illite–montmorillonite derived from contemporaneous volcanics and older montmorillonite sediments.

The overwhelming majority of the illite clays have the 2M structure; the mixed-layer illite–montmorillonite clays have a 1M structure, and nearly all of the chlorite and mixed-layer chlorite–montmorillonite appears to be the trioc-tahedral variety.

Lithology

The composition of sedimentary rocks is estimated to be 14–40% sandstone, 15–29% limestone, and 40–56% shale (PETTIJOHN, 1949). The sandstones are classified into three broad groups: orthoquartzite, graywacke, and arkose. The orthoquartzites typically contain 90–95 % quartz and minor amounts of chert, feldspar, and calcite. The grains are usually held together with silica or calcite cement. 1–5 % clay occurs as discrete nests or coating the individual quartz grains. Seldom is there enough clay present to act as a matrix. Orthoquartzites are commonly derived by the reworking of older sediments; however, they can be derived from any type of source rock if the climate is humid and there exists a long period of tectonic stability (FOLK, 1961).

There is considerable difference of opinion as to what constitutes a graywacke. Metamorphic rock fragments are the major essential constituent of graywackes. Shale, slate, phyllite, and schist fragments, in addition to quartz and chert, make up the bulk of the grains. The soft clay and mica-rich rock fragments may range from 5 to 60%. An abundance of clay matrix (5–40%) is also common in graywackes (KRYNINE, 1948). This clay is commonly illite and fine-grained muscovite and chlorite which is derived from the break-up of the soft rock fragments. Sorting is poor and there is relatively little grain-to-grain contact. When sands of this type are deposited in high-energy environments they may be "cleaned-up" and the residium composed largely of quartz and chert (quartzose graywacke).

KRYNINE (1948) states: "Graywackes are formed during the stage of moderate deformation of the diastrophic cycle, the stage of subsidence, filling, and very early deformation of the geosynclines. Low-rank or common, non-feldspathic graywackes are related to broad and gently subsiding geosynclines (miogeosyncline). High-rank or feldspathic graywackes are formed in narrow and rapidly subsiding geosynclines, frequently connected with volcanic activity (eugeosynclines)".

Feldspar is the essential mineral of the arkose. It is present in amounts ranging from 25 to 50% and along with quartz comprises 80–98% of the rock (PETTIJOHN, 1949). The clay content of the arkose is variable but generally less than in the graywackes. Arkoses are derived from granitic rocks and where chemical weathering is mild (arid climate) little clay is formed. Under humid conditions some of the feldspars are weathered to form kaolinite, illite, and montmorillonite which are deposited as a matrix material. Arkoses are related to the stage of violent block faulting where basement granite is raised to the surface. They may also form on peneplaned granitic land areas if the climate is arid (FOLK, 1961).

Rocks containing more than 50% calcite or dolomite are called limestones. In addition to carbonate minerals they commonly contain quartz, chert, clay, and feldspar. The calcite in limestones occurs in six main forms: fossil fragments, oolites, pellets, intraclasts, mud-size grains, and sparry cement. The latter two types are true chemical constituents formed by precipitations. The other four types are those which have been suffered some transport or are biological in origin (FOLK, 1961).

These six constituents can occur in wide varieties of combinations and as a result this has led to the construction of a large number of classifications. Not enough work has been done to establish if any relation exists between the amount of clay and the type of carbonate constituent.

All carbonate rocks contain clay minerals. The amounts may range from 0.01 to 40%. Bioherms of reef limestone (shallow water, high-energy environment) may contain very little clay; whereas some deep-water limestones composed largely of pelagic Foraminifera contain an abundance of silicate clay minerals. It seems certain that the clay-mineral distribution in limestones has some useful genetic significance.

Most dolomites are secondary in origin formed by the replacement of calcite rather than by direct precipitation. They contain no distinctive clay-mineral type.

Relation of clays to lithology

Illite is generally the dominant mineral in carbonate rocks (for review see WEAVER, 1959) though all other clay-mineral types are present and often dominant through thousands of feet of section; i.e., montmorillonite is the dominant clay in much of the Upper Cretaceous limestones of Florida, mixed-layer chlorite–montmorillonite is the most abundant clay in the lower Ordovician limestones, and dolomites of the Warrior Basin and Arbuckel mountains. Illite does not appear to be more abundant in carbonate rocks than in shales. Most of the illites are the 2M variety and apparently detrital in origin. Much of the mixed-layer chlorite–montmorillonite is believed to have been formed from volcanic material. More magnesium was apparently present than necessary for the formation of montmorillonite and not enough to form chlorite. Chlorite formed from volcanic ash is common in the Ordovician K-bentonite beds.

The clay minerals in sandstones are frequently different from those found in shales. GLASS (1958) recently has presented an excellent example from some Pennsylvanian cyclothems of Illinois which illustrates such differences. He found that kaolinite was more abundant in the sandstones than in the shales and quite convincingly showed that "... kaolinite crystals form in sand bodies prior to exposure and that exposure in outcrop augments the process. Permeability, therefore, must be considered as a factor in clay mineral formation not only in outcrop but also in subsurface".

In many Cretaceous sediments, the kaolinite content is usually much greater in the sandstones than in the adjacent shales. Table II shows a typical example of the kaolinite distribution through a sand-shale section.

This phenomenon of kaolinite being concentrated in the sands occurs not only in thicker rock units but also in laminae-size units. In Table III is listed the percent kaolinite (in the less than 2 μ fraction) in adjacent sand and shale laminae (1–5 mm) from rocks with various types of primary bedding structures.

Although the kaolinite ratio varies considerably, the sand laminae consistently

TABLE II

RELATION OF KAOLINITE TO LITHOLOGY
(Cretaceous, Almond Formation, Wyo.)

Sample interval core footage	Lithology	Percent kaolinite
0	Shale	18
3	Shale	16
6	Shale	17
7	Silty shale	28
11	Siltstone	75
14	Sandstone	91
19	Sandstone	83
24	Sandstone	87
31	Sandstone	89
33	Sandstone	82
34	Shale	22
36	Siltstone	63
37	Siltstone	53
40	Shale	12
45	Shale	17

have a higher relative kaolinite content than the shale laminae. Whether this type of kaolinite distribution is due to segregation of the clay-mineral types during deposition or whether it is due to post-depositional alteration by fluids has not been satisfactorily answered although the latter explanation is the most likely.

The relative scarcity of clays other than kaolinite in Cretaceous sands plus the presence of fresh feldspar would suggest that if post-depositional alteration has occurred, it was the clays and not the feldspars which were altered to kaolinite. Illite and mixed-layer illite–montmorillonite are the dominant clay minerals in some of the less permeable sands and probably are the clays originally deposited with the sand.

TABLE III

KAOLINITE CONTENT OF ADJACENT SAND AND SHALE LAMINAE

	Percent kaolinite		
	Sandstone	Shale	Ratio
Regular bedded	73	11	6.6
Slightly irregular	43	16	2.7
Mottled	60	31	1.9
Slumped	63	14	4.5

SMOOT and NARAIN (1960) examined the clay in some Palaeozoic oil-bearing sandstones, non-oil-bearing sandstones, and shales from the Illinois Basin. Their results are summarized in Table IV.

Their data, as well as the data of others, indicate that the increase in kaolinite and mixed-layer clay (leached illite and chlorite) in the sands relative to the shales is due to post depositional leaching. They believe the clays in the oil-bearing sands are more completely altered because these sands tend to be more permeable and thus likely to have been leached more thoroughly.

TABLE IV

CLAY SUITES OF OIL-BEARING AND NON-OIL-BEARING SANDS AND ASSOCIATED SHALES

	Illite	Chlorite	Kaolinite	Expanded clays (mostly mixed layer)
Chester Sandstone				
Oil-bearing sandstone	0.7	1.6	3.2	4.2
Non-oil-bearing sandstone	1.7	2.7	2.5	2.5
Shales	4.3	3.6	0.7	1.4
Aux Vases Sandstone				
Oil-bearing sandstone	2.4	1.1		6.4
Non-oil-bearing sandstone	4.5	1.1		4.6
Shales	6.5	0.5		2.9

The occurrence of secondary kaolinite and dickite in sandstones is a common phenomenon. In many cases it has formed by the alteration of feldspar and other clay minerals; although occasionally in sub-surface sands, it appears to have grown from solutions which have not affected the feldspars. Kaolinite formed by the alteration of feldspars and other clays is apparently caused by acid intrastratal solutions. In continental sandstones these acid solutions would be available and could begin leaching the permeable sandstones immediately after deposition. In deltaic and marine sandstones acid solutions are not so readily available, but it is possible that the destruction of organic material by bacteria in the muds would produce the neutral–slightly acid condition which favors the formation of kaolinite. In other instances it is likely that the leaching is done by meteoric waters that have migrated from the sandstone outcrops. KULBICKI and MILLOT (1961) report that the Cambrian oil-bearing sandstones of the Sahara contain kaolinite and the non-oil-bearing sandstones illite. Thin-section studies suggest the kaolinite is secondary and formed from the alteration of feldspars, micas, and illite. Where oil migrated into the sandstone, the kaolinite was preserved; where salt waters fills the pore space, they believe the kaolinite was changed into illite.

QUAIDE (1956), BURST (1958a), and MILNE and EARLEY (1958) have reported the concentration of secondary chlorite in sandstones. Secondary poorly-crystallized chlorite and mixed-layer chlorite–montmorillonite is relatively common in marine sands. In many cases the chlorite is formed from the alteration of volcanic material. It is found in the volcanic-rich Tertiary sands and in older sands such as those in the Upper Mississippian montmorillonite-rich Springer formation.

Secondary illite occurs in sandstones (KRYNINE, 1940; WEAVER, 1955; R.L. Folk, personal communication, 1956) but it is considerably less common than kaolinite and chlorite.

In many instances it appears that the clean, more quartzose sandstones are more apt to contain secondary kaolinite. Secondary chlorite is usually found in "dirtier" sands than is kaolinite. The clay-mineral suite in most argillaceous sandstones is similar to that in the adjacent shale. This presumably reflects the relative lack of permeability.

Orthoquartzites may contain kaolinite but the clay suite is often composed entirely of illite or mixed-layer illite–montmorillonite (9:1–4:1) or both. Also, as was discussed before, much of the kaolinite in orthoquartzites has a post-depositional origin and thus does not reflect the character of the source material. Graywackes eroded from older metamorphosed geosynclinal rocks generally contain an illite and chlorite clay-mineral suite, but the younger graywackes (post-Mississippian) have relatively complex clay-mineral suites. Illite, chlorite, mixed-layer illite–montmorillonite, montmorillonite and kaolinite commonly are all present and in many instances montmorillonite and mixed-layer illite–montmorillonite are predominant. The clay content of only a few arkosic sandstones has been determined in detail but if the relative lack of kaolinite in Permian, Jurassic, and Triassic red shales is any indication, then kaolinite is probably relatively rare as a detrital constituent of arkoses. Nearly any of the other clay-mineral types can occur as the dominant clay mineral in these red shales. HOOKS and INGRAM (1955), in their study of Triassic arkosic rocks of North Carolina, concluded that: "Arkosic sediments, in general, can have almost any type of clay mineral in the clay fraction, depending on the nature of the source rock, the climate and topography of the source area, and the chemical environment of the depositional site".

Although some "granite wash" sandstones in California contain kaolinite, many of them also contain either montmorillonite, illite, or mixed-layer illite–montmorillonite as the major clay constituent.

Shales associated with orthoquartzite sandstones tend to have a relatively high illite content; those associated with sub-graywacke sands have a relatively high chlorite content.

RELATION OF CLAY MINERALS TO DEPOSITIONAL ENVIRONMENTS

MILLOT (1949, 1953) seems to have been the first to make a detailed attempt to relate clay minerals to environments of deposition. He found kaolinite to be dominant in fluvio-lacustrine deposits where acid leaching was active. In all other environments except basic lakes (which contained montmorillonite) illite was reported to be the major clay present (MILLOT, 1953). Numerous studies since then have indicated this relation exists in many instances. MURRAY (1954) showed that in some Pennsylvanian cyclothems from Illinois illite was always dominant but that chlorite and kaolinite decreased in going from non-marine to brackish to marine shales. GLASS (1958) found that in some Pennsylvanian sediments kaolinite was slightly more abundant in the non-marine than in the marine shales. KELLER'S (1956) study of the Pennsylvanian Cheltenham formation of Missouri indicated that in passing from a non-marine to a marine environment the clay suites changed from a diaspore, boehmite, well-crystallized kaolinite suite to a good to moderately crystallized kaolinite suite to an illite and moderately crystallized kaolinite suite to a largely illitic suite. DEGENS et al. (1957) found that in 70 Pennsylvanian samples the illite–kaolinite ratio was statistically higher in marine and brackish-water shales than in fresh-water shales. BURST (1958a) reports the reverse of this trend in some Gulf Coast Eocene shale where he found that the chlorite and kaolinite to illite ratio (7 Å/10 Å) increases (1.1 vs. 1.3) in passing from a deltaic to a marine environment. The contrast is more marked in the sandstones than in the shales. Illite is most abundant in the deltaic sandstones and chlorite in the beach sandstones. In much of the Pennsylvanian of West Texas the deltaic shales contain illite and chlorite and the marine shales only illite. In the deltaic facies of the Green River Formation chlorite is more abundant than in the surrounding lacustrine facies.

WEAVER (1960) reported that organic-rich marine black shales are composed almost entirely of illite or mixed-layer illite–montmorillonite, or both, and few contain kaolinite. Continental shales of this type commonly contain abundant kaolinite. Brackish-water black shales usually have a mixture of these two clay types.

KELLER (1953) found that either illite, montmorillonite or kaolinite could occur as the dominant clay mineral in the non-marine Morrison shales. SIMONS and TAGGART (1954) found in the marine Gulf Coast Tertiary shales that either illite, montmorillonite or kaolinite could predominate. LEMCKE et al. (1953), in a study of Molasse sediments, reported that the clay-mineral suites bore no significant relation to the environment of deposition. RIVIÈRE (1953) reported that the marine graptolitic clays of the Sahara are almost pure kaolinite. RIVIÈRE and VISSE (1954) have examined marine sediments in which illite, montmorillonite, kaolinite and palygorskite are predominant.

MILLOT et al. (1961) found that in the Eocene chemical sediments of North Africa, montmorillonite is dominant in the near-shore facies; farther from shore attapulgite is developed and finally sepiolite. These sediments were deposited in an evaporite basin and much of the clay material was believed to have been formed in the basin. The Al/Mg ratio of these three minerals varies from high for mont-morillonite to slightly larger than 1 for atapulgite and low for sepiolite. This presumably reflects the increase in the availability of magnesium farther from the basin edge. DROSTE (1961) conducted a study of seven Recent saline lake deposits in order to evaluate the relative effectiveness of source and depositional environ-ment. He concluded: "The clay-mineral composition of desert saline sediments of southern California is controlled almost entirely by the composition of the source rocks. The evaporites of this region are rich in sodium and calcium, and magnesium salts are extremely rare. The high sodium and calcium environment does not produce significant diagenetic change in the clay minerals deposited in these desert basins".

In the Lower Ordovician carbonate rocks of the southern United States mixed-layer chlorite–vermiculite (or montmorillonite) is a dominant clay mineral. These rocks are thought to be mostly tidal flat deposits. Evaporitic, magnesium-rich solutions might be expected to be common in such an environment and thus favor the development of magnesium rich clays.

The Cretaceous sediments in the Upper Mississippi Embayment (PRYOR, 1960) have clay suites that are closely related to environments. Kaolinite is dominant in the continental, montmorillonite in the marine and illite with kao-linite and montmorillonite in the near-shore transitional environment. In the Gulf Coast Wilcox sediments GRIFFIN (1960) found that the clays in the fluviatile shales are almost entirely kaolinite. Kaolinite decreases and montmorillonite increases seaward. The same clay-environmental relations occur in most of the Cretaceous sediments of the Rocky Mountain area. In the Upper Cretaceous of the Washakie Basin, Wyoming (WEAVER, 1961) the relation of average percent kaolinite is given in Table V.

A plot showing the percent distribution of kaolinite in the Upper Cretaceous always shows a minimum (5–10%) in the open marine facies of the Lewis shale. Above and below this minimum the kaolinite gradually increases indicating a continually decreasing marine influence. This wedge-shaped profile reflects the last major westward transgression and regression of the Cretaceous sea. The period of maximum transgression is indicated by the minimum kaolinite content of the shales. Montmorillonite is restricted to the open marine sediments. The presence of numerous thin bentonite beds in these open-marine sediments suggest that much of the montmorillonite was formed by the alteration of volcanic ash. Apparently only in the open marine environment was deposition slow enough and magnesium sufficiently available to cause the alteration to montmorillonite.

It appears that in the Cretaceous, kaolinite and montmorillonite have fairly consistent environmental significance. This specific relationship is evident in other age sediments but there are many exceptions.

The considerable data on glauconite has recently been reviewed by WER-MUND (1961). On the basis of his work on the Gulf Coast Tertiary he concluded

TABLE V

RELATION OF KAOLINITE TO ENVIRONMENT

Environment	Kaolinite ($^o/_o$) (in shales)
Open marine	6
Shallow marine to lagoon	16
Marsh to continental	27

that most glauconite is deposited in normally saline water and only a few in brackish water; that glauconite can be composed of any of the major clay-mineral types; and that the mineralogy of the glauconite is not related to depositional environments.

FACTORS AFFECTING THE DISTRIBUTION OF CLAYS

There has been considerable discussion concerning the origin of clays and particularly on why clay-mineral suites are so closely related to their depositional environments. GRIM (1953) and MILLOT (1953) suggested on the basis of their pioneering work that most clays were authigenic and formed or strongly modified in their depositional environment. RIVIÈRE (1953), RIVIÈRE and VISSE (1954) and WEAVER (1958b, 1959) contended that most of the clays in sediments were detrital in origin and only slightly modified in their depositional environment. There is no question that clay minerals are formed authigenically but only in a relatively few instances are they the predominant mineral in a clay suite. None of the major clay-mineral types are restricted to particular environments. Illite, montmorillonite, and mixed-layer illite–montmorillonite occur in abundance, and commonly occur as the dominant clay in all of the major marine and non-marine-type environments. Kaolinite is abundant in sediments of all environments but is most likely to be dominant in fluviatile environments. Chlorite, although commonly present in all environments, is seldom a predominant clay mineral. The magnesium rich minerals—mixed-layer chlorite–vermiculite, attapulgite, and sepiolite—are frequently abundant in some evaporatic environments.

Relatively unaltered detrital clays, slightly modified detrital clays, and strongly altered or authigenic clays are all found in sedimentary rocks. The first two types are quantitatively the most important. Studies of Recent sediments indicate that well over half, perhaps 70–100%, of the clays being deposited in the Gulf of Mexico and Atlantic Ocean are detrital in origin and unmodified except for some changes in the variety of exchangeable cation.

No direct evidence has been obtained to indicate that the basic lattice of clay minerals is being changed in Recent marine environments. Most of the chemical modification of pre-existing lattices that occurs under marine conditions is a form of rejuvenation. Weathered illites and micas with a portion or all of the potassium removed and chlorite with all or a portion of the magnesium and iron in the brucite layer removed are the second most abundant clay types being supplied to the present oceans. Water enters between the illite and mica layers from which the potassium is leached and these expanded layers resemble montmorillonite with which they are sometimes confused. When these expanded illites and micas reach marine waters, they obtain enough potassium to cause the layers to contract and the clay reverts to its non-expanded form. The same cyclic process appears to apply to chlorite. It is possible that under some conditions the expanded illite and expanded chlorite layers act as host for cations other than their original type.

It is likely that during times when the land surface had less relief than now and weathering conditions were suitable, the percentage of weathered, stripped clays carried to the seas was greater than the unweathered clays.

Authigenic montmorillonite formed by the alteration of volcanic material under marine conditions is relatively common in ancient sediments. Authigenic montmorillonite is apparently forming today in the southern Pacific (GRIFFIN and GOLDBERG, 1963). Much of the mixed-layer chlorite–vermiculite in the Palaeozoic carbonate rocks may be in a large part authigenic. How much of it formed from pre-existing clay lattices or from volcanic material is not certain. The magnesium-rich clays, attapulgite and sepiolite, can be formed authigenically (MILLOT et al., 1961) in magnesium-rich evaporatic environments.

The major natural chemical environments range from acid, well-leached continental conditions through alkaline, poorly-drained continental, to normal marine, and to magnesium-rich evaporatic conditions. Kaolinite is formed in the first environment. Attapulgite, sepiolite, chlorite and mixed-layer chlorite–vermiculite can be formed in the marine evaporatic environment. In the two intermediate environments chemical alteration is relatively minor and the great bulk of clays in these two environments is detrital in origin. Most of the chemical change in these two environments affects only the interlayer cations. Illite, montmorillonite, and mixed-layer illite–montmorillonite are apparently the clay minerals which are most stable under these environmental conditions.

Regardless of the mode of origin of the clay minerals there is in almost all instances a difference between the clay suites found in adjacent environments. These differences may be small, in the order of 2–20%, when the clays are predominantly detrital in origin or they may be quite large, as much as 100%, if the clays are predominantly authigenic. The pure detrital or predominantly detrital clay suites are by far the most abundant and for that reason clay changes between adjacent environments are usually relatively small.

There are three source materials for clay minerals: non-clay minerals, clay minerals and micas, and glassy volcanic material. When weathering solutions are acid to neutral and leaching is sufficient to carry away cations taken into solution, aluminum-rich minerals, kaolinite, and aluminum oxides will be formed from all source materials. When the solutions are basic, leaching moderate, and sufficient potassium is present, illite will be formed from volcanic material and some non-clay minerals (primarily potassium feldspar and micas). Under the same conditions, with magnesium present, montmorillonite will usually be formed. Where leaching is poor to moderate, or strong but of short duration, most clay minerals are only slightly modified. The first stages of alteration consist in leaching the interlayer cations from the 2:1 clays and the brucite layers from chlorite. The iron in the octahedral layer is also oxidized early. Under these conditions expanded and mixed-layer and expanded and non-expanded clays are formed. Magnesium and iron may be precipitated between these expanded layers forming pseudo-chlorites.

EPIGENESIS IN SHALES

Post-depositional alterations in sandstones have been discussed. Modification of the clay minerals in shales after burial is little understood. BURST (1958a), POWERS (1958), and WEAVER (1958b) showed that in the Gulf Coast Tertiary mont-morillonite decreases with depth and mixed-layer illite–montmorillonite increases. Discrete montmorillonite was found to be absent below a 9,000–12,000-ft. depth. WEAVER (1958b) has found the same situation in the Upper Mississippian Springer shales of southern Oklahoma and (WEAVER, 1961) the Upper Cretaceous of Wyoming.

   Fig.10 shows the relation of montmorillonite to the structural configurations of the Washakie Basin of Wyoming and the Anadarko Basin of Oklahoma. In both instances montmorillonite is abundant on the relatively shallow-basin flanks and is absent in the more deeply-buried center of the basins.

   The collapse of expanded montmorillonite layers may start as shallow as 5,000 ft. (or shallower). There appears to be a gradual increase in the percentage of contracted layers with depth until approximately 70% of the montmorillonite layers is collapsed. This usually takes place between 12,000–14,000 ft. but may occur at shallower depths. Below this depth, to at least 20,000 ft., there is no further contraction, though there is some increase in the regularity of the mixed-layer clay (as indicated by the increased sharpness of the X-ray reflections). Further expulsion of interlayer water is accomplished by extreme depth of burial or by low-grade regional metamorphism. As the relation between degree of contraction and depth of burial is the same for Tertiary, Cretaceous, and Mississippian shales, the process is primarily related to depth of overburden rather than age. Other factors such as the sandstone content, rate of deposition and type of exchange cation may modify the rate of contraction.

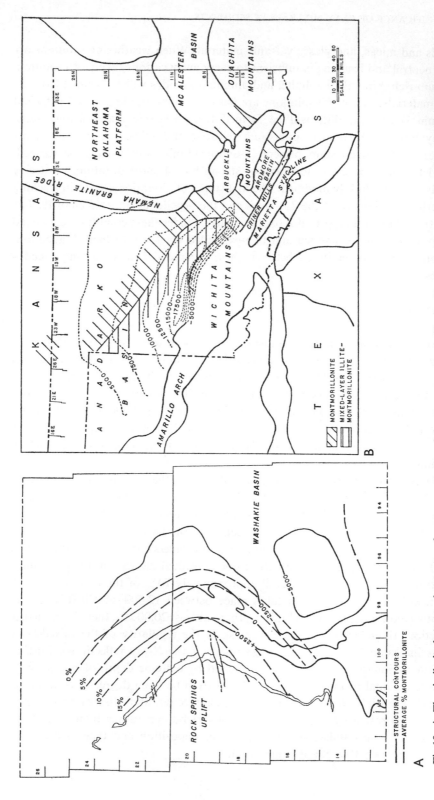

Fig.10. A. The similarity between the structural contour pattern and the percent montmorillonite (Lewis shale) contour pattern in the Washakie Basin, Wyoming. B. The relation between the montmorillonite and mixed-layer illite–montmorillonite facies of the Springer shales and the structural contour pattern.

TABLE VI

AVERAGE STRUCTURAL FORMULAS OF SOME $2:1$ CLAYS

Montmorillonite[1] (5)
   −0.33   −0.06
   $(Al_{1.48}Fe_{0.16}Mg_{0.38})$ $(Si_{3.94}Al_{0.06})O_{10}(OH)_2$

Beidellite[2] (2)
   −0.24   −0.47
   $(Al_{1.37}Fe_{0.50}^{3+}Fe_{0.02}^{2+}Mg_{0.22})$ $(Si_{3.53}Al_{0.47})O_{10}(OH)_2$

Mixed-layer illite–montmorillonite[3] $1:2$–$4:1$ (5)
   −0.36   −0.39
   $(Al_{1.60}Fe_{0.07}^{3+}Fe_{0.02}^{2+}Mg_{0.34})$ $(Si_{3.60}Al_{0.39})O_{10}(OH)_2$

Illite[1] (5)
   −0.25   −0.55
   $(Al_{1.44}Fe_{0.35}Mg_{0.22})$ $(Si_{3.45}Al_{0.55})O_{10}(OH)_2$

[1] FOSTER (1954).
[2] ROSS and HENDRICKS (1945), Putnam Clay, Missouri; Java soil.
[3] GRIM and ROWLAND (1942), WEAVER (1953a), BYSTROM (1956).

There is little or no data available to indicate what processes are operative during this contraction. POWERS (1958) has speculated that major chemical changes take place so that clay with a montmorillonite composition is converted to a clay with an illite composition (Table VI). On the basis of our present knowledge of the chemical composition of clays we do not know if any chemical change is necessary. Most analyses of montmorillonite are of commercial grade, relatively pure deposits and are probably not typical. Many analyses of soil montmorillonites (ROSS and HENDRICKS, 1945; GORBUNOV, 1956) indicate that these montmorillonites are frequently beidellitic (have a high aluminum content, Table VI). Samples of Recent and Tertiary montmorillonitic muds and shales were leached with LiCl, dried at 250–300 °C, and glycolated. The swelling capacity of these samples was only slightly affected and, according to the work of GREENE-KELLY (1955), they would be classed as beidellites. If illite and mixed-layer illite–montmorillonite are forming from montmorillonite, then, in addition to potassium, additional aluminum is also necessary. If most of the expanded clays carried into a marine environment are beidellitic in composition which would include those formed from volcanic material and stripped illites and micas, they would obtain sufficient potassium from sea water so that little or no chemical change would be necessary in the subsurface. Just the physical expulsion of interlayer water due to overburden pressure may be the only process affecting the expanded clays.

Though expanded clay layers have been found in samples from as deep as

20,000 ft., apparently only relatively mild shearing pressure is necessary to expel interlayer water. Studies of low-grade regional metamorphic argillaceous rocks in the Ouachita Mountains show that first effects of metamorphism are detected by a loss of interlayer water and a contraction of all expanded layers to 10 Å. With increasing metamorphism, the 10 Å illite peak becomes sharper and eventually attaining the sharpness characteristics of muscovite.

There has been considerable speculation on the role of clay minerals as a catalyst in the formation of hydrocarbons and as a fractionating agent. WEAVER (1960) has suggested that clay type might be important in controlling the migration of hydrocarbons.

In the United States more oil occurs in the Tertiary than any other age, and the Tertiary sediments contain much more montmorillonite and mixed-layer illite–montmorillonite than rocks of any other age. Most of the Cretaceous producing intervals that have been examined have abundant expanded clay in adjoining shales. In the Illinois Basin, the most prolific producing formation is the Chester (SWANN and BELL, 1958) and the Chester clay suite contains a higher percentage of expanded clays than any other formation in the basin. The Permian formations are the most prolific producers in the Permian basin of western Texas (GALLEY, 1958). The Permian contains more expanded clay than the other age sediments in the basin. In Oklahoma the Springer, lower Morrow, and Simpson Formations are prolific producers and contain more expanded clay minerals than the other formations in this area.

There is little Paleozoic production from the Black Warrior Basin of Mississippi and Alabama and there is also very little expanded clay in these sediments. Most of the production that has been found is from Chester sands. These sands and the enclosing shales contain a larger amount of expanded clay than is found anywhere else in the basin. Similar relations exist in most of the basins in the United States.

A plot of past production plus proven reserves for the various geologic periods and an estimate of the relatively amount of expanded clay in the sediments of these periods (WEAVER, 1960) show in a general way a coincidence between the expanded clay content and amount of oil. The relation is actually better than indicated. For example, the Jurassic and Triassic sediments have a fair montmorillonite content, but the total volume of marine sediments is relatively small. The amount of expanded clay estimated for the Mississippian and Ordovician is high for the periods as a whole, but most of the Mississippian oil is from Chester age sediments. These sediments contain the great bulk of expanded clay in the Mississippian. In the Ordovician most of the production is from the Middle Ordovician, which contains the bulk of the Ordovician expanded clays.

SARKISSIAN (1958) reported: "Clay minerals of clayey rocks of the most important petroliferous deposits of the U.S.S.R. are represented by hydromicas (hydromuscovite, hydrobiotite, illite) and montmorillonite (including also ferri-montmorillonite) . . ." All of these clay minerals, with the exception of illite which is commonly found in nearly all sediments, are expanded-type clays.

Montmorillonite not only holds more pore water (factor of 10) than the non-expanded clays (kaolinite, chlorite, and illite), but also a greater pressure is required to squeeze this pore water from between the clay particles (MIELENZ and KING, 1955; CHILINGAR and KNIGHT, 1960). Water is presumably necessary to move hydrocarbons from shales to sands. There is considerable argument whether hydrocarbons are formed at shallow depths or relatively deep depths. If it is assumed that a considerable depth of burial is necessary before any appreciable amounts of hydrocarbons are formed, it may be that in muds devoid of expanded, water-bearing clays most of the pore water that is present escapes after only shallow burial and before most of the hydrocarbons are formed. This may explain why formation such as the Chattanooga shale and the Green River shale, which contain little expanded clay, are oil shales—by the time the oil was formed there was not enough water left to remove the oil from the shales. On the other hand, greater overburden pressure is required to remove pore water from montmorillonite muds (in the Miocene, montmorillonite muds from as deep as 7,000 ft. are still pliable) and sufficient water would presumably be available to flush out hydrocarbons which were formed at depths of burial exceeding several thousand feet.

Time does not appreciably influence the rate of conversion of montmorillonite to illite; however, it does appear that time is an important factor in determining the density of shales. Though the Pliocene–Miocene and the Springer (Mississippian) shales have a similar clay composition and a similar rate of conversion of expanded clay to non-expanded clay with depth, their velocity values (and density values) are quite different. For a given depth the velocity and density values increase with increasing age, whereas the amount of expanded clay layers at a given depth is the same regardless of age. This suggests that the expulsion of the pore water is not related to the collapse of montmorillonite. The contraction of the expanded layers (diagenesis of montmorillonite to illite?) has little effect on the overall bulk density of the shale. For example, a shale that is composed of 60% clay, of which 70% is montmorillonite, would lose approximately 5% by volume between 100 ft. and 20,000 ft. by contraction of the montmorillonite layers. Though volumetrically this change may be minor, it may be important if it is the mechanism by which hydrocarbons are moved from between the expanded clay layers (if that is where they are formed) to the pores.

It is also likely that for a given depth the pore water content of illitic and kaolinitic shales will show a decrease with increasing age. As illitic and kaolinitic muds contain less water to start with, their water content for a given age and a given depth will be less than for montmorillonitic shales.

It appears that when composition and over-burden pressure are relatively constant, time is the important factor in the migration of pore water from shales.

REFERENCES

BURST JR., J. F., 1958a. Post diagenetic clay mineral—environmental relationships in the Gulf Coast Eocene in clays and clay minerals. In: *Clays Clay Minerals, Proc. Natl. Conf. Clays Clay Minerals*, 6 (1958): 327–341.

BURST JR., J. F., 1958b. Mineral heterogeneity in glauconite pellets. *Am. Mineralogist*, 43: 481–497.

BYSTROM, A. M., 1956. Mineralogy of the Ordovician bentonite beds at Kinnekulle, Sweden. *Sveriges Geol. Undersokn., Arsbok*, 48 (05): 1–62.

CAN, H. N., DONOSO, W. et SABATIER, G., 1959. Minéralogie de quelques vases marines de la région de Monaco. *Bull. Soc. Franç. Minéral. Crist.*, 82: 380–383.

CHILINGAR, G. V. and KNIGHT, L., 1960. Relationship between pressure and moisture content of kaolinite, illite, and montmorillonite clays. *Bull. Am. Assoc. Petrol. Geologists*, 44: 101–106.

CORRENS, C. W., 1937. Die Sedimente des Atlantischen Ozeans. *Deut. Atlantische Expedition "Meteor", 1925–1927, Wiss. Ergeb.*, 3 (3).

CORRENS, C. W., 1939. Pelagic sediments in the North Atlantic Ocean. In: P. D. TRASK (Editor), *Recent Marine Sediments*. Am. Assoc. Petrol. Geologists, Tulsa, Okla., pp.373–395.

COWAN, C. T. and WHITE, D., 1958. The mechanism of exchange reactions between sodium-montmorillonite and various n-primary aliphatic amine salts. *Trans. Faraday Soc.*, 54 (5): 691–698.

DEGENS, E. T., WILLIAMS, E. G. and KEITH, M. L., 1957. Environmental studies of Carboniferous sediments. 1. Geochemical criteria for differentiating marine from fresh-water shales. *Bull. Am. Assoc. Petrol. Geologists*, 41: 2427–2455.

DIETZ, R. S., 1941. *Clay Minerals in Recent Marine Sediments*. Ph. D. Thesis, Univ. Ill., Urbana, Ill.

DROSTE, J. B., 1961. Clay mineral composition of sediments in some desert lakes in Nevada, California and Oregon. *Science*, 133: 1920.

EARDLY, A. J., 1951. *Structural Geology of North America*. Harper, New York, N.Y., 624 pp.

EROSCHEV-SHAK, V. A., 1961a. Kaolinite in Atlantic bottom sediments. *Dokl. Akad. Nauk SSSR*, 137 (3): 695–697.

EROSCHEV-SHAK, V. A., 1961b. Illite in Atlantic Ocean sediments. *Dokl. Akad. Nauk SSSR*, 137 (4): 951–953.

FOLK, R. L., 1961. *Petrology of Sedimentary Rocks*. Hemphill's, Austin, Texas, 154 pp.

FOSTER, M. D., 1954. The relation between illite, beidellite and montmorillonite. In: *Clays Clay Minerals—Natl. Acad. Sci.—Natl. Res. Council, Publ.*, 327: 386–397.

FOSTER, M. D., 1956. Correlation of dioctahedral potassium micas on the basis of their charge relations. *U.S., Geol. Surv., Bull.*, 1036D: 57–67.

GALLEY, J. E., 1958. Oil and geology of the Permian basin of Texas and New Mexico. In: L. G. WEEKS (Editor), *Habitat of Oil*. Am. Assoc. Petrol. Geologists, Tulsa, Okla., pp.395–446.

GLASS, H. D., 1958. Clay mineralogy of Pennsylvanian sediments in southern Illinois. In: *Clays Clay Minerals—Natl. Acad. Sci.—Natl. Res. Council, Publ.*, 566: 227–241.

GORBUNOV, N. I., 1956. Patterns in the distribution of clay minerals in the main soil types of the U.S.S.R. *Pochvovedenie*, 2: 75–89.

GORBUNOVA, Z. I., 1960. Clay minerals at various levels in Indian Ocean bottom sediments. *Dokl. Akad. Nauk SSSR*, 134 (5): 1201–1203.

GREENE-KELLY, R., 1955. Dehydration of the montmorillonite minerals. *Mineral. Mag.*, 30: 604–615.

GRIFFIN, G. M., 1960. *Clay Mineral Facies Development in Recent Surface Sediments of the Northeastern Gulf of Mexico*. Ph. D. Thesis, Rice Inst., Houston, Texas, 210 pp.

GRIFFIN, G. M., 1962. Regional clay-mineral facies—products of weathering intensity and current distribution in the northeastern Gulf of Mexico. *Bull. Geol. Soc. Am.*, 73: 737–768.

GRIFFIN, G. M. and INGRAM, R. L., 1955. Clay minerals of the Neuse River estuary. *J. Sediment. Petrol.*, 25: 194–200.

GRIFFIN, J. J. and GOLDBERG, E. D., 1963. Clay mineral distributions in the Pacific Ocean. In: M. N. HILL, E. D. GOLDBERG, C. O'D. ISELIN and W. H. MUNK (Editors), *The Sea, Ideas and Observations on Progress in the Study of the Seas*. Wiley, New York, N.Y., 3: 728–741.

GRIM, R. E., 1953. *Clay Mineralogy*. McGraw-Hill, New York, N.Y., 384 pp.

GRIM, R. E. and JOHNS, W. D., 1954. Clay mineral investigation of sediments in the northern Gulf of Mexico. In: *Clays Clay Minerals—Natl. Acad. Sci.—Natl. Res. Council, Publ.,* 327: 81–108.

GRIM, R. E. and ROWLAND, R. A., 1942. Differential thermal analyses of clay minerals and other hydrous materials. *Am. Mineralogist,* 27: 746–761, 801–818.

GRIM, R. E., DIETZ, R. S. and BRADLEY, W. F., 1949. Clay mineral composition of some sediments from the Pacific Ocean off the California coast and the Gulf of California. *Bull. Geol. Soc. Am.,* 60: 1785–1808.

HAWKINS, D. B., 1961. *Experimental Hydrotherm Studies bearing on Rock, Weathering, and Clay Mineral Formation.* Ph. D. Thesis, Penna. State Univ., University Park, Pa., 138 pp.

HEEZEN, B. C., NESTEROFF, W. D. et SABATIER, G., 1960. Répartition des minéraux argileux dans les sédiments profonds de l'Atlantique Nord et Équatorial. *Compt. Rend.,* 251: 410–412.

HENDRICKS, S. B. and ROSS, C. S., 1941. Chemical composition and genesis of glauconite and celadonite. *Am. Mineralogist,* 26: 683–708.

HEY, M. H., 1954. A new review of the chlorites. *Mineral. Mag.,* 30: 277–292.

HOOKS, W. G. and INGRAM, R. L., 1955. The clay minerals and the iron oxide minerals of the Triassic "Red Beds" of the Durham Basin, North Carolina. *Am. J. Sci.,* 253: 19–25.

HOWER, J., 1961. Some factors concerning the nature and origin of glauconite. *Am. Mineralogist,* 46: 313–334.

HURLEY, P. M., HART, S. R., PINSON, W. H. and FAIRBAIRN, H. W., 1959. Authigenic versus detrital illite in sediments. *Bull. Geol. Soc. Am.,* 70: 1622.

HURLEY, P. M., BROOKINS, D. G., PINSON, W. H., HART, S. R. and FAIRBAIRN, H. W., 1961. K–Ar age studies of Mississippi and other river sediments. *Bull. Geol. Soc. Am.,* 72: 1807–1816.

JOHNS, W. D. and GRIM, R. E., 1958. Clay mineral composition of Recent sediments from the Mississippi River delta. *J. Sediment. Petrol.,* 28: 186–199.

KELLER, W. D., 1953. Clay minerals in the type section of the Morrison Formation. *J. Sediment. Petrol.,* 23: 93–105.

KELLER, W. D., 1956. Clay minerals as influenced by environments of their formation. *Bull. Am. Assoc. Petrol. Geologists,* 40: 2689–2710.

KELLEY, W. P. and LIEBIG JR., G. F., 1934. Base exchange in relation to composition of clays with special reference to effect of sea water. *Bull. Am. Assoc. Petrol. Geologists,* 18: 358–367.

KRYNINE, P. D., 1940. Petrology and genesis of the third Bradford sand. *Penna. State Univ., Mineral Ind. Expt. Sta., Bull.,* 29: 134 pp.

KRYNINE, P. D., 1948. The megascopic study and field classification of sedimentary rocks. *J. Geol.,* 56: 112–117.

KULBICKI, G. and MILLOT, G., 1961. Diagenesis of clays in sedimentary and petrol series. In: *Clays Clay Minerals, Proc. Natl. Conf. Clays Clay Minerals,* 10: 329–332.

LEMCKE, K., VON ENGELHARDT, W. und FUCHTHAVEN, H., 1953. Geologische und sediment-petrographische Untersuchungen im Westteil der ungefalteten Molasse des süddeutschen Alpenvorlandes. *Geol. Jahrb., Beih.,* 11: 56–57.

LIPPMANN, F., 1954. Über einen Keuperton von Zaiserweiher bei Maulbronn. *Heidelberger Beitr. Mineral. Petrog.,* 4: 130–134.

MIELENZ, R. C. and KING, M. E., 1955. Physical–chemical properties and engineering performance of clays. *Proc. Natl. Conf. Clays Clay Tech.—Calif. Dept. Nat. Resources, Bull.,* 169: 196–254.

MILLOT, G., 1949. Relations entre la constitution et la genèse des roches sédimentaires argileuses. *Géol. Appl. Prospection Minière, Univ. Nancy,* 2: 352 pp.

MILLOT, G., 1953. Héritage et néoformation dans la sédimentation argileuse. *Compt. Rend., Congr. Géol. Intern., 19, Alger, 1952,* 18: 163–217.

MILLOT, G., LUCAS, J. and WEY, R., 1961. Some researches on the evolution of clay minerals and argillaceous and siliceous neoformation. In: *Clays Clay Minerals, Proc. Natl. Conf. Clays Clay Minerals,* 10: 399–412.

MILNE, I. H. and EARLY, J. W., 1958. Effect of source and environment on clay minerals. *Bull. Am. Assoc. Petrol. Geologists,* 42: 328–338.

MILNE, I. H. and SHOTT, W. L., 1958. Clay mineralogy of Recent sediments from the Mississippi sound area. In: *Clays Clay Minerals—Natl. Acad. Sci.—Natl. Res. Council, Publ.*, 566: 253–265.

MOORE, J. E., 1960. Clay mineralogy—problems in oil recovery. *Petrol. Eng. Management*, 1960: B40–B47; B78–B101.

MORRIS, F. G., QUINTIN, A. A. and GATES, G. L., 1959. Clay in petroleum reservoir rocks. *U.S., Bur. Mines, Rept. Invest.*, 5425.

MURRAY, H. H., 1954. Genesis of clay minerals in some Pennsylvanian shales of Indiana and Illinois. In: *Clays Clay Minerals—Natl. Acad. Sci.—Natl. Res. Council, Publ.*, 327: 47–67.

NELSON, B. W. and ROY, R., 1954. New data on the composition and identification of chlorites. In: *Clays Clay Minerals—Natl. Acad. Sci.—Natl. Res. Council, Publ.*, 327: 335–348.

PETTIJOHN, F. J., 1949. *Sedimentary Rocks*. Harper, New York, N.Y., 526 pp.

PETTIJOHN, F. J., 1957. *Sedimentary Rocks*, 2 ed. Harper, New York, N.Y., 718 pp.

PINSAK, A. P. and MURRAY, H. H., 1958. Regional clay mineral patterns in the Gulf of Mexico. In: *Clays Clay Minerals, Proc. Natl. Conf. Clays Clay Minerals*, 5 (1958): 162–177.

POWERS, M. C., 1954. Clay diagenesis in the Chesapeake Bay area. In: *Clays Clay Minerals—Natl. Acad. Sci.—Natl. Res. Council, Publ.*, 327: 68–80.

POWERS, M. C., 1958. Adjustments of clays to chemical change and the concept of the equivalence level. In: *Clays Clay Minerals, Proc. Natl. Conf. Clays Clay Minerals*, 6 (1958): 309–326.

PRYOR, W. A., 1960. Cretaceous sedimentation in Upper Mississippi embayment. *Bull. Am. Assoc. Petrol. Geologists*, 44: 1473–1504.

QUAIDE, W. L., 1956. *Petrography and Clay Mineralogy of Pliocene Sedimentary Rocks from Ventura Basin, California*. Ph. D. Thesis, Univ. California, Berkeley, Calif.

REITEMEIER, R. F., 1951. The chemistry of soil potassium. In: A. G. NORMAN (Editor), *Advances in Agronomy*. Academic Press, New York, N.Y., 3: 113–159.

REYNOLDS, W. R. and GOODELL, H. G., 1962. *The Lithostratigraphy and Clay Mineralogy of the Tampa–Harothorn Sequence of Peninsular Florida*. M.S. Thesis, Florida State Univ., Gainesville, Fla., 126 pp.

RIVIÈRE, A., 1953. Sur l'origine des argiles sédimentaires. *Compt. Rend., Congr. Géol. Intern.*, 19, *Alger, 1952*, 18: 177–180.

RIVIÈRE, A. and VISSE, L., 1954. Origin of the minerals in marine sediments. *Soc. Géol. Franç.*, 4: 467–473.

ROSS, C. S. and HENDRICKS, S. B., 1945. Minerals of the montmorillonite group, their origin and relation to soils and clays. *U.S., Geol. Surv., Profess. Papers*, 205B: 23–79.

ROY, D. M. and ROY, R., 1954. An experimental study of the formation and properties of synthetic serpentines and related layer silicate minerals. *Am. Mineralogist*, 39: 957–975.

SARKISSIAN, S. G., 1958. Mineralogic composition of clays in petroliferous deposits of the U.S.S.R.—Some data on geology, mineralogy and utilization of clays in the U.S.S.R. *Rept. Intern. Meeting Clays, Brussels*, p.57.

SHAW, D. B., 1959. *A Study of the Variations in the Mineralogical Composition of Shales*. M.S. Thesis, Univ. Houston, Texas.

SHAW, D. B. and WEAVER, C. E., 1965. The mineralogical composition of shales. *J. Sediment. Petrol.*, 35: 213–222.

SIMONS, L. H. and TAGGART JR., M. S., 1954. Clay mineral content of Gulf Coast outcrop samples. In: *Clays Clay Minerals—Natl. Acad. Sci.—Natl. Res. Council, Publ.*, 327: 104–110.

SMITH, J. B. and BADER, R. G., 1961. Preliminary investigations of the association of organic material and carbon dioxide with sedimentary particles. *Agr. Mech. Coll. Texas, Tech. Rept.*, 3: 221 pp.

SMOOT, T. W., 1959. *Clay Mineralogy of Pre-Pennsylvanian Sandstones and Shales of the Illinois Basin*. Ph. D. Thesis, Univ. Illinois, Urbana, Ill.

SMOOT, T. W. and NARAIN, K., 1960. Clay mineralogy of pre-Pennsylvanian sandstones and shales of the Illinois Basin, II. *Illinois State Geol. Surv., Circ.*, 287: 14 pp.

SWANN, D. H. and BELL, A. H., 1958. Habitat of oil in the Illinois Basin. In: L. G. WEEKS (Editor), *Habitat of Oil*. Am. Assoc. Petrol. Geologists, Tulsa, Okla., pp.447–472.

TAGGART JR., M. S. and KAISER, A. D., 1960. Clay mineralogy of Mississippi River deltaic sediments. *Bull. Geol. Soc. Am.*, 71: 521–530.

TRASK, P. D., 1939. Organic content of Recent marine sediments. *Bull. Am. Assoc. Petrol. Geologists*, 23: 428–453.

VAN ANDEL, TJ. and POSTMA, H., 1954. *Recent Sediments of the Gulf of Paria. Reports of the Orinoco Shelf Expedition*. North Holland, Amsterdam, 1: 245 pp.

WALKER, G. F., 1950. Trioctahedral minerals in the soil-clays of northeast Scotland. *Mineral. Mag.*, 29: 72–84.

WALKER, G. F., 1958. Reactions of expanding-lattice clay minerals with glycerol and ethylene glycol. *Clay Minerals Bull.*, 3: 302–313.

WARSHAW, C. M., 1957. *The Mineralogy of Glauconite*. Thesis, Pennsylvania State Univ., University Park, Pa., 167 pp.

WARSHAW, C. M. and ROY, R., 1961. Classification and a scheme for the identification of layer silicates. *Bull. Geol. Soc. Am.*, 72: 1455–1492.

WEAVER, C. E., 1953a. Mineralogy and petrology of some Ordovician K-bentonites and related limestones. *Bull. Geol. Soc. Am.*, 64: 921–943.

WEAVER, C. E., 1953b. A lath-shaped non-expanded dioctahedral 2:1 clay mineral. *Am. Mineralogist*, 38: 279–289.

WEAVER, C. E., 1955. Mineralogy and petrology of the rocks near the Quadrant–Phosphoria boundary in southwest Montana. *J. Sediment. Petrol.*, 25: 163–193.

WEAVER, C. E., 1958a. The effects and geological significance of potassium "fixation" by expandable clay minerals derived from muscovite, biotite, chlorite, and volcanic material. *Am. Mineralogist*, 43: 839–861.

WEAVER, C. E., 1958b. A discussion on the origin of clay minerals in sedimentary rocks. In: *Clays Clay Minerals—Natl. Acad. Sci.—Natl. Res. Council, Publ.*, 566: 159–173.

WEAVER, C. E., 1959. The clay petrology of sediments. In: *Clays Clay Minerals, Proc. Natl. Conf. Clays Clay Minerals*, 6 (1958): 154–187.

WEAVER, C. E., 1960. Possible uses of clay minerals in search for oil. *Bull. Am. Assoc. Petrol. Geologists*, 44: 1505–1518.

WEAVER, C. E., 1961. Clay mineralogy of the late Cretaceous rocks of the Washakie Basin. *Wyoming Geol. Assoc., Guidebook Ann. Field Conf.*, 16, pp.148–152.

WERMUND, E. G., 1961. Glauconite in early Tertiary sediments of Gulf Coastal province. *Bull. Am. Assoc. Petrol. Geologists*, 45: 1667–1696.

WHITEHOUSE, U. G. and JEFFREY, L. M., 1953. Relative adsorption tendencies of settling clays for selected organic materials. *Agr. Mech. Coll. Texas, Tech. Rept.*, 3: 1–17.

Chapter 3

PETROLEUM HYDROCARBONS

M. A. BESTOUGEFF

Compagnie Française de Raffinage, Paris (France)

INTRODUCTION

Hydrocarbons are the principal constituents of petroleum, usually exceeding 75%. The proportions of minor constituents such as sulfur, oxygen and nitrogen compounds, the organometallic complexes, and the organic salts vary considerably according to the type of petroleum.

The non-hydrocarbon heteroatomic compounds form the greater part of certain heavy crude oils in which the hydrocarbons represent only secondary constituents. For example, in the Tertiary crude oil from Boscan (Venezuela), the hydrocarbon content is only 35–38% (M. A. Bestougeff, unpublished data).

The hydrocarbons found in the various crude oils belong to five principal classes:

(*1*) normal paraffins (normal alkanes).

(*2*) branched chain paraffins (branched chain alkanes).

(*3*) cycloparaffins (cycloalkanes or naphthenes) (mono-, bi- and polycyclic).

(*4*) aromatics (mono-, bi- and polycyclic).

(*5*) naphtheno-aromatics (or mixed structures, sometimes described as "hybrid" hydrocarbons. ANDREEV, et al., 1958; SERGIENKO, 1959).

These naphtheno-aromatic compounds may simultaneously contain in their molecules up to ten aromatic and naphthenic rings as well as aliphatic groups. Indane, tetralin, etc., and their homologs fall into this category.

Unsaturated hydrocarbons (olefins, diolefins, etc.,) have been found in small quantities in the Pennsylvania (Bradford) crude oil (HOLLIMAN et al., 1950; PUTSCHER, 1952).

FRED and PUTSCHER (1949); HAAK and VAN NES (1951); and FRANCIS (1956) also have identified cyclic olefins in fractions of some lubricating oils from other locations. However, this refers to very small quantities of these hydrocarbons not actually affecting the overall composition of petroleum.

The five groups of hydrocarbon compounds previously outlined correspond to seventeen homologous series ranging from C_nH_{2n+2} to C_nH_{2n-30}. Fig.1 shows the distribution of hydrocarbon compounds in a medium crude oil according to these series. The number of carbon atoms in the hydrocarbons of petroleum for all these series can vary from C_1–C_4 (the gases) to C_{60} as the maximum, with a molecular weight of approximately 800–850. The molecular weight of the hetero-

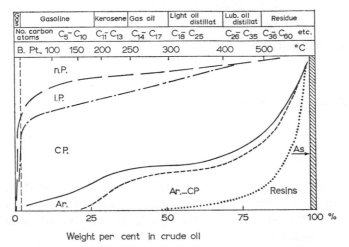

Fig.1. Distribution of hydrocarbon classes in a medium crude oil. *n.P.* = normal paraffins; *i.P.* = iso-paraffins; *CP.* = cycloparaffins; *Ar.* = aromatics; *Ar.–CP.* = naphtheno-aromatics; *Resins* = heterocyclic compounds; *As* = asphaltenes.

atomic constituents of petroleum can exceed this limit reaching two or three thousand in the asphaltenes.

The determination of the chemical composition of petroleum has progressed very rapidly during the last 25 years due to new fractionation and identification methods and to the systematic work of large research teams. These new methods include azeotropic distillation, thermal diffusion, the formation of complexes with urea, etc., ultra-violet and infra-red spectrometry, mass spectrometry, as well as liquid and gas chromatography (HOOD et al., 1959; DESTY et al., 1962; BESTOUGEFF, 1961, 1964). Nuclear magnetic and electronic spin resonance spectroscopy (JONES, 1957; WILLIAMS, 1957; KEARNS et al., 1959; BESTOUGEFF, 1961) have also been employed.

Although there has been great progress in petroleum research, the opinions voiced in numerous organic chemical treatises (even fairly recent editions) contain out-of-date statements reflecting theories and ideas formulated in past decades. For example, L. FIESER and M. FIESER (1944, p.85) state in their well-known book, *Organic Chemistry*, that it is quite difficult to separate the hydrocarbon compounds from petroleum when they contain more than six carbon atoms since the number of isomers increases greatly as a function of the increasing chain length. WHITMORE (1951, p.6) states that the present ignorance of petroleum constituents is great. He pointed out the great number of theoretically possible isomeric structures, as do most other authors, with the number of isomers reaching 75 at $C_{10}H_{22}$ and about 4 billion for the C_{30} paraffins.

This is understandable since a great variety of crude oils exists, and early investigators isolated in the light fractions most of the possible isomers of different classes of hydrocarbons. It was therefore generally assumed that crude oils were composed of millions of isomeric hydrocarbons containing mainly paraffins or consisting of aromatics and naphthenes. Certain theories concerning the origin of petroleum based on extraordinary organic and inorganic reactions also contributed to the establishment of erroneous beliefs concerning the formation and composition of petroleum.

In accordance with recent scientific data, it now appears that the composition of petroleum is not exceptional and is the result of normal and regular processes. The total number of constituents and their isomers, although somewhat high, represents only a negligible portion of theoretically possible structures (BESTOUGEFF, 1961).

As early as 1925 the formation of petroleum was considered a common natural process. Later DOBRYANSKY (1961) concluded that all petroleum properties are intimately linked together in a casual manner, because petroleum evolves and "lives" in the same manner as all natural objects, and that each analysis of a given crude oil is simply a reflection of a determined stage of this evolution. Thus, the hydrocarbons in petroleum are a mixture of different types of chemical structures, selected by nature according to certain rules, and preferably responding to the principle of the greatest thermodynamic stability.

THE HYDROCARBONS IN PETROLEUM

Principles of composition

The present knowledge of the chemical composition of petroleum is still insufficient to permit establishing a complete picture of the compositional principles. However, it is possible to formulate a certain number of correlations concerning the content of the various series of hydrocarbon compounds in petroleum oils, their molecular weight, structure, and isomerism. The following are the compositional principles for crude oils:

(1) The composition of each crude oil is affected by a set of homologous series. This is an important fact; namely, that the homologous series of hydrocarbon compounds found in petroleums form a series of isologs (BESTOUGEFF, 1951).

(2) Each homologous series is represented in a given crude oil by one or several families of homologs; i.e., isomeric groups. Members of these groups in a given crude oil always form a continuous succession of compounds varying according to the type of crude oil.

(3) The first members of the homologous series are always found to be proportionally lower in concentration than the higher molecular weight members. In certain crude oils these lower members may be absent.

(4) The cyclic structures are more predominant in oils found in relatively young (Tertiary) reservoirs; and the aliphatic structures in older (Palaeozoic) rocks.

TABLE I

PREDOMINANT CONSTITUENTS OF PETROLEUM

No.	Series and hydrocarbon	Carbon atom number	Percent of crude oil	
			min.	max.
	Normal paraffins			
1	Pentane	C_5	0.2	3.2
2	Hexane	C_6	0.04	2.6
3	Heptane	C_7	0.03	2.5
4	Octane–Decane	C_8–C_{10}	0	1.8–2.0
5	Undecane–Pentadecane	C_{11}–C_{15}	0	0.8–1.5
6	Hexadecane and higher	C_{16} and higher	0	<1.0
	Isoparaffins			
1	2-Methylpentane	C_6	0.2	1.16
2	3-Methylpentane	C_6	0.06	0.9
3	2-Methylhexane	C_7	0.03	1.1
4	3-Methylhexane	C_7	0.02	0.9
5	2-Methylheptane	C_8	0.03	1.0
6	3-Methylheptane	C_8	0.02	0.4
7	2-Methyloctane	C_9	0.02	0.4
8	3-Methyloctane	C_9	0.01	0.2
9	2-Methylnonane	C_{10}	—	0.3
10	3-Methylnonane	C_{10}	—	0.1
11	4-Methylnonane	C_{10}	—	0.1
12	Pristane (isoprenoid)	C_{19}	—	1.12
	Cycloparaffins			
1	Methylcyclopentane	C_6	0.11	2.35
2	Cyclohexane	C_6	0.08	1.4
3	Methylcyclohexane	C_7	0.25	2.8
4	1, trans-2-dimethylcyclopentane	C_7	0.05	1.2
5	1, cis-3-dimethylcyclopentane	C_7	0.04	1.0
6	1, cis-3-dimethylcyclohexane	C_8	—	0.9
7	1, cis-2-dimethylcyclohexane	C_8	—	0.6
8	1, 1, 3-trimethylcyclohexane	C_9	—	0.7
	Aromatics			
1	Benzene	C_6	0.01	1.0
2	Toluene	C_7	0.03	1.8
3	Ethylbenzene	C_8	0.01	1.6
4	m-Xylene	C_8	0.02	1.0
5	1-Methyl-3-ethylbenzene	C_9	—	0.3
6	1, 2, 4-Trimethylbenzene	C_9	—	0.6
7	1, 2, 3-Trimethylbenzene	C_9	—	0.4
8	1, 2, 3, 4-Tetramethylbenzene	C_{10}	—	0.3
9	2-Methylnaphtalene	C_{11}	—	0.3
10	2, 6-Dimethylnaphtalene	C_{12}	—	0.4
11	Trimethylnaphtalene	C_{13}	—	0.3

Predominant constituents

The abundance of the different members of the same homologous series varies considerably in absolute and relative values. Thus in a given oil fraction there may be a small number of constituents forming the greater part of the fraction. The author has proposed to designate these hydrocarbons as "predominant constituents" (BESTOUGEFF, 1961). They are the same in most oils of the same type (see Table I). The unequal distribution of the different series of hydrocarbons in crude oils and the varied members and isomers in the same series leads to the conclusion that the major part of petroleum is composed of a relatively moderate number of constituents. ROSSINI and MAIR (1959) undertook the most complete identification of the compounds of one crude oil, and found that about 50% of the total hydrocarbons of this petroleum is composed of only 150 individual compounds.

Of the light gasoline fractions (boiling point $\sim 150\,^{\circ}$C), derived from various crude oils, 50–70% contain only ten to twenty components (BESTOUGEFF, 1961). At present, only approximately 340 individual hydrocarbons have been identified in crude oils; only some have been isolated and purified (see Table II). About 200 individual sulfur constituents have also been isolated (H. M. SMITH et al., 1959;

TABLE II

INDIVIDUAL HYDROCARBONS ISOLATED OR IDENTIFIED FROM VARIOUS CRUDE OILS

Hydrocarbons	Series	Number of carbon atoms per molecule	Number of constituents[1]
Normal paraffins	C_nH_{2n-2}	C_1-C_{35}	35 (5)
Branched paraffins	C_nH_{2n-2}	C_4-C_{10}	50 (24)
Branched paraffins	C_nH_{2n-2}	$C_{11}-C_{15}$	2 (9)
Branched paraffins	C_nH_{2n-2}	$C_{16}-C_{20}$	2 (5)
Branched paraffins	C_nH_{2n-2}	$C_{21}-C_{23}$	— (3)
Cycloparaffins (monocyclic)	C_nH_{2n}		
Cycloparaffins (cyclopentanes)	C_nH_{2n}	C_5-C_{10}	35 (5)
Cycloparaffins (cyclohexanes)	C_nH_{2n}	C_6-C_{10}	25 (18)
Cycloparaffins (cycloheptanes)	C_nH_{2n}	C_7	2
Cycloparaffins (bicyclic)	C_nH_{2n-2}	C_8-C_{11}	8 (6)
Cycloparaffins (tricyclic)	C_nH_{2n-4}	$C_{10}-C_{12}$	1 (1)
Aromatics monocyclic	C_nH_{2n-6}	C_6-C_{12}	45 (5)
Aromatics bicyclic (naphthalenes)	C_nH_{2n-12}	$C_{10}-C_{16}$	12 (9)
Aromatics bicyclic (diphenyls)	C_nH_{2n-14}	$C_{12}-C_{14}$	2 (2)
Aromatics tricyclic	$\left\{ \begin{array}{l} C_nH_{2n-18} \\ C_nH_{2n-20} \end{array} \right.$	$C_{14}-C_{18}$	8 (3)
Aromatics tetracyclic	C_nH_{2n-24}	$C_{16}-C_{18}$	7 (4)
Naphtheno-aromatics			
Indane group	C_nH_{2n-8}	C_9-C_{13}	4 (1)
Tetraline group	C_nH_{2n-8}	$C_{10}-C_{14}$	8 (2)

[1] In parentheses the number of constituents only identified but not separated in pure state.

H. M. SMITH, 1965). Developments in fractionation and separation techniques of compounds from their mixtures suggest the possibility of determining the structure of the principal constituents of petroleum in a relatively short time.

Normal paraffin hydrocarbons

Normal paraffins are found in most petroleums and particularly in the light types. The chemical study of this group is currently well advanced due to new separation and identification methods, especially treatment with urea and molecular sieve adsorbents, and elution and gas chromatography (BROOKS, 1954a, b; O'CONNOR and NORRIS, 1960; BOLSHAKOVA and STAROBINETZ, 1961; BESTOUGEFF, 1964).

The members of the n-paraffin C_1-C_{35} group (molecular weight 16–492) have been separated and identified in several crude oils (see Table III) (MAIR and ROSSINI, 1957; MAIR et al., 1957; RAMPTON, 1957). The total content of n-paraffins of a crude oil can reach 25% (not taking into account the gases). The light gasoline fractions can contain up to 80% and the lubricating oil distillates from 0 to 25% n-paraffins.

The lower members (C_5-C_{20} range) constitute by weight the greater part of the n-paraffins in light paraffin-rich oils. They are the predominant constituents; for example, five hydrocarbons (C_5-C_9) account for 9–12% of the Ponca City or Hassi Messaoud crude oils (Table III). The highest concentration of a single paraffin hydrocarbon found up to now is 2.5–3.2% (C_5-C_7), in the crude oils of Ponca City, Teas, Hassi Messaoud, and Beaver Lodge.

On the other hand the concentration of a single n-paraffinic constituent in heavy crude oils may decrease to 0.7–0.1% (H. M. SMITH and RALL, 1953; MARTIN and WINTERS, 1959; YATSENKO and CHERNOZHUKOV, 1960a).

TABLE III

NORMAL PARAFFINS DISTRIBUTION IN LIGHT CRUDE OILS ACCORDING TO THE MOLECULAR WEIGHT

Fraction of n-paraffins	*Content in crude oil (vol. percent)*		
	Iraq (Tertiary)	*Ponca City (Ordovician)*	*Hassi Messaoud (Cambrian)*
C_5-C_{10}	9.55	11.5	14.05
$C_{11}-C_{20}$	7.50	10.13	5.07
$C_{21}-C_{30}$	2.10	~ 2.23	~ 1.82
C_{31} etc.	~ 0.6	~ 0.25	~ 0.7
Total content in crude oil	19.75	24.11	21.64

In certain intermediary types of petroleums the *n*-paraffins may fall in the middle weight range. Thus MARTIN et al. (1963) and also YATSENKO and CHERNOZHUKOV (1960a) have found in the Uinta Basin, and in the Dolinska and Bitkov crude oils, the high concentrations of normal paraffins in the C_{10}–C_{28} range. However, the data of the quantitative determinations of the *n*-paraffins in the higher boiling point fractions are not precise in many instances, and probably are rather exaggerated due to the presence of crystalline naphthenic constituents. For example, when using a molecular sieve separation technique, the author found that the total paraffin wax derived from vacuum residues of the Hassi Messaoud and Qatar crude oils contained only 26 % and 16 % of *n*-paraffins, respectively.

Branched-chain paraffin hydrocarbons

The hydrocarbons of this group are commonly present in petroleum, particularly in light and middle boiling point fractions. In a Pennsylvania gas oil (in the C_{17}–C_{20} range), HAAK and VAN NES (1951) found 17 % branched-chain paraffins with the concentration considerably decreasing in the range of C_{20}–C_{23}. It is unlikely that crude oils would be found with high concentrations of branched-chain paraffins above C_{25}.

Ceresins, the solid crystalline constituents of high molecular weight, are considered by some authors (SACHANEN, 1945) to be higher members of the isoparaffinic series, but these compounds contain, in fact, principally cyclic hydrocarbons. Several samples of ceresin, originating from petroleum or natural ozokerites and analysed by CHERNOZHUKOV et al. (1959), contained from 80 to 93 % cyclic constituents, and a fraction which could have contained not more than 10 % isoparaffins.

Among the individual branched chain hydrocarbons isolated and identified in petroleums, all possible isomers are present in the C_4, C_5, and C_6 range, seven isomers in C_7 (out of the possible nine); sixteen in C_8 (out of the possible eighteen); nine isomers in C_9; and four in C_{10}.

The isoparaffins above C_{14} possessing the isoprenoid structure 2, 6, 10-trimethylundecane and 2, 6, 10-trimethyldodecane have lately been separated in a Ponca City crude oil by MAIR et al. (1962). Two other hydrocarbons of the same structure, pristane and phytane, C_{19} and C_{20}, have previously been discovered in notable quantities in several crude oils (BENDORAITIS et al., 1962).

The presence of slightly branched paraffins in the C_{12}–C_{20} range (containing one or two methyl groups) has been shown in kerosene and gas-oil fractions by the examination of narrow distillation cuts (MAIR et al., 1962) and by gas chromatographic analysis of urea adducts (M. A. Bestougeff, unpublished data). However, these hydrocarbons have not yet been isolated in a pure state.

Among the various isomers of branched-chain paraffins in petroleums, the 2- and 3-methyl substituted compounds are often predominant. The compounds with 4-methyl substitutions are less abundant. Generally, the concentration of the various branched-chain paraffinic hydrocarbons decreases considerably from mono-substituted to poly-substituted via bi- and tri-substituted compounds. ROSSINI et al. (1952) established the relationships for the C_6–C_9 branched-chain paraffins in a Ponca City crude oil, shown in Table IV. The known C_{10}, C_{11} paraffins in petroleum seem to follow the same pattern.

TABLE IV

RELATIONSHIPS FOR C_6–C_9 BRANCHED-CHAIN PARAFFINS IN PONCA CITY CRUDE OIL

	Monosubstituted $(^o/_o)$	Bisubstituted $(^o/_o)$	Trisubstituted $(^o/_o)$	Total $(^o/_o)$
C_6	86	14	—	100
C_7	84	16	—	100
C_8	72	27	1	100
C_9	67	31	2	100

MARTIN and WINTERS (1959), conducting their analyses on light fractions of twenty crude oils of different ages have found, with a few exceptions, the following relationships between mono- and poly-substituted branched-chain paraffins:

C_6: 2-methylpentane > 3-methylpentane > 2, 3-dimethylbutane > 2, 2-dimethylbutane.

C_7: 3-methylhexane > 2-methylhexane > 2,3 dimethylpentane > 2, 4-dimethylpentane > ethylpentane > 2, 2-dimethylpentane > 3, 3-dimethylpentane > 2, 2, 3-trimethylbutane.

ROSSINI et al. (1952); FROST (1956); H. M. SMITH et al. (1959); and BOGO-MOLOV and PANINA (1961b) have all attempted to find the correlations between the relative content of the different constituents.

Certain authors have thought that quantitative relationship exists between different petroleum constituents. It was later shown that this ratio was only approximate (Fig.2). Perhaps Rossini was too speculative in asserting that "a liter of all the branched paraffins from the kerosene fraction of one petroleum will be substantially the same as a liter of all the branched paraffins from the same kerosene fraction of another petroleum". He also suggested an analogous pattern for the alkylnaphthalene content of the gas oil fractions (ROSSINI and MAIR, 1959).

As for the relative proportions of the total normal paraffins and total branched-chain paraffins, three possible cases are found in nature; i.e., crude oils with high concentration of n-paraffins, those rich in branched-chain paraffins, and those with practically equal contents of these hydrocarbon groups (FORZIATI et al., 1944).

The distribution of branched-chain paraffins in different fractions of a crude

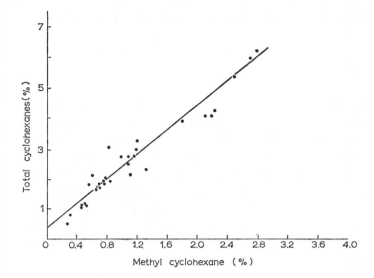

Fig.2. Percentages of methylcyclohexane and cyclohexanes in crude oils.
(After SMITH and RALL, 1953.)

oil is unequal, and, as in the case of *n*-paraffins (light crude oils), drops rapidly as a function of the molecular weight. Rossini gave the distribution for the Ponca City crude oil (Table V).

As can be seen from this tabulation, ca. 50% of the branched-chain paraffins are concentrated in the light gasoline fractions. The maximum concentration of a single isoparaffinic hydrocarbon in petroleum may be as high as 0.6–1.2% in the lower ranges C_6 and C_7 (2- and 3-methyl). The concentration of individual bi- and tri-substituted hydrocarbons does not exceed 0.5% and usually amounts to only tenths or hundredths of a percent. The discovery of a relatively high quantity of the C_{19} branched-chain paraffin (pristane, 1.12%) presents a new factor not yet ob-

TABLE V

DISTRIBUTION OF BRANCHED-CHAIN PARAFFINS IN THE PONCA CITY CRUDE OIL

	In crude oil (%)	In relation to total of the isoparaffins (%)	Average per carbon atom (%)
C_6–C_{10}	6.7	51.1	1.3
C_{11}–C_{12}	1.9	14.6	0.85
C_{13}–C_{17}	2.3	17.6	0.46
C_{18}–C_{25}	1.42	10.8	0.22
C_{26}–C_{38}	0.83	5.9	0.06 (approx.)

served for this type of structure in light fractions of crude oils (BENDORAITIS et al., 1962).

Cycloparaffin hydrocarbons

The cycloparaffins (naphthenes) are represented in all fractions from C_5 upwards. One finds several series of cycloparaffins usually containing five or six membered rings or their combinations in the polycyclic structures. The content of cycloparaffins in petroleums all over the world varies from 30 to 60%. Thus, one can state that the hydrocarbons of this series are one of the principal constituents of crude oils. The cycloparaffin content of different boiling range fractions of a crude oil does not vary considerably, and generally remains within rather close limits (see Table VI). On the other hand, the structure of these constituents may change from one petroleum to another, as well as in the same crude oil as a function of the molecular weight of the fractions.

The principal factor in the variation of the structure of naphthenes is the number of rings present in the molecule. The mono- and bicyclic naphthenes form the major part of cycloparaffins of petroleum (RAMPTON, 1957). However, the higher boiling point fractions such as the lubricating oils may contain up to ten rings in a molecule according to MELPOLDER et al. (1957). Fractions of naphthenes, derived from a lubricating oil and separated by thermal diffusion, contained on the average two to six rings per molecule according to elementary analysis. However, mass spectrometry gave an indication of the existence of higher numbers of rings in some of these compounds. For example, the composition of one of the last fractions containing an average of six rings was shown by mass spectral data to be a mixture of the following naphthenes:

tetracyclic $= 10\%$
pentacyclic $= 32\%$
hexacyclic $= 25\%$
heptacyclic $= 17\%$
octacyclic $= 10\%$
nonacyclic $= 5\%$

These and other data concerning the interpretation of mass spectra of the high boiling point compounds must be accepted with the greatest caution until verified by other methods.

YATSENKO and CHERNOZHUKOV (1960b) have separated from the Dolinska and Bitkov crude oils 0.24% of a tricyclic naphthenic fraction $C_{41}H_{78}$, ($n_D^{20} = 1.4990$), and 0.77% of a pentacyclic naphthenic fraction $C_{32.6}H_{57}$ ($n_D^{20} = 1.5220$).

Apart from the number of rings in the molecules, the nature and the distribution of chains attached to the rings also play an important role. The monocyclic naphthenes of petroleum, homologs of cyclopentane and cyclohexane, are those that have been the most thoroughly investigated in this connection.

TABLE VI

DISTRIBUTION OF THE CYCLOPARAFFINS IN FRACTIONS OF VARIOUS CRUDE OILS
(According to DOBRYANSKY, 1961)

Fractions		Origin of cycloparaffinic hydrocarbons (weight percent in fraction)								
Boiling point (°C at 1 atm.)	Average number of carbon atoms	Sura-chany	Bala-chany	Grozny non pa-raffin	paraf-fin	Dos-sor	Ishim-bay	Iskine I	Shugu-rovo	Iskine II
95–122	C_7	81	68	48	37	63	29	35	23	37
122–150	C_8	51	66	45	30	67	24	23	21	30
150–200	C_9	66	55	55	29	69	28	33	29	28
200–250	C_{11}–C_{12}	66	74	63	36	72	35	35	42	34
250–300	C_{14}	70	78	59	44	78	28	38	41	44
300–350	C_{17}–C_{18}	70	78	65	54	80	30	38	40	54
350–400	C_{22}	74	76	62	62	83	40	54	—	57
400–450	C_{26}	78	74	57	71	83	33	87	33	44
450–500	C_{31}	81	74	56	70	80	30	86	35	34
500–550	C_{36}	78	76	56	71	82	30	84	32	24

A number of isomers in the range C_6, C_7, C_8, and C_9 have been isolated and identified in several crude oils. Many monocyclic hydrocarbons in the C_6–C_8 range which are mono-, bi- and tri-substituted can be classed as predominant constituents (see Table I). The methylcyclohexane content is especially high in naphthenic type crude oils and it reaches 2.7–2.8% in Tertiary crudes from Wade City and Plymouth, Texas (H. M. SMITH and RALL, 1953). The gasolines (B.P.~150°) derived from Surachany (Baku) and Koschagyl crude oils contain 20 and 13%, respectively, of this hydrocarbon (PLATE, 1957). Among the monocyclic naphthenic constituents in the C_7–C_{11} range, the most abundant isomers are those having relatively little strain energy in the molecules. The compounds substituted in 1, 3 and 1, 1, 3 positions clearly predominate.

LINDEMAN and LE TOURNEAU (1963) recently established the presence of 1, 1, 2 trimethylcyclohexane and n-propyl- and isopropylcyclohexanes in California crude oils.

The higher members of moncyclic naphthenes belong mainly to the polysubstituted series with two to four side chains, one long chain of which is straight or slightly branched (MAIR and ROSSINI, 1957; SERGIENKO and LEBEDEV, 1958). Usually the short chains are methyl and ethyl groups.

The cyclopentane homologs are often more abundant than those of cyclohexane, and their relative ratios vary between 25 and 40%. The long chain monocyclic naphthenes in the C_{20}–C_{30} range are crystalline and can be separated from the technical grade "paraffin waxes" during crystallization. They are constituents of ceresins and paraffin waxes of high melting points.

The bicyclonaphthenes appear to have the number and structure of chains similar to the monocyclic group. It is assumed that their rings are mainly condensed and correspond to the decalin, bicyclononane (4-3-0) and bicyclo-octane (3-3-0) types. These bicyclic hydrocarbons have recently been found in petroleum (ROSSINI and MAIR, 1959). Bicycloheptane, four methylbicyclo (2-2-1) heptane and two bicyclo-octanes (2-2-2 and 3-2-1) have also been found in California crude oil (LINDEMAN and LE TOURNEAU, 1963). This crude oil contains quite high quantities of the trimethylhexanes, bicyclo-octanes and nonanes. SERGIENKO and LEBEDEV (1958) also obtained high proportions of trisubstituted homologs of naphthalene by catalytic dehydrogenation of naphthenes in the C_{22}–C_{24} range which were derived from the Romashkino crude oil. The presence in petroleum of polycycloparaffins possessing one or three carbon-atom linkages in their rings has also been reported (MAIR and ROSSINI, 1957).

Methylbicyclo (2-2-1) heptane and bicyclo (3-2-1) octane have been separated in very small quantities from a Ponca City crude oil (ROSSINI and MAIR, 1959). The tricyclic saturated hydrocarbon adamantane ($C_{10}H_{16}$) has been identified in the Hodonin (Czechoslovakia) crude oil by LANDA and MACHACEK (1933). A polycyclic crystalline hydrocarbon (four to five rings) has been isolated by OAKWOOD et al. (1952) from a lubricating oil fraction. This compound, having a molecular weight of 392, showed high optical rotation and contained 88% C and 12% H. Non-condensed ring systems have also been shown to be present in certain naphthenic fractions, since catalytic dehydrogenation has yielded both diphenyl and phenyl cyclopentyl homologs.

The nature of the rings of tri- and polycyclic naphthenes is not yet well-known. According to spectrometric indications these constituents should primarily contain condensed rings. With the increasing number of these rings, the chains become shorter, ultimately resulting in methyl groups. In addition, the chains may become more numerous.

Aromatic hydrocarbons

There is some confusion regarding the use of the term "aromatic hydrocarbons" in connection with petroleum constituents. Among chemists engaged in the study of "aromatic portions" of petroleum, it is customary to call all compounds "aromatics" which have aromatic rings in addition to the presence of naphthenic rings within the same molecule. Strictly speaking, one should classify in the aromatic group only those hydrocarbons which contain aromatic rings, side chains and aliphatic bridges. One may distinguish mono-, bi-, tri-, and poly-aromatics belonging respectively to the benzene, naphthalene, diphenyl, fluorene, phenanthrene, chrysene, etc., series. Thus all the mixed constituents containing aromatic and naphthenic rings in the same molecule (tetralin, phenylcyclopentane, etc.) should be excluded from the aromatic group. In the author's opinion, this distinction is very important in order to interpret correctly the composition of the higher boiling point petroleum fractions.

The monocyclic aromatics and homologs of benzene are characteristic for the light crude oils. Benzene and all of its isomers in the C_7, C_8, C_9, and in part, C_{10} range (ROSSINI and MAIR, 1960) have been separated and identified in numerous petroleums. The relative proportions of these aromatic hydrocarbons are very close in all oils.

Toluene, m-xylene and 1, 2, 4-trimethylbenzene are among the major petroleum constituents (see Table I). The maximum concentration of a single mono-aromatic hydrocarbon in a crude oil may reach 1.6–1.8 % for toluene and 1.0 % for benzene and xylene. This concentration decreases considerably for C_9 and C_{10} mono-aromatics. It is to be noted that the presence of benzene homologs with one straight chain longer than five carbon atoms has never been proven. MAIR and BARNEWALL (1963) have shown that the di- and tri-substituted alkylbenzenes are the major components of the mono-aromatic series in the C_{13}, C_{14} and C_{15} range. The aromatics of the higher boiling point petroleum fractions are mainly tri- and polycyclic.

The bicyclic aromatics such as naphthalene and diphenyl, as well as certain of their homologs in the C_{11}, C_{12}, C_{13}, and C_{14} range, have been identified in several crude oils (BIRCH and NORRIS, 1926; COSCIUG, 1935; GARAT and IRIMESCU, 1941, 1942; VAN NES, 1951; ADAMS and RICHARDSON, 1953; CARRUTHERS and DOUGLAS, 1955; CARRUTHERS et al., 1955). Also the di-, tri-, and sometimes tetramethyl naphthalenes have been found in the Grozny, Maikop, Baku, Ehaby, Volga–Ural, etc., kerosene distillate fractions (NAMETKIN et al., 1949; TOPCHIEV, 1955; ROBINSON, 1956; TOPCHIEV et al., 1957; MUKHAMEDOVA et al., 1958; MAIR and MARTINEZ-PICO, 1962; YATSENKO and DONTSEVA, 1962). TOPCHIEV et al. (1957) found in a Devonian crude oil (Romashkinskaya) 1-ethylnaphthalene, dimethylisopropyl naphthalene (for the first time) and probably tetramethyl naphthalene (TOPCHIEV, 1955). 2, 3, 6, 7-tetramethyl naphthalene has also been identified in the Ponca City crude oil (MAIR and MARTINEZ-PICO, 1962).

CARRUTHERS et al. (1955) and CARRUTHERS (1956) have separated tricyclic aromatics from the Kuwait crude oil; 1, 8 dimethyl and 1, 2, 8-trimethylphenanthrenes; 2, 6- and 2, 7-dimethyl; 2, 3, 6-trimethyl as well as three tetramethylanthracenes.

A series of polycyclic aromatics has been isolated from the Ponca City crude oil (MAIR and MARTINEZ-PICO, 1962); monomethyl, 4, 6-dimethyl and trimethyl fluorenes, phenanthrene, 1-methyl, 2-methyl, 3-methyl, as well as 1, 8-dimethyl phenanthrenes were separated and identified.

In general, ultra-violet spectra and other analytical data permit the assumption that the homologs of phenanthrene are far more abundant than those of anthracene. Also fluorene-type structures are present in significant concentrations in crude oils.

The polycyclic aromatic hydrocarbons, pyrene, methylchrysene, methyl- and dimethylperylenes and benzofluorenes have been identified in Kuwait, California, West Beaumont, and Ponca City crude oils. The polycyclic aromatic hydrocarbons are found generally in rather small quantities in petroleum (a few fractions of a percent) and are chiefly represented by their methyl homologs. Higher members of these polyaromatic series with side chains longer than two or three carbon atoms probably do not exist. Chrysene and benzofluorene homologs seem to predominate over those of pyrene.

It should be emphasized that in the higher boiling point petroleum fractions, all these structures may be found in the naphtheno-aromatic constituents because each aromatic structure may be part of one or several mixed compounds containing naphthenic rings of a different nature. For example it has been shown by mass spectrometry (ORKIN et al., 1957) that among the compounds containing the benzene ring, there are many constituents that belong to the tetralin, indane, di- and tri-naphtheno-benzene series (cyclanobenzenes).

Naphtheno-aromatic hydrocarbons

The naphtheno-aromatic hydrocarbons, together with the naphthenic hydrocarbon series, form the major content of higher boiling point petroleum fractions. They are very important from the geochemical point of view, due to their complex and varied structures and their high chemical reactivity.

Usually the different naphtheno-aromatic components are classified according to the number of aromatic rings in their molecules. The first to be distinguished is the series with an equal number of aromatic and naphthenic rings. The first members of the bicyclic series C_9-C_{11}, are the simplest, such as the 1-methyl, 2- methyl, and 4-methyl indanes, and 2-methyl, and 6-methyl tetralins which have been isoated and identified in Ponca City and West Edmont crude oils (ADAMS and RICHARDSON, 1953; ROSSINI and MAIR, 1959, 1960). Tetralin, methyl-, dimethyl,- methylethyl- and tetramethyltetralins have been found in several Soviet crude oils, in particular that from Romashkino (TOPCHIEV et al., 1957; MUKHAMEDOVA and BAIBUROVA, 1960). In this case, catalytic dehydrogenation and separation by means of picrates have been used for identification. Spectrometric studies and in particular mass spectrometry have led to the finding of C_{12} acenaphthene homologs in kerosene and gas-oil fractions (CARLSON and O'NEAL, 1957; ORKIN et al., 1957).

TABLE VII

CYCLIC SYSTEMS IN THE C_{25}–C_{35} RANGE FROM PONCA CITY CRUDE OIL

Ring systems		Relative proportions (%)
1 aromatic ring	2 cycloparaffinic rings	27
1 aromatic ring	3 cycloparaffinic rings	
2 aromatic rings	2 cycloparaffinic rings	40.4
3 aromatic rings	1 cycloparaffinic ring	32.6

Although up to now only the two higher C_{17} and C_{18} naphtheno-aromatics, the cyclopenteno-phenanthrene and the methyl 1-1-2-cyclopenteno-phenanthrene have been isolated, their type of structures has been determined with rather good precision regarding the number and structure of the rings, their bonds, and the number and nature of the chains, as well as the distribution of the latter relative to the rings (MAIR and MARTINEZ-PICO, 1962).

The narrow naphtheno-aromatic fractions in the C_{25}–C_{35} range obtained from the Ponca City crude oil contained the cyclic systems mentioned in Table VII. The total number of rings in the higher naphtheno-aromatic molecules may be as high as six. But such highly condensed structures are difficult to separate from complex mixtures containing heterocyclic constituents of a resinous character. The chemical analysis of these mixtures is not yet sufficiently advanced.

An examination of the ultra-violet and infra-red spectra of polycyclic naphtheno-aromatic hydrocarbons shows that the rings in these constituents are mainly condensed (LUMPKIN and JOHNSON, 1954; BESTOUGEFF, 1957).

It is interesting that the distribution of the chains between aromatic and naphthenic rings within the same molecules follow the same pattern as in the single ring compounds. The short chains (methyl and ethyl) are characteristic constituents of the aromatic portion of the molecule, whereas a limited number (one or two) of rather long chains are commonly attached to the cycloparaffin rings. The total number of chains, which is in general four to six, as well as their length, increases according to the molecular weight of the naphtheno-aromatic compounds (BROWN and KNOBLOCH, 1957; MAIR and ROSSINI, 1957). The length of the chains and their abundance in relationship to the rings of the naphtheno-aromatic group occupy an intermediary position between the naphthenes and aromatics of petroleum.

The hydrocarbon composition of various types of petroleum

The various types of crude oils differ not only in the concentrations of individual hydrocarbons, but also in the presence or absence of certain constituents. Although one finds most of the same type of hydrocarbons in all petroleums, it can still be said that there are no two identical crude oils, either quantitatively or qualitatively.

For example, the heavy naphtheno-aromatic type crude oils, without low boiling point fractions, do not contain the lower members of the series C_nH_{2n+2} and C_nH_{2n}. Even in naphthenic crude oils containing low boiling fractions and the higher homologs of the C_nH_{2n} series, cyclopentane and cyclohexane are often absent.

The different classifications of crude oils are based on the predominance of a more or less well-defined group of constituents; this is not really satisfactory. For example, it is not correct to describe and compare as "aromatic" two crude oils, one having a high content of benzene and naphthalene homologs, and the other being a heavy oil of high aromaticity due to polycyclic compounds, the aromatic rings of which may only represent a small portion of the molecules. Nevertheless, some classification of the various types of petroleums is possible. The C_nH_{2n+2} hydrocarbons are always abundant when normal paraffins predominate over the aromatic hydrocarbons, especially over the homologs of benzene and naphthalene. In the case of cycloparaffinic (naphthenic) petroleums, the branched-chain paraffins may become one of the major constituents. The concentration of the naph-

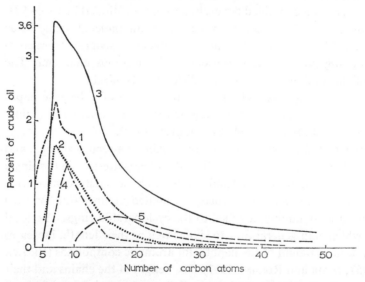

Fig.3. Distribution of hydrocarbons in a light (Ordovician) crude oil.
(By class and number of carbon atoms per molecule.)

Curve No.	Constituents	Weight percent	Curve No.	Constituents	Weight perc
1	normal paraffin hydrocarbons	23.3	4	aromatics	6.4
2	iso-paraffin hydrocarbons	12.8	5	aromatic cycloparaffins	8.1
3	cycloparaffins	41.0		resins asphaltenes	8.4
				total	100.0

thenic hydrocarbons is highest in the naphthenic crude-oil distillates. The aromatic and naphtheno-aromatic heavy crude oils are richer in polycyclic constituents. This is true not only in the distillation residues, but also in the kerosene, gas oil and lubricating oil fractions. In addition, as a general rule, naphtheno-aromatic and aromatic crude oils contain a significant content of heteroatomic constituents and asphaltenes. Fig.3 and 4 show the distribution of the different hydrocarbon groups in relation to the number of carbon atoms in two petroleums.

ORIGIN OF THE HYDROCARBONS AND THE GENETIC RELATIONS BETWEEN PETROLEUM CONSTITUENTS

Petroleum constituents

When one reviews the chemical composition of petroleums, it is necessary to classify their primary, secondary, and tertiary constituents according to their possible

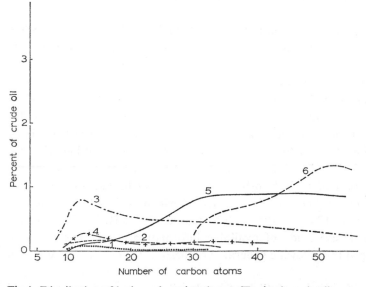

Fig.4. Distribution of hydrocarbons in a heavy (Tertiary) crude oil.
(By class and number of carbon atoms per molecule.)

No.	Constituents	Weight percent	Curve No.	Constituents	Weight percent
	normal paraffin hydrocarbons	0.95	5	aromatic cycloparaffins	
	iso-paraffin hydrocarbons	3.20		+ sulfur compounds	27.90
	cycloparaffins	19.20		heterocyclics (resins)	23.10
	aromatics	9.15		asphaltenes	16.50
				total	100.00

origins. However, our present knowledge is far too incomplete to carry out this classification. Thus the problem of genetic relations between different petroleum constituents, and especially between hydrocarbons and non-hydrocarbons, still remains unsolved.

Certain authors proposed that several of the hydrocarbons may have originated directly from living matter (WHITMORE, 1944); or from metal carbides (KUDRYAVTSEV, 1962). These authors, unfortunately, have not solved the problem but have merely displaced it because the question is not to determine the origin of isolated compounds, but to explain the whole chemical composition of petroleums. For example, STEVENS (1956) notes that "there is no evidence for the generation of oil as such by biochemical process although specific hydrocarbons are produced metabolically by numerous organisms". In spite of the widespread and almost universal occurrence of biochemically produced hydrocarbons in the organic debris of soils and Recent sediments, as a whole they differ in type from those present in recognized source beds and in the oil itself. Some of these hydrocarbons may have been preserved from the organic debris and accumulated in the oil, but it appears that the bulk of the petroleum hydrocarbons was formed by other means.

If the crude oils are considered to be formed from complex organic materials in marine muds, the proteins, carbohydrates, lipids, sterols, lignin and pigments could be expected to contribute to the formation of the oil (BREGER, 1960). The transformation of these heteroatomic systems (progenitors) to the different types of non-hydrocarbon and hydrocarbon petroleum constituents can be accomplished by different means, directly or indirectly through intermediary stages of polymerized substances (primary resins, etc.). A number of investigations has been conducted to explore the reaction mechanisms which are compatible with the physical and biological media of diagenesis. One of the current views is that the organic debris, or part of it, is transformed to a heavy bitumen-like material (malts, primary resins) or "embryonic petroleum" which evolves to form lighter and more paraffinic oils (BROOKS 1952; McNAB et al., 1952; H. M. SMITH et al., 1959). From an extensive study of available information, DOBRYANSKY (1948, 1962, 1963) developed the following general hypothesis of the origin and evolution of hydrocarbons:

(1) The formation and evolution of crude oil are oriented and universal phenomena, related to the parent substance and form systems of the lowest level of free energy possible in the given conditions.

(2) The mechanism of the evolution involves two basic phenomena mutually related and developing at the same rate. First, the formation of small molecules (low boiling point paraffins, gases, mono- and bicyclic aromatics, etc.) from the larger ones; and second, the condensation of average-sized molecules containing polycyclic rings to more voluminous and complex polycyclic structures containing aromatic, cycloparaffinic, heterocyclic rings, and short side chains.

(*3*) The chemical transformation of the substances takes place by a mechanism of intermolecular redistribution of hydrogen (hydrogen transfer) and the radicals, as well as by condensation and polymerisation. These processes appear to be favorable from the point of view of energy considerations in the reducing conditions of deeply buried rocks.

(*4*) Two groups of external factors affect the evolution of petroleums: The first group consists of the physico-chemical factors: temperature, pressure and catalysts, the action of which is constantly and regularly exercised. It is necessary to emphasize the thermocatalytic action (BROOKS, 1954; FROST, 1956; BOGOMOLOV and PANINA, 1960), without which the composition of petroleums would probably not have greatly exceeded the state of semi-solid maltha. The second group of factors is characterized by a mode of intermittent and local environments incapable of either modifying the direction or the overall nature of the evolution controlled by the factors of the first group. In this group of factors one can include oxidation, sulfurization, selective adsorption and the thermal diffusion of crude oils (VAN EGGELPOEL, 1959, 1960; DOBRYANSKY, 1961).

These general assumptions and the results of recent experiments might perhaps permit one to outline an initial, tentative scheme of the genetic relationships of petroleum compounds. This outline can be divided into four stages. The first stage contains the assumed "progenitors"; the number of carbon atoms of these compounds generally exceeds C_{18}. The second stage consists of the principal constituents of maltha or primary oils; i.e., the principally heteroatomic substances with high molecular weights. The two latter stages include the major portion of hydrocarbons and the heteroaromatic constituents (sulfur, oxygen compounds, etc.) ultimately formed during the course of evolution. The last stage includes substances having completely transformed structures which are not known to be products of living organisms (ERDMAN, 1961), for example, lower aromatic hydrocarbons, pyridine bases, etc.

Classification principles

The consideration of molecular weights permits making a rough selection of the "progenitor" substance, taking into consideration that low molecular weight hydrocarbons (lower than C_{12}–C_{15} excluding methane) have not apparently been found in Recent sediments and soils. P. V. SMITH (1954) found only hydrocarbons in the C_{15}–C_{30} range; on the other hand, VEBER and TURKELTAUB (1958) and SOKOLOV (1959) reported finding traces of C_3–C_{14} hydrocarbons. ERDMAN (1961) further emphasized the lack of low molecular weight hydrocarbons by pointing out the absence of certain aromatic hydrocarbons such as benzenes, xylenes, and naphthalenes in the parent organic debris. HUNT (1963) examined Recent sediments from several areas and he concluded in agreement with the preceding investigations that hydrocarbons in the C_3–C_8 range are formed at depth after burial. Apparently they are not present in near-surface Recent sediments. The same appears to be true for constituents having high molecular weights; for example, the paraffins in the range C_{40}–C_{45} and higher, the cycloparaffins, aromatics with a high number of rings, and the asphalthenes, etc.

In the authors's opinion it is evident that the substances with an average molecular weight of the C_{18}–C_{35} range, such as the naphtheno-aromatic hydrocarbons, appear to be nearest to the parent organic substances. Besides the size of the molecules and their high optical and chemical activity, these hydrocarbons may also have structures similar to those of steroids and vegetable resins.

The degree of substitution of the molecules can also be used as a criterion for the genetic classification. For example, the non-substituted cyclic hydrocarbons, benzene, naphthalene, cyclohexane, cyclopentane, etc., or the poly-substituted ones such as tetra- and penta-methylnaphthenes, can apparently form only by radical transfer reactions probably from mono- and tri-substituted molecules.

The degree of cyclization and the ramification of the chains in certain cases constitute genetic indicators. It appears that polycyclic structures with five to six or more condensed rings of the same kind (for example, polycyclic naphthenes), are secondary or tertiary products, as their structures are rather remote from possible parent substances.

Hydrocarbons

Normal paraffins

Normal paraffin hydrocarbons up to C_{12}–C_{14} probably originate either by the degradation of higher *n*-paraffins, or from other hydrocarbons by the cleaving of the side chains. Methane may also be directly derived from various parent substances. The fermentation of plant debris supplies copious quantities of methane (STEVENS, 1956). The average normal paraffins in the C_{16}–C_{35} range are sometimes considered being the direct derivatives of fatty acids. However, according to Bogomolov's studies, the thermo-catalysis of fatty acids (stearic, oleic) gives mainly iso-paraffins (BOGOMOLOV et al., 1960a; BOGOMOLOV and PANINA, 1961a). Fatty acids most common in nature contain twelve, sixteen and eighteen carbon atoms. Their transformation mechanism into hydrocarbons is not yet known. BREGER (1960) assumed that fatty acids and related substances may be transformed into aliphatic chains by a combined reaction, first biological, then chemical reactions of the Diels–Alder type. BOGOMOLOV and PANINA (1962) have succeeded in obtaining from stearic acid a small yield of a C_{34} paraffin with the aid of an aluminosilicate catalyst at 275 °C. It was assumed that the reaction passed through the following stages: acid → anhydride → ketone (stearone) → ketone decomposition and condensation of two C_{17} radicals → C_{34} hydrocarbon. The phenomenon of direct biochemical conversion of these acids into hydrocarbons has not yet been demonstrated in quantities sufficient for oil formation (BREGER, 1960, p.304).

STEVENS (1956) stated that both fatty acids and wax esters may be produced bio-chemically from carbohydrates.

The origin of the higher members of the *n*-paraffin series still remains un-explained. According to theoretical calculations, the thermodynamic possibilities of an increase or decrease in the chain length are practically identical above the C_{38}–C_{40} molecules. The actual chemical reactions, which could lead to a lengthen-ing of the chains in a geochemical environment, are still not known.

An explanation of the formation of long paraffin chains, either free or attached to naphthenic rings, is one of the most difficult problems in petroleum geochemistry.

Branched-chain paraffins

The genetic considerations concerning branched-chain paraffins are similar to those of the straight-chain molecules. The difficulties in explaining the origins of branched chains in the C_{16} and higher ranges are, however, facilitated because of the possibility of explaining the formation of these compounds from cyclic structures.

The branched-chain paraffins of the "isoprenoid" series (such as pristane and phytane, etc.) in petroleum are genetically related to the pigments, more specifically to the "phytol" group of the porphyrinic (chlorophyll) type complexes (BENDORAITIS et al., 1962).

Cycloparaffins

The formation of lower mono- and bicyclic naphthenes from mixed naphtheno-aromatic structures has been demonstrated experimentally by thermo-catalytic experiments (BOGOMOLOV et al., 1960b). A large number of cycloparaffins has been obtained by this method using acids as the starting substance (BOGOMOLOV et al., 1960a; BOGOMOLOV and PANINA, 1961a).

In the case of the higher molecular weight cycloparaffins, it is necessary on the one hand to examine separately the long-chain mono- and bicyclic structures, and on the other hand the polycyclic structures having relatively short chains.

A large portion of the tetracycloalkanes in sediments and crude oils is prob-ably derived from parent sterol compounds. The most abundant steranes contain the same number of carbon atoms (27–29) as the natural sterols, and their mass spectra resemble those of cholestane. The C_{30} tetracyclic naphthenes in crude oil have molecular weights of the same order of magnitude as that of certain bile acids and sex hormones. The structures of these tetracyclic compounds, according to mass-spectrometric data, could be similar to those of the C_{30} steranes. However, they are often classified with the perhydrotriterpenes or triterpenes, because C_{30} steroids have not yet been found in nature (MEINSCHEIN, 1959).

Through a condensation mechanism, hydrogen transfer or hydrogenation, the naphtheno-aromatic and aromatic compounds can give, rather easily, higher polycyclic or mono- and bicyclic cycloparaffins with branched chains. But, as has been previously mentioned, it does not seem possible that long-chain mono- and bicyclic naphthenes of high molecular weights were produced by these re-actions. Yet these structures form the major portion of the cycloparaffinic con-stituents of the higher boiling point fractions of light crude oils. To make the problem more difficult, experiments and thermodynamic calculations have shown that the synthesis of these cycloparaffins is not possible from n- and branched-chain paraffin hydrocarbons under geochemical environments.

Aromatic hydrocarbons

Experimental and theoretical considerations indicate a major difference between mono- and bicyclic, and polycyclic aromatic hydrocarbons. The structures of the first group of compounds seem to be present without much alteration in the prob-able parent substances (such as lignin, kerogen, transformed fatty acids, "primary resins", and naphtheno-aromatic hydrocarbons). The polycyclic aromatic hydro-carbons can only result by a major alteration of the parent substances. The struc-ture of these polycyclic compounds is not characteristic for either the products of biological or thermocatalytic reactions. The quantitative difference between the two groups should be noted in particular. The mono- and bicyclic aromatic hydro-carbons are the major constituents of crude oils; whereas the polyaromatic con-tent is usually very low. The molecules containing condensed aromatic rings linked with naphthenic or heteroaromatic rings are especially rare. This leads one to specu-late that the polycyclic aromatic hydrocarbons may be transient constituents in the process of the formation of the more "graphite-like" substances (this will be further discussed in this chapter in connection with the asphaltenes).

Naphtheno-aromatic hydrocarbons

This group of compounds is abundantly present in the medium and higher boiling point petroleum fractions. It seems to constitute an important step in hydrocarbon formation which apparently permits the development of a large variety of structures (BOGOMOLOV and PANINA, 1962).

The chemical structures and properties of these substances suggest that these compounds may be genetically related to resins, kerogen and sterols. It appears that practically all geochemical paths leading to the formation of different hydro-carbon classes involve, to some degree, the formation of the naphtheno-aromatic structures. According to O'NEAL and HOOD (1956) and to MEINSCHEIN and KENNY (1957), the sediments and the oils contain sterol-like compounds with aromatic nuclei. Their structures can be compared with some of the aromatic hydrocarbons. $C_{25}H_{24}$ hydrocarbons were found for the first time by Otto Diels and then by other investigators in dehydrogenated products of sapogenins, sterols, and triterpenes, and consequently they may be of interest in this connection.

The condensation of naphtheno-aromatic hydrocarbons with sulfur or oxygen-containing compounds probably leads to a substance of the type of second-ary resins.

Heteroatomic constituents

To complete a survey of possible hydrocarbon development processes, one must consider briefly the heteroatomic molecules in oils.

Oxidized products, acids and derivatives

Crude oils contain relatively small quantities (up to 2%) of oxidized compounds in the form of acids, phenols, ketones (H. M. SMITH, 1965) and esters. Acids, which constitute the greater portion, have been studied rather extensively. It has been ascertained that fatty acids, cyclic acids with naphthenic and aromatic rings as well as asphaltogenic acids of a complex nature and high molecular weight were present in various distillates and residues. The naphthenic acids are by far the most abundant. Small quantities of phenols of different structures have been found in kerosene and gas oils (LOCHTE, 1952). FERRANTE (1960) and HUBRECHT (1960) have shown that heavy oil residues contain appreciable quantities of slightly acidic constituents. Heavy crude oils from geologically young formations seem to contain the highest acid content. Light oils from older reservoirs contain only traces of these substances (DOBRYANSKY, 1961).

Opinions regarding the origin of the acids differ substantially. It is assumed that they result from oxidation of the petroleum hydrocarbons, but there is no direct proof that this reaction is possible. It may be that naphthenic acids have formed at the beginning of the diagenesis from already oxidized substances (camphors, cetons, etc.), or originate directly from pre-existent acid groups in the parent substances (fatty acids).

Resinous constituents

The term "resins" is not clearly defined; it usually includes substances of different structures which are strongly retained on silica gel and other adsorbents. Theoreti-cally, the resins should contain only neutral, oxygenated, polycyclic compounds, including heterocyclics with sulfur and nitrogen atoms. Such resins are soluble in light paraffinic solvents and have molecular weights in the range of 500–1000. Unfortunately, the standard methods yield complex mixtures, containing substan-ces other than resins (as defined above). Polycondensed aromatic and naphtheno-aromatic hydrocarbons as well as sulfur and nitrogen-bearing compounds with structures different from that of resins are often present in these mixtures.

A certain degree of separation of the resinous constituents may be obtained be elution chromatography on silica gel or alumina columns (M. A. Bestougeff, unpublished data). The first fractions obtained from the columns by elution with low polarity solvents contain sizeable quantities of hydrocarbons. More polar solvents are used to elute the non-hydrocarbon and then the resinous substances. The analyses of the non-hydrocarbons is often difficult. The concentration of sulfur and nitrogen in most of the non-hydrocarbon eluate fractions does not usually exceed one atom of these elements per molecule (SERGIENKO, 1959). The number of the oxygen atoms varies between one and three, on the average, per molecule in these fractions. The average content of heteroatoms increases in the last fractions eluted by the more polar solvents such as acetone and alcohol. The intermediate fractions eluted by benzene are high in aromatic substances; whereas the subsequent polar fractions have considerably lower aromaticity.

The presence of oxygen and the aromatic and naphthenic rings (mixed polycyclic structures) are characteristics of resins. It is likely that the resins eluted by benzene, being more cyclic and of higher molecular weight, can be classified as secondary products formed from naphtheno-aromatic hydrocarbons of a polycyclic structure. On the other hand resin fractions desorbed by acetone and alcohol may be nearer in composition to the parent substance or to the residues of this matter.

A thorough study of the resins, and in particular, better separation of the different constituents of resinous substances will certainly help to establish the genetic relations between primary and secondary resins and naphtheno-aromatic hydrocarbons.

Sulfur compounds

Sulfur compounds are among the most important heteroatomic constituents of petroleum. They are found in increasing quantities in the higher molecular weight fractions. The sulfur content of crude oils varies from traces up to 5%. Therefore, there are petroleums which contain up to 30–40% sulfur compounds in addition to those in the resins and asphaltenes. Sulfur-rich crude oils appear in different geological strata, and it is apparently impossible to establish a relation between the sulfur content and the age of the oil.

The principal groups of sulfur compounds identified in crude oils are the following:

(*1*) Thiols.

(*2*) Aliphatic, monocyclic, bi- and polycyclic sulfides.

(*3*) Disulfides.

(*4*) Monocyclic, bicyclic (benzothiophene), and tricyclic (dibenzothiophenes) thiophenes.

The first three groups of compounds are less abundant than the cyclic compounds containing aromatic rings (BESTOUGEFF, 1959). It is generally considered that most of the sulfur compounds, particularly in sulfur-rich crude oils, are of secondary origin. (This will be discussed in greater detail in the next chapter.) It is possible that the enrichment of the crude oil with sulfur compounds has occurred during geological time by the reaction of the hydrocarbons with hydrogen sulfide or elementary sulfur. EREMENKO (1960) found that the isotopic compositions of sulfur in crude oils coming from formations of the same age seem to be identical, even if these formations are located far apart. On the other hand, Eremenko reported that the isotopic composition of sulfur varied considerably in oils of different ages.

Certain investigators did not exclude the possibility that a part of the sulfur compounds was derived from the parent organic substance (such as proteins), but this source probably played only a negligible role (JAVILLIER et al., 1962). It is necessary to note that all sulfur compounds undergo an evolution process as do all petroleum constituents. This evolution must be very involved for the groups of the rather unstable sulfur compounds with the possible exception of the thiophenic and benzo-thiophenic compounds. The elimination of sulfur from these latter types requires high energy.

It is interesting that the sulfur content of asphaltenes varies proportionally with the sulfur-compound content of petroleum. This fact indirectly indicates that the transformation of cyclic sulfur compounds may also lead to the formation of asphaltic complexes.

Nitrogen compounds

The nitrogen compounds in petroleum are mainly concentrated in distillation residues and are part of the resins and asphaltenes. (The nitrogen compounds will be discussed in greater detail in the next chapter.) The nitrogen content of crude oils generally varies between 0.01 and 0.2%. This percentage corresponds to a few percent of nitrogen compounds. The crude oil from Wilmington (California) contains 0.65% nitrogen; i.e., its nitrogen compound content exceeds 10%.

Three-quarters of the nitrogen constituents are neutral and only the remaining quarter is of basic character. Nitrogen bases have been identified in distillates and are composed mainly of pyridine homologs in the C_6-C_{10} range and quinolines in the $C_{10}-C_{17}$ range and their hydrogenated derivatives (LOCHTE, 1952). Among the non-basic nitrogen compounds the carbazoles were first identified in the Wilmington crude oil (SAUER et al., 1952). Spectrographic studies have also shown the presence of indoles and pyrroles.

The nitrogen compounds appear to be of biogenic origin. The proteins and the pigments are the probable sources of pyrroles and indoles, if not the pyridine derivatives (STEVENS, 1956; BREGER, 1960). The transformation mechanism of the parent substance into nitrogen constituents is not yet known. The anaerobic fermentation of proteins results in amino acids as well as stable nitrogen compounds containing pyrrol rings. In the presence of air, degradation proceeds as far as ammonia. RICHTER et al. (1952) made the interesting observation that the ratio of basic nitrogen to total nitrogen is substantially constant and suggested that this indicates a common mechanism for the formation of all crude oils. According to other observations, nitrogen bases can form during distillation. They may also be the products of degradation of pre-existent nitrogen compounds, the nature of which is unknown.

Porphyrins

Porphyrins were first discovered in crude oils by TREIBS (1934, 1935). These compounds have been studied extensively during the past few years. Practically all porphyrins are associated with high molecular weight constituents, however, a portion of these substances, according to the investigation of BIEBER et al. (1958) can be recovered by molecular distillation. The presence of porphyrins is generally assumed to be proof of the biogenic origin of petroleum.

The porphyrin content varies in petroleums. It may attain the relatively high concentration of 0.04 % (in the Trinidad crude oil). DUNNING et al. (1954), DUNNING and ROBON (1956), and BALL et al. (1959) suggested that the highest porphyrin content is found in asphaltic petroleums from the young geological reservoirs. In light and methane-rich oils, porphyrins may be entirely absent.

The porphyrins are genetically related to certain natural pigments (chlorophyll, etc.), the degradation of which may furnish porphyrins and branched-chain paraffin hydrocarbons of the isoprenoid type (phytane, C_{20}). The organic debris appear to change in such a manner that phytane, by continuous degradation, yields the lower members of this series (C_{19}, C_{18}, etc.); whereas the prophyrins may condense with the polycyclic aromatic and naphtheno-aromatic molecules, thus forming asphaltene-type constituents. Some of these latter constituents may give the characteristic spectra of the porphyrins. It is also possible that a small portion of the porphyrins may be degraded to pyrrol derivatives. ERDMAN (1961) reports that nitrogen-containing heterocyclic compounds may also be derived from the purines and pyrimidines.

Asphaltenes

Heterocyclic substances containing oxygen, sulfur, nitrogen, and metals, and possessing molecular weights of approximately 900–3000, constitute the major portion of the asphaltenes. They can be precipitated from crude oils and bitumens by C_5–C_7 paraffinic solvents. These precipitates contain a complex mixture of semi-solid to solid organic substances which are soluble in benzene and polar solvents. The asphaltene content of crude oils varies between 0 and 20%.

Apparently, the asphaltenes contain numerous aromatic and naphthenic rings and short aliphatic chains grouped in several systems. (The asphaltenes will be discussed in greater detail in Chapter VI.) The cyclic systems, varying considerably regarding their structures and aromaticity, are only partially condensed and may contain the heterocyclic rings of five or six atoms. The linkage between the different groups of condensed rings appears to be rather loose considering the easy degradation of these compounds by hydrogenation at low temperatures. It is possible to dissociate the asphaltene particles with hydrogen in the presence of Raney nickel catalyst at 100 °C at atmospheric pressure.

The products, listed in Table VIII, have been obtained from a fraction of the Boscan asphalt. Similar results have been reported by SERGIENKO (1959).

TABLE VIII

PRODUCTS OBTAINED FROM A FRACTION OF THE BOSCAN ASPHALT

	Yield $(\%)$	Mol. weight	Fusion $(°C)$	$C(\%)$	$H(\%)$	$S(\%)$	$(O+N)$ $(\%)$	Solubility in heptane
Initial product	100	990	160	79.0	8.3	6.4	6.3	insoluble
Fraction *1* (heptane precipitable)	38	1010	220			5.6		insoluble
Fraction *2* (chromatographic)	18.6	590	120			2.5		soluble
Fraction *3* (chromatographic)	39.0	330	140	79.0	9.0	3.9	8.1	soluble
Fraction *4* (chromatographic)	4.4		semi-solid					soluble

From the genetic point of view, asphaltenes are of considerable interest because they contain the largest amount of the trace elements in petroleum, particularly vanadium and nickel. These metals are found in asphaltenes in the porphyrin complexes and also in greater quantities associated with large polycyclic molecules, which do not give the characteristic spectra of porphyrins.

It is very likely that asphaltenes are secondary products derived by the condensation and polymerization of the heavy organic debris during diagenesis. The variety and complexity of the asphaltene structures are rather extensive, taking into account that the substances of different nature, such as primary and secondary resins, polycyclic aromatic and naphtheno-aromatic hydrocarbons, porphyrins, asphaltogenic acids, etc., may contribute to their formation.

One should emphasize that not only the asphaltenes in a given crude oil contain different groups of substances, but that the corresponding asphaltene fractions separated from different petroleum may also vary considerably. Thus the asphaltenes from old formations (for example, the Hassi Messaoud petroleum which is in Cambrian strata) have a more graphitic character and contain less metals and sulfur than asphaltenes in younger oils (BESTOUGEFF et al., 1962). Furthermore, the properties of sulfur-rich asphaltenes differ considerably from those poor in this element.

These facts lead one to assume that asphaltenes have been subjected to a substantial transformation, as were also the hydrocarbons, during petroleum evolution. The secondary character of asphaltenes has been emphasized by ERDMAN (1961) who stated that "these substances definitely are not produced by plants and animals and no true asphaltic material has been observed in any uncontaminated Recent sediments".

REFERENCES

ADAMS, N. G. and RICHARDSON, D. M., 1953. Isolation and identification of biphenyls from West Edmond crude oil. *Anal. Chem.*, 25: 1073–1074.
ANDREEV, P. F., BOGOMOLOV, A. I., DOBRYANSKY, A. F. and KARTSEV, A. A., 1958. *Transformation of Petroleum in the Nature.* Gostoptekhizdat, Leningrad, 416 pp.
BALL, J. S., HAINES, W. E. and HELM, R. V., 1959. Minor constituents of a California petroleum. *World Petrol. Congr. Proc., 5th, N.Y., 1959*, pp.175–189.
BENDORAITIS, J. G., BROWN, B. L. and HEPNER, L. S., 1962. Isoprenoid hydrocarbons in petroleum. *Anal. Chem.*, 34: 49–53.
BESTOUGEFF, M. A., 1951. Isomérie des constituants des pétroles. *World Petrol. Congr., 3rd, The Hague, 1951*, 4: 12.
BESTOUGEFF, M. A., 1957. Identification des hydrocarbures aromatiques à l'aide des spectres ultra-violets. *Congr. Intern. Chim. Pure Appl., 16e, Paris, 1957, Mém. Sect. Chim. Minérale*, 2: 306.
BESTOUGEFF, M. A., 1959. Constitution of the sulfur cyclic compounds of petroleum. *World Petrol. Congr., Proc., 5th, N.Y., 1959*, 5: 143–164.
BESTOUGEFF, M. A., 1961. Contribution des méthodes chromatographiques à l'étude de l'isomérie des constituants des pétroles. *Journées Internat. Études Méthodes Séparation Immédiate Chromatographie, Compt. Rend., Paris, 1961*, pp.55–63.
BESTOUGEFF, M. A., 1964. Étude sur les "paraffines" du pétrole. *Proc. Intern. Congr. Org. Geochem., Paris, 1964 (Pub. 1965)*, pp.197–211.
BESTOUGEFF, M. A., GUIOCHON, G. et JACQUE, L., 1962. Étude thermogravimétrique des asphaltènes. *Compt. Rend.*, 254: 266–268.
BIEBER, H., HARTZBAND, H. M. and KRUSE, E. C., 1958. The volatility of porphyrins in petroleum. *Am. Chem. Soc., Div. Petrol. Chem.*, 3: 268–281.
BIRCH, S. F., and NORRIS, W. S., 1926. Chemistry of petroleum aromatic hydrocarbons. *J. Chem. Soc.*, 127: 2545–2554.
BOGOMOLOV, A. I. and PANINA, K. I., 1960. Catalytic transformation of the naphthenic hydrocarbons of petroleum on natural clay at low temperature. *Zh. Prikl. Khim.*, 33: 2757–2762.
BOGOMOLOV, A. I. and PANINA, K. I., 1961a. Thermocatalytic transformation of the oleic acid at low temperature. *Tr. Vses. Nauchn. Issled. Geologorazved. Inst.*, 7 (174): 17–25.
BOGOMOLOV, A. I. and PANINA, K. I., 1961b. Catalitic transformation of waxes on natural clay at low temperature. *Tr. Vses. Nauchn. Issled. Geologorazved. Inst.*, 7 (174): 26–34.
BOGOMOLOV, A. I. and PANINA, K. I., 1962. Catalytic transformation of mixed naphthenoaromatic hydrocarbons of petroleum. *Bull. Univ. Leningrad*, pp.82–94.
BOGOMOLOV, A. I., KHOTINTCEVA, A. I. and PANINA, K. I., 1960a. Thermocatalytic transformation of the stearic acid at low temperature. *Tr. Vses. Nauchn. Issled. Geologorazved. Inst.*, 6 (155): 163–193.
BOGOMOLOV, A. I., PANINA, K. I. and BATALIN, O. E., 1960b. Thermocatalytic transformation of polycyclic naphthenic hydrocarbons of petroleum. *Tr. Vses. Nauchn. Issled. Geologorazved. Inst.*, 6 (155): 194–211.
BOLSHAKOVA, T. A. and STAROBINETZ, G. L., 1961. Distribution chromatography of solid petroleum paraffinic hydrocarbons on urea. *Khim. Tekhnol. Topliv. Massel*, 6 (5): 17–21.

BREGER, I. A., 1960. Diagenesis of metabolities and a discussion of the origin of petroleum hydrocarbons. *Geochim. Cosmochim. Acta*, 19: 297–308.

BROOKS, B. T., 1952. Evidence of catalytic action in petroleum formation. *Ind. Eng. Chem.*, 44: 2570–2576.

BROOKS, B. T., 1954a. Origin of petroleum In: R. BROOKS, C. BOORD, S. KURTZ and L. SCHMEZLING (Editors), *The Chemistry of Petroleum Hydrocarbons*. Reinhold, New York, N.Y., 1: 93–101.

BROOKS, B. T., 1954b. Composition of petroleum waxes. In: R. BROOKS, C. BOORD, S. KURTZ and L. SCHMEZLING (Editors), *The Chemistry of Petroleum Hydrocarbons*. Reinhold, New York, N.Y., 1: 37–47.

BROWN, A. B. and KNOBLOCH, J. O., 1957. The composition of petroleum distillates as revealed by their sulfonates. *Am. Soc. Testing Mater., Spec. Tech. Publ.*, 224: 213–229.

CARLSON, E. G. and O'NEAL, M. J., 1957. Analysis of petroleum oils by mass spectrometry. *Am. Soc. Testing Mater., Spec. Tech. Publ.*, 224: 151–167.

CARRUTHERS, W., 1956. Anthracene homologues in a Kuwait oil, *J. Chem. Soc.*, 1956: 603–607.

CARRUTHERS, W., 1957. Some polycyclic aromatic hydrocarbons in a Kuwait oil. *J. Chem. Soc.*, 1957: 278–281.

CARRUTHERS, W. and COOK, J. W., 1954. The constitution of high boiling petroleum distillates. *J. Chem. Soc.*, 1954: 2047–2052.

CARRUTHERS, W. and DOUGLAS, A. G., 1955. Trimethylnaphthalenes in Trinidad oil. *J. Chem. Soc.*, 1955: 1847–1850.

CARRUTHERS, W., CERIGO, D. G., KING, P. J., MORTON, F., PELL, A. W. and SAGARRA, A., 1955. The constitution of petroleum fractions structural group analysis of a Kuwait heavy gas oil. *World Petrol. Congr., Proc., 4th, Rome, 1955*.

CHERNOZHUKOV, N. J., KREIN, C. E. and LOSSIKOV, B. V., 1959. *Chemistry of Mineral Oils*, 2 ed. Gostoptekhizdat, Moscow.

COSCIUG, T., 1935. Naphthalene and methylnaphthalene from Romanian petroleum. *Petr. Z.*, 31: 5–7.

COSCIUG, T., 1938a. Dimethylnaphthalenes from Romanian crude oils. *Petr. Z.*, 34: 5–7.

COSCIUG, T., 1938b. Chemical constituents of Romanian oil. *Petr. Z.*, 34: 1–5.

DESTY, D. H., GOLDUP, A. and SWANTON, W. T., 1962. Performance of coated capillary columns, examination of Ponca Crude, gas chromatography. *Proc. Instr. Soc. Am. Natl. Symp. Progr. Trends Chem. Petrol. Instr., 3rd, 1961*, pp.105–134.

DOBRYANSKY, A. F., 1948. *The Geochemistry of Petroleum*. Gostoptekhizdat, Moscow, 476 pp.

DOBRYANSKY, A. F., 1961. *Chemistry of Petroleum*. Gostoptekhizdat, Leningrad, 224 pp.

DOBRYANSKY, A. F., 1962. Low temperature catalytic transformation of hydrocarbons (progenitors of petroleum). *Bull. Univ. Leningrad*, pp.5–11.

DOBRYANSKY, A. F., 1963. La transformation du pétrole brut dans la nature. *Rev. Inst. Franç. Pétrole Ann. Combust. Liquides* 18: 41–49.

DUNNING, H. N. and ROBON, N. A., 1956. Porphyrin–metal complexes in petroleum stocks. *Ind. Eng. Chem.*, 48: 951–955.

DUNNING, H. N., MOORE, J. W. and MYERS, A. T., 1954. Properties of porphyrins in petroleum. *Ind. Eng. Chem.*, 46: 2000–2007.

ERDMAN, J. G., 1961. Some chemical aspects of petroleum genesis as related to the problem of source bed recognition. *Geochim. Cosmochim. Acta*, 22: 16–36.

EREMENKO, N. A., 1960. Variation of the isotope composition in U.S.S.R. crude oils according to the stratigraphic sequence. *Geol. Nefti i Gaza*, 4 (11): 9–10.

FERRANTE, J., 1960. Détermination potentiométrique de l'indice d'acide des bitumes en milieu non aqueux. *Centre Rech. Routières (Brussels), Note Lab. C.R.R.*, M 2/60: 1–19.

FIESER, L. and FIESER, M., 1944. *Organic Chemistry*, 1 ed. Reinhold, New York, N.Y., 1118 pp.

FORZIATI, A. F., WILLINGHAM, C. B., MAIR, B. J. and ROSSINI, F. D., 1944. Hydrocarbons in the gasoline fraction of seven representative crudes including all the distillates to 102°C and aromatics to 160°C. *J. Res. Natl. Bur. Std.*, 32: 11–37.

FRANCIS, S. A., 1956. Interpretation of 10.3-micron infra-red absorption band in lubricating oils. *Anal. Chem.*, 28: 1171.

FRED, M. and PUTSCHER, R. E., 1949. Identification of Pennsylvania lubricating oils by infra-red absorption. *Anal. Chem.*, 21: 900–911.

FROST, A. V., 1956. Works on the cinetic and catalysis. *Acad. Sci. U.S.S.R.*, pp.402–405.

GARAT, I. G. and IRIMESCU, I., 1941. Separation of the dimethylnaphtalenes from Romanian petroleum. *Chem. Ber.*, 74: 1812.

GARAT, I. G. and IRIMESCU, I., 1942. Separation of the trimethylnaphthalenes and phenanthrene from gas oil. *Chem. Ber.*, 75: 820.

HAAK, F. A. and VAN NES, K., 1951. Investigation into the olefinic components of a Pennsylvania crude oil. *J. Inst. Petrol.*, 37: 245.

HEADLE, A. J. W. and MCCLELAND, R. E., 1951. Quantitative separation of West Virginia petroleum into several hundred fractions, isolation and properties of C_5 to C_{27} normal paraffins and other hydrocarbons. *Ind. Eng. Chem.*, 43: 2547–2552.

HOLLIMAN, W. C., SMITH, H. M., MCKINNEY, C. M. and SPONSLER, C. R., 1950. Composition of petroleum: properties of distillates to 600 °F. *U.S., Bur. Mines, Tech. Papers*, 722.

HOOD, A., CLERC, R. J. and O'NEAL, M. J., 1959. The molecular structure of heavy petroleum compounds. *J. Inst. Petrol.*, 45: 168–172.

HUBRECHT, L., 1960. L'indice d'acide des bitumes pour route; série de bitumes de différentes origines. *Centre Rech. Routières (Brussels)*, 71: 1–24.

HUNT, J. M., 1963. Geochemical data on organic matter in sediments. *Proc. Intern. Conf. Geochem., Microbiol. Petrol. Chem., Budapest, 1962*, 2: 394–412.

JAVILLIER, M., POLONOVSKI, M., FLORKIN, M. et BOULANGER, P., 1962. *Traité de Biochimie Générale*. Masson, Paris, V (3).

JONES, A. L., 1957. New thermal diffusion techniques applicable to high-boiling petroleum fractions. *Am. Soc. Testing Mater., Spec. Tech. Publ.*, 224: 83–93.

KEARNS, G. L., MARANOVSKI, N. C. and CRABLE, G. F., 1959. Application of F.I.A. separatory and low voltage mass spectrometric techniques. *Anal. Chem.*, 31: 1646–1651.

KUDRYAVTSEV, N. A., 1962. Study of relationship in the distribution of oil and gas fields. *Geol. Nefti i Gaza*, 6 (1): 23–28.

LANDA, S. and MACHACEK, U., 1933. Adamantane, a new hydrocarbon extracted from petroleum. *Collection Czech. Chem. Commun.*, 5: 1–5.

LINDEMAN, L. P. and LE TOURNEAU, R. L., 1963. New information on the composition of petroleum. *World Petrol. Congr., 6th, Frankfurt, 1963*, 5: 281–292.

LOCHTE, H. L., 1952. Petroleum acids and bases. *Ind. Eng. Chem.*, 44: 2597–2601.

LUMPKIN, H. E., 1956. Determination of saturated hydrocarbons in heavy petroleum fractions by mass spectrometry. *Anal. Chem.*, 28: 1946–1948.

LUMPKIN, H. E. and JOHNSON, B. H., 1954. Identification of compound types in a heavy petroleum gas oil. *Anal. Chem.*, 26: 1719–1722.

MAIR, B. J. and BARNEWALL, J. M., 1963. Composition of the mononuclear aromatic material in the light gas oil range. *Meeting Am. Chem. Soc., New York, N.Y.*, pp.C5–C28.

MAIR, B. J. and MARTINEZ-PICO, J. L., 1962. Composition of the trinuclear aromatic portion of the heavy gas oil and light lubricating distillate. *J. Chem. Eng. Data*, 7 (4): C115–C137.

MAIR, B. J. and ROSSINI, F. D., 1957. Summary of work on the hydrocarbons in the C_{13}–C_{38} fraction of petroleum. *Am. Soc. Testing Mater., Spec. Tech. Publ.*, 224: 10–48.

MAIR, B. J., KROUSKOP, N. C. and MAYER, J. T., 1962. Composition of the branched paraffin–cycloparaffin portion of the light gas oil fraction. *J. Chem. Eng. Data*, 7 (3): 420–426.

MAIR, B. J., MARCULAITIS, W. J. and ROSSINI, F. D., 1957. Separation of the C_{18} to C_{25} fraction of petroleum. *Anal. Chem.*, 29: 92–100.

MARTIN, R. L. and WINTERS, J. C., 1959. Composition of crude oil through seven carbons as determined by gas chromatography. *Anal. Chem.*, 31: 1954–1960.

MARTIN, R. L., WINTERS, J. C. and WILLIAMS, J. A., 1963. Distribution of *n*-paraffins in crude oils and their implications to origin of petroleum. *Nature*, 199: 110–113.

MCNAN, J. G., SMITH JR., P. V. and BETTS, R. L., 1952. Evolution of petroleum. *Ind. Eng. Chem.*, 44: 2556–2563.

MEINSCHEIN, W. G., 1959. Origin of petroleum. *Bull. Am. Assoc. Petrol. Geologists*, 43: 925–943.

MEINSCHEIN, W. G. and KENNY, G. C., 1957. Analysis of a chromatographic fraction of organic extracts of soils. *Anal. Chem.*, 29: 1153–1161.

MELPOLDER, F. W., SAUER, R. W. and WASHALL, T. A., 1957. The separation of high boiling petroleum oils by thermal diffusion. *Am. Soc. Testing Mater., Spec. Tech. Publ.*, 224: 94–110.

MUKHAMEDOVA, L. A. and BAIBUROVA, M. K., 1960. Hydrocarbons of the tetralin series in the kerosene fraction of Romashkinskaya crude. *Khim. i Technol., Topliv i Masel*, 5 (3): 5–8.

MUKHAMEDOVA, L. A., BAIBUROVA, M. K. and ROBINSON, E. A., 1958. Study of the hydrocarbons of the naphthalene series from kerosene fraction of Romachkinskaya crude, Minnibaev field. *Khim. i Technol., Topliv i Masel*, 3 (9): 18–24.

NAMETKIN, S. S., POKROVSKAYA, E. S. and STEPANTSEVA, T. G., 1949. Naphthalene series hydrocarbons of Surakhan petroleum. *Dokl. Akad. Nauk, SSSR*, 67: 847–850.

NAMETKIN, S. S., POKROVSKAYA, E. S. and STEPANTSEVA, T. G., 1950a. Hydrocarbons of the naphthalene series in Maikop petroleum. *Dokl. Akad. Nauk, SSSR*, 73: 715–717.

NAMETKIN, S. S., POKROVSKAYA, E. S. and STEPANTSEVA, T. G., 1950. Characterization of aromatic hydrocarbons from Emba petroleum. *Dokl. Akad. Nauk, SSSR*, 74: 69–71.

OAKWOOD, T. S., SHRIVER, O. S., FALL, H. H., McCLEER, W. J. and WUNZ, P. K., 1952. Optical activity of petroleum. *Ind. Eng. Chem.*, 44 (11): 2568–2570.

O'CONNOR, J. G. and NORRIS, M. S., 1960. Molecular sieve adsorption. Application to hydrocarbon type analysis. *Anal. Chem.*, 32: 701–706.

O'NEAL, M. J. and HOOD, A., 1956. Mass spectrometric analysis of polycyclic hydrocarbons. *Meeting Am. Chem. Soc., Atlantic City, 1956*, pp.127–131.

ORKIN, B. A., BENDORAITIS, J. G., BROWN, B. and WILLIAMS, R. H., 1957. Composition of an East Texas lubricating oil distillate. *Am. Soc. Testing Mater., Spec. Tech. Publ.*, 224: 59–82.

PLATE, A. F., 1957. Study of the composition of gasolines by combined methods. Composition and properties of crude petroleums and its gasoline and kerosene fractions. *Petrol. Inst., Acad. Sci., Moscow*, 1957: 217–235.

PUTSCHER, R. E., 1952. Isolation of olefins from Bradford crude oil. *Anal. Chem.*, 24: 1551–1558.

RAMPTON, H. C., 1957. Determination of the paraffin, monocyclic and dicyclic. Naphthene contents of a Middle East gas oil by selective adsorption. *Am. Soc. Testing Mater., Spec. Tech. Publ.*, 224: 49–58.

RICHTER, F. P., CAESAR, P. D., MAISAL, S. L. and OFFENHAUER, R. D., 1952. Distribution of nitrogen in petroleum according to viscosity. *Ind. Eng. Chem.*, 44 (11): 2601–2605.

ROBINSON, E. A., 1960. Crude oils of Tatar A.S.S.R. *Akad. Nauk USSR*, 1960: 1–274.

ROSSINI, F. D. and MAIR, B. J., 1959. The work of the API research project 6 on the composition of petroleum. *World Petrol. Congr., Proc., 5th, N.Y., 1959*, 5: 223–245.

ROSSINI, F. D. and MAIR, B. J., 1960. 17 aromatic hydrocarbons in fraction 180–200° of Ponca City crude. *J. Chem. Eng. Data*, 5: 186–190.

ROSSINI, F. D., MAIR, B. J. and STREIFF, A. J., 1952. *Hydrocarbons from Petroleum*. Reinhold, New York, N.Y., 572 pp.

SACHANEN, A. N., 1945. *The Chemical Constituents of Petroleum*. Reinhold, New York, N.Y., 451 pp.

SAUER, R. W., MELPOLDER, F. W. and BROWN, R. A., 1952. Nitrogen compounds in domestic heating oil destillates. *Ind. Eng. Chem.*, 44: 2606–2609.

SERGIENKO, S. R., 1959. *High Molecular Weight Substances in Petroleum*. Gostoptekhisdat, Moscow, 410 pp.

SERGIENKO, S. R. and LEBEDEV, E. B., 1958. *Tr. Inst. Nefti, Akad. Nauk SSSR*, 12 pp.

SMITH, H. M., 1965. Crude oil—qualitative and quantitative aspects. *U.S., Bur. Mines, Rept. Invest.*, 1–55.

SMITH, H. M. and RALL, H. T., 1953. Relationship of hydrocarbons with six to nine carbon atoms. *Ind. Eng. Chem.*, 45: 1491–1497.

SMITH, H. M., DUNNING, H. M., RALL, H. T. and BALL, J. S., 1959. Keys to the mystery of crude oil. *Proc., Am. Petrol. Inst., Sect. VI*, pp.1–33.

SMITH JR., P. V., 1954. Studies on origin of petroleum occurrence of hydrocarbons in recent sediments. *Bull. Am. Assoc. Petrol. Geologists*, 38 (3): 377–404.

SOKOLOV, V. A., 1959. Possibilities of formation and migration of oil in young sedimentary deposits. *Proc. Conf. Lvov, Gostoptekhizdat, Moscow*, pp.59–63.

STEVENS, N. P., 1956. Origin of petroleum. *Bull. Am. Assoc. Petrol. Geologists*, 40: 51–61.

STEVENS, N. P., BRAY, E. E. and EVANS, E. D., 1955. Hydrocarbons in sediments of the Gulf of Mexico. *Am. Assoc. Petrol. Geologists, Ann. Meeting, 40th*, pp.28–31.

THOMPSON, S. A., 1925. *Oil Field Exploration and Development*. Van Nostrand, New York, N.Y., 42 pp.

TOPCHIEV, A. V., 1955. A study of hydrocarbons composition of the kerosene fractions of some crude oils of the U.S.S.R. *World Petrol. Congr., Proc., 4th, Rome, 1955*, pp.23–39.

TOPCHIEV, A. V., KUSAKOVA, M. M., NIFONTOVA, S. S., SUCHKOVA, A. A. and SHISHKINA, N. V., 1957. Study of condensed aromatic hydrocarbons of Romashkinskaya crude. *Khim. i Tekhnol. Topliv i Masel*, 9: 1–8.

TREIBS, A., 1934. Chlorophyll and hemin derivatives in bituminous rocks, petroleums, mineral waxes, and asphalts. *Ann. Chem.*, 510: 42–62.

TREIBS, A., 1935. Chlorophyll and hemin derivatives in bituminous rocks, petroleums, coals and phosphorites. *Ann. Chem.*, 517: 172–196.

VAN EGGELPOEL, A., 1959. Étude sur l'évolution des huiles au cours des migrations et application à la détermination graphique des migrations. *Rev. Inst. Franç. Pétrole Ann. Combust. Liquides*, 14 (12): 1595–1614.

VAN EGGELPOEL, A., 1960. Étude sur l'évolution des huiles au cours des migrations et application à la détermination graphique des migrations. *Rev. Inst. Franç. Pétrole Ann. Combust. Liquides*, 15 (1): 69–92.

VAN NES, K., 1951. Researches on constitution of petroleum fractions beyond the gasoline range. *World Petrol. Congr., Proc., 3rd, The Hague, 1951*, pp.21–39.

VAN NES, K. and VAN WESTEN, H. A., 1951. *Aspects of the Constitution of Mineral Oils*. Elsevier, Amsterdam, 483 pp.

VEBER, V. V. and TURKELTAUB, N. M., 1958. Gaseous hydrocarbons in Recent sediments. *Geol. Nefti*, 8: 39–44.

WHITMORE, F. C., 1944. *Review of API Research Project 43B: Trassformation of Organic Materials into Chemical and Biochemical Phases: Fundamental Research on Occurrence and Recovery of Petroleum*. Am. Petrol. Inst., New York, N.Y., 124 pp.

WHITMORE, F. C., 1951. *Organic Chemistry*, 2 ed. Van Nostrand, New York, N.Y., 1005 pp.

WILLIAMS, R. B., 1957. Characterization of hydrocarbons in petroleum by nuclear magnetic resonance spectrometry. *Am. Soc. Testing Mater., Spec. Tech. Publ.*, 224: 168–194.

YATSENKO, E. F. et CHERNOZHUKOV, N. J., 1960a. Les paraffines supérieures normales des pétroles Bitkova et Dolinska. *Khim. i Tekhnol. Topliv i Masel*, 3: 1–5.

YATSENKO, E. F. and CHERNOZHUKOV, N. J., 1960b. Naphthenic hydrocarbons from the lubricating fractions of Dolinska and Bitkov crudes. *Khim. i Tekhnol. Topliv i Masel*, 5 (10): 6–10.

YATSENKO, E. F. and DONTSEVA, G. M., 1962. Composition and properties of Karpatian crude oils. *Geol. Nefti i Gaza*, 6 (10): 29–33.

Chapter 4

NON-HYDROCARBON COMPOUNDS IN PETROLEUM

G. COSTANTINIDES AND G. ARICH

Research Laboratory, Aquila SpA, Trieste (Italy)
Institute of Applied Chemistry, University of Trieste, Trieste (Italy)

INTRODUCTION

The significance of non-hydrocarbon compounds in petroleum

Crude oils consisting chiefly of hydrocarbons, and the non-hydrocarbon constituents account for only 5–10%. In other crude oils these constituents represent a predominant percentage that may reach 10% in atmospheric distillates, 30–40% in heavy distillates, and almost 100% in residues. This is usually the case with younger crude oils which also have less paraffinic volatile constituents than older crude oils. Consequently, studies for separating, classifying, and identifying the non-hydrocarbon compounds as well as investigating their properties are of almost equal importance and interest as those concerning the hydrocarbons.

Investigation of the non-hydrocarbon fraction in crude oil should also be concerned with the solution of the following three important problems:

(*1*) For the refiner, non-hydrocarbon compounds are usually harmful in two aspects. First, frequent and costly shutdowns and replacement of equipment are necessitated due to the corrosive effect of the non-hydrocarbons; and second, resultant poor performance of products caused by such undesirable features as unpleasant odors, instability, corrosivity, etc. Occasionally, even traces of non-hydrocarbons have catalytic effects (metals poison or lessen the life and effectiveness of cracking catalysts; nitrogen bases shorten the life of polymerization catalysts, etc.). Adequate methods must be found to remove these compounds.

(*2*) Once the non-hydrocarbons are removed, especially those present in greater quantities, the problem is utilization. For this reason it becomes important to know their structure and properties.

(*3*) The presence of certain compounds and their concentrations may be essential in solving the classical problem of the source matter of petroleum and the transformation processes it may have undergone in the course of its maturation period.

Up to the present time no systematic investigation of the non-hydrocarbon fraction of the various types of crude oils has been carried out. The available data are rather fragmentary in that they concern either the constituents of a single fraction; a single series of compounds (e.g., sulfur or nitrogen compounds only);

or data obtained on a single type of crude oil. It is hoped that with the improvement of analytical techniques and particularly the introduction of gas chromatography and mass spectrometry, rapid progress will be made in this field.

Classes of non-hydrocarbon compounds found in crude oil

Excluding C and H, the elements found in petroleum are mainly O, N, and S, plus small amounts of metals. (The metals can usually be determined by ashing.)

The sulfur content may vary from less than 0.1 % to nearly 10 % in petroleum. While there is a certain quantity of free sulfur (from 2–3 up to 30% of total S) most of the sulfur is in organic sulfur compounds such as sulfides (open-chain, monocyclic, bicyclic and tricyclic sulfides) and thiophenes. Disulfides and mercaptans (thiols) as well as hydrogen sulfide occur in much lower concentrations.

The oxygen content usually does not exceed 3% with most of it accommodated in acids (fatty, naphthenic and naphthenic–aromatic acids). Phenols are present in smaller amounts, normally below 0.1%, while ketones occur only in traces.

The nitrogen content of petroleum is rarely higher than 1% and is concentrated chiefly in distillation residues. A fraction of the nitrogen compounds (about 25% in almost all crude oils) is of basic nature and can be separated by extraction with sulfuric acid. In this fraction derivatives of monocyclic (pyridines, pyrroles), bicyclic (quinolines, indoles), and tricyclic compounds (carbazoles) are detectable.

The metallic constituents are chiefly V, Ni, Fe, Na, Ca, and Cu, occurring in oil-soluble form mainly as metal porphyrin and other complexes with N-containing compounds or as metal soaps and, possibly, as alkyl metals. Al and Si also occur to some extent in practically all crude oils while Mg, Mn, and Cr only occur in some. Other metals (Co, Mo, Pt, K, Ag, Sr, Ti) are rarely detected and then only in small traces.

While some of the non-hydrocarbons initially present may be partially removed during refining operations, new ones are often formed or introduced. Thus, for example, phenols, peroxides, disulphides and traces of new metallo-organics are likely to be formed. Similarly, after treatments with such solvents as furfural and nitrobenzene, traces of ketones remain in the refinery products.

Preliminary analysis of petroleum for non-hydrocarbons

The O, N, S, and metallic element contents of a crude oil are of relatively little significance even for a mere comparison between different crude oils. The point of interest from both an analytical and industrial standpoint is the distribution of non-hydrocarbons among the distilled fractions of various petroleums. With this in mind it is of value first to subject the crude oil to fractional distillation and then to determine the percentage of O, N, S, and possibly the metals in each fraction.

Since it is possible to establish the molecular weight range of non-hydro-carbon constituents in each fraction fairly well, these data can indicate the non-hydrocarbon content. In this calculation, non-hydrocarbon constituents are assumed to contain only one heteroatom per molecule; when this assumption is not true, the actual content of non-hydrocarbons will be lower than the calculated value. This is well illustrated graphically in Fig.1 where the quantities of the various constituents are represented by differently shaded areas. This type of representation has been adopted by BALL et al. (1959) for the identification of minor constituents of Wilmington (California), Wasson (Texas), and Ponca City (Oklahoma) crude oils. These authors also extrapolate the curves to the distillation residues, but this does not seem to be correct as here the assumption of one heteroatom per molecule is undoubtedly not true. It is better to carry the distillation as far as possible and to investigate the composition of the residue by different techniques.

It should be pointed out that this procedure may involve several difficulties. There is the presence of solid materials to be considered, and an aqueous phase present in a more or less fine suspension in crude oils. To separate these substances is, generally, very difficult; washing with water is to be avoided because some of the components may be dissolved. The best separation method is probably centrifugation which does not effect the composition of the principal phase. An even greater difficulty is that in the course of fractionation some compounds, especially non-hydrocarbons, may undergo thermal decomposition. Consequently, the analytical results will not correspond to the original composition of the crude oil. These phenomena become noticeable if a crude oil is fractioned under two different

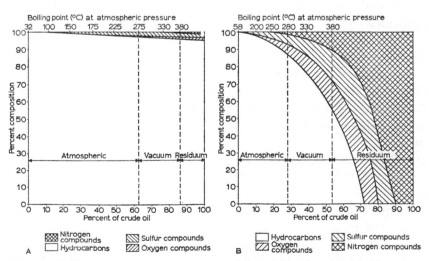

Fig.1. Distribution of non-hydrocarbon components in two different crude oils.
A = Ponca City crude oil; B = Wilmington crude oil.

pressures. If distillation at higher temperatures increases the O, N, and S contents of the more volatile fractions, decomposition may have occurred. In order to prevent the crude oil from thermal decomposition during fractionation, the preliminary separation of the residue can be most useful, either by precipitation (with a suitable solvent such as propane), or by continuous high-vacuum distillation (isothermal distillation). Since the results of this technique depend on the efficiency of fractionation, distillation over an infinite number of plates with infinite reflux and the collection of very narrow fractions would lead to the best isolation of the individual components. The curves shown in Fig.1 would be discontinuous at the loss of each individual component. In practice, the efficiency of fractionation is always limited unless it is carried out with great care by temperature-programmed gas chromatography. Only the most volatile fractions, containing relatively few individual components, can give peaks indicating the presence of non-hydrocarbon compounds. On the other hand, the concentration of non-hydrocarbons in these low-boiling-point fractions is usually quite low but with the types of curves shown in Fig.1 appearing continuous and increasing regularly. It is then convenient to operate the distillation with a limited efficiency on large volumes of crude oil, and the fractions can then be used for analytical studies.

Fractionation of a crude oil and the systematic analysis of its fractions

The O, N, and S content of a fraction can only give an approximate picture of the molecular composition. To achieve more accurate and extensive information it is necessary to separate, or at least concentrate, the non-hydrocarbon constituents by further fractionation from the preliminary distillates. The choice of the most suitable fractionation technique depends on the types of constituents present in the crude oil; the molecular weight of the fraction; the interest in a particular constituent; etc. (The techniques which can be used for concentrating, separating, and iendtifying the various types of non-hydrocarbons will be described in detail in the sections concerned with the various compounds with only the more general criteria being discussed in this section.) Generally, in the course of such a fractionation, a classification of the hydrocarbon constituents can usually be obtained. The analytical techniques most widely used for a wide volatility range of fractions are the following:

(*1*) Column chromatography, either by displacement or by elution with solvents of variable polarity. The stationary phase is usually silica gel, alumina, or molecular sieves. For example SNYDER and BUELL (1963) established a relative separation sequence in eluates from alumina columns where various solvents were used. Compound types were eluted in this consecutive order: hydrocarbons, sulfur compounds, ethers, N-alkyl substituted pyrrole, phenols, carboxylic acids. Good results can be obtained occasionally by using as stationary phases liquids adsorbed on a solid phase (e.g., a polar solvent on silica gel).

(2) The solvent extraction technique enables the separation of acid and basic compounds such as the caustic wash for phenols, or the extraction of basic nitrogen by sulfuric acid. A further fractionation can be achieved by means of selective solvents such as aniline, furfural, dimethylformamide, glycols, etc. In such cases, to obtain sufficiently sharp separations, it is necessary to perform multi-stage fractionation. Good results can also be obtained with two solvents in counter-current extraction using automatic instruments having 50 or more stages.

The chromatographic method leads to far better results but is usually slow and has the disadvantage of incomplete recovery of the sample, this being particularly true for non-hydrocarbons. In contrast to chromatography, extraction enables the concentration of the products in large quantities. Other methods of separation such as fractional crystallization, azeotropic and extractive distillation, thermal diffusion, formation of complexes and adducts, etc., may be very efficient under certain circumstances but generally cannot be applied to the entire boiling range of a crude oil.

The analysis of the non-hydrocarbon compounds is facilitated by concentrating them in a few fractions. Suitable ways can then be chosen to investigate the structure types present. Besides elemental analyses, methods generally based on the measurements of some physical property such as infrared and ultraviolet spectra and the formation of chemical derivatives can be used.

One of the best analytical techniques in this field is gas chromatography. Recently developed procedures permit the analysis of samples having molecular weights of as high as 500 or even higher. Temperature-programmed operations especially with capillar columns provide high resolutions. By the proper choice of the stationary phase, it is possible to achieve a separation either in an order of volatility or according to the different structures of the components. With gas chromatography a very large number of components can be separated. If the components can be collected at the exit port of the chromatograph and then subjected to elemental analysis and to infrared, ultraviolet, mass-spectroscopic, and nuclear magnetic resonance analysis, one can obtain an analysis of crude oil as complete as is possible today.

Because a complete systematic analysis of the petroleum non-hydrocarbon fractions would be most complex and time consuming due to the large number of components present, it is customary to confine the analysis to the most abundant components with other components being analyzed in groups.

The research sponsored by the American Petroleum Institute (A.P.I.) may serve as a guide for a systematic analysis of non-hydrocarbon compounds in different crude oils. These studies included the analysis of hydrocarbons as well as sulfur and nitrogen-containing compounds. A.P.I. Research Project 48, established in 1948, selected the Wasson (Texas) crude oil as a representative sample for an investigation of the synthesis, properties, and identification of sulfur compounds in petroleum. A.P.I. Research Project 52, established in 1954, centered on the nitrogen-containing constituents of petroleum and was based on a Wilmington (California) crude oil. In addition to the identification and semi-quantitative estimation of several petroleum components, the A.P.I. research projects provided accurate information on the chemical behavior, physical properties, and thermo-dynamic data of hydrocarbons and related compounds. These data were placed on I.B.M. cards, and in addition to the periodic distribution of loose-leaf data sheets, a bound book was issued at about 5-year intervals summarizing all the existing information.

SULFUR COMPOUNDS

Methods for determining sulfur

Determination of the sulfur content of petroleum and petroleum products is very frequently necessary. Total sulfur may have to be determined in concentrations ranging from 1 p.p.m. up to 4% and, occasionally, even higher. The samples may be petroleum products extending from gases to bitumens. It would be desirable if a single determination technique could be used for different quantities of sulfur, but unfortunately, this is not yet possible. In this chapter the various methods of sulfur determination will be outlined (FRANKS and GILPIN, 1962; LIDDEL, 1962). The methods for sulfur determination are based on the following techniques: (*1*) combustion methods—(*a*) lamp combustion, (*b*) bomb combustion, (*c*) quartz-tube combustion, and (*d*) flask combustion (Schöniger); (*2*) X-ray methods—(*a*) absorption and (*b*) fluorescence; and (*3*) reduction methods.

Combustion methods
The combustion methods are based on the general principle of the combustion of sulfur compounds in air, oxygen–carbon dioxide mixtures, or in oxygen alone. The product is SO_2 which is adsorbed in and reacted with a suitable liquid reagent and converted into SO_3. Then the quantitive determination can be made by different techniques; acidimetric titration of the acids that are formed, or precipitation with barium chloride. In the latter case the barium sulfate is determined either gravimetrically or by nephelometric or turbidimetric procedures, depending on the amount of sulfur present in the sample. Another method of quantitative determination consists of titration with special reagents such as lead nitrate or barium perchlorate, in which case dithizone and thorin, respectively, are used for indicators. Combustion methods are widely used in sulfur analysis.

X-ray methods
The X-ray absorption method is based on the principle that X-rays are strongly absorbed by sulfur atoms so that even small changes in sulfur content significantly

affect the intensity of the beam passing through the sample. On the other hand the carbon and hydrogen atoms have much lower absorptivity. The X-rays used in the experiments may be emitted by a customary cathode-ray tube or by a radioactive source, most frequently tritium. X-radiations of suitable wavelength are formed when β-rays from tritium strike a target of zirconium or titanium on which the tritium is adsorbed. The radiation is then detected by a Geiger–Müller counter and is recorded. The absorption method is suitable for samples which contain amounts of sulfur higher than 0.1 % (PYRAH et al., 1961; BURCKHARDT et al., 1962).

The X-ray fluorescence method consists of the excitation of a secondary X-radiation containing the characteristic wavelength of sulfur by means of the primary X-ray beam. The intensity of this secondary radiation is measured and from this the sulfur content is estimated. The X-ray fluorescence method is applicable to the same types of samples as the X-ray absorption method.

Reduction methods

The reduction methods are based on the catalytic reduction of sulfur compounds resulting in the evolution of hydrogen sulfide. Hydrogen sulfide in solution is determined either by titration with mercuric acetate and dithizone or by gas–liquid chromatography.

Elementary sulfur

The presence of elementary sulfur in crude oils has long been the subject of disagreement. Studies of various petroleums have shown that crude oils evolve large quantities of hydrogen sulfide when heated at temperatures near 200 °C. In addition, elemental sulfur had been detected in some distillates of higher sulfur content. These observations led to the theory that in most, if not all, cases the evolution of hydrogen sulfide at approximately 200 °C was due to reaction between sulfur and certain components of the oil.

This theory was confirmed when a polarographic method was finally developed for determining free sulfur in crude oils. ECCLESTON et al. (1952) determined sulfur in a number of crude oils by polarography. The electrolyte consisted of benzene, methanol, pyridine, and hydrogen chloride. (The results are summarized in Table I.) Sulfur can also be determined by polarography using a sodium-acetate and hydrogen-chloride solution having a pH of 6–6.5 as the supporting electrolyte. The crude oils are first extracted with diethylamine–water mixtures, and then the sulfur content determined in the buffered aqueous layer. ECCLESTON et al. (1952), on the other hand, made the determination directly on crude oil.

The evolution of hydrogen sulfide from crude oils when heated is of importance, for this phenomenon may delineate the maximum temperatures to which a petroleum was subjected. For example, experiments show that a Wasson (Texas) crude oil begins to decompose with the evolution of hydrogen sulfide at approxi-

TABLE I

ELEMENTAL SULFUR CONTENT OF VARIOUS CRUDE OILS

Field	Total sulfur (weight %)	Elemental sulfur (weight %)	Author
Spraberry (U.S.A.)	0.24	0.000	ECCLESTON et al. (1952)
Dune (U.S.A.)	1.65	0.045	ECCLESTON et al. (1952)
Saudi Arabia	1.78	0.08	Schultze and Irion (personal communication, 1962)
Meckfeld Sud (Germany)	2.30	0.10	Schultze and Irion (personal communication, 1962)
Ras Garib (Egypt)	3.07	0.14	ECCLESTON et al. (1952)
Means (U.S.A.)	2.48	0.17	ECCLESTON et al. (1952)
Etzel (Germany)	10.20	0.48	Schultze and Irion (personal communication, 1962)
Goldsmith (U.S.A.)	1.82	0.70	ECCLESTON et al. (1952)
Fuhrman-Mascho (U.S.A.)	4.09	1.31	ECCLESTON et al. (1952)

mately 200°C, whereas in the Wilmington (California) crude oil decomposition commences at 260°C. It is interesting to note that neither of these crude oils contain free sulfur. When elemental sulfur is present, as is the case of the Goldsmith (U.S.A.) crude oil, decomposition begins at 150°C. The same effect can be observed if elemental sulfur is added to an originally sulfur-free petroleum. It has been demonstrated that sulfur begins to react with n-tetradecane and tetraline at 100°C temperature. It may be possible that in petroleum even more reactive hydrocarbons are present. Consequently, the identification and quantitative estimation of elementary sulfur in some crude oils points to a low temperature origin of petroleum. This is in agreement with the low temperature history deduced from the presence of carboxylated porphyrins.

Sulfur compounds in crude oil

Investigations to identify classes and individual sulfur compounds in crude oils were confined for many years to the types of compounds found mainly in gasoline. Odorous sulfur compounds had to be removed from crude oil by refining processes to obtain petroleum products which are commercially acceptable. Since there was also a possibility of interference with anti-knock agents, these compounds could not be present in gasoline. Later, following the development of improved analytical techniques, sulfur compounds present in the 200–350°C boiling range fractions were investigated (by this time low-sulfur kerosenes and gas-oils also had to be produced from crude oils). Still relatively unknown, however, are the sulfur compounds occurring in even higher boiling range lubricating oil fractions and distillation residues (residual fuel oils, bitumens). Before a detailed description is presented it is desirable to present a general view of the sulfur contents of some typical crude oils. The information appears rather incomplete because no adequate classifying criterion has yet been found. The sulfur content of a crude oil appears to be related to the particular conditions under which the original organic matter was deposited, and the environmental conditions present during the petroleum evolution processes. However, it does not depend on the geological age of the oils at least insofar as geographic considerations are concerned.

Low A.P.I. gravity crude oils usually contain more sulfur than high-gravity crude oils though there are exceptions to this rule. Table II shows the average sulfur contents of a number of crude oils grouped according to typical producing regions. Note that this table summarizes the average percentages of the sulfur contents of various crude oils. If the various crude oils were listed separately instead of by the averages, the variations would be even more apparent.

The distribution of sulfur compounds in the different fractions of petroleum varies mainly with the boiling range of the fractions. The lighter fractions, i.e., those having lower boiling ranges, contain fewer sulfur compounds. As the boiling point or density (or better, the molecular weight) of the fractions increases, the sulfur-compound content also increases.

In the following discussion concerning the distribution of sulfur compounds in crude oils, the chemical structure will be taken into account; the various classes of compounds in which sulfur is bound; and the molecular weight of the fractions in which they occur will be considered. Discussion will be confined first to the

TABLE II

AVERAGE PERCENTAGE OF SULFUR IN VARIOUS CRUDE OILS

Source	Average ° A.P.I.	Average % sulfur
Gulf Coast	—	0.19
Far East (India, Pakistan, Burma)	—	< 0.2
East Texas	38.0	0.26
U.S.S.R. and Eastern Europe	—	< 0.40
Average U.S.A.	34.7	0.75
Western Europe	—	< 1.0
California	26.2	1.05
Venezuela	25.3	1.36
West Texas	36.0	1.38
Mississippi heavy oils	26.0	1.60
Middle East (Iran, Saudi Arabia, Kuwait, Iraq, Bahrein and Egypt)	35.0	1.60
South America (including Trinidad)	—	1.80

general identification methods of the various classes, and then to the analytical techniques suitable for the identification of the individual compounds.

The classes of compounds so far identified in petroleum are thiols (mercaptans), disulfides, sulfides and thiophenes.

The relative concentration of these compounds in a crude oil may be estimated from Fig.2 which illustrates a hypothetical distribution of sulfur compounds in the Wasson (Texas) petroleum according to SMITH et al. (1961).

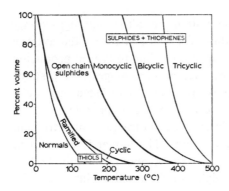

Fig.2. Hypothetical distribution of sulfur compounds in the Wasson crude oil.

To avoid any chemical interferences when attempting any separations or identifications of sulfur compounds in light distillates, such as gasoline and kerosene, hydrogen sulfide must be removed from the sample. This can be done by stirring the gasoline with cadmium chloride in an acidic solution. If hydrogen sulfide is present, a yellow cadmium-sulfide precipitate will be formed and may be quantitatively analyzed by the usual iodometric reaction for sulfides. Elementary sulfur must also be removed. Sulfur may either be originally present in the distillate or it may evolve from the oxidation of the hydrogen sulfide in air (some is always dissolved in the distillates). Elemental sulfur is removed by shaking the mixture with metallic mercury to form mercury sulfide. After decanting and filtering, the solution should be free of elementary sulfur. The quantitative estimation of sulfur has been discussed previously.

Next the distillate fraction can be treated with either a silver nitrate solution, acidified with nitric acid or with an aqueous cadmium–acetate solution buffered with sodium acetate. The first procedure causes the mercaptans (thiols) to precipitate as silver mercaptides. The latter results in a gelatinous precipitate of the cadmium mercaptides from which the mercaptans may be recovered with dilute hydrochloric acid. The reaction between mercaptans and silver nitrate is the following:

$$RSH + AgNO_3 \rightarrow RSAg + HNO_3$$

This reaction may be used for the quantitative estimation of mercaptans with the application of colorimetric, amperometric, or potentiometric methods.

After the mercaptans have been removed the residue is reduced with zinc in acetic acid. In this way the disulfides are reduced to mercaptans and then can be removed and analysed by the methods described above. It is generally thought that disulfides are not originally present in the distillate fractions but are formed through the oxidation of mercaptans.

After the removal of the disulfides the other sulfides can be identified. The mixture is vigorously shaken with mercurous nitrate monohydrate and the open-chain and cyclic sulfides precipitate as complexes. The residual sample is then separated by filtration from the sulfide complexes and washed with a sodium-carbonate solution. The mercurous nitrate monohydrate has no effect on thiophenes or aromatic sulfides. Thiophenes are removed by shaking the sample with a basic mercuric sulfate solution. The sample is filtered by suction and the thiophenes then separated. The filtrate is now treated with an equal weight of mercuric nitrate monohydrate which precipitates the aromatic sulfides as complexes. For a summary of the procedure see Fig.3. This method was first reported by EMMOTT (1953) and later modified by BIRCH et al. (1955). For the separation of sulfides and thiophenes, however, the latter authors worked on heavier distillate fractions which boiled in the 140–250°C range. The higher molecular weight sulfides still form complexes with mercurous nitrate but these complexes are soluble in the hydro-carbon solution. Thus the separation process after the removal of disulfides may be achieved by a fractional extraction process with an aqueous solution of mercuric acetate. The extraction sequence was found to be:

tricyclic > bicyclic > monocyclic > open-chain sulfides

Recovery of the sulfides from the complexes follows the reverse order. Sulfides were recovered from the aqueous extract in two stages; first, by steam distillation alone, then in the presence of hydrochloric acid. Trialkylthiophenes react with the mercuric acetate solution to form the acetoxymercury derivative. Normally this compound remains dissolved in the sulfides and does not precipitate until the sulfides have been removed from the aqueous extract. However, the acetoxymercury trialkylthiophene can be removed before this stage by distilling the sulfides at reduced pressures and leaving the thiophene derivative as a solid residue. After crystallization the thiophene can be recovered from the purified acetoxymercury compound by distillation with hydrochloric acid. The tetraalkylthiophenes remain unaffected in the hydrocarbon phase.

HALE et al. (1951) performed a quantitative study of the distribution of various types of sulfur compounds in gasoline distillates which had a maximum boiling point of 250°C. These authors used fractional vacuum distillation of the gasolines in which they separated the constituents in each of the fractions according to the method of EMMOTT (1953). However, they did not extract thiophenes; these

Fig.3. Separation of different classes of sulfur compounds.

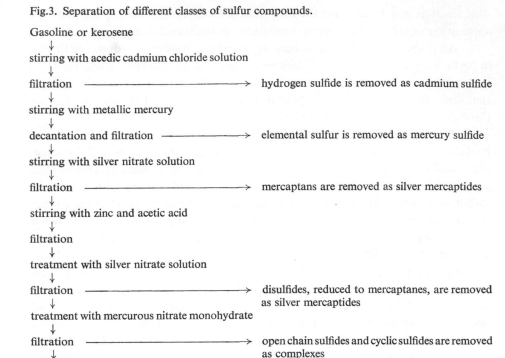

compounds were included with residual sulfur together with those components that could not be determined with this method. They refer to aliphatic and saturated cyclic sulfides as "sulfides I", and to aromatic sulfides as "sulfides II". The authors admit that some aliphatic sulfides, especially those of higher molecular weights, are probably removed with the aromatic sulfides and they express the opinion that there is little evidence for the presence of thiophenes in straight-run distillates. The results obtained are summarized in Table III and in Fig.4. The analyses show that the quantity of sulfur compounds which cannot be determined with these methods rapidly increases with higher boiling points until, in the range between 200°C and 250°C, they account for 20–80% of the total organic sulfur content. Furthermore, EMMOTT (1953) and BIRCH et al. (1955) were of the opinion that disulfides were not originally present in the crude oil but were the results of the oxidation of mercaptans. They also pointed out that the distribution of sulfur

TABLE III

PER CENT SULFUR (BASED ON TOTAL SULFUR) PRESENT IN VACUUM DISTILLATES

Field	Sulfur in fraction (weight $^o/_o$)	Residual sulfur	R–S–R II	R–S–R I	R–S–H	R–S–S–R	H₂S	Elemental sulfur
Heidelberg	0.523	80.3	11.7	7.8	0.0	0.2	0.0	0.0
Hawkins	0.377	73.8	14.6	11.1	0.3	0.3	0.0	0.0
Rangely	0.271	72.0	20.3	7.7	0.0	0.0	0.0	0.0
Oregon Basin	1.048	68.2	13.5	15.0	1.7	1.3	0.0	0.3
Wilmington	0.387	66.7	19.9	12.7	0.3	0.5	0.0	0.0
Midway–Sunset	0.385	66.5	26.0	7.3	0.2	0.0	0.0	0.0
Schuler	0.313	66.4	22.7	9.3	0.6	1.0	0.0	0.0
Agha Jari	0.353	65.7	9.6	12.8	8.5	3.4	0.0	0.0
Santa Maria	2.014	58.2	35.5	6.1	0.2	0.0	0.0	0.0
Elk Basin	0.725	54.9	25.1	1.4	11.3	7.2	0.0	0.1
Wasson	0.857	52.6	13.0	11.6	15.3	7.4	0.0	0.1
Slaughter	1.020	48.8	22.5	7.5	10.8	9.2	0.0	1.2
Velma	0.554	43.9	41.5	12.4	1.1	0.7	0.0	0.4
Kirkuk	0.368	41.0	24.7	20.9	7.9	5.5	0.0	0.0
Deep River	0.231	28.6	3.0	0.0	45.9	22.5	0.0	0.0
Yates	1.297	20.5	20.1	9.2	7.5	6.9	1.2	34.6
Goldsmith	0.729	17.3	11.6	9.6	10.6	8.4	0.0	42.5

compounds in gasolines varies widely according to the original composition of the crude oil. Perhaps the gas-chromatographic method of determining the volatile organic sulfur compounds reported by RYCE and BRYCE (1957) may be a useful technique to alleviate some of the current analytical difficulties.

Sulfur compounds in gas-oil distillate fractions

It is more difficult to develop a scheme for separation techniques and analysis of the various types of sulfur compounds occurring in the gas-oil fractions, i.e., the fractions distilling approximately in the range of 250–370°C normally known as light gas-oils, and those distilling in the range 370–540°C normally known as heavy gas-oils.

The first attempt to extract sulfur compounds from gas-oils was made by HOOG et al. (1951). Later, LUMPKIN and JOHNSON (1954); HASTINGS and JOHNSON (1955); and HASTINGS et al. (1956) reported experiments based on more advanced techniques. These authors separately determined the aliphatic sulfides on unfractionated samples using the strong and characteristic ultraviolet adsorption band of the complex formed between these sulfides and molecular iodine.

The sulfide sulfur determined according to this method may be in an

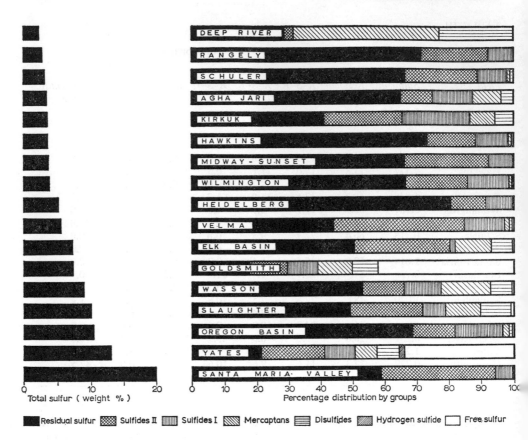

Total sulfur (weight %)   Percentage distribution by groups

■ Residual sulfur ▨ Sulfides II ▥ Sulfides I ▧ Mercaptans ☰ Disulfides ▨ Hydrogen sulfide ☐ Free sulfur

Fig.4. Composition of sulfur compounds in distillates from different crude oils.

acyclic or cyclic satured system, or in side chains attached to aromatic nuclei;
however, it is not in an aromatic ring. See Table IV where the results are listed.
The aromatic fraction of gas-oils, or more precisely the compounds which have
sulfur directly connected to an aromatic ring, may be analyzed by a technique
proposed by the latter authors. This technique is more complicated since it requires
a preliminary separation of the various compound types which are subsequently
examined by ultraviolet and mass-spectrometry. The technique involves the
chromatographic separation of the gas-oil fraction on silica-gel columns followed
by elution with iso-octane, iso-octane and benzene, benzene and cthanol mixtures.
This is followed by a subsequent fractionation of the eluates on alumina columns.
(See Table V.)

Similar analyses were reported by MUSAYEV et al. (1963) for a gas-oil from
a Romashkino (U.S.S.R.) crude oil (Table VI). With the increasing boiling points
of the fractions the sulfide-sulfur content decreased to some degree relative to
total sulfur content. In comparing the data of Table VI with those reported by

TABLE IV

ALIPHATIC SULPHIDE SULFUR CONTENT OF VIRGIN GAS OILS[1]

Source of gas oils	Sulfur, weight %		$\dfrac{\text{Sulphide sulfur}}{\text{Total sulfur}} \times 100$
	Sulphides	Total	
West Texas	0.46	2.15	21.4
Panhandle	0.25	0.43	58.1
Tomball	0.07	0.17	41.1
Heavy coastal	0.16	0.27	59.2
Hawkins	0.56	2.41	23.2
West Texas	0.61	2.05	29.7

[1] Distillation range: 371–537°C

TABLE V

ANALYSES OF GAS OIL AROMATIC FRACTIONS FROM VARIOUS CRUDE OILS

Compound type (weight %)	Crude oil source						
	Louisiana	Iraq	Canada	South America	East Texas	West Texas	California
Benzenes	11.8	18.0	15.4	12.2	10.6	11.1	8.7
Indanes, etc.	8.9	8.3	8.5	7.3	7.4	6.0	8.4
Dinaphthenebenzenes	12.9	8.3	9.4	7.9	11.9	7.7	7.7
Naphthalene	4.6	2.7	2.0	1.7	5.2	1.8	3.1
Acenaphthenes	8.2	5.1	9.1	8.3	12.4	0.1	10.8
Acenaphthylenes	17.6	10.4	19.0	15.8	24.9	11.6	10.4
Phenanthrenes	15.0	2.8	13.8	9.7	14.6	7.1	7.4
Pyrenes	11.0	0.8	6.1	3.4	5.4	3.8	4.2
Chrysenes	3.1	0.7	3.2	1.8	3.0	3.4	5.3
Benzothiophenes	0.4	14.4	3.3	10.2	0.0	9.9	5.9
Naphthothiophenes	1.2	19.6	4.1	14.2	2.3	14.4	5.7
Benzonaphthothiophenes	4.1	3.9	2.9	0.0	0.0	5.0	0.6
Sulfides	1.2	5.0	3.2	7.5	2.3	12.1	21.8
S, weight %	0.55	3.98	1.39	3.42	0.49	4.63	2.86
C_A (% of carbon in aromatic rings)							
mass spectra	42.0	32.2	38.0	38.7	38.6	35.8	32.5
nuclear magnetic resonance	41.3	36.4	39.0	40.0	39.5	36.0	32.7
n–d–M	50.6	37.7	46.6	48.4	49.0	46.5	33.9

TABLE VI

DISTRIBUTION OF SULFUR COMPOUNDS IN VIRGIN GAS OIL FROM THE ROMASHKINO CRUDE OIL[1]

Compound	Weight $\%$
Total sulfur	1.46
Mercaptan sulfur	0.004
Disulphide sulfur	0.01
Sulphide sulfur	1.19
Residual sulfur	0.25
(mainly thiophene homologues)	
$\dfrac{\text{sulphide sulfur}}{\text{total sulfur}} \times 100$	81.5

[1] Distillation range: 180–340°C.

HASTINGS et al. (1956) (Table V), one must take into account that the gas-oils studied by the two groups of authors had different boiling ranges.

This brief survey of the classes of sulfur compounds shows that traces of mercaptans (thiols), greater amounts of aliphatic sulfides, aromatic sulfides, thiophenes, and higher homologues of thiophene can be detected in the kerosene and gas-oil boiling-range fractions. The relative quantities of the sulfur compounds vary, largely as a result of the geographic origin of the oil.

Sulfur compounds in lubricating oils and distillation residues

As far as the present authors know, a complete investigation has not yet been made on lubricating oil fractions. BESTOUGEFF (1959) studied the sulfur compounds in an aromatic extract of a deasphalted residue of the Qatar (Middle East) crude oil and in an extract of a heavy lubricating distillate from an Iraq crude oil. This investigator separated various types of cyclic compounds containing one to four aromatic rings per molecule by vacuum distillation, chromatography on alumina, and thermal diffusion. The chemical structure of these compounds has been determined by conventional chemical analyses and by spectroscopic methods. It has been shown that most of these sulfur compounds contained one or more naphthenic rings per molecule in addition to the aromatic rings, and that the sulfur compounds which contained two and three aromatic rings were the most abundant. Also the condensed ring systems were more common than the non-condensed ones. Individually identified thiophenes will be discussed later.

A better knowledge of this subject would be most useful because many properties of lubricating oils which are little understood will likely be influenced by the distribution of the various types of sulfur compounds. More information, although consisting mainly of approximations, is available on bitumens. O'DON-

NELL (1951) attempted to separate sulfur compounds from asphalts. After the asphaltenes were precipitated with iso-pentane, bitumen was fractionated in a molecular still. The distilled maltene fractions were diluted with iso-pentane and were vigorously shaken with an equal volume of saturated aqueous mercuric chloride solution. This resulted in the formation of a solid complex which was separated by filtration. The sulfur compounds were recovered from this complex by treatment with hydrochloric acid and hydrogen sulfide. Treatment of a number of asphalts with mercuric chloride showed that the amount of sulfur compounds which form complexes was not proportional to the sulfur content of the maltenes. In some cases 80% of the sulfur was removed whereas in others, very few of the sulfur compounds reacted. There are indications that disubstituted benzothiophenes and substituted dibenzothiophenes are the main sulfur compounds which do not participate in complex formation. Nitrogen compounds also react with mercuric chloride.

Mercaptans (thiols)

Following the survey of the general methods for separating sulfur compounds in petroleum, specific methods for detecting individual compounds will now be outlined. First, the identification of mercaptans in light distillates (gasolines) will be considered.

All techniques used for the separation and identification of sulfur compounds have some common features. In all cases the first step is to separate a sulfur-rich fraction from the crude oil. Care must be taken that during this separation the compounds do not become altered due to high temperatures or overlong heating. Consequently, investigators at the Petroleum Experiment Station of the U. S. Bureau of Mines in Bartlesville, Oklahoma, developed a process called "isothermal distillation". The isothermal distillation system utilizes the principle of flash evaporation of the distillate from a heated, descending film of crude oil; the vapors being removed continuously by a counter-current stream of inert gas. The temperature is easily maintained at 100°C and no excessive heating can occur; the heating time is relatively short, about 30 seconds, and the process is continuous so that large quantities may be distilled. This technique fulfills the need for a method which eliminates to a large degree the possibility that heat decomposes the sulfur compounds and that elementary sulfur would react with crude oil producing sulfur compounds.

After this step, there is a choice between two separation techniques depending on whether the boiling points of the compounds which are to be separated are lower or higher than 100°C. In fact, above this temperature the number of compounds present in the fraction is usually so large that it is necessary to devise specific methods to further separate the mixture into type and sub-fractions, each of which must then be distilled and studied separately.

TABLE VII

THIOLS IDENTIFIED IN WASSON (TEXAS) CRUDE OIL

Name	Boiling Point (°C)	Weight % in crude oil
methanethiol	5.96	0.00240
ethanethiol	35.0	0.00530
2-propanethiol	52.56	0.00199
2-methyl-2-propanethiol	64.22	0.00055
1-propanethiol	67.5	0.00041
2-butanethiol	85.15	0.00386
2-methyl-1-propanethiol	88.72	0.00003
1-butanethiol	98.4	trace
2-methyl-2-butanethiol	99.0	0.00064
3-methyl-2-butanethiol	109.8	—
2-pentanethiol	112.9	0.0014
3-pentanethiol	113.9	0.00057
4-methyl-2-pentanethiol	—	—
3-methyl-3-pentanethiol	—	—
cyclopentanethiol	132.2	—
2-hexanethiol	138.9	0.0028
cyclohexanethiol	158.8	0.0012

In the first case the isothermal distillation product is subjected to fractional distillation in a column with an efficiency of about 30 theoretical plates. Each of the fractions is chromatographed on activated alumina which is capable of separating sulfur compounds from aromatic hydrocarbons. The fraction eluted by iso-pentane contains the paraffinic, naphthenic and aromatic hydrocarbons and is discarded. The fraction containing the sulfur compounds is eluted by ethyl alcohol and is then subjected to further fractional distillation in a semi-micro column. The mercaptans are identified in the proper fractions by vapor-phase chromatography, infrared spectrometry, or chemical methods such as the precipitation of the mercaptans. For example, reactions with 2,4-dinitrochlorobenzene and the subsequent identification of the crystalline sulphides is such a method.

When the mercaptans occur in fractions of boiling points higher than 100°C, separation is more involved. As a general rule the mercaptans are extracted either with a concentrated solution of KOH in ethyl alcohol, or with sodium amino-ethoxide ($H_2NC_2H_4ONa$) dissolved in anhydrous ethylene diamine (HOPKINS and SMITH, 1954). The mercaptans are then recovered from this extract by steam distillation and are redistilled in a high-efficiency column after removal of traces of phenols and hydrocarbons by a suitable treatment. Selected fractions are subjected to chromatographic analysis on a silica-gel column and individual compounds are identified according to the techniques described above (e.g., the thiols found by C. J. THOMPSON et al. (1955) in a gasoline from the Wasson (Texas) crude oil are listed in Table VII).

Examination of this table may furnish some indication concerning the relative abundance of 1-, 2-, and 3-alkane thiols. The concentration of 1-alkane thiols decreases appreciably with increasing molecular weight and becomes negligible for compounds with 5–6 C atoms. Of all thiols, 2-alkane thiols are apparently the most abundant, particularly those with even numbers of C atoms. The content of 2-alkane thiols also decreases with increasing molecular weight and appears to become negligible for compounds with approximately 12–15 C atoms per molecule. There are not sufficient data on 3-alkane thiols to establish a definite trend. Probably cycloalkane thiols predominate in the fractions boiling above 200°C. Thiols have also been detected in both kerosene and gas-oils, although only in very small amounts in the latter. Table VIII summarizes all mercaptans which had been identified with certainty in various fractions of crude oils.

Sulfides

Neutral sulfur compounds were first described by THIERRY (1925) from the acid used to treat a naphtha from a Masjid-i-Sulaiman (Iraq) crude oil. Later, a similar investigation was made on sulfur compounds in an acid sludge obtained during the refining of an SO_2-extract of a light straight-run naphtha from an Iranian petroleum (HARESNAPE et al., 1949). The compounds isolated were found to be mainly open-chain and cyclic sulfides; the remainder consisted of dialkyldisulfides formed by oxidation of mercaptans during the refining process. The sulfides isolated from these acid sludges were open-chain sulfides (methyl ethylsulfide, ethyl-*n*-propylsulfide, isopropyl-*n*-propylsulfide) and cyclic sulfides (thiacyclopentane, 2-methylthiacyclopentane, 3-methylthiacyclopentane, thiacyclohexane).

Previous to the work of HARESNAPE et al. (1949) all these cyclic sulfides had been isolated from straight-run distillates by POLLY et al. (1942); FRIDMAN and CANSECO (1943); FRIDMAN and RODRIGUEZ (1946); NAMETKIN and SOSNINA (1948).

An important contribution to the understanding of sulfides resulted from the investigations of BIRCH (1953) and BIRCH et al. (1952, 1955, 1959) who studied an acid sludge from an Agha Jari (Iran) kerosene SO_2 extract. These compounds will be considered during discussions of sulfides in various boiling fractions.

Before considering the detailed study of various types of sulfides found in crude oils, the work of C. J. THOMPSON et al. (1955) and COLEMAN et al. (1956) should be noted. Working in connection with the American Petroleum Institute Research Project 48, these authors identified and quantitatively estimated the sulfides present in a straight-run gasoline from a Wasson (Texas) crude oil. For a summary of their results see Table IX. The separation and identification techniques used by these authors will be discussed later. From data still incomplete,

TABLE VIII

THIOLS IDENTIFIED IN CRUDE OILS

Compound	Source
Primary	
methanethiol (methyl mercaptan)	Wasson, Naft Khaneh
ethanethiol (ethyl mercaptan)	Wasson, Naft Khaneh, Tuimaza
1-propanethiol (*n*-propyl mercaptan)	Wasson, Naft Khaneh, Tuimaza, Agha Jari
2-methyl-1 propanethiol (isobutyl mercaptan)	Wasson, Naft Khnaneh, Agha Jari
1-butanethiol (*n*-butyl mercaptan)	Wasson, Naft Khaneh, Tuimaza
2-methyl-1 butanethiol (x)	
2,2 dimethyl-1 propanethiol (x)	Agha Jari
pentanethiol (*n*-amyl mercaptan)	Tuimaza, Ishimbaevsk
Secondary	
2-propanethiol (isopropyl mercaptan)	Wasson, Naft Khaneh, Agha Jari, Tuimaza
2-butanethiol (secondary butyl mercaptan)[1]	Wasson, Naft Khaneh, Tuimaza, Agha Jari
3-methyl-2 butanethiol	Wasson
2-pentanethiol	Wasson
3-pentanethiol	Wasson
4-methyl-2 pentanethiol	Wasson
2-methyl-2 pentanethiol	Wasson
2-hexanethiol	Wasson
3-hexanethiol (x)	Wasson
2-octanethiol (x)	Wasson
Tertiary	
2-methyl-2 propanethyl (tertiary butyl mercaptan)	Wasson, Agha Jari, Tuimaza
2-methyl-2 butanethiol (tertiary amyl mercaptan)	Wasson
3-methyl-3 pentanethiol	Wasson
2-methyl-3 pentanethiol	Wasson
Cyclic	
cyclopentanethiol	Wasson
cyclohexanethiol	Wasson
cis-2 methylcyclopentanethiol (x)	Wasson

[1] Tentatively identified.

it may be deduced that the alkyl-side chain substitutions are usually located in position *2* in the open-chain sulfides.

In an investigation of an acid sludge obtained from the sulfuric acid treatment of an SO_2 kerosene extract of Iranian crude oils, BIRCH et al. (1959) identified a series of monocyclic and bicyclic sulfides, and one tricyclic sulfide. Other tricyclic sulfides were also thought to be present but were not definitely identified. It may be of some interest to point out the bridged structure of the thioadamantane, a sulfide isolated from Agha Jari (Iran) crude oil by BIRCH et al. (1952):

Author

BIRCH (1953); COLEMAN et al. (1956)
BIRCH (1953); COLEMAN et al. (1956); PRINZLER and HÄNEL (1961)
BIRCH (1953); COLEMAN et al. (1956, 1958); PRINZLER and HÄNEL (1961)
BIRCH (1953); COLEMAN et al. (1956, 1958)
BIRCH (1953); COLEMAN et al. (1956); PRINZLER and HÄNEL (1961)
NAMETKIN and SOSNINA (1948b)
COLEMAN et al. (1958)
NAMETKIN and SOSNINA (1948b); PRINZLER and HÄNEL (1961)

BIRCH (1953); COLEMAN et al. (1956, 1958); PRINZLER and HÄNEL (1961)
BIRCH (1953); COLEMAN et al. (1956, 1958); PRINZLER and HÄNEL (1961)
THOMPSON et al. (1955)
THOMPSON et al. (1955)
THOMPSON et al. (1955)
THOMPSON et al. (1955)
THOMPSON et al. (1955)
THOMPSON et al. (1955)
THOMPSON et al. (1955)
THOMPSON et al. (1955)

COLEMAN et al. (1956, 1958); PRINZLER and HÄNEL (1961)
COLEMAN et al. (1956)
THOMPSON et al. (1955)
BALL et al. (1959)

THOMPSON et al. (1955)
ARNOLD et al. (1952); THOMPSON et al. (1955)
THOMPSON et al. (1955)

The physical properties of this compound resemble the hydrocarbon adamantane isolated by LANDA and MACHACEK (1933) from a Hudonin naphtha.

TABLE IX

SULPHIDES IDENTIFIED IN WASSON (TEXAS) CRUDE OIL

Name	Boiling point (°C)	Weight % in crude oil
2-thiapropane	37.31	0.00088
2-thiabutane	66.65	0.00222
3-methyl-2 thiabutane	84.81	0.00064
3-thiapentane	92.10	0.00075
2-thiapentane	95.52	0.00030
3, 3-dimethyl-2 thiabutane	99.0	—
2-methyl-3 thiapentane	107.4	—
3-thiahexane	118.50	0.00012
2, 4-dimethyl-3 thiapentane	120.02	0.00053
2, 2-dimethyl-3 thiapentane	120.41	0.000058
thiacyclopentane	121.12	0.000077
2-thiahexane	123.2	0.000077
2-methyl-3 thiahexane	132.05	0.000078
2-methylthiacyclopentane	133.23	0.0023
4-methyl-3 thiahexane	133.65	0.00050
3-methylthiacyclopentane	138.67	0.00046
thiacyclohexane	141.75	0.00032
trans-2, 5 dimethylthiacyclopentane	142.0	0.0025
cis-2, 5 dimethylthiacyclopentane	142.28	0.0024
3-thiaheptane	144.24	0.000078
2-methylthiacyclohexane	153.04	0.0029
3-methylthiacyclohexane	158.04	0.000024
4-methylthiacyclohexane	158.64	0.000048

The sulfides present in the middle boiling-point distillates from a Romashkino (U.S.S.R.) crude oil were investigated by KARAULOVA et al. (1962). These authors reached certain conclusions regarding compound types and suggested that the saturated sulfides in the Romashkino (U.S.S.R.) crude oil can be represented by two pairs of similar structures:

and by a third pair with isolated rings:

R and R' are CH_3 or C_2H_5 groups; the value of n varies from 2 to 6 and m, p from 0 to 4 (in accordance with the molecular weight of the sulfide); however, the structures with thiacyclopentane rings appear more probable than the others.

The unsaturated sulfides apparently consist of a partially aromatic structure which might be represented in the following manner:

where $R = CH_3$, C_2H_5.

In summary, one may conclude that at the present time the structures of the sulfides present in gasolines is rather well known whereas the sulfides present in gas-oils and lubricating oils are still almost entirely unknown. There is some limited knowledge of the sulfide content in crude oils in general, but the structures of many of these compounds are uncertain. See Tables X and XI for a list of sulfides identified in crude oils.

Individual sulfide compounds in the various petroleum fractions can be identified through the following two stages: (1) concentration of the sulfur compounds, and (2) identification of the individual compounds in the enriched fractions.

Concentrated fractions can generally be obtained by two different methods. Some investigators start from the crude oils directly, while others use as starting material the sludges from acid refining or SO_2 extracts. The first method has the advantage that with it the concentration of the sulfur compounds in the original crude oil can be calculated. The second method has the advantage that the starting material is already a sulfur-compound concentrate.

When the concentration is carried out on the crude oil directly, the first operation generally consists of an isothermal distillation by which a distillate and a residue are obtained as previously noted. The distillate is separated from mercaptans by extraction and then subjected to fractional distillation. Each of the fractions is then passed through alumina columns and eluted with an appropriate paraffin hydrocarbon (iso-pentane, n-pentane, etc.) until the refractive index of the eluate approaches that of the eluent. Next, ethyl alcohol is used to displace the remaining sulfur compounds from the column. The fractions eluted by the alcohol, rich in sulfides and possibly thiophenes, are then diluted with iso-pentane or n-pentane and washed with an aqueous salt solution to remove the ethyl alcohol. Activated alumina is an effective adsorbent for separating sulfur compounds from aromatics;

TABLE X

OPEN CHAIN SULPHIDES IDENTIFIED IN CRUDE OILS

Compound	Source
Primary	
2-thiapropane (methyl sulphide)	Wasson
2-thiabutane (methyl ethyl sulphide)	Wasson, Masjid-i-Sulaiman, Tuimaza, Agha Jari
3-thiapentane (ethyl sulphide)	Wasson, Tuimaza, Agha Jari
2-thiapentane (methyl *n*-propyl sulphide)	Wasson, Agha Jari
3-thiahexane (ethyl *n*-propyl sulphide)	Wasson, Masjid-i-Sulaiman
2-thiahexane	Wasson
3-thiaheptane	Wasson
Primary–secondary	
3-methyl-2 thiabutane (methyl isopropyl sulphide)	Wasson, Tuimaza, Agha Jari
2-methyl-3 thiapentane (ethyl isopropyl sulphide)	Wasson, Tuimaza, Agha Jari
2-methyl-3 thiahexane (isopropyl *n*-propyl sulphide)	Wasson, Masjid-i-Sulaiman, Tuimaza
4-methyl-3 thiahexane	Wasson
Primary–tertiary	
3, 3-dimethyl-2 thiabutane (methyl-tertiary butyl sulphide)	Wasson
2, 2-dimethyl-3 thiapentane	Wasson
Secondary–secondary	
2, 4-dimethyl-3 thiapentane	Wasson

however, a single elution procedure will not remove all aromatics from the sulfur-compound concentrate and it then becomes necessary to repeat this procedure two or three times. The sulfur-compound concentrate combined with the isopentane extracts from the alcohol fraction is rechromatographed, reducing the aromatic content to a negligible value. The resulting sulfur-compound concentrate is then subjected to a further fractional distillation. If the boiling point of one of the fractions is higher than that of gasoline, the latter must be removed by isothermal distillation. The distillation residue is then treated with *n*-pentane to remove the asphaltic matter. Asphaltenes precipitate and are discarded. The residue consists of an oily fraction. This residue is passed through an alumina column and eluted with solvents of increasing polarity such as *n*-pentane, mixed amylenes, benzene, and ethyl alcohol–benzene mixtures. Normal pentane is a specific eluent in separating saturated from aromatic hydrocarbons. Mixed amylenes separate monocyclic aromatic hydrocarbons from bicyclic aromatic hydrocarbons and displace sulfides and thiophenes with one and two rings per molecule. Benzene and ethyl alcohol–benzene mixtures displace aromatic hydrocarbons with three and more rings and the corresponding thiophenes and sulfides.

Author

COLEMAN et al. (1956); THOMPSON et al. (1955)
BIRCH (1953); COLEMAN et al. (1956, 1958)
PRINZLER and HÄNEL (1961); THOMPSON et al. (1955)
COLEMAN et al. (1956, 1958); PRINZLER and HÄNEL (1961); THOMPSON et al. (1955)
COLEMAN et al. (1956, 1958); THOMPSON et al. (1955)
BIRCH (1953); THOMPSON et al. (1955)
THOMPSON et al. (1955)
THOMPSON et al. (1955)

COLEMAN et al. (1956, 1958); PRINZLER and HÄNEL (1961); THOMPSON et al. (1955)
COLEMAN et al. (1956); PRINZLER and HÄNEL (1961); THOMPSON et al. (1955)
BIRCH (1953); PRINZLER and HÄNEL (1961); THOMPSON et al. (1955)
THOMPSON et al. (1955)

COLEMAN et al. (1958); THOMPSON et al. (1955)
THOMPSON et al. (1955)

THOMPSON et al. (1955)

Thermal diffusion has also been investigated as a possible separation method and offers some distinct advantages for certain types of separations such as the separation of chain sulfides from aromatics, but unfortunately not cyclic sulfides from thiophenes.

As previously mentioned, some investigators have used for the starting material the sulfur-rich oil obtained when the acid sludge from the refining distillates is diluted with water. The oil is neutralized with NaOH, then distilled under reduced pressure. Each of the fractions is extracted with an aqueous mercuric acetate solution. Not only are the open-chain sulfides partially separated from the cyclic sulfides but also the monocyclic and the bicyclic sulfides are concentrated in different fractions by this procedure. After each extraction the aqueous layer is separated and the sulfides recovered first by steam distillation alone and then in the presence of acids. The distilled sulfides are recovered, washed with a NaOH solution, and analyzed.

Trialkylthiophenes are not recovered by distillation; tetrasubstituted thiophenes do not react with the aqueous mercuric acetate solution and can therefore be separated from the sulfides. The sulfides can also be separated from thiophenes by

TABLE XI

CYCLIC SULPHIDES IDENTIFIED IN CRUDE OILS

Compound	Source
Monocyclics	
thiacyclopentane	Wasson, Masjid-i-Sulaiman
2-methylthiacyclopentane	Wasson, Masjid-i-Sulaiman
3-methylthiacyclopentane	Wasson, Masjid-i-Sulaiman
thiacyclohexane	Wasson, Masjid-i-Sulaiman
trans-2, 5-dimethylthiacyclopentane	Wasson
cis-2, 5-dimethylthiacyclopentane	Wasson
2-methylthiacyclohexane	Wasson
3-methylthiacyclohexane	Wasson
4-methylthiacyclohexane	Wasson
2, 4-dimethylthiacyclopentane	Agha Jari
2, 3-dimethylthiacyclopentane	Agha Jari
2-ethylthiacyclopentane	Agha Jari
2, 3, 5-trimethylthiacyclopentane	Agha Jari
3,4-dimethylthiacyclohexane and/or	
2,3,4-trimethylthiacyclopentane	Iran
2, 6-dimethylthiacyclohexane and/or	
2-ethyl-5-methylthiacyclopentane	Iran
3-methyl-4-ethylthiacyclopentane and/or	
3-isopropylthiacyclopentane	Iran
2, 3-dimethyl-5-ethyl and/or 2, 4-diethylthiacyclopentane	
and/or 2, 3, 6-trimethylthiacyclohexane	Iran
2, 5-dimethyl-3-ethyl and/or 2, 3-diethyl thiacyclopentane	Iran
Bicyclics	
cis-1-thiahydrindane	Iran
trans-1-thiahydrindane	Iran
Tricyclics	
thia adamantane	Agha Jari

another procedure based on the fact that sulfides possess a lower oxidation potential than aromatic hydrocarbons and thiophenes. Therefore, sulphides may be converted quantitatively and selectively into sulfoxides with hydrogen peroxide in acetic acid. Aromatic hydrocarbons and thiophenes are not oxidized under the same conditions. The sulfoxides possess a polarity which more than twice exceeds the polarity of the corresponding sulfides. This means that they can easily be separated by chromatography on silica gel from aromatic hydrocarbons and thiophenes. From silica gel, benzene generally elutes aromatic hydrocarbons and non-sulfide sulfur compounds whereas ethyl alcohol elutes the sulfoxides. Once the sulfoxides have been separated from the other sulfur compounds, they can be reconverted into sulfides by a reaction with lithium–aluminum hydride in an ether–

Author

BIRCH (1953); THOMPSON et al. (1955)
BIRCH (1953); THOMPSON et al. (1955)
BIRCH (1953); THOMPSON et al. (1955)
BIRCH (1953); THOMPSON et al. (1955)
THOMPSON et al. (1955)
THOMPSON et al. (1955)
THOMPSON et al. (1955)
THOMPSON et al. (1955)
THOMPSON et al. (1955)
BIRCH (1953)
BIRCH (1953)
BIRCH (1953)
BIRCH (1953)

BIRCH et al. (1955)

BIRCH et al. (1955)

BIRCH et al. (1955)

BIRCH et al. (1955)
BIRCH et al. (1955)

BIRCH et al. (1955)
BIRCH et al. (1955)

BIRCH et al. (1952)

benzene solution or by the action of potassium iodide in a mixture of acetic and hydrochloric acids.

In these concentrates of sulfur compounds, the individual compounds can be identified by infrared and ultraviolet spectroscopy and by reaction with mercuric chloride. The melting point of the mercuric chlorides can then be determined which provides a characteristic property. Another analytical process is hydrogenation and desulfurization with Raney nickel, determination of the boiling points, and refractive indices of the hydrocarbons formed. In some cases a solid compound can be obtained such as that of thioadamantane which is then purified by sublimation and recrystallization, and identified by the previously described methods.

Thiophenes

Thiophene was first discovered by MEYER (1882) in a coal-tar, light-oil distillate. This discovery initiated intensive research in thiophene chemistry and attempts to find this compound in certain natural products followed. As a result of this research the presence of thiophene was established in pyrolysis products such as in coal tars, shale oils, and cracked petroleum.

The presence of thiophene in samples which had not been subjected to pyrolysis was only indicated at first. CHARITSCHKOFF (1899) first reported the isolation and identification of thiophene in a Grozny (U.S.S.R.) crude oil by precipitation of the mercuric chloride complex from a distillate fraction. Upon decomplexing and recovery of the product in thiophene-free benzene, Charitschkoff obtained a positive color reaction with isatin. He estimated the quantity of thiophene in the Grozny gasoline as 0.0001 %. This value turned out to be a good approximation when compared with the data obtained much later by C. J. THOMPSON et al. (1956) on a 38/111 °C gasoline from a Wilmington (California) crude oil. They found the following concentrations: thiophene, not less than 0.000032% in crude oil; 2-methylthiophene, not less than 0.0001 % in crude oil.

In 1900 EDELEAN and FILITI reported that thiophene derivatives may possibly be present in a Roumanian petroleum. On the other hand NAMETKIN and SOSNINA (1948a, b) reported that the isatin test was negative on all distillate fractions of the Ishimbaevs (U.S.S.R.) crude oil. This finding is not surprising in the light of results obtained by C. J. THOMPSON et al. (1956) for although 2-methyl- and 3-methylthiophene do give a color reaction with isatin, the colors obtained are of a different hue than those obtained with thiophene alone. It has also been shown that thiols interfere when they are present in sufficient concentration and will cause the isatin reaction for thiophenes to fail. The study of thiophenes in light distillate fractions was resumed later by C. J. THOMPSON et al. (1959) and led to the identification of thiophene, 2-methylthiophene, and 3-methylthiophene in the gasoline from a Wilmington (California) crude oil. Subsequently 3-methylthiophene was identified by PRINZLER and HÄNEL (1961) in a gasoline from a Tuimasy (U.S.S.R.) crude oil.

Thiophenes present in the higher boiling-point fractions were first studied by EMMOTT (1953) who reported the presence of thiophenes in SO_2 extracts of Iraq middle distillates. At approximately the same time BIRCH (1953) and BIRCH et al. (1955) identified several individual alkylthiophenes in an acid sludge from a kerosene boiling-range distillate from mixed Iranian crude oils. RICHTER et al. (1956) identified benzo (*b*) thiophene in the kerosene from a Santa Maria Valley (California) crude oil. COLEMAN et al. (1961) confirmed this finding on a Wasson (Texas) crude oil. These latter investigators also identified 2-methyl- and 3-methyl-benzo (*b*) thiophene and also were the first to report quantitative data on the presence of the following thiophene compounds in petroleum: benzo (*b*) thiophene,

0.00002 % in crude oil; 2-methyl-benzo (*b*) thiophene, 0.00063 % in crude oil; and 3-methyl-benzo (*b*) thiophene, 0.00009 % in crude oil.

In recent years knowledge concerning the structure of thiophenes has been extended over the gas-oils and heavy gas-oils as a result of investigations by BIRCH et al. (1955); CARRUTHERS (1955); CARRUTHERS and DOUGLAS (1959); ESPAGNO and POQUET (1962); and MAIR and MARTINEZ-PICO (1962). Table XII lists all the thiophenes that have so far been identified in crude oils.

Approximately 70% of the sulfur compounds in crude oils are thiophenes. This is based primarily on studies of the Wasson (Texas) crude oil and is in agreement with the findings of C. J. THOMPSON et al. (1955). If thiophenes are differentiated into groups according to the number of rings per molecule, the ratio of the one-, two- and three-ring thiophenes is 1/9/9. To demonstrate this finding, Table XIII is quoted from C. J. THOMPSON et al. (1955).

The identification of individual thiophenes, like that of sulfides, is carried out in two stages: first, the thiophenes are concentrated in a particular fraction; second, the thiophene-rich fraction is analyzed for the individual compounds. The starting materials used by the various investigators were either crude-oil fractions or acid sludges.

When an oil fraction is used for the starting material, the technique for enriching it in sulfur compounds is identical with that previously described for the separation of sulfides up to the step of the chromatography on activated alumina. At this point one may choose from several procedures, depending mainly upon the molecular weight of the mixture, which is a function of its complexity, and the particular type of thiophenes that may be present in the mixture. The thiophene-rich fraction resulting from the chromatography may be further concentrated by precipitating the thiophenes with picrates. For example benzo (*b*) thiophene may be isolated by means of naphthalene picrate which is capable of coprecipitating benzo (*b*)-thiophene from an ethanol solution essentially quantitatively. Thiophene can then be recovered from the picrate and further purified through the formation of the diacetoxymercury derivative.

If the fractions contain naphthalene or methylnaphthalenes (boiling range 200–250 °C), the eluates from alumina are diluted with *n*-butane and chilled to remove the naphthalenes by crystallization. The filtrate can then be treated with trinitrobenzene to form adducts and thereby remove part of the naphthalenes and benzothiophenes. The adducts are recovered and redistilled.

In some cases, as in the isolation of dibenzothiophene from a Lacq (France) crude oil, vacuum fractional distillation and fractional crystallization from an ethyl-alcohol solution proved to be sufficient in obtaining a concentrate satisfactorily pure to be suitable for subsequent analysis.

When an acid sludge is used for the starting material, the same technique as applied to a separation of the sulfides can be used until the stage of treatment with aqueous mercuric acetate solution is reached. The complexes, formed by the reaction

TABLE XII

THIOPHENES IDENTIFIED IN CRUDE OILS

Compound	Source	Author
Thiophene	Wilmington, Tuimaza	PRINZLER and HÄNEL (1961); THOMPSON et al. (1956)
2-methylthiophene	Wilmington, Tuimaza	PRINZLER and HÄNEL (1961); THOMPSON et al. (1956)
3-methylthiophene	Tuimaza	PRINZLER and HÄNEL (1961); THOMPSON et al. (1956)
2, 3, 4-trimethylthiophene	Iran	PRINZLER and HÄNEL (1961);
2-ethyl-3, 4-dimethylthiophene	Iran	BIRCH (1953)
3-ethyl-2, 4-dimethylthiophene	Iran	BIRCH (1953)
4-ethyl-2, 3-dimethylthiophene	Iran	BIRCH (1953)
2, 3, 4, 5-tetramethylthiophene	Iran	BIRCH (1953)
2-ethyl-3, 4, 5-trimethylthiophene	Iran	BIRCH (1953)
benzo(b)thiophene	Wasson, S. Maria Valley	COLEMAN et al. (1961); RICHTER et al. (1956)
2-methyl benzo(b)thiophene	Wasson	COLEMAN et al. (1961)
3-methyl benzo(b)thiophene	Wasson	COLEMAN et al. (1961)
1, 4, 4-trimethyl-4, 5, 6, 7-tetrahydro isothianaphthene	Iran	BIRCH (1953)
methyl-3, 4, 5-trimethyl-2-thienyl sulfide	Iran	BIRCH (1953)
dibenzothiophene	Lacq	ESPAGNO and POQUET (1962)
2-methyldibenzothiophene (probable)	Lacq	ESPAGNO and POQUET (1962)
4-methyldibenzothiophene	Lacq	ESPAGNO and POQUET (1962); MAIR and MARTINEZ-PICO (1962)
1, 8-dimethyldibenzothiophene	Kuwait	CARRUTHERS (1955)
4, 6-dimethyldibenzothiophene	Lacq	ESPAGNO and POQUET (1962); MAIR and MARTINEZ-PICO (1962)
1, 2, 6, 7-tetramethyldibenzothiophene	Kuwait	CARRUTHERS and DOUGLAS (1959)
1, 3, 6, 7-tetramethyldibenzothiophene	Kuwait	CARRUTHERS and DOUGLAS (1959)
1, 3, 6, 8-tetramethyldibenzothiophene	Kuwait	CARRUTHERS and DOUGLAS (1959)
9-thia-1, 2-benzofluorene	S. Maria Valley	CARRUTHERS and DOUGLAS (1959)
3-ethyl-6, 8-dimethyl naphtho (1 : 2-b) thiophene	Kuwait	CARRUTHERS and DOUGLAS (1959)
benzo(b)naphtho (2:1-d) thiophene		MAIR and MARTINEZ-PICO (1962)

TABLE XIII

RESULTS OF A MASS SPECTRAL STUDY OF ALUMINA CHROMATOGRAPHIC FRACTIONS OF TOPPED
DEASPHALTENED CRUDE OIL

Fraction No.	Weight $\%$ on sample	Thiophenes				Sulphide (weight $\%$)[4]
		1 ring[1]	2 rings[2]	3 rings[3]	4 rings	
1	13.1	0.0	0.0	0.0	0.0	0.0
2	13.4	0.0	0.0	0.0	0.0	0.0
3	12.6	0.0	0.0	0.0	0.0	0.0
4	5.6	0.0	0.0	0.0	0.0	0.0
5	1.7	2.3	0.0	0.0	0.0	0.0
6	11.3	3.2	0.0	0.0	0.0	2.4
7	13.9	0.0	22.3	2.5	0.0	14.4
8	11.2	0.0	4.7	29.0	0.0	9.6
9	17.2	—	—	—	—	—

[1] Estimated from ultraviolet spectra.
[2] Benzothiophenes.
[3] Dibenzothiophenes or thiophenonaphthalenes.
[4] Determined by the iodine complex method.

of trialkylthiophenes with mercuric acetate, remain dissolved in the sulfides. Precipitation occurs only after the sulfides have been removed from the aqueous extract, then thiophene can be recovered from the acetoxymercury derivative by distillation in the presence of hydrogen chloride. It should be pointed out that tetraalkylsulfides do not react with the mercuric acetate solution.

When a fraction rich in a particular thiophene has been obtained, it is identified by either physical methods such as infrared and ultraviolet spectroscopy; mass spectrography; gas chromatography; or by chemical methods such as the formation of picrates; complexes with s-trinitrobenzene; or chlorimercury derivatives whose melting points are characteristic and can be determined. Still another method may be applied based on the desulfurization of the thiophenes and subsequent identification of the resultant hydrocarbons.

Origin of the sulfur compounds

The form in which sulfur occurs in the various petroleums is of considerable interest not only for the refining chemist but also for the geologist. They may well be one of the keys to unlock the mystery of the origin of petroleum although the available information is far from complete.

BIRCH (1953) reviewed this subject and suggested that sulfur compounds could have been present at the time of deposition of the organic source material of petroleum although it does seem doubtful that sufficient sulfur was present at this early stage to account for the quantity of combined sulfur found in the majority of crude oils. It is then necessary to assume that sulfur was introduced at a later stage in connection with the in situ oxidation of petroleums. Anaerobic bacteria could have oxidized hydrocarbons to carbon dioxide, utilizing the oxygen in sulfates in rock or in the formation waters, and accompanied by the evolution of hydrogen sulfide. The reaction of hydrogen sulfide with oxygen and possibly nitrogen-containing substances may explain the presence of the various sulfur compounds.

The presence of sulfur compounds in the original source materials appears doubtful not only because of their significant concentrations in petroleum but also because sulfur compounds of the types found in crude oils are usually not found in nature. For example very few natural substances have been found which contain cyclic sulfides such as thiacyclopentane or thiacyclohexane. The question arises as to when cyclic sulfides were formed in the oil. The authors believe that they are probably not the products of some decomposition reaction because of the apparent absence of other degradation products. Further, it is unlikely that they have been formed by the hydrogenation of thiophenes, followed, as in the case of thiacyclohexane derivatives, by isomerization. Perhaps the catalytic hydrogenation of thiophenes is possible (MOLDOVSKII and PROKONCHUCK, 1932; MOZINGO et al., 1945). Birch was unable to convert methylthiacyclopentane into thiacyclohexane or vice versa by isomerization with a strong catalyst such as aluminium chloride. When these hypotheses are discarded, attention must be focussed on the oxygen- or nitrogen-containing compounds from which the cyclic sulfides might have been formed.

Furan-ring containing compounds have actually been found in many carbohydrates while sylvan (2-methylfuran) is only found in certain distillates of the oils of the *Pinus sylvestris* and in beachwood tars. Dimethylfurans have been found in other similar distillates and the pyran ring is found in carbohydrates, plant pigments, etc. Furthermore the dehydration–isomerization of tetrahydrofurfuryl alcohol to dihydropyran is readily effected. The corresponding nitrogen compounds, i.e., pyrrols and pyridines also occur in some natural substances.

It may be of interest to explore the possibility of the conversion of these oxygen- and nitrogen-containing compounds into the petroleum type cyclic sulfides. YUR'EV et al. (1939) have shown that, at 400–450 °C in the presence of an alumina catalyst, hydrogen sulfide leads to the replacement of the oxygen atom of the tetrahydrofuran and pyran rings by sulfur. Tetrahydrofurfuryl alcohol undergoes ring expansion and a mixture of 2-thiacyclopentane and thiacyclohexane is obtained although this reaction does not proceed so easily.

All of these transformations have been observed at much higher temperatures than those presumably existing during the formation of oil. Thermodynamic calculations have shown that the conversion of tetrahydrofuran to thiacyclopentane can also occur at lower temperatures falling within the limits usually assumed during the conversion of the sedimentary organic matter into crude oil.

The formation of thiophenes still cannot be explained. There is no way of determining whether the thiophenes have been formed directly from the corresponding
furans and pyrrolidines through a reaction with hydrogen sulfide or by secondary
reactions such as the dehydrogenation of thiacyclopentanes. Thiophenes are not
considered to have been present in the source material because of the thiophene
nucleus. Its derivatives are most uncommon in nature. FRIDMAN (1951) found that
thiacyclopentane is dehydrogenated by sulfur at 160°C to give thiophene and
hydrogen sulfide; consequently this may be one way by which thiophenes could
have evolved. Other possible ways of thiophene formation may be the action of
sulfur on paraffins or hydrogen sulfide on diolefins. The origin of the other sulfur
compounds will not be discussed because they are found in much smaller amounts
in petroleum in comparison with those already considered.

From this brief study it appears clear that the understanding of the origin
of sulfur compounds in crude oils is still at an unsatisfactory stage. For the present,
it can only be suggested that they were not all existing in the original organic
matter but have been formed, at least partially, by secondary processes in the
course of the transformation of the organic matter into crude oil.

OXYGEN COMPOUNDS

Determination of oxygen

The accurate determination of the oxygen content in organic compounds is important.
Although various methods of oxygen analysis were tried and extensively studied
in the past, none of them proved wholly satisfactory. It became a common practice
to obtain the oxygen by difference, i.e., by substracting the sum of the other
elements from 100%. Direct oxygen determination methods in use before 1939
were based either on the complete oxidation of the sample accompanied by the
measurement of the amount of oxygen consumed during this reaction or on the
catalytic hydrogenation to form water (TER MEULEN, 1924).

The oxidation method requires the accurate determination of hydrogen,
carbon, and of the consumed oxygen, and the determination of sulfur and nitrogen
if present. Catalytic hydrogenation determines oxygen directly, however, other
elements may interfere in the original Ter Meulen method. Furthermore, sulfur
and halogens poison the hydrogenation catalyst. The catalytic hydrogenation
method has been subsequently improved to overcome some of these difficulties
and is still in use. At present, instead of a calcined nickel-nitrate catalysts, thoria-
activated nickel catalyst is used which is not affected by sulfur and the halogens.
The sample is hydrogenated at 320°C in the presence of this catalyst leading to
the formation of methane and water. A simplified scheme of this reaction is:

$$(C–H–O–X)_n + H_2 \rightarrow CO + H_2O$$

$$CO + 3H_2 \rightarrow CH_4 + H_2O$$

where X represents elements other than C, H, and O, i.e., nitrogen, sulfur, halogens, etc. In contrast to the original Ter Meulen method the water is determined quantitatively in the modified method with an electrolytic cell and not by adsorption and gravimetric procedures.

In 1939, SCHÜTZE proposed a method which involved the passing of the vapors, that arose from the decomposition of a pyrolyzed sample, over carbon at 1,000 °C. The resulting carbon monoxide was then oxidized to carbon dioxide. In 1940, UNTERZAUCHER, by improving the apparatus, adapted this method for microchemical analysis. These determinations are based on the thermal decomposition of the sample in an inert gas atmosphere and the subsequent reaction of the gaseous decomposition products with carbon at 1,120 °C. At this temperature the carbon dioxide–carbon monoxide equilibrium is displaced in favor of carbon monoxide. The latter compound is converted to carbon dioxide by passing it over red-hot copper oxide. Carbon dioxide can then be determined either gravimetrically by adsorption on ascarite or volumetrically with iodine pentoxide. The following reactions are involved in pyrolysis and in the conversion of CO:

$$\text{oxygen in organic compounds} \xrightarrow[\text{C}]{1120\,°C} CO$$

$$CO + CuO \longrightarrow CO_2 + Cu$$

It must be noted that the Schütze–Unterzaucher procedure can give incorrect results when applied to certain types of samples such as high ash-containing asphalts.

A rapid and non-destructive method of oxygen determination can be performed by neutron-activation analysis (GUINN et al., 1963). This is based on the irradiation of the sample in a 14 meV neutron flux of approximately 10^8 neutrons per cm^2 per second followed by scintillation counting of the N^{16} product. The following reaction is involved:

$$^{16}O + n \xrightarrow{\hspace{1cm}} {}^{16}N + p - 9.62 \text{ meV}$$

The radioactive product, ^{16}N, decays with a half life of 7.4 sec by the emission of beta particles and gamma rays having energies greater than 5 meV. The fast neutrons for this analysis are most conveniently produced by the bombardment of a tritiated target with deuterons in a relatively low-voltage accelerator. Oxygen concentrations greater than 100 p.p.m. can be estimated with 10% error, smaller ones with 25% error.

Oxygen compounds in petroleum

Because of the difficulties of oxygen analysis, few reliable analytical data are available on the oxygen content of crude oils. BALL et al. (1959) reported that a Ponca City (Oklahoma) and a Wilmington (California) crude oil had total oxygen contents of 0.06% and 0.44%, respectively (Fig.1).

The problem can also be approached from another point of view. The oxygen compounds in crude oils are apparently mainly acids and phenols; the latter compounds are present in much lower concentrations than the former ones. Accordingly, the quantity of the oxygen compounds in a crude oil is usually indicated by the quantity of the acids. Table XIV illustrates the range of acidity normally encountered in crude oils. Crude oils with the highest acid contents are found in the western United States (California), the northern part of South America (Venezuela), and southeastern Europe (Roumania). One may further generalize by saying that paraffinic crude oils usually have low acid contents.

TABLE XIV

ACIDITY OF VARIOUS CRUDE OILS

Source	Acidity of crude oil (weight %)
Pennsylvania (U.S.A.)[1]	0.03
Mid Continent (U.S.A.)[1]	0.03
Iraq[2]	0.03
Boryslav (U.S.S.R.)[1]	0.07
Lobitos (Peru)[2]	0.37
Bibi Eibat (U.S.S.R.)[1]	0.50
Gulf Coast (U.S.A.)[1]	0.60
Balachany (U.S.S.R.)[1]	0.70
Lagunillas (Venezuela)[2]	1.20
Kettleman Hills (U.S.A.–Calif.)[2]	3.01

[1] The weight % data were calculated from the acid numbers and an assumed average molecular weight of 280 for the acids listed.
[2] The weight % data were calculated from the acid numbers and an assumed molecular weight of 250.

The distribution of the acids in crude oils is interesting. SCHMITZ (1938) has shown that the acidity of the gasoline-range fractions is very low, the kerosene and gas-oil fractions have the highest acid concentrations, and the heavy lubrication oils and distillation residues usually have relatively low acid contents.

Petroleum acids

It is fairly well established that the aliphatic acids ($C_nH_{2n+1}COOH$) are the only acids in petroleum which may contain less than six carbon atoms per molecule. The petroleum fatty acids make up a large portion of the acids which contain six to ten carbon atoms. This distribution is particularly common in Japanese crude oils. Some of these acids occur even in high boiling-point fractions.

The simplest naphthenic acid is the monocyclic acid, $C_nH_{2n-1}COOH$, cyclopentane carboxylic acid. Other cyclic acids may contain up to twenty carbon atoms. In some acid fractions, bicyclic acids with twelve or more carbon atoms per molecule are present. These higher molecular-weight acids deserve particular attention and will be discussed separately.

The basic process used for the isolation of naphthenic acids involves extraction of the oil with an alkali solution and subsequent acidification of the aqueous extract with a mineral acid. In commercial operations not the crude oil but a distillate fraction boiling in the range of approximately 200–370 °C temperature is extracted. Dilute solutions (2–8 %) are used for the caustic wash. More concentrated solutions may cause emulsification, bring about a salting-out effect of the dissolved sodium naphthenates, and increase the solubility of the oil in the dissolved or salted-out sodium naphthenate. Such extractions can be made either in batch mixers or by a continuous operation in orifice mixers. Extraction separates an alkaline layer containing the sodium salts of the naphthenic acids from the oil fraction. These naphthenates must then be recovered from the alkaline solution. The solution is acidified with sulfuric acid and the supernatant layer, consisting of an oily acidic substance, is separated from the two phases. It may be necessary to remove dissolved or admixed oil from the spent soda or sodium naphthenate prior to the acidification in order to reduce the oil content of the final naphthenic acid fraction. After the separation the naphthenic acids are washed with water to remove mineral acids and then dried. For several industrial processes this crude naphthenic acid fraction is still too impure. The normal impurities consist chiefly of iron salts, phenols, basic nitrogen and sulfur compounds. There are essentially two commercial purification methods:

(*1*) Extraction of this fraction with 1–5 % sulfuric acid to remove iron salts, phenols, basic nitrogen, and most of the sulfur compounds, leaving the oil content unaffected.

(*2*) Distillation under reduced pressure. This process removes, at least to an acceptable level, the oil content as well as other impurities.

Naphthenic acids and their salts have extensive industrial applications. Neutral or basic salts of manganese, zinc, cobalt and iron are used for drying agents in the varnish industry, the principal user of naphthenic acids. Calcium and magnesium naphthenates are used in the paint industry as flotation agents. Other naphthenates such as copper naphthenate and, to a smaller extent, zinc and mercury naphthenates, are used as fungicides and insecticides for the preservation of wood and textiles. In the manufacture of lubricants, salts of naphthenic acids are often utilized. Sodium naphthenate is used as an emulsifying agent in the manufacture of cutting oils; sodium, calcium, zinc, or aluminium naphthenates are employed for manufacturing lubricating greases; calcium or zinc naphthenates are sometimes used as dispersants in motor oils. In the military field, Napalm, an incinerating substance, is manufactured because of the ability of aluminium dinaphthenate and other aluminium soaps to increase the viscosity of gasoline to the point where it forms a gel.

For the purposes of this chapter, the analytical separation and the identification of individual acids in the crude oils is the more important consideration. It is of some interest that only the simple aliphatic acids are found among the compounds containing up to six carbon atoms. The six to ten carbon atom-containing compounds consist of a mixture of fatty and naphthenic acids. Information regarding acids with more than ten carbon atoms is seriously lacking. Except for some solid aliphatic acids investigated by TANAKA and KUWATA (1928), fatty acids containing more than twelve carbon atoms have not yet been identified in petroleum.

It is generally believed that naphthenic acids are monocyclic up to C_{12}–C_{14} and bicyclic from C_{12} to C_{18}. The present discussion is concerned only with aliphatic and monocarboxylic naphthenic acids; acids of higher molecular weights will be discussed later. The various acids identified in petroleum are listed in Table XV.

Separation and identification procedures normally involve the following steps: (1) removal of the acids from the alkaline extract; (2) removal of the neutral oils and phenols which contaminate the acid fraction; (3) further fractionation of the purified acids into narrower fractions; (4) esterification of the acids in order to separate them from traces of phenols which may still be present, and from unreacted tertiary acids partially dissolved in the ester layer; (5) careful fractional distillation of the esters; (6) saponification of each of the ester fractions and subsequent fractional distillation of the regenerated acids; (7) suitable analytical steps to isolate and identify the individual acids by converting them into solid derivatives (various salts, such as amides), or by characterizing them through degradation reactions.

Normally the samples for these analyses are the alkaline solutions from the caustic washes of distilled gasolines supplied by the refinery. These alkaline solutions are acidified to separate the acids as noted previously. The acids are dissolved again in a sodium-carbonate solution and extracted with petroleum ether to remove the neutral oils and part of the phenols. The sodium-carbonate solution is then acidified and the acids fractionated either by distillation or by fractional extraction with NaOH. The acids are next esterified usually with methanol and anhydrous hydrogen chloride. During this step the acids may already be

TABLE XV

ACIDS IDENTIFIED IN CRUDE OILS

Compound	Source	Author
Aliphatic monocarboxylic acids		
formic acid	California, Caucasus	HANCOCK and LOCHTE (1939); MARKOWNIKOW and OGLOBLIN (1883)
acetic acid	California, Caucasus	HANCOCK and LOCHTE (1939); MARKOWNIKOW and OGLOBLIN (1883)
propionic acid	California	HANCOCK and LOCHTE (1939)
butyrric acid	California, Texas	HANCOCK and LOCHTE (1939); SCHUTZE et al. (1940)
isobutyrric acid		HANCOCK and LOCHTE (1939)
n-valeric acid	California, Texas	HANCOCK and LOCHTE (1939); SCHUTZE et al. (1940)
isovaleric acid	California	HANCOCK and LOCHTE (1939)
2-methylpentanoic acid	California	QUEBEDEAUX et al. (1943)
3-methylpentanoic acid	California	QUEBEDEAUX et al. (1943)
4-methylpentanoic acid	Ploesti	NENITZESCU et al. (1938)
3-ethylpentanoic acid	Romania, Baku	VON BRAUN et al. (1933); CHICHIBABIN (1932)
hexanoic acid	California	QUEBEDEAUX et al. (1943)
2-methylhexanoic acid	California	QUEBEDEAUX et al. (1943)
3-methylhexanoic acid	California, Romania	VON BRAUN et al. (1933); QUEBEDEAUX et al. (1943)
4-methylhexanoic acid	California	QUEBEDEAUX et al. (1943)
5-methylhexanoic acid	California, Ploesti, Baku	NENITZESCU et al. (1938); CHICHIBABIN (1932)
heptanoic acid	California	QUEBEDEAUX et al. (1943)
octanoic acid	California, Texas	HANCOCK and LOCHTE (1939); QUEBEDEAUX et al. (1943)
nonanoic acid	California	QUEBEDEAUX et al. (1943)
palmitic acid	Ishikari (Japan)	TANAKA and KUWATA (1928)
stearic acid	Ishikari	TANAKA and KUWATA (1928)
myristic acid	Ishikari	TANAKA and KUWATA (1928)
arachidic acid	Ishikari	TANAKA and KUWATA (1928)

Aliphatic dicarboxylic acids		
dimethylmaleic anhydride	California	HANCOCK and LOCHTE (1939)
dimethylmaleic acid	Texas	SCHUTZE et al. (1940)
1, 2, 2-trimethyl cyclopentane-1, 3-dicarboxylic acid		HANCOCK and LOCHTE (1939)
Cycloalkane monocarbolxylic acids		
cyclopentane carboxylic acid	California, Ploesti	NENITZESCU et al. (1938); NEY et al. (1943)
2-methylcyclopentane carboxylic acid	California	NEY et al. (1943)
3-methylcyclopentane carboxylic acid	California	NEY et al. (1943)
cyclopenthylacetic acid	California, Ploesti	NENITZESCU et al. (1938); NEY et al. (1943)
cyclohexane carboxylic acid	California, Baku	VON BRAUN et al. (1933); NEY et al. (1943)
3-methyl cyclopenthyl acetic acid	California, Ploesti	NENITZESCU et al. (1938); NEY et al. (1943)
2, 3-dimethyl cyclopenthyl acetic acid	California	NEY et al. (1943)
4-methyl cyclohexane carboxylic acid	Texas	SCHUTZE et al. (1940)
cis-2, 2, 6-trimethylcyclohexane carboxylic acid	California	NEY et al. (1943)
trans-2, 2, 6-trimethyl cyclohexane carboxilic acid	California	SHIVE et al. (1942a)

separated to a certain extent due to their different esterification rates. The esters are then subjected to fractional distillation which removes further impurities that may still be present such as neutral oils, phenols, or unesterified tertiary acids. The boiling point of the esters is approximately 50 °C lower than that of the impurities. After this step both the esterified fraction and the unesterified fraction are analyzed. The latter can be analyzed for tertiary acids whereas the former must be saponified to recover the original acids. The latter acids are then subjected to a further fractional distillation and identified by conversion into various solid derivatives such as amides, magnesium salts, silver salts, or cadmium salts.

These procedures were used mainly during the period 1925–1949 when the first aliphatic and monocyclic naphthenic acids were identified. At the present time identification of the acids can be performed more accurately and simply by gas chromatography. Special procedures have been developed to identify low molecular-weight acids (formic, acetic) which would otherwise be lost due to their solubility in water. The details of the various analytical steps may be obtained from the original papers. (See the references in Table XV.)

High molecular-weight acids

Success in separating individual compounds from mixtures of acids containing more than ten carbon atoms per molecule has not yet been achieved. One must be satisfied to examine mixtures which may at the best be separated into a number of type fractions.

Acids are present not only in kerosene and in the gas-oil fractions from which they are routinely recovered in industrial operations, but also in the lubricating oil fractions and distillation residues. CARO (1962) separated acids from soaps obtained from vacuum distillation residues of acidified lubricating oil fractions saponified with NaOH. These alkaline residues were treated with an excess of sulfuric acid, and the oil portion separated by chromatography into neutral oils and polar compounds; the latter fraction contained the acids and other compounds. This polar fraction was esterified to form methyl esters and then subjected to molecular distillation to purify the esters. The ester fractions were first reduced to primary alcohols with lithium–aluminum hydride, then to hydrocarbons by iodination followed by reduction with Zn and HCl. The products were separated into various molecular types by chromatography. A comparison of the chromatograms of these hydrocarbon products, with those of the original hydrocarbons in the oil from which the acids were separated, showed a notable similarity. Alkyl-substituted naphthenes, mono- and bicyclic aromatic hydrocarbons, and also sulfur compounds (for example, benzothiophenes) were present in both substances. Consequently the acids present in the lubricating oil fractions appear to be carboxylic acids originally derived from all of these molecules. The view that they have been derived mainly from alkyl-substituted cycloparaffins with the exclusion of most other compounds cannot be substantiated. Because of these genetic reasons the term naphthenic acids appears to be misleading, and perhaps the suggestion of KNOTNERUS (1957) proposing the term "petroleum acids" may be worthy of consideration.

Acids occurring in bitumens are of significance because they play an important role in emulsifying the bitumens. In order to isolate these acids CARO (1962) placed a toluene solution of bitumen on an alumina column removing other components by eluting first with toluene and then with a toluene–ethanol mixture (1/1, v/v). The acids were eluted with a toluene–acetic-acid mixture (3/1, v/v). Acetic acid was removed from the eluate by water extraction and then the toluene by distillation. The acids were left behind in the distillation residue. The molecular weight of these acids ranged between 700 and 1,400. When these acids were subjected to the same purification and reduction procedures as applied to the acids in the lubricating oil fractions, the resultant hydrocarbon reduction products were again markedly similar to the original hydrocarbons in the bitumen; however, the ratios of the hydrocarbon constituents were different in the reduced sample. This shows that the acids in bitumens contain substituted naphthenic and mono-, bi-, and tricyclic aromatic structures and are not pure naphthenic acids as was assumed before the work of CARO (1962).

TABLE XVI

ACID CONTENT OF ASPHALT CONSTITUENTS

Source	Acid number of bitumen (mg KOH/g)	Acid content of unfractionated bitumen (weight %)	Acid content of maltenes (weight %)	Acid content of asphaltenes (weight %)
Argentina	1.0	2.48	2.4	2.9
Middle East	0.2	0.38	0.2	3.8
Venezuela I	1.7	2.34	1.9	6.0
Venezuela II	2.9	3.26	3.1	4.6

Based on solubilities in light saturated hydrocarbon solvents or simply on molecular weights, the acid contents of maltenes and asphalthenes have also been estimated. The information is incomplete (CARO, 1962; see Table XVI), but it may be sufficient to indicate that the ratio of the acids in these two components of bitumen varies with different samples. This may also help to explain why some bitumens have the tendency to form more stable emulsions than others and why some adhere more firmly to the rock-forming minerals.

Origin of the acids occurring in petroleum

It should be noted that the long-accepted assumption that acids do not actually occur in crude oils but are artifacts formed in the various refining processes has been proved to be incorrect. There is evidence that most of the acids identified in petroleum distillates are also present in the original crude oil. Only a small quantity of acids appears to be formed during refining processes. Another important fact is that optically active acids are present in crude oils, showing that a small part of the petroleum parent material had a biogenic origin. Any assumption regarding the formation of acids must therefore be consistent with this concept; i.e., that petroleum originated from animal or perhaps more likely, plant matter. Petroleum evolution must have been a most complex process; no doubt the formation of acids from the parent organic substances occurred via numerous intermediates. The following data may support this opinion. BROOKS (1949) pointed out that while crude oils have been reported to contain 5-membered ring naphthenic hydrocarbons and cyclopentanecarboxylic acids, the occurrences of cyclopentane-type structure in biological matter is very rare. Most likely the significant quantity of cyclopentane-type acids in crude oils was not formed by the degradation of substances originally containing this ring system but, in the authors' opinion, by the rearrangement of cyclohexane in the presence of some natural catalysts. This hypothesis may also explain the fact that certain crude oils contain aliphatic but no naphthenic acids. In such cases petroleum evolution would have occurred in the absence of the natural catalysts.

There are other facts which also show that transformation of the parent material into acids has not been a simple process. It was noted previously that petroleum contains certain optically active acids; however, most of the individual acids so far isolated are optically inactive though many of them have asymmetric molecular structures. These acids would be optically active if they had been synthesized by enzymatically catalyzed processes. It must be remembered that the available data are not sufficient for establishing the origin of these acids; they only prove that in many cases the acids have not been formed by a simple degradation process, but by an extensive rearrangement of the molecules.

Some of the acids may have been derived directly from a parent substance such as the palmitic, stearic, myristic and arachic acids, which were isolated by TANAKA and KUWATA (1928) from Japanese crude oils. These acids could have originated from, for example, fish oils. Few of the other acids seem to have such a relatively simple origin. A more elaborate hypothesis is required to explain the presence of 2, 2, 6-trimethylcyclohexanecarboxylic acid which has been isolated in large quantities from a Signal Hills (California) crude oil. This acid may have originated from β-carotene. The β-ionone ring in the β-carotene molecule may be oxidized in the following manner:

This hypothesis, suggesting the derivation of an acid from a hydrocarbon, might be of some interest. It is possible that other aromatic hydrocarbons such as toluene, *m*-xylene, 2, 5- and 2, 6-dimethylnaphthalene could also have been derived from β-carotene. On the other hand, the fact that petroleum evolution appears to have taken place in a non-oxidizing environment argues against this hypothesis.

It may be permissible to state that, in general, acids occurring in petroleum could have originated from lipids contained in the biological source material. The reaction processes involved in their transformation are still unknown and they probably differed with source materials and environment conditions. In some instances acids might have been formed by the degradation of complex, non-lipid compounds.

Phenols

Phenols may also be considered indigenous components of crude oils. They have been found in significant concentrations in casing head gasolines from high-pressure gas wells and in formation waters. Little, if any, knowledge is available concerning their origin.

Because crude oils contain usually less than 0.1 % phenols, their isolation is difficult. Although phenols are present in crude oils and distillate fractions they are isolated customarily from cracked products because the phenol content of light oil fractions appears to increase after the cracking reactions. The isolation of phenols and cresols from gasolines may be summarized by the following steps: (*1*) extraction of the phenols from gasoline by caustic washing; (*2*) recovery of the so-called cresylic acids from the alkaline solution by acidification with carbon dioxide and/or mineral acids; (*3*) removal of the contaminations.

The major difficulties are encountered in the last step. The impurities usually are sulfur compounds (thiocresols and mercaptans) neutral compounds (i.e., hydrocarbons) and fatty acids. Only the sulfur compounds are present in significant quantities. This is shown in Table XVII.

TABLE XVII

ESTIMATED COMPOSITION (BY WEIGHT %) OF SPENT CAUSTIC FROM CATALYTICALLY CRACKED
GASOLINE

Component	Weight %
NaOH	3–7
Na-phenolates	15–30
Na-thiophenolates	1–5
Na-mercaptides	0.5–2
Na_2S	0.3–1.5
Neutral oils	0.2–3
Nitrogen bases	0–2.5
Water	65–90
Sediments	0.1

The sulfur-containing impurities can be removed by any one of the following methods: (1) air blowing and subsequent washing with "light" gasoline of the caustic solution prior to the separation of the cresylic acids; (2) carefully adjusting the pH of the caustic solution; (3) distillation where the sulfur compounds are removed in the highest and lowest boiling point fractions. A combination of these methods can, of course, also be applied.

The cresylic acids find industrial application as germicides, fungicides, disinfectants and insecticides. Crude cresylic fractions are also used for cleaning engines, various machinery, and parts made of ferrous and non-ferrous metals because they are effective neutral solvents.

The various phenol compounds identified in crude oils are summarized in Table XVIII. For the separation and identification of phenols alkaline washing solutions containing NaOH or Na_2CO_3 were used by many investigators. First the neutral compounds must be removed. Hydrocarbons can either be removed by steam distillation of the alkaline solution or extracted with petroleum ether, then both the acids and phenols are separated by treating the alkaline solution with an acid (usually sulfuric acid). After this step there are various techniques available for separating the acids from phenols and purifying the phenols. NE-NITZESCU et al. (1938) converted the acids into methyl esters from which the phenols were separated by extraction with dilute alkali. The esterification was repeated several times to insure the quantitative removal of the acids. TANAKA and KOBA-YASHI (1928) carefully neutralized the carboxylic acids and then extracted the phenols with ether. The process of fractional neutralization was repeated several times. STORY and SNOW (1928) extracted acids and phenols from an aqueous acid phase with benzene. The carboxylic acids were removed from the benzene with a solution of sodium bicarbonate and the phenols were extracted from the residual

TABLE XVIII

PHENOLIC COMPOUNDS IDENTIFIED IN CRUDE OILS

Compound	Source	Author
phenol	California	FIELD et al. (1940); SHIVE et al. (1942a)
o-cresol	Boryslav, California, Japan, Ploesti	FIELD et al. (1940); HOLZMAN and VON PILAT (1930); NENITZESCU et al. (1938); TANAKA and KOBAYASHI (1928)
m-cresol	Boryslav, California, Japan, Ploesti	FIELD et al. (1940); HOLZMAN and VON PILAT (1930); NENITZESCU et al. (1938); TANAKA and KOBAYASHI (1928)
p-cresol	Boryslav, California, Japan, Ploesti	FIELD et al. (1940); HOLZMAN and VON PILAT (1930); NENITZESCU et al. (1938); TANAKA and KOBAYASHI (1928)
1, 2, 3-xylenol	Japan, Ploesti	NENITZESCU et al. (1938); TANAKA and KOBAYASHI (1928)
1, 2, 4-xylenol	Boryslav, California	FIELD et al. (1940); HOLZMAN and VON PILAT (1930)
1, 3, 4-xylenol	Boryslav, California, Japan	FIELD et al. (1940); HOLZMAN and VON PILAT (1930); TANAKA and KOBAYASHI (1928)
1, 3, 5-xylenol	California, Ploesti	FIELD et al. (1940); NENITZESCU et al. (1938)
1, 4, 5-xylenol	Boryslav	NENITZESCU et al. (1938)
beta naphthol	California	FIELD et al. (1940)

benzene solution with strong alkali. HOLZMANN and PILAT (1930) subjected the crude acids to steam distillation, then treated the distillate with a solution of sodium bicarbonate and removed the neutral oils and phenols by extraction with ether. The ether extract was made alkaline and was repeatedly extracted with ether to remove additional neutral compounds. The remaining phenols were finally isolated with dilute sulfuric acid.

The final step consists of the separation and identification of phenols. Separation can be accomplished either by distillation (WOOLFOLK et al., 1950), or by counter-current extraction (GOLUMBIC et al., 1950). Phenol itself can be identified by forming its trinitro derivative; p-cresol by its acetate, phenylurethane, and aryloxyacetic acid derivatives; m-cresol by the formation of phenylurethane or trinitro derivatives; o-cresol by the formation of aryloxyacetic acid and naphthylurethane derivatives. 1, 2, 4-; 1, 3, 4-; and 1, 4, 5-xylenols were identified by their aryloxyacetic acid derivatives. The various compounds were separated mainly by the different solubilities of their sodium salts. Similar methods may be used to identify related compounds. 1, 4, 5-xylenol forms a potassium salt of its sulfonic acid derivative which is insoluble in concentrated potassium-chloride solution. 1, 2, 3-xylenol was identified by its oxyacetic acid derivative, and 1, 3, 5-xylenol by its tribromo and beta naphthol derivatives. FIELD et al. (1940) noted that the oxyacetic acid and other simple derivatives of xylenols and higher phenols are difficult to separate from their mixtures. Consequently the phenols usually were sulfonated and separated by Brückner's acid splitting method. Each of the lower molecular-weight phenol derivatives was decomposed at a specific temperature upon heating. The products were further separated by steam distillation.

Phenol, cresols and xylenols can be qualitatively identified and their concentrations determined by infrared spectroscopy using the method of FRIEDEL and PIERCE (1950). Analysis of the relatively volatile phenols may be done by simple gas-chromatographic methods (KARR et al., 1958). BROOKS (1959) separated 2, 4-xylenol from 2, 6-xylenol and m-ethylphenol from p-ethylphenol on columns containing phosphoric esters on a celite stationary phase. Retention data of phenols with different partition liquids has been reported by JONAK and KOMERS (1958). They also describe a method for separating mono-phenols. Physical constants for a series of phenols have been tabulated by PARDEE and WEINRICH (1944).

Ketones

The presence of ketones in crude oils was first reported by LOCHTE and MEYER (1953) who found in a gas-well condensate various methylketones ranging from acetone to methyl-n-butylketone. LATHAM et al. (1962) identified alkyl-substituted fluorenones in a Wilmington (California) crude oil by a combined mass, infrared, and ultraviolet spectroscopic analysis. They separated their samples for analysis by distillation at 320–330 °C temperature and then by a chemical reaction with sodium amide in liquid ammonia, followed by extraction and gas–liquid chromato-graphy. Fluorenones were the first aromatic ketones identified in petroleum. The first cycloalkylketone has been isolated from a Wilmington (California) petroleum by BRANDENBURG et al. (1963) who identified acetylisopropyl-methyl-cyclopentane by a combination of mass, infra-red, and nuclear magnetic resonance spectroscopy. The analytical sample was first isolated by distillation, elution chromatography, and gas–liquid chromatography. The content of this compound was found to be 0.0005% in the Wilmington (California) crude oil. BARTON et al. (1956) isolated a high melting point crystalline compound from high boiling point distillates of a West Baumont (U.S.A.) crude oil which had the approximate composition of $C_{30}H_{46}O_2$. This compound was subsequently identified as oxyallobetul-2-ene, a triterpenoid lactone. The identification of this compound is of considerable interest. It could have been derived from a typical plant triterpenoid such as betulline, and its presence in a crude oil could be construed as evidence that at least a portion of petroleum must have been derived from a parent plant matter.

The presence of ketones in distillation residues and bitumens has not yet been established with any degree of certainty. It should be noted that the infrared spectra of bitumens show adsorption bands at 5.8 and 5.9 μ which may be attributed to stretching of the C=O bond, and adsorption bands at 9.6–9.8 μ usually attrib-uted to C—O stretching. On the basis of these data, some authors claimed that aromatic ketones were present in bitumens, but undoubtedly this interpretation is still not final.

NITROGEN COMPOUNDS

Determination of nitrogen

The nitrogen content of crude oils can be determined by the Kjeldahl, Dumas, or the Ter Meulen method. The Kjeldahl method was originally developed for the determination of protein nitrogen and has undergone various modifications to make it suitable for determining nitrogen in substances which could not be analyzed by the original method. It is based on the destruction of the organic matter with sulfuric acid. Nitrogen compounds are converted to ammonium sulfate; then by means of an alkaline treatment and subsequent steam distillation, the ammonia is liberated from the ammonium sulfate and determined according to conventional methods. In the original Kjeldahl method, pyridinic nitrogen and that linked in –N=N– and NO_2 groups could not be destroyed. LAKE et al. (1951) modified the method by introducing a mercury catalyst and carefully controlling the digestion temperatures.

The Dumas method involves the combustion and ignition of a mixture of the nitrogen compounds and copper oxide in a stream of carbon dioxide, followed by volumetric determination of the nitrogen gas evolved. One must note that the Dumas method will lead to reliable results only if the sample is burned slowly at sufficiently high temperatures with large volumes of copper oxide present, and if very pure carbon dioxide is passed through the combustion tube. The error due to adsorbed nitrogen must be held to a minimum. This method becomes more sensitive and rapid if the amount of nitrogen evolved is measured by gas–liquid chromatography (REITSEMA and ALLPHIN, 1961).

The Ter Meulen method (HOLOWCHAK et al., 1952) is particularly well suited for samples which have low nitrogen contents. This technique consists of the thermal decomposition of the sample in a hydrogen atmosphere and conversion of nitrogen to ammonia by passage of the pyrolysis products over a nickel–magnesium catalyst at 280–300 °C. Ammonia is determined by conventional procedures. The original method involved the use of a nickel oxide catalyst which was quite susceptible to poisoning by sulfur and halogens.

Nitrogen compounds in crude oils

The presence of nitrogen in petroleum was demonstrated as early as 1817 when Saussure observed that ammonia formed upon the burning of naphtha. In 1872

TABLE XIX

NITROGEN CONTENTS OF CRUDE OILS FROM VARIOUS FIELDS

Field	State or Country	Geological formation	Nitrogen (weight % of crude oil)	Gravity (° A.P.I.)
Atlanta	Arkansas	Smackover (Jurassic)	0.003	51.1
Schuler	Arkansas	Jones (Jurassic)	0.063	33.2
Wilmington	California	Terminal (Tertiary)	0.44	25.6
Gato Ridge	California	Chert Shale (Tertiary)	0.67	13.8
Oxnard	California	Miocene (Tertiary)	0.88	7.1
Chromo	Colorado	Greenhorn (Cretaceous)	0.08	31.5
Heidelberg	Mississipi	Eutaw (Cretaceous)	0.11	25.7
Hogback	New Mexico	Dakota (Cretaceous)	0.000	60.2
Agha Jari	Iran	Asmari (Tertiary)	0.14	36.0
Midway Sunset	California	Etchegoin (Tertiary)	0.58	20.3
Wasson	Texas	Permian (Carboniferous)	0.08	34.2
Velma	Oklahoma	Red Beds (Carboniferous)	0.27	28.2
Deep River	Michigan	Dundee (Devonian)	0.12	34.2
Dublin	New Mexico	Ellenberger (Ordovician)	0.002	51.8
Apache	Oklahoma	Wilcox (Ordovician)	0.087	38.8
Lost Soldier	Wyoming	Cambrian (Cambrian)	0.097	35.6
Keri	Greece		0.17	7.9
Kirkuk	Iraq		0.094	36.6

TABLE XX

DISTRIBUTION OF NITROGEN IN THE VARIOUS BOILING RANGE FRACTIONS OF THREE CRUDE OILS

Crude oil	Winkleman Dome (Wyo.)		Sage Creak (Wyo.)		Steamboat Butte (Wyo.)	
Boiling range, (°C at 760 mm Hg)	Nitrogen (weight %)	Nitrogen (% of total)	Nitrogen (weight %)	Nitrogen (% of total)	Nitrogen (weight %)	Nitrogen (% of total)
Crude oil	0.23	100.0	0.28	100.0	0.16	100.0
Initial boiling point –275	0.005	0.1	—	—	0.003	0.1
275–310	0.026	0.4	0.01	0.4	0.024	0.6
310–338	0.036	1.0	0.02	0.4	0.030	1.1
338–365	0.058	1.4	0.05	1.1	0.059	1.9
365–393	0.105	2.5	0.09	1.8	0.096	3.1
393–422	0.144	4.0	0.13	2.9	0.136	6.3
Residuum after 422°C	0.50	91.3	0.53	92.9	0.44	87.5
		100.7		99.5		100.6

various investigators noticed the evolution of ammonia during the distillation of Galician crude oils. Quantitative analyses of the total nitrogen content of crude oils and of distillate fractions of crude oils were repeatedly reported from 1890 on, but the first results were not reliable because of the inaccuracy of the analytical methods that were available at that time.

It appears that practically all crude oils contain at least traces of nitrogen compounds but never more than 0.88 %.

Table XIX shows that all the reliable results seem to indicate that the nitrogen content of petroleums depends largely on the geographical location and, to a lesser extent, on the geological formation from which the oil was obtained. Crude oils containing the highest percentages of nitrogen compounds are produced in California from Tertiary formations. High nitrogen contents have for a long time been known to be associated with high quantities of non-distillable residues in petroleum.

It is interesting to consider the distribution of nitrogen in the various boiling range fractions. Table XX, quoted from the work of LOCHTE and LITTMANN (1955) indicates that nitrogen compounds are generally absent in the lighter fractions; i.e., those boiling up to approximately 225 °C. With increasing boiling points the amount of nitrogen compounds slowly increases with most of the nitrogen concentrated in the residue; i.e., in the fraction boiling above 422°C. This is illustrated in Table XXI, reported by BALL et al. (1951). The fact that the nitrogen content of fractions boiling above 225°C increases regularly, even when one changes from atmospheric to vacuum distillation techniques, suggests that the more complex nitrogen com-

TABLE XXI

PERCENT OF NITROGEN PRESENT IN RESIDUUM

Source of crude oil	Nitrogen (weight °/$_o$)	Nitrogen in residuum (weight °/$_o$)	Nitrogen in residuum (weight °/$_o$ of total nitrogen)
Schuler (Arkansas)	0.06	0.16	88.3
Heidelberg (Mississippi)	0.11	0.24	106.0
Deep River (Michigan)	0.12	0.32	90.8
Midway Sunset (California)	0.58	1.15	84.5
Velma (Oklahoma)	0.27	0.60	88.9
Chromo (Colorado)	0.08	0.20	100.0
Keri (Greece)	0.17	0.25	94.1

pounds are not seriously decomposed during distillation. For this reason nitrogen compounds found in distillates were likely indigenously present in the crude oil and are not decomposition products of more complex molecules.

Separation and identification of basic and non-basic nitrogen compounds in petroleum and various petroleum products was carefully studied by RICHTER et al. (1952). They suggested that the old definition by Bailey of the basic N compounds, "those which can be extracted with dilute sulfuric acid", should be changed to, "compounds which can be titrated with perchloric acid when dissolved in a 50:50 solution of glacial acetic acid and benzene". Indoles, some pyrroles, and carbazoles behave as non-basic compounds during this titration, whereas pyridines, quinolines (and presumably isoquinolines) and some substituted pyrroles, such as 2, 4-dimethylpyrrole, can be titrated and thus are considered as basic compounds. This definition of basicity and non-basicity is, of course, arbitrary in that it is dependent upon a particular method. When the perchloric acid titration is used, basic compounds are defined as those which have a pKa (H_2O) higher or equal to 2, and non-basic compounds those having a pKa (H_2O) lower or equal to 2. Using this titration method RICHTER et al. (1952) found that the ratio of basic nitrogen to total nitrogen is approximately constant regardless of the source of crude oil (see Table XXII). This ratio, however, varies in the different boiling-range fractions of the same crude oil.

One may conclude that the ratio of basic to total nitrogen is quite similar in a number of crude oils from widely different areas. It appears that the character and relative proportions of nitrogen compounds present in various crude oils are essentially the same although the actual amounts may vary considerably. This may indicate that petroleums in various areas of the earth were formed by a common mechanism.

TABLE XXII

RATIO OF BASIC NITROGEN COMPOUNDS TO TOTAL NITROGEN IN CRUDE OILS

Source of crude oil	Basic nitrogen (weight %)	Total nitrogen (weight %)	N_B/N_T
Kuwait	0.03	0.12	0.25
Tibu Petrolea	0.033	0.13	0.25
Mid Continent mix	0.025	0.10	0.25
East Texas	0.02	0.08	0.25
West Texas	0.03	0.11	0.27
Wilmington	0.14	0.50	0.28
Santa Maria Valley	0.19	0.66	0.29
Ventura	0.13	0.42	0.31
Kansas	0.04	0.12	0.33
Kettleman Hills	0.14	0.41	0.34

Identification of nitrogen compounds

Only basic nitrogen compounds have so far been isolated from petroleum. The non-basic compounds were identified only as classes but not as individual compounds. The only exception to this is carbazole (see Table XXIII).

It would be impossible to describe in this chapter all the analytical techniques used for separating and identifying the various individual nitrogen compounds. The discussion will therefore be confined to a summary. The primary separation of heterocyclic compounds from the hydrocarbon mixture can be achieved by extraction with liquid sulfur dioxide. Unlike the treatment with concentrated sulfuric acid, this technique does not affect the structure of the compounds. From the SO_2 extract, the basic N compounds may be roughly separated by extraction with dilute mineral acids. The steps involved in the isolation of pure bases include one or more of the following procedures but not necessarily in this order:

(1) Separation of the basic from the neutral compounds by neutralization of bases.

(2) Fractional distillation in order to separate the components of the mixture on the basis of their differences in vapor pressure.

(3) Fractional precipitation and recrystallization, etc.

After a concentrate of the basic compounds has been obtained by a combination of these methods to a point where a solid salt or other derivatives are available, the problem usually arises as to how to purify and identify the components of the concentrates. The basic nitrogen compounds most commonly are precipitated as picrates, but other reagents have also been used; sulfuric acid, hydrochloric acid, zinc chloride, methyl iodide, and mercury chloride which, in some cases, yield pure crystalline compounds.

TABLE XXIII

NITROGEN COMPOUNDS IDENTIFIED IN CRUDE OILS

Compound	Source	Author
Monocyclics		
3-methylpyridine	California	LOCHTE and LITTMANN (1955)
2, 3-dimethylpyridine	California	LOCHTE and LITTMANN (1955)
3, 5-dimethylpyridine	California	LOCHTE and LITTMANN (1955)
2, 3, 4-trimethylpyridine	California	LOCHTE and LITTMANN (1955)
2, 3, 5-trimethylpyridine	California	LOCHTE and LITTMANN (1955)
3-methyl-5-ethylpyridine	California	LOCHTE and LITTMANN (1955)
3-ethyl-5-methylpyridine		LOCHTE and LITTMANN (1955)
2, 3-dimethyl-6-isopropylpyridine	California	LOCHTE et al. (1950)
d1-2-*s*-buthyl-4, 5-dimethylpyridine	California	LOCHTE et al. (1942)
2-(2, 2, 6-trimethylcyclohexyl-) 4, 6-dimethylpyridine		PERRIN and BAILEY (1933); SHIVE et al. (1942a); SHIVE et al. (1942b); THOMPSON and BAILEY (1931)
Bicyclics		
quinoline	California	LOCHTE and LITTMANN (1955)
2-methylquinoline		LOCHTE and LITTMANN (1955)
2, 3-dimethylquinoline		BIGG and BAILEY (1933); PERRIN and BAILEY (1933)
2, 4-dimethylquinoline		BIGG and BAILEY (1933)
2, 8-dimethylquinoline		LAKE and BAILEY (1933)
2, 3, 8-trimethylquinoline		KING and BAILEY (1930)
2, 4, 8-trimethylquinoline		PERRIN and BAILEY (1933)
2-methyl-8-ethylquinoline		GLENN and BAILEY (1941b)
2, 3-dimethyl-8-ethylquinoline		KEY and BAILEY (1938)
2, 4-dimethyl-8-ethylquinoline		AXE (1939)
2, 3-dimethyl-8-*n*-propylquinoline		AXE and BAILEY (1938)
2, 4-dimethyl-8-*n*-propylquinoline		AXE and BAILEY (1939)
2, 4-dimethyl-8-*s*-buthylquinoline		SCHENCK and BAILEY (1940)
2, 3, 4, 8-tetramethylquinoline		AXE and BAILEY (1938); GLENN and BAILEY (1939)
2, 3, 4-trimethyl-8-ethylquinoline		GLENN and BAILEY (1939); SCHENCK and BAILEY (1939)
2, 3, 8-trimethyl-4-ethylquinoline		GLENN and BAILEY (1941a)
2, 3, 4-trimethyl-8-isopropylquinoline		SCHENCK and BAILEY (1941a)
2, 3, 4-trimethyl-8-*n*-propylquinoline		SCHENCK and BAILEY (1939)
2, 3-dimethyl-4, 8-diethylquinoline		SCHENCK and BAILEY (1941b)
2, 3-dimethyl-4-ethyl-8-*n*-propylquinoline		SCHENCK and BAILEY (1941b)
2, 3-dimethylbenzo(h)quinoline		SCHENCK and BAILEY (1941c)
2, 4-dimethylbenzo(h)quinoline		SCHENCK and BAILEY (1941c)
5, 6, 7, 8-tetrahydroquinoline	California	LOCHTE and LITTMANN (1955)
Tricyclics		
Carbazole	Wilmington	HELM et al. (1960)

Individual basic nitrogen compounds have been identified in low molecular weight (or boiling-point) fractions. Compounds having higher boiling points than kerosene have been identified only as classes of compounds. Particular attention was directed to N compounds occurring in fuel oils, simply because pyrroles and indoles seem to decrease the storage stability by gum formation.

SAUER et al. (1952) reported the classification of nitrogen compounds in a 152–327°C gas-oil distillate from a Cretaceous Kuwait crude oil. The Kuwait gas-oil was passed through an alumina column, then eluted with iso-hexane, carbon tetrachloride, benzene, chloroform, and methanol. The fractions were analyzed by mass spectrography and total nitrogen contents determined.

TABLE XXIV

NITROGEN COMPOUNDS IN VIRGIN KUWAIT GAS-OIL

Compounds	Concentration (g/100 ml)	Percent
Pyridines	0.079	43.9
Carbazoles	0.053	29.4
Indoles	0.017	9.4
Pyrroles	0.016	8.9
Quinolines	0.015	8.3

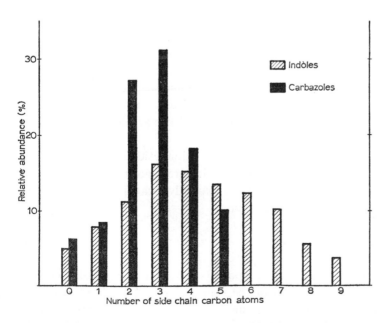

Fig.5. Distribution of substituted carbozoles and indoles in distillates.

Carbazoles can be identified not only by mass spectrography but also from their strong adsorption band in the ultraviolet spectra in the region between 291 and 294 mμ. The nitrogen compounds found in the Kuwait gas-oil are shown in Table XXIV. Fig.5 shows the distribution of indoles and carbazoles according to their molecular weights or more precisely, according to the number of C atoms in the side chains. Carbazoles and indoles containing chains with three C atoms were the most abundant. Carbazoles are the only non-basic compounds which could be identified in petroleum distillates. Carbazole was identified by HELM et al. (1960) in a Wilmington (California) petroleum. A 320–330°C boiling-range fraction was dissolved in *n*-pentane which was then reacted with sodium amide in liquid ammonia to give a concentrate of nitrogen compounds. This material was further separated by gas–liquid chromatography. The presence and quantity of carbazole was confirmed by mass, infrared, and ultraviolet spectra with the quantity of carbazole of at least 2 p.p.m.

Analysis of distillation residues

There is little, if any, available knowledge concerning nitrogen compounds present in distillation residues. It appears that a part of the nitrogen is bound to the metallic constituents in the form of metal-porphyrin complexes which will be discussed later in this chapter; however, these compounds only account for about 20% of the nitrogen content.

Distillation residues are usually analyzed first by separating a series of fractions of increasing molecular weights. This may be accomplished by molecular distillation; fractional precipitation with a mixture of solvents of variable cohesive energies; thermal diffusion; or by ultracentrifugation. The lower molecular weight fractions can also be fractioned by chromatography on alumina columns (O'DON-NELL, 1951; CHELTON and TRAXLER, 1959). The molecular weight and the elementary composition of each of these fractions can be determined. The location of nitrogen and sulfur, etc., in the large complex molecules which make up the residues are determined by indirect methods.

In conclusion it is probable that in the distillation residues, oxygen is present chiefly in CO and OH groups as is shown by the infrared spectra; sulfur is present mainly in thiophenic rings; and nitrogen is apparently located on the outer rings of these highly condensed aromatic structures.

Origin of the nitrogen compounds

Any theory of the origin of nitrogen compounds occurring in petroleum must be consistent with the general theories of the origin of petroleum itself. The view held at present is that nitrogen compounds have been derived from biogenic matter. The processes involved in the transformation of the parent organic matter into the nitrogen compounds must have been very complex. It is also possible that the nitrogen compounds may have been derived from such compounds as purines and pyrimidines. The transformation temperature could not have been very high otherwise non-decarboxylated porphyrins could not have survived in crude oils. The complexity of the transformation cycle is further emphasized by the fact that apparently none of the individual nitrogen bases so far identified in crude oil occur in biological substances.

In summary, it may be stated that at the present time no definite conclusion can be reached regarding the origin of nitrogen compounds in petroleum. Different transformation processes may have occurred in different geographical areas during different geological times; this view is indicated by the varying nitrogen contents of crude oils. However, one can perhaps state that the basic nitrogen compounds originated from animal and/or plant sources that formed the parent matter of petroleum. Possibly a better knowledge of the non-basic compounds will shed more light on the origin of the nitrogen compounds and of petroleum itself.

METALLIC CONSTITUENTS OF PETROLEUM

Inorganic analysis of petroleum

The metal content of crude oils normally varies from 0.1 to 100 p.p.m. Usually the metallic elements must be separated from the bulk of the organic material before the inorganic analyses are performed. Probably the simplest procedure for removing organic matter is direct ashing. The process of dry ashing consists of burning a weighed sample of oil in a tared dish and igniting the residue in a furnace until all carbonaceous material has been oxidized. The possible loss of certain metallic constituents in the form of volatile compounds can be avoided by sulfating the oil before igniting it (MILNER et al., 1952). This constitutes the wet ashing method. In another method, the oil is first treated with benzenesulfonic acid which destroys the porphyrin metallo complexes and renders the metals non-volatile (SHOTT et al., 1961). The basic procedure for direct ashing can also be modified by addition of certain reagents; notably calcium or zinc oxide in order to prevent the volatilization of phosphorus, or sulfur to prevent the loss of nickel and vanadium (AGAZZI et al., 1963). The following conditions must be carefully controlled in the course of ashing: the burning rate; the temperature of the final ignition; and the composition of the crucible used. If losses during the ignition procedures can still not be avoided, one may use wet oxidation which unfortunately is a rather time-consuming process. Usually the sample is charred by heating it with sulfuric acid and adding concentrated nitric acid in 1 or 2 ml increments; alternatively or consecutively. Concentrated hydrogen peroxide is added drop by drop to the charred digestion mixture. The organic material in small-sized samples can also be oxidized by perchloric acid (FORRESTER and JONES, 1960).

Once the sample has been ashed and the ash dissolved in a suitable solvent, the metals can be determined by several well-known methods. However, because only small amounts of metals are present in the sample, colorimetric methods are usually preferred by most analysts. The colorimetric reagents most commonly used are the following: dimethylglyoxime for nickel (WRIGHTSON, 1949; ARICH and COSTANTINIDES, 1960); thiocyanate (SANDELL, 1950) and ortho-phenanthroline for iron; diphenylbenzidine (WRIGHTSON, 1949; ARICH and COSTANTINIDES, 1960); or 3, 3'-dimethylnaphthidine (FEIGL, 1954); or other redox indicators (MILAZZO et al., 1958) for vanadium; sodium diethyldithiocarbamate for copper (SANDELL, 1950). Unless special precautions are taken, the colorimetric methods do not give a reproducibility better than 5%, this is due in part to errors in ashing procedures.

Because of its rapidity and general applicability (KARCHMER and GUNN, 1952), emission spectroscopy is a most suitable method for the routine analysis of low concentrations of metallic elements in petroleum. Spectroscopy can be conveniently applied for the determination of Al, Ba, Ca, Cr, Co, Cu, Fe, Pb, Mn, Mo, Ni, Si, Na, V, and Zn. It is difficult to evaluate the accuracy of this method since there are many variables in the technique but, in general, the reproducibility of routine data on most metallic elements is in the order of 10 to 15%.

The metallic elements can also be determined by X-ray analysis, either by X-ray absorption or by fluorescence. DAVIS and CROSS-HOECK (1955) suggested that V and Ni can be determined by this method with a reproducibility that is equal to that of the emission spectroscopic methods. Neutron activation can also be applied to the determination of trace metals in petroleum (COLOMBO et al., 1964). The results of inorganic analyses of petroleum have been summarized in detail in the review papers of McCoy (1962) and MILNER (1963).

Metallic compounds in crude oils

Among the various heavy metals in crude oils only vanadium and nickel have been studied in detail because these elements are almost always present, and usually in significant concentrations. In 1934, TREIBS observed the presence of these metals in porphyrin complexes. Considerable work has been done to clarify the nature, behavior, and origin of these compounds which could provide the most useful information regarding the origin and environmental conditions of petroleum formation. The presence of metal complexes in crude oils is also of industrial interest. Small amounts of heavy metals in the feed stocks introduced to catalytic cracking, adversely affects the catalysts (MILLS, 1950), and the ashes of V-containing fuels have strong corrosive effects on gas turbines. Finally the V and Ni complexes apparently affect the oil–water interfacial tension and thereby the stability of emulsions.

Occasionally, traces of metals are found in the gas-oil fractions. Metal contents increase regularly with increasing molecular weight of the distillate fractions and reaches its maximum in the residue (WOODLE and CHANDLER, 1952). When the residue is fractionated by precipitation with propane or butane the metals are found preferentially concentrated in the asphaltenes. The occurrence of metals in distillates may be explained by a mechanical entrainment of residue or by distillation of the metals in the form of volatile metal-organic compounds. The latter process is generally accepted as a result of investigations by DUNNING and MOORE (1957b), and BEACH and SHEWMAKER (1957) indicating that some metal complexes, isolated by elution chromatography and by extraction with aqueous pyridine, are concentrated in the more volatile distillate fractions. ERD-MAN et al. (1955) achieved the sublimation of certain complexes of etioporphyrin I without decomposition with copper, nickel, vanadium, and iron. These findings lead to the conclusion that both V and Ni compounds of widely varying molecular weights exist in crude oils.

Determination and classification of metal complexes

Porphyrins are compounds containing four condensed pyrrol rings and have the general structure:

Different porphyrin molecules are formed by substitution on different side-chains on the ring system. Their spectra are not identical although all show similar absorption bands in the visible region. In acid solutions, or when porphyrins are complexed with metals, the spectral bands shift to different wavelengths. The characteristic absorption spectra of the complexes may be used for their identification in distillates and residues, (SUGIHARA and BEAN, 1962), however the spectra of the residues show strong background adsorption. There is a method (COSTAN-TINIDES and ARICH, 1963) by which this intense background adsorption can be subtracted from the spectrum and by applying this correction the bands of the complexes become more noticeable. (The corrected spectra of various crude oils are shown in Fig.6.)

The GROENNINGS' (1953) method is usually employed for estimating the amount of metal-porphyrins in a crude oil. The complexes are extracted and demetallated by digestion with a mixture of acetic and hydrobromic acids, the porphyrins are purified, then identified by spectrophotometry. If these methods are carefully applied the results are in good agreement within experimental error. (Table XXV).

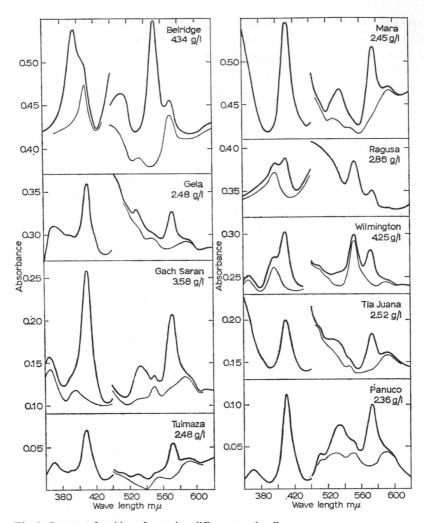

Fig.6. Spectra of residues from nine different crude oils.

It has been noticed that during treatment with acetic and hydrochloric acids other metal-organic compounds must also be liberated since the acid solution contains an excess of metals which cannot be accounted for by the porphyrins (HOWE and WILLIAMS, 1960). Because the nitrogen to metal ratio in the acid extracts is 4/1 it may be assumed that these compounds also contain four pyrrol rings; the N atoms are coordinated with the metals (COSTANTINIDES and ARICH, 1963). It is likely that these compounds were derived from the metal-porphyrin complexes for it has been observed that when a distillation residue is oxidized by air blowing, the porphyrins are destroyed following a first order kinetic reaction; whereas the total amount of extractable metals remains unchanged (COSTANTINIDES et al., 1959).

TABLE XXV

DETERMINATION OF METAL AND PORPHYRIN CONTENTS IN NINE DIFFERENT RESIDUES

Residue	North Bel-ridge	Gela	Gach Saran	Tui-maza	Mara maza	Ra-gusa	Wil-ming-ton	Tia Juana	Panuco
Yield of crude (weight %)	67.2	77.4	47.5	20.7	29.4	46.3	81.0	58.7	77.0
Total metal contents (moles/g)									
vanadium	0.89	2.49	4.33	3.14	11.0	0.49	1.12	6.06	7.52
nickel	2.77	1.28	1.24	1.62	0.94	2.49	1.28	0.66	1.43
total	3.66	3.77	5.57	4.76	11.94	2.98	2.40	6.72	8.95
Metal porphyrin complexes (moles/g)									
vanadium	0.36	0.69	1.00	0.56	1.40	0.26	0.38	0.61	1.19
nickel	1.26	0.09	0.20	0.12	0.07	0.44	0.43	0.06	0.14
total	1.62	0.78	1.20	0.68	1.47	0.70	0.81	0.67	1.33
Porphyrins (moles/g)	1.27	0.57	0.87	0.68	1.03	0.59	0.64	0.52	0.90
Metal in acid extract (moles/g)									
vanadium	0.73	1.40	2.17	1.04	2.84	0.38	0.62	1.41	2.29
nickel	2.51	0.86	0.84	1.05	0.56	1.73	1.10	0.32	0.79
total	3.24	2.26	3.01	2.09	3.40	2.11	1.72	1.73	3.08

A third fraction of metals is not affected by acid but the idea can not be dismissed that these metals may also be bound, at least partially, to N atoms. In fact, SARACENO et al. (1961), using quantitative electron paramagnetic resonance spectroscopy, have demonstrated that with very few exceptions all the vanadium in petroleum (distillates, residues and crude oils) exists in a single valence state; namely the $+4$ oxidation state. The crystal field environment around the vanadium is essentially the same in all samples. ERDMAN and HARJU (1962) also noticed that certain residues can take up additional amounts of metals which would then be coordinated in a molecular aggregate consisting of a series of aromatic sheets surrounded by paraffinic groups.

Thus the metallic compounds in crude oils can be classified in three main groups:

(1) Metal-organic compounds unaffected by acid.

(2) Metal-porphyrin complexes.

(3) Metal complexes with porphyrin-like systems.

Table XXV shows the distribution of metal-porphyrins and other metal compounds.

In the past few decades numerous analytical studies have been made to improve the separation and identification of the different metal complexes in crude oils. While partly concerned with the fractionation of the aggregates obtained after the complexes were degraded, the separation of the metal complexes themselves were also studied. This perhaps is more interesting to the geochemist because the degradation of the complexes by acid may lead to the loss or alteration of a part of the compounds. The fractionation of the complexes may be based on their volatility (see the preceding descriptions), or on their molecular weight. ELDIB et al. (1960) fractionated the residues by ultracentrifugation; DUNNING and RABON (1956) obtained sharp separation between Ni and V complexes; BEACH and SHEWMAKER (1957) experimented with aqueous pyridine; SKINNER (1952) extracted a fraction of the complexes with alcohol; GARNER et al. (1953) evaluated a series of solvents in this connection. Other separation techniques are elution chromatography, and solvent extraction. COSTANTINIDES and ARICH (1963) achieved sharper separations and higher yields by countercurrent multistage partitioning extraction between a paraffinic phase and a polar solvent such as dimethylformamide. The results of ERDMAN et al. (1957) show that a separation of complexes containing various metals can also be obtained according to their different stability to the acid attack.

To separate the decomplexed porphyrins, either extraction with solutions of varying pH or chromatography is used. HOWE (1961) separated petroleum porphyrins into the spectral types of rhodo, etio, phyllo, etc., by column chromatography using silica gel. Others have used paper chromatography (BLUMER, 1950; and FISHER and DUNNING, 1959), or chromatography on cellulose (DUNNING and CARLTON, 1956).

At present it is still difficult to critically compare the results obtained by the various analytical techniques and to arrive at a complete picture regarding the nature of the porphyrinic aggregates in petroleum. It seems that they consist mainly of decarboxylated porphyrins. Perhaps one of the most significant results obtained so far is that carboxylated porphyrins have been found in several crude oils. Such compounds undergo decarboxylation at temperatures of 200–300°C; consequently, one may conclude that these crude oils have not been subjected to temperatures higher than these during geological time. (A complete discussion of porphyrins will be presented in Chapter 5.)

Origin of metal complexes in crude oils

The problem of the origin of the metal-porphyrins is closely related to that of the origin of petroleum and is one of the most basic and interesting questions of petroleum geochemistry. Important contributions to the understanding of this problem were made by a number of investigators such as DUNNING and MOORE (1957a) and HODGSON and PEAKE (1961). The most probable conclusion seems to be that the nickel and vanadium–porphyrin complexes are formed by metal exchange reactions from animal and/or plant metabolic pigments such as hemoglobin and chlorophyll. To investigate what may have been involved in the transformation of chlorophyll to porphyrin, experiments with pigments extracted from recent sediments have been conducted (HODGSON and PEAKE, 1961). The fact that sediments of Lake Wabamun near Edmonton, Canada, contained not only free chlorins but also chlorins complexed with metals suggests that the transformation may have undergone the following stages: chlorophyll was converted to pheophytin by the loss of magnesium; the pheophytin formed a metal–pheophytin complex (a chlorin complex); and was next reduced and dehydrogenated to a metal-containing porphyrin. In addition to the metal complexes of chlorins, the Lake Wabamun sediments also contained small amounts of a metal complex of a carboxylated porphyrin. The proposed transformation has been confirmed experimentally by reacting various chlorophyll containing mixtures with various vanadium salts in the presence of sodium sulfide in an aqueous system at temperatures ranging between 90 to 150 °C.

Several attempts have been made to find a relationship between the age of a crude oil and its metal content. The vanadium to nickel ratios particularily have been examined. The relationships seem to be meaningful only for crude oils in the same region. For example, KATCHENKOV (1949) found that crude oils from the oldest formations had a high vanadium-to-nickel ratio. On the other hand, HODGSON (1954) found the oils from western Canada to exhibit the reverse pattern; i.e., the crude oils from the oldest formations generally had a lower ratio. BALL et al. (1960) found that crude oils from the United States differed in this respect according to the geographic location of the field. Better relationship is likely to be discovered not only when the total amount of vanadium and nickel will be considered, but also the different forms of metal complexes. It was observed (COSTANTINIDES and ARICH, 1963) that the metal complexes are converted to a form which is unaffected by acid when they are first treated at temperatures at approximately 400 °C. Such transformation follows first-order kinetics, and the degradation rate is higher for vanadium than for nickel complexes.

REFERENCES

AGAZZI, E. J., BURTNER, D. C., CRITTENDEN, D. J. and PATTERSON, D. R., 1963. Determination of trace metals in oils by sulfur incineration and spectrophotometric measurements. *Anal. Chem.*, 35: 332–335.
ARICH, G. e COSTANTINIDES, G., 1960. Microanalisi di nichel e vanadio nei residui petroliferi. *Riv. Combust.*, 14: 695–716.
ARNOLD, R. C., LAUNER, P. J. and LIEN, A. P., 1952. Identification of cyclohexanethiol in virgin naphtha. *Anal. Chem.*, 24: 1741–1744.
AXE, N., 1939. The nitrogen compounds in petroleum distillates, 14. Isolation of 2, 4-dimethyl-8-ethylquinoline from the kerosene distillate of California petroleum. *J. Am. Chem. Soc.*, 61: 1017–1019.

AXE, N. and BAILEY, J. R., 1938. The nitrogen compounds in petroleum distillates, 13. Isolation of four quinoline homologs and two aromatic bases of probable trinuclear cyclic structure. *J. Am. Chem. Soc.*, 60: 3028–3032.

AXE, N. and BAILEY, J. R., 1939. The nitrogen compounds in petroleum distillates, 15. Counter-current acid extraction of kero bases. Isolation of 2, 4-dimethyl-8-*n*-propylquinoline. *J. Am. Chem. Soc.*, 61: 2609.

BALL, J. S., WHISMAN, M. L. and WENGER, W. J., 1951. Nitrogen content of crude petroleum. *Ind. Eng. Chem.*, 43: 2577–2581.

BALL, J. S., WENGER, W. J., HYDEN, H. J., HORR, C. A. and MYERS, A. T., 1956. Metal content of twenty-four petroleums. *J. Chem. Eng. Data*, 5: 553–557.

BALL, J. S., HAINES, W. E. and HELM, R. V., 1959. Minor constituents of a California petroleum. *World Petrol. Congr., Proc., 5th, N.Y., 1959*, 5: 175–189.

BARTON, D. H. R., CARRUTHERS, W. and OVERTON, K. H., 1956. Triterpenoids, 21. A triterpenoid lacton from petroleum. *J. Chem. Soc.*, 1956: 788.

BEACH, L. K. and SHEWMAKER, J. E., 1957. The nature of vanadium in petroleum. *Ind. Eng. Chem.*, 49: 1157–1164.

BESTOUGEFF, M., 1959. Constitution des composés soufrés cycliques du pétrole. *World Petrol. Congr., Proc., 5th, N.Y., 1959*, 5: 143–164.

BIGG, B. and BAILEY, J. R., 1933. The nitrogen compounds in petroleum distillates, 5. The use of sulfur dioxide in the separation of petroleum bases. *J. Am. Chem. Soc.*, 55: 4141–4142.

BIRCH, S. F., 1953. Sulfur compounds in petroleum. *J. Inst. Petrol.*, 39: 185–201.

BIRCH, S. F., CULLUM, T. V., DEAN, R. A. and DENYER, R. L., 1952. Thiaadamantane. *Nature*, 170: 629–630.

BIRCH, S. F., CULLUM, T. V., DEAN, R. A. and DENYER, R. L., 1955. Sulfur compounds in kerosine boiling range of Middle East crude. *Ind. Eng. Chem.*, 47: 240–249.

BIRCH, S. F., CULLUM, T. V., DEAN, R. A. and REDFORD, D. G., 1959. Sulfur compounds in the kerosine boiling range of Middle East distillates. *Tetrahedron*, 7: 311–318.

BLUMER, M., 1950. Porphyrinfarbstoffe und Porphyrin-Metallcomplexe in schweizerischen Bitumina. *Helv. Chim. Acta*, 33 (4): 1627.

BRANDENBURG, C. F., LATHAM, D. R., COOK, G. L. and HAINES, W. E., 1963. Identification of a cycloalkylketone in Wilmington petroleum through use of chromatography and spectroscopy. *Am. Chem. Soc., Div. Petrol. Chem., Preprints*, 8: C53.

BROOKS, B. T., 1949. Cyclopentanes and petroleum origin. *J. Am. Chem. Soc.*, 71: 4143.

BROOKS, B. T., 1959. Some open questions regarding petroleum origin. *J. Inst. Petrol.*, 45: 42–46.

BURCKHARDT, CH., GRÜTTER, A. and STOESSEL, H., 1962. Determination of sulfur in petroleum by X-ray analysis. *Nature*, 196: 825–826.

CARO, J. H., 1962. Hochmolekular säure Verbindungen aus Erdöl. *Erdöl Z.*, 7: 435–440.

CARRUTHERS, W., 1955. 1:8-dimethyldibenzothiophen in a Kuwait mineral oil fraction. *Nature*, 176: 790–791.

CARRUTHERS, W. and DOUGLAS, A. G., 1959. The constituents of high boiling petroleum distillates, 5. Semicondensed thiophen derivates in a Kuwait oil. *J. Chem. Soc.*, 1959: 2813–2821.

CHARITSCHKOFF, K. W., 1899. Argument: character of naphta von Grozny. *J. Russ. Phys. Chem. Soc.*, 31 (6): 665–668; *J. Soc. Chem. Ind. (London)*, 18: 907.

CHELTON, H. M. and TRAXLER, R. N., 1959. Composition of chromatographic and thermal diffusion fractions of typical asphalts. *World Petrol. Congr., Proc., 5th, N.Y., 1959*, 5 (19): 247–257.

CHICHIBABIN, A. E., 1932. General method for obtaining γ-ketonic acids and their eters. *Chim. Ind. (Paris)*, 1932 (306): 563–568.

COLEMAN, H. J., ADAMS, N. G., ECCLESTON, B. H., HOPKINS, R. L., MIKKELSEN, L., RALL, H. T., RICHARDSON, D., THOMPSON, C. J. and SMITH, H. M., 1956. Analytical separation and identification of sulfur compounds in a petroleum distillate boiling to 100°C. *Anal. Chem.*, 28: 1380–1384.

COLEMAN, H. J., THOMPSON, C. J., WARD, C. C. and RALL, H. T., 1958. Identification of low-boiling sulfur compounds in Agha Jari crude oil by gas-liquid chromatography. *Anal. Chem.*, 30: 1592–1594.

COLEMAN, H. J., THOMPSON, C. J., HOPKINS, R. L., FOSTER, N. G., WHISMAN, M. L. and RICHARDSON, D. M., 1961. Identification of benzo(b)thiophene and its 2- and 3-methyl homologs in Wasson, Texas, crude oil. *J. Chem. Eng. Data*, 6: 464–468.

COLOMBO, U., SIRON, G., FASOLO, G. B. and MALVANO, R., 1964. Systematic neutron activation technique for the determination of trace metals in petroleum. *Anal. Chem.*, 36: 806–807.

COSTANTINIDES, G. and ARICH, G., 1963. Research on metal complexes in petroleum residues. *World Petrol. Congr., Proc., 6th, Frankfurt, 1963*, 5: 65–77.

COSTANTINIDES, G., ARICH, G. and LOMI, C., 1959. Detection and behaviour of porphyrin aggregates in petroleum residues and bitumens. *World Petrol. Congr., Proc., 5th, N.Y., 1959*, 5: 131–142.

DAVIS, E. N. and CROSS HOECK, B., 1955. X-ray spectrographic method for the determination of vanadium and nickel in residual fuels and charging stocks. *Anal. Chem.*, 27: 1880–1884.

DUMAS, M., 1847. *Traité de Chimie Appliquée aux Arts*, Tome 1. Felix Oudart, Liège, 554 pp.

DUNNING, H. N. and CARLTON, J. K., 1956. Paper chromatography of a petroleum porphyrin aggregate. *Anal. Chem.*, 28: 1362–1366.

DUNNING, H. N. and MOORE, J. W., 1957a. Metal-porphyrin complexes in an asphaltic mid-continent crude oil. *U.S. Bur. Mines, Rept. Invest.*, 1957: 5370.

DUNNING, H. N. and MOORE, J. W., 1957b. Porphyrin research and origin of petroleum. *Bull. Am. Assoc. Petrol. Geologists*, 41: 2403–2412.

DUNNING, H. N. and RABON, N. A., 1956. Porphyrin-metal complexes in petroleum stocks. *Ind. Eng. Chem.*, 48: 951–955.

ECCLESTON, B. H., MORRISON, M. and SMITH, H. M., 1952. Elemental sulfur in crude oil. *Anal. Chem.*, 24: 1745–1748.

EDELEANU, L. and FILITI, G. A., 1900. Argument: sulphur compounds in petrol. *Bull. Soc. Chim.*, 3 (23): 382–403.

ELDIB, I. A., DUNNING, H. N. and BOLEN, R. J., 1960. Nature of colloidal materials in petroleum. *J. Eng. Chem. Data*, 5: 550–553.

EMMOTT, R., 1953. Investigations of the sulphur compounds present in middle distillate SO_2 extracts. *J. Inst. Petrol.*, 39: 695–715.

ERDMAN, J. G. and HARJU, PH. H., 1962. The capacity of petroleum asphaltenes to complex heavy metals. *Am. Chem. Soc., Div. Petrol. Chem., Gen. Papers*, 7: 43–55.

ERDMAN, J. G., RAMSEY, V. G. and HANSON, W. E., 1955. Volatility of metallo-porphyrin complexes. *Science*, 123: 502.

ERDMAN, J. G., WALTER, J. W. and HANSON, W. E., 1957. The stability of the porphyrin metallic complexes. *Am. Chem. Soc., Div. Petrol. Chem., Preprints*, 2: 259–267.

ESPAGNO, L. et POQUET, B., 1962. Identification du dibenzothiophene et certains de se dérivés dans le pétrole de Lacq. *J. Chim. Phys.*, 59: 509.

FEIGL, F., 1954. *Spot Tests. I. Inorganic Applications*. Elsevier, New York, N.Y., 500 pp.

FIELD, E., DEMPSTER, F. H. and TILSON, G. E., 1940. Phenolic compounds from petroleum sources. *Ind. Eng. Chem.*, 32: 489–496.

FISHER, L. R. and DUNNING, H. N., 1959. Chromatographic resolution of petroleum porphyrin aggregates. *Anal. Chem.*, 31: 1194–1197.

FORRESTER, J. S. and JONES, J. L., 1960. The determination of iron, nickel and vanadium in petroleum oils. *Anal. Chem.*, 32: 1443–1446.

FRANKS, M. C. and GILPIN, R. L., 1962. The determination of sulphur in petroleum products. *J. Inst. Petrol.*, 48: 226–236.

FRIDMAN, W., 1951. Dehydrogenation of tetrahydrothiophene. *J. Inst. Petrol.*, 27: 239–241.

FRIDMAN, W. and CANSECO, C., 1943. Sulfur compounds from Panuco gasoline. *Petrol. Refiner*, 22:1.

FRIDMAN, W. and RODRIGUEZ, C., 1946. Sulfur compounds from Panuco gasoline. *Petrol. Refiner*, 26: 52–60.

FRIEDEL, R. A. and PIERCE, L., 1950. Infrared analysis of phenol, cresols, xylenols and ethyl-phenols. *Anal. Chem.*, 22: 418–420.

GARNER, F. H., GREEN, S. J., HARPER, F. D. and PEGG, R. E., 1953. The metallic elements in residual fuel oils. *J. Inst. Petrol.*, 39: 278–293.

GLENN, R. A. and BAILEY, J. R., 1939. The nitrogen compounds in petroleum distillates, 16.

Use of multiple acid extraction in isolation of 2, 3, 4-trimethyl-4-ethylquinoline. *J. Am. Chem. Soc.*, 61: 2612–2613.

GLENN, R. A. and BAILEY, J. R., 1941a. The nitrogen compounds in petroleum distillates, 19. The isolation from California petroleum of 2, 3, 8-trimethyl-8-ethylquinoline. *J. Am. Chem. Soc.*, 63: 637–638.

GLENN, R. A. and BAILEY, J. R., 1941b. The nitrogen compounds in petroleum distillates, 20. Isolation of 2-methyl-8-ethylquinoline from California petroleum and proof of structure through degradation and synthesis. *J. Am. Chem. Soc.*, 63: 639–641.

GOLUMBIC, C., WOOLFOLK, E. O., FRIEDEL, R. A. and ORCHIN, M., 1950. Partition studies on phenols, 4. Isolation of indanols from coal hydrogenation oils. *J. Am. Chem. Soc.*, 72: 1939–1942.

GROENNINGS, S., 1953. Quantitative determination of the porphyrin aggregate in petroleum. *Anal. Chem.*, 25: 938–941.

GUINN, V. P., JOHNSON, R. A. and MULL, G. C., 1963. A rapid and comprehensive activation analysis method using fast and slow neutrons. *World Petrol. Congr., Proc., 6th, Frankfurt*, 5: 93–102.

HALE, J. H., THOMPSON, C. J., BARKER, M. G., SMITH, H. M. and BALL, J. S., 1951. Distribution and types of sulfur compounds in straight-run naphthas. *Anal. Chem.*, 23: 287–293.

HANCOCK, K. and LOCHTE, H. L., 1939. Acidic constituent of a California straight-run distillate. *J. Am. Chem. Soc.*, 61: 2448–2452.

HARESNAPE, D., FIDLER, F. A. and LOWRY, A. R., 1949. Separation of sulfur compounds by adsorption on silica gel. *Ind. Eng. Chem.*, 41: 2691–2697.

HASTINGS, S. H. and JOHNSON, B. H., 1955. Spectrophotometric determination of aliphatic sulfides. *Anal. Chem.*, 27: 564–565.

HASTINGS, S. H., JOHNSON, B. H. and LUMPKIN, H. E., 1956. Analysis of the aromatic fraction of virgin gas oil by mass spectrometer. *Anal. Chem.*, 28: 1243–1247.

HELM, R. V., LATHAM, D. R., FERRIN, C. R. and BALL, J. S., 1960. Identification of carbazole in Wilmington petroleum through use of gas–liquid chromatography and spectroscopy. *Anal. Chem.*, 32: 1765–1767.

HODGSON, G. W., 1954. Vanadium, nickel and iron trace metals in crude oils of western Canada. *Bull. Am. Assoc. Petrol. Geologists*, 38: 2537–2554.

HODGSON, G. W. and PEAKE, E., 1961. Metal chlorin complexes in recent sediments as initial precursors to petroleum porphyrin pigments. *Nature*, 191: 766–767.

HOLOWCHAK, J., WEAR, G. E. C. and BALDESCHWIELER, E. L., 1952. Application of Ter Meulen nitrogen method to petroleum fractions. *Anal. Chem.*, 24: 1754–1757.

HOLZMANN, E. and VON PILAT, J., 1930. Higher alcohols from petroleum hydrocarbons. *Brennstoff Chem.*, 11: 409.

HOOG, H., REMAN, G. H. and BREZESINSKA-SMITHUYSEN, W. C., 1951. Desulphurization of gas oil by hydrogenation and by extraction. Some aspects of their sulphur type analysis. *World Petrol. Congr., Proc., 3rd, The Hague, 1951*, 5: 282–294.

HOPKINS, R. and SMITH, H. M., 1954. Extraction and recovery of thiols from petroleum distillates. *Anal. Chem.*, 26: 206–207.

HOWE, W. W., 1961. Improved chromatographic analysis of petroleum porphyrin aggregates and quantitative measurement by integral absorption. *Anal. Chem.*, 33: 255–260.

HOWE, W. W. and WILLIAMS, A. R., 1960. Classes of metallic complexes in petroleum. *J. Eng. Chem. Data*, 5: 106–110.

JONAK, J. and KOMERS, R., 1958. Separation of mono- and difunctional phenols by means of gas chromatography. *Z. Anal. Chem.*, 164: 69–72.

KARAULOVA, E. N., GALPERN, G. D. and SMIRNOV, B. A., 1962. Investigation of sulphides of the middle distillates of petroleum. *Tetrahedron*, 18: 1115–1129.

KARCHMER, J. H. and GUNN, E. L., 1952. Determination of trace metals in petroleum fractions. *Anal. Chem.*, 24: 1733–1741.

KARR, C., BROWN, H. M. and ESTEP, P. A., 1958. Identification and determination of low-boiling phenols in low-temperature coal tar. *Anal. Chem.*, 30: 1413–1416.

KATCHENKOV, S. M., 1949. Correlation of petroleum by the micro-elements. *Dokl. Akad. Nauk S.S.S.R.*, 1949 (67): 503–505.

KEY, C. and BAILEY, J. R., 1938. The nitrogen compounds in petroleum distillates, 11. Isolation of 2, 3-dimethyl-8-ethylquinoline from kerosene distillate of California petroleum. *J. Am. Chem. Soc.*, 60: 763–765.

KING, W. A. and BAILEY, J. R., 1930. Isolation and synthesis of 2, 3, 8-trimethyl-quinoline. *J. Am. Chem. Soc.*, 52: 1245–1246.

KJELDAHL, 1883. Neue Methode zur Bestimmung der Stickstoffs in organischen Korpern. *Z. Anal. Chem.*, 22: 366.

KNOTNERUS, J., 1957. The chemical constitution of the higher naphthenic acids. *J. Inst. Petrol.*, 48: 307–312.

LAKE, G. and BAILEY, J. R., 1933. The nitrogen compounds in petroleum distillates, 6. The occurrence of 2, 8-dimethylquinoline in the crude kerosene distillate of California petroleum. *J. Am. Chem. Soc.*, 55: 4143–4145.

LAKE, G., CUTCHAN, P. M., VAN METER, R. and NEEL, J. C., 1951. Effects of digestion temperature on Kjeldahl analyses. *Anal. Chem.*, 23: 1634–1638.

LANDA, S. and MACHACEK, V., 1933. Adamantane, a new hydrocarbon extracted from petroleum. *Collection Czech. Chem. Commun.*, 15: 1–5.

LATHAM, D. R., FERRIN, C. R. and BALL, J. S., 1962. Identification of fluorenones in Wilmington petroleum by gas chromatography and spectrometry. *Anal. Chem.*, 34: 311–313.

LIDDEL, C., 1962. The application of the Schöniger flask combustion procedure to the analysis of petroleum products. *J. Inst. Petrol.*, 48: 221–225.

LOCHTE, H. L. and LITTMANN, E. R., 1955. *Petroleum Acids and Bases.* Chem. Publ. Co. Inc., New York, N.Y., 368 pp.

LOCHTE, H. L. and MEYER, H. W. H., 1953. Condensate well corrosion. *Natl. Gasoline Assoc., Publ.*

LOCHTE, H. L., CROUCH, W. W. and THOMAS, D., 1942. The nitrogen compounds in petroleum distillates, 24. Isolation and identification of a $C_{11}H_{17}N$ bases from California petroleum. *J. Am. Chem. Soc.*, 64: 2753–2755.

LOCHTE, H. L., BARTON, A. D., ROBERTS, S. M. and BAILEY, J. R., 1950. The nitrogen compounds in petroleum distillates, 27. Isolation and identification of 2, 3-dimethyl-6-isopropyl-pyridine from California petroleum. *J. Am. Chem. Soc.*, 72: 3007–3009.

LUMPKIN, H. E. and JOHNSON, B. H., 1954. Identification of compound types in a heavy petroleum gas oil. *Anal. Chem.*, 26: 1719–1722.

MAIR, B. J. and MARTINEZ-PICO, J. L., 1962. Petroleum fractions yield 21 compounds. *Chem. Eng.*, 1962 (5): 54–56.

MARKOWNIKOW, W. und OGLOBLIN, W., 1883. Untersuchung des Kaukasischen Erdöls. *Chem. Ber.*, 16: 1873–1879.

McCOY, J. W., 1962. *The Inorganic Analysis of Petroleum.* Chem. Publ. Co. Inc., New York, N.Y., 271 pp.

MEYER, V., 1882. Über Benzole verschiedenen Ursprungs. *Chem. Ber.*, 15: 2893–2894.

MILAZZO, G., SPINELLI, F., TROYLI, M. e VERGA, C., 1958. Microanalisi di vanadio in prodotti combustibili. *Riv. Combust.*, 9: 690–698.

MILLS, G. A., 1950. Aging of cracking catalysts. *Ind. Eng. Chem.*, 42: 182–187.

MILNER, O. I., 1963. *Analysis of petroleum for Trace Elements.* Pergamon, London, 128 pp.

MILNER, O. I., GLASS, J. R., KIRCHNER, J. P. and YURICK, A. N., 1952. Determination of trace metals in crudes and other petroleum oils. *Anal. Chem.*, 24: 1728–1732.

MOLDOVSKII, B. L. and PROKONCHUCK, N., 1932. Catalytic desulfuration of benzene containing thiophene by destructive hydrogenation. *J. Appl. Chem. U.S.S.R. (English Transl.)*, 5: 619–627.

MOZINGO, R., HARRIS, S. A., WOLF, D. E., HOFFHINE, C. E., EASTON, N. R. and FOLKER, K., 1945. Hydrogenation of compounds containing divalent sulfur. *J. Am. Chem. Soc.*, 67: 2092–2095.

MUSAYEV, J. A., ROSENBERG, L. M., SANIN, P. I., NIFONTOVA, S. S., GALPERN, G. D., KUSAKOV, M. M., USHALOVA, I. B. and SUCHKOVA, A. A., 1963. Investigation of the chemical composition of middle distillates of a sulphur-bearing crude oil of the U.S.S.R. *World Petrol. Congr., Proc., 6th, N.Y., 1963*, 5: 31–40.

NAMETKIN, S. S. and SOSNINA, A. S., 1948a. Sulfides from Ishimbaevsk petroleum. *Dokl. Akad. Nauk S.S.S.R.*, 63: 391–394.

NAMETKIN, S. S. and SOSNINA, A. S., 1948b. Mercaptans from Ishimbaevsk petroleum. *Dokl. Akad. Nauk S.S.S.R.*, 63: 775–778.

NAPHTHALI, M., 1927. *Chemie, Technologie und Analyse der Naphthensäuren.* Wiss. Verlag, Stuttgart, 52 pp.

NAPHTHALI, M., 1927–1933. *Naphthensäuren und Naphthensulfosäuren.* Supplement. Wiss. Verlag, Stuttgart, 28 pp.

NELSON, W. L., THÉRY FOMBONA, G. and CORDERO, L. J., 1955. Relationship between sulfur content of crude oils and the sulfur content of conventional refinery products. *World Petrol. Congr., Proc., 4th, Rome,* 5: 13–26.

NENITZESCU, C. D., ISACESCU, D. A. and VOLRAP, T. A., 1938. Über die Isolierung einiger Säuren aus dem Erdöl. *Chem. Ber.,* 71: 2056–2062.

NEY, W. O., CROUCH, W. W., RANNEFELD, C. E. and LOCHTE, H. L., 1943. Petroleum acid, 6. Naphthenic acids from California petroleum. *J. Am. Chem. Soc.,* 65: 770–777.

O'DONNELL, G., 1951. Separating ashphalts into their chemical constituents. *Anal. Chem.,* 23: 894–898.

PARDEE, W. A. and WEINRICH, W., 1944. Physical properties of alkylated phenols. *Ind. Eng. Chem.,* 37: 595–603.

PERRIN, T. S. and BAILEY, J. R., 1933. Cumulative extraction of kero-bases. The isolation of 2, 4, 8-trimethylquinoline among the kero-bases. *J. Am. Chem. Soc.,* 55: 4136–4140.

POLLY, O. L., BYRUS, A. C. and BRADLEY, W. E., 1942. Isolation of sulfur compounds from California straight-run gasoline. *Ind. Eng. Chem.,* 34: 755–758.

PRINZLER, H. und HÄNEL, R., 1961. Schwefelhaltige Inhaltsstoffe des Benzins aus Tuimasy Erdöl (U.S.S.R.). *Chem. Tech. (Berlin),* 13: 439–442.

PYRAH, A. F., ROBERTSON, R. S. and WISEMAN, J., 1961. The rapid determination of sulfur in petroleum fractions by X-ray absorption of Tritium Bremsstrahlung. *Anal. Chem.,* 33: 1355–1360.

QUEBEDEAUX, W. A., WASH, G., NEY, W. O., CROUCH, W. W. and LOCHTE, H. L., 1943. Petroleum acid, 5. Aliphatic acids from California petroleum. *J. Am. Chem. Soc.,* 65: 767–770.

REITSEMA, R. H. and ALLPHIN, N. L., 1961. Determination of nitrogen with gas chromatography. *Anal. Chem.,* 33: 355–359.

RICHTER, F. P., CAESAR, P. D., MEISEL, S. L. and OFFENHAUER, R. D., 1952. Distribution of nitrogen in petroleum according to basicity. *Ind. Eng. Chem.,* 44: 2601–2605.

RICHTER, F. P., WILLIAMS, A. L. and MEISEL, S. L., 1956. The isolation of thionaphthene (benzo-(b)thionaphthene) from a crude petroleum. *J. Am. Chem. Soc.,* 78: 2166–2167.

RYCE, S. A. and BRYCE, W. A., 1957. Analysis of volatile organic sulfur compounds by gas partition chromatography. *Anal. Chem.,* 29: 925–928.

SANDELL, E. B., 1950. *Colorimetric Determination of Traces of Metals,* 2nd ed. Interscience, New York, N.Y., 363 pp.

SARACENO, A. J., FANALE, D. T. and COGGESHALL, N. D., 1961. An electron paramagnetic resonance investigation of vanadium in petroleum oils. *Anal. Chem.,* 33: 500–505.

SAUER, R. W., MELPOLDER, F. W. and BROWN, R. A., 1952. Nitrogen compounds in domestic heating oil distillates. *Ind. Eng. Chem.,* 44: 2606–2609.

SCHENCK, L. M. and BAILEY, J. R., 1939. The nitrogen compounds in petroleum distillates, 17. The use of multiple acid extraction in isolation of 2, 3, 4-trimethyl-8-*n*-propylquinoline. *J. Am. Chem. Soc.,* 61: 2613–2615.

SCHENCK, L. M. and BAILEY, J. R., 1940. The nitrogen compounds in petroleum distillates, 18. Isolation, ozonization and synthesis of a 2, 4-dimethyl-8-*s*-butylquinoline. *J. Am. Chem. Soc.,* 62: 1967–1969.

SCHENCK, L. M. and BAILEY, J. R., 1941a. The nitrogen compounds in petroleum distillates, 21. Isolation and synthesis of a 2, 3, 4-trimethyl-8-*i*-propylquinoline. *J. Am. Chem. Soc.,* 63: 1364–1365.

SCHENCK, L. M. and BAILEY, J. R., 1941b. The nitrogen compounds in petroleum distillates, 22. Isolation and synthesis of 2, 3-dimethyl-4-ethyl-8-*n*-propylquinoline. *J. Am. Chem. Soc.,* 63: 1365–1367.

SCHENCK, L. M. and BAILEY, J. R., 1941c. The nitrogen compounds in petroleum distillates, 23. Isolation of 2, 3-dimethylbenzo(h)quinoline and 2, 4-dimethylbenzo(h)quinoline from California petroleum. *J. Am. Chem. Soc.,* 63: 2331–2333.

SCHMITZ, P. M. E., 1938. Naphthenic acids. *Bull. Assoc. Franç. Techniciens Pétrole,* 46: 93–148.

SCHÜTZE, M., 1939. Direct oxygen determination in metal oxides and organic substances. *Naturwissenschaften*, 27: 822.

SHIPP, V. L., 1936. The naphthenic acid industry. *Oil Gas J.*, 19: 56–60.

SHIVE, W., HORECZY, J., WASH, G. and LOCHTE, H. L., 1942a. Trans 2, 2, 6-trimethyl-cyclohexanecarboxylic acid: a second solid naphthenic acid from California petroleum. *J. Am. Chem. Soc.*, 64: 385–391.

SHIVE, W., ROBERTS, S. M., MAHAN, R. I. and BAILEY, J. R., 1942b. The nitrogen compounds in petroleum distillates, 23. The structure of a $C_{16}H_{25}N$ bases from California petroleum. *J. Am. Chem. Soc.*, 64: 909–912.

SHOTT, J. E., GARLAND, T. J. and CLARK, R. O., 1961. Determination of traces of nickel and vanadium in petroleum distillates. *Anal. Chem.*, 33: 506–510.

SKINNER, D. A., 1952. Chemical state of vanadium in Santa Maria Valley crude oil. *Ind. Eng. Chem.*, 44: 1159–1165.

SMITH, H. M., DUNNING, H. N., RALL, H. T. e BALL, J. S., 1961. Richerche delle chiavi per chiarire il mistero del petrolio. Composti dello zolfo. *Riv. Combust.*, 15: 282–296.

SNYDER, L. R. and BUELL, B. E., 1963. Characterization and routine determination of non-basic nitrogen types in cracked gas oils. *Am. Chem. Soc., Div. Petrol. Chem., Preprints*, 8: 6–95.

STORY, L. G. and SNOW, R. D., 1928. Phenols in petroleum distillates. *Ind. Eng. Chem.*, 20: 359–364.

SUGIHARA, J. M. and BEAN, R. M., 1962. Direct determination of metallo-porphyrins in Boscan crude oil. *J. Chem. Eng. Data*, 7: 269–271.

TANAKA, Y. and KOBAYASHI, R., 1928. Phenols from natural petroleum. *J. Fac. Eng., Univ. Tokyo*, 17: 127–133.

TANAKA, Y. and KUWATA, T., 1928. Occurrence of higher fatty acids in natural petroleum and origin of petroleum. *J. Fac. Eng., Univ. Tokyo*, 17: 293–303.

TER MEULEN, H., 1924. The determination of oxygen in organic compounds. *Rev. Trav. Chim.*, 43: 899–904.

THIERRY, E. H., 1925. Sulfur compounds removed from Persian petroleum by means of sulfuric acid. *J. Chem. Soc.*, 127: 2756–2759.

THOMPSON, C. J., COLEMAN, H. J., RALL, H. T. and SMITH, H. M., 1955. Separation of sulfur compounds from petroleum. *Anal. Chem.*, 27: 175–185.

THOMPSON, C. J., COLEMAN, H. J., MIKKELSEN, L., DON YEE, WARD, C. C. and RALL, H. T., 1956. Identification of thiophene and 2-methylthiophene in virgin petroleum. *Anal. Chem.*, 28: 1384–1387.

THOMPSON, C. J., COLEMAN, H. S., WARD, C. C. and RALL, H. T., 1959. Identification of 3-methylthiophene in Wilmington, California, crude oil. *J. Eng. Chem. Data*, 4: 347–348.

THOMPSON, W. C. and BAILEY, J. R., 1931. The nitrogen compounds in petroleum distillates, 3. The structure of a hydroaromatic base of the formula $C_{16}H_{25}N$. *J. Am. Chem. Soc.*, 53: 1002–1011.

TREIBS, A., 1934. Chlorophyll und Häminderivate in bituminosen Gesteinen, Erdölen, Erdwachsen und Asphalten. *Ann. Chem.*, 510: 42.

UNTERZAUCHER, J., 1940. Die mikroanalytische Bestimmung des Säuerstoff. *Chem. Ber.*, 73: 391–404.

VON BRAUN, J., MANNES, L. und REUTER, M., 1933. Untersuchungen über die Bestandteile des Erdöls, 2. Mitteil: Darstellung der ersten einheitlichen Naphthensäure. *Chem. Ber.*, 66: 1499–1501.

WOODLE, R. A. and CHANDLER, W. B., 1952. Mechanism of occurrence of metals in petroleum distillates. *Ind. Eng. Chem.*, 44: 2591–2596.

WOOLFOLK, E. O., ORCHIN, M. and DULL, M. F., 1950. Phenols in oil obtained from hydrogenation of coal. *Ind. Eng. Chem.*, 44: 552–556.

WRIGHTSON, F. M., 1949. Determination of traces of iron, nickel and vanadium in petroleum oils. *Anal. Chem.*, 21: 1543–1545.

YUR'EV, YU. K. and BUGORKOVA, A. A., 1949. Catalytic transformation of tetrahydrofuran, pyrroline and thiophene. *J. Gen. Chem. (U.S.S.R.)*, 19: 720–723.

YUR'EV, YU. K., MINACHEV, KH. M. and SAMURSKAYA, K. A., 1939. Catalytic reaction of heterocyclic compounds, 14. Mechanism of transformation of oxygen-containing five-membered heterocyclic rings to nitrogen- and sulfur-containing heterocycles. *J. Gen. Chem. (U.S.S.R.)*, 9: 1710–1716.

Chapter 5

GEOCHEMISTRY OF PORPHYRINS[1]

G. W. HODGSON, B. L. BAKER AND E. PEAKE

Research Council of Alberta, Edmonton, Alta. (Canada)

INTRODUCTION

Among the multitude of compounds occurring in petroleum there are a few which are unique. Of these, the porphyrin compounds are distinctive, offering some hope of defining more clearly the genesis of petroleum. Although there are many possible structures for porphyrins, only a limited number occur in petroleum. However, these few may have had both an active and a passive role to play in the development of crude oil from its source biogenic material. The evidence is strong that the petroleum porphyrin pigments came from precursor pigments present in the source material. The passive role played by the pigments was that in which the precursor molecules underwent a series of systematic changes until they became the stable and easily recognizable trace compounds of crude oil. In an active sense, the developing pigments may have had a surfactant role to play during the mobilization, migration and accumulation of the crude oil hydrocarbons.

The purpose of this chapter is to review the current knowledge of petroleum porphyrins in terms of their structure, properties, origin and natural occurrence in relation to the geochemistry of petroleum. The structure and properties of porphyrins and metal porphyrin complexes depend on the basic porphyrin nucleus and groups in peripheral positions of this nucleus, as recently and comprehensively reviewed by FALK (1964). The transformation of porphyrin precursors to porphyrins, as well as the occurrence of these compounds in possible petroleum source materials and in petroleum, have considerable geochemical significance in the history of the origin and accumulation of petroleum.

PHYSICAL AND CHEMICAL PROPERTIES OF PORPHYRINS AND METAL PORPHYRIN COMPLEXES

Free porphyrins and related compounds

Basic structure

Pyrrole, the chief constituent of the porphyrin molecule, is a cyclic structure

---

[1] Contribution No. 339, Research Council of Alberta.

consisting of four carbon atoms and a nitrogen atom linked together in an aromatic type of bonding described by alternating single and double bonds as shown
in Fig.1. The pyrrole structure is marked by high stability due to its aromatic
character, and therefore resembles molecules such as benzene and pyridine illustrated in Fig.2. As a result of aromatization arising from the conjugated bond system,
pyrrole is not strongly basic even though it is a seondary amine. Pyrrole, like
other heterocyclic molecules, differs from homocyclic aromatic compounds in
that it is quite reactive at the position alpha to the nitrogen atom and tends to form
dimers, trimers and higher condensation products in which the fundamental
pyrrole structure is preserved to a marked degree.

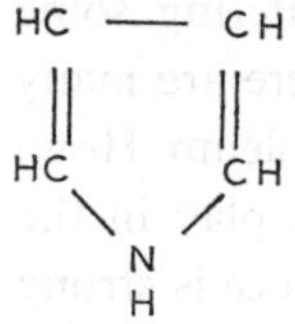

Fig.1. Structure of pyrrole.

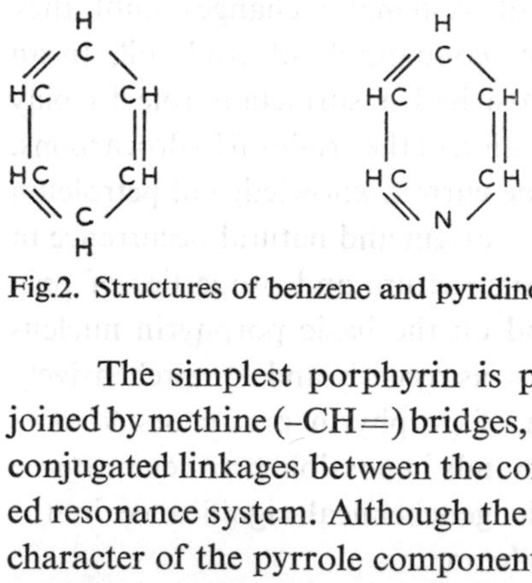

Fig.2. Structures of benzene and pyridine, respectively.

The simplest porphyrin is porphin. It consists of four pyrrole molecules
joined by methine (–CH=) bridges, as shown in Fig.3. The methine bridges establish
conjugated linkages between the component pyrrole nuclei forming a more extended resonance system. Although the resulting structure retains much of the inherent
character of the pyrrole components, the larger conjugated system gives increased
aromatic character to the porphin molecule. The reactivity of the pyrrole nuclei
in porphin is greatly reduced, partially because of the increased aromatic character
but primarily because the reactive alpha positions are occupied.

Two closely related classes of tetrapyrrole compounds are the dihydroporphyrins and the tetrahydroporphyrins. The dihydroporphyrins, commonly
known as chlorins, include two "extra" hydrogen atoms on one of the pyrrole
rings, saturating one of the double bonds thus impairing the resonance stability
of the porphyrin structure by interfering with the conjugated bond system. The
tetrahydroporphyrins carry four "extra" hydrogen atoms. As would be expected,
the resonance stability is further impaired.

The bond distances and bond angles of porphyrins were believed to be

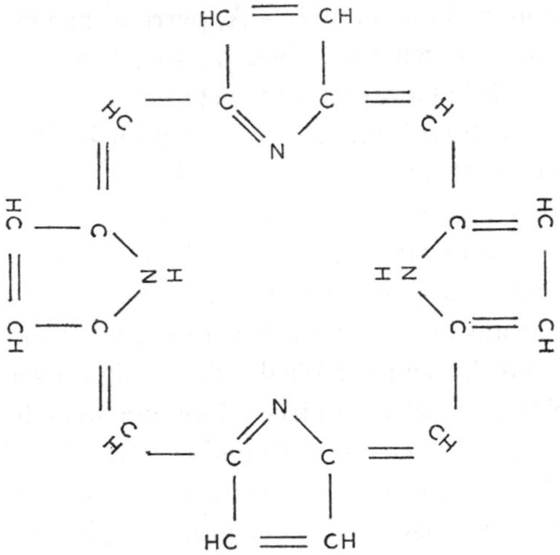

HC ═══ CH

Fig.3. Structure of porphin.

similar to those of phthalocyanine, the dimensions of which have been studied by ROBERTSON (1936), and ROBERTSON and WOODWARD (1937) using X-ray diffraction. As illustrated in Fig.4, phthalocyanine includes the fundamental porphyrin assemblage of conjugated single and double bonds in a tetrapyrrole arrangement. In addition, a benzene ring is fused to the base of each pyrrole component. The phthalocyanine molecule is essentially planar with the following bond distances

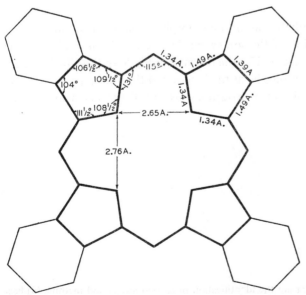

Fig.4. Structure of phthalocyanine (ROBERTSON and WOODWARD, 1937).

as reported by Robertson: methine carbon–carbon about 1.34 Å, pyrrole carbon–carbon 1.49 Å and 1.39 Å, and the carbon–nitrogen bond about 1.34 Å. The bond angles within the pyrrole components of phthalocyanine vary between 104° and 111.5°. These angles are much the same as those found for pyrrole itself by BAK et al. (1956). The nitrogen separation in phthalocyanine appeared to be 2.7 Å for adjacent pyrrole rings and about 3.8 Å for opposite pyrrole rings.

CORWIN et al. (1962) used an analog computer to examine the bond distances and angles of porphin and related structures, with some attention being given to the position of the two imine hydrogen atoms in the central part of the molecule. Since the N–H bond distance is 1.02 Å and the Van der Waal radius of hydrogen is 1.20 Å some deformation of the molecule must take place. Consequently, the hydrogens are forced slightly out of the plane of the molecule and the N–N bond distances are altered in agreement with Robertson's assignment of N–N bond lengths of 2.65 and 2.76 Å to different pairs of adjacent nitrogen atoms in phthalocyanine. Evidently, the hydrogen atoms are accommodated on opposite pairs of nitrogen atoms, rather than on adjacent pairs according to the analog model. Nevertheless, the possibility of tautomerism, the simultaneous existence of two or more forms of a compound, remains to be considered. DOROUGH and SHEN (1950) found spectroscopic evidence for such tautomeric structures in which one showed hydrogen atoms on adjacent nitrogens, and the other on opposite.

CORWIN et al. (1962) found that a minor distortion of the porphyrin structure occurred when their analog model was modified to represent a dihydroporphyrin (i.e., a chlorin) pigment. Appropriate changes in bond character and angles of the peripheral carbon bonds in the model resulted in an overall shrinking of the molecule.

Assuming that the phthalocyanine and porphin analog structures give a reasonable physical description of the somewhat flexible porphyrin molecule, the porphin structure may be represented by the drawing in Fig.5. In this illustration it is understood that the carbon atoms lie at the junction of the lines representing the bonds, and that there are sufficient hydrogen atoms to satisfy the carbon atoms,

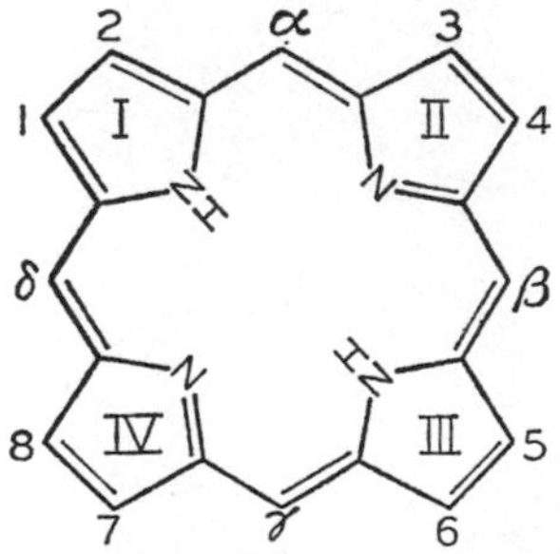

Fig.5. Structure of porphin illustrating the identification of carbon atoms and methine bridges for nomenclature of porphyrins.

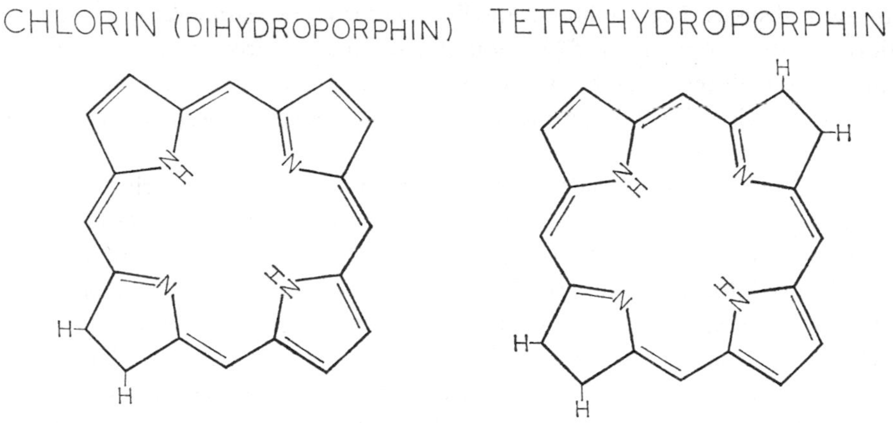

CHLORIN (DIHYDROPORPHIN)   TETRAHYDROPORPHIN

Fig.6. Structures of chlorin and tetrahydroporphin.

i.e., one at each peripheral position in porphin. The corresponding chlorin and tetrahydroporphyrin structures are illustrated in Fig.6. The placing of the second pair of "extra" hydrogen atoms on the opposite pyrrole is in accordance with the findings of BARNARD and JACKMAN (1956).

Although the foregoing figures suggest that the porphyrin and chlorin molecular structures are clearly defined insofar as their single and double bond orientations are concerned, this is not the case. Fig.7 illustrates three types of resonant structures in which there are two forms of A, eight of B and two of C resulting from the many possibilities of assigning the locations of single and double bonds (DOROUGH and SHEN, 1950). The heavy lines in the diagram indicate the path of the single–double bond conjugated system. DOROUGH and SHEN (1950) discussed these forms and noted that the assignment of specific contributions of each type is difficult. If one assumes that exchange integrals between wave functions representative of resonance forms for each type are about the same, simplified quantum mechanical treatment indicates that types A and B probably contribute equal amounts of energy to the ground state whereas type C contributes only

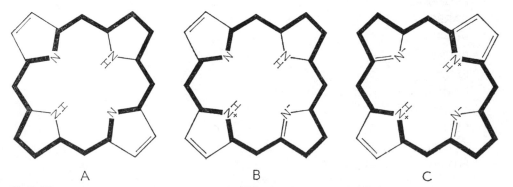

A   B   C

Fig.7. Three types of resonating structures of porphyrins (DOROUGH and SHEN, 1950).

to the excited states. The amphoteric qualities of porphyrins support these findings, with observation of the ready formation of sodium salts through the replacement of the imine hydrogens (> N–H) with sodium hydroxide, and the formation of hydrochloric acid salts through the addition of two extra protons to the centre of the porphyrin ring.

Extensive resonance lends remarkable stability to the porphyrin molecule. DOROUGH and SHEN (1950) reported that the porphin-free base is stabilized by resonance to the extent of 250 kcal./mole below the classical structure given in Fig.3. Such stabilization is important in considering the existence of such pigments in the petroleum environment. Direct measurements of the stability of porphyrin pigments in petroleum environments have been made; however, these have dealt with further modifications of the porphyrin molecule and will be considered later.

Many structural modifications of the molecules within the three major classes—porphyrins, chlorins, and tetrahydroporphyrins—can be envisaged. Such modifications include the substitution of various functional groups for the hydrogen atoms on the methine bridge carbons as well as those on the carbon atoms of the pyrrole molecules. The functional groups could be alkyl radicals such as methyl, ethyl, propyl, etc.; the corresponding carboxylic acids; unsaturated groups such as vinyl groups; phenyl or benzyl groups; and oxygenated groups such as aldehydes and ketones. These functional groups are illustrated in Fig.8. Mass-spectral measurements have become possible for elucidating such structures (THOMAS and BLUMER, 1964).

A further kind of substitution is possible in which the methine bridge carbon is linked by a two-carbon chain to the base of a pyrrole component of the porphyrin molecule resulting in the formation of a fifth ring in the molecule. CORWIN et al.

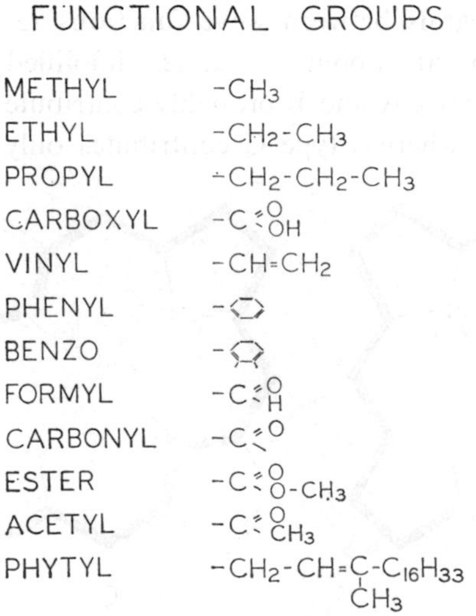

FUNCTIONAL GROUPS

METHYL $\quad$ $-CH_3$

ETHYL $\quad$ $-CH_2-CH_3$

PROPYL $\quad$ $-CH_2-CH_2-CH_3$

CARBOXYL $\quad$ $-C{\lessgtr}^O_{OH}$

VINYL $\quad$ $-CH=CH_2$

PHENYL $\quad$ $-\bigcirc$

BENZO $\quad$ $-\bigcirc$

FORMYL $\quad$ $-C{\lessgtr}^O_H$

CARBONYL $\quad$ $-C{\lessgtr}^O$

ESTER $\quad$ $-C{\lessgtr}^O_{O-CH_3}$

ACETYL $\quad$ $-C{\lessgtr}^O_{CH_3}$

PHYTYL $\quad$ $-CH_2-CH=C-C_{16}H_{33}$
$\qquad\qquad\qquad CH_3$

Fig.8. Functional groups for peripheral substitution on the porphin molecule.

(1962) in analysing the internal stresses in such a structure concluded that the basic porphyrin framework was warped.

It has now been established that the porphyrin structure is a tetrapyrrole structure in which the pyrrole rings are joined together by methine groups. Substitution is possible on the peripheral positions of the pyrrole components, as well as on the methine bridges. Location of peripheral substituents for nomenclature of porphyrins is aided by the numbering of carbon atoms and methine bridges as illustrated in Fig.5.

The most significant properties of porphyrins and related compounds in a discussion of petroleum geochemistry are absorption spectra, ionization behavior, acid separation numbers and chromatographic behavior.

Spectra

Porphyrins, chlorins and tetrahydroporphyrins are highly conjugated tetrapyrrole compounds and therefore have a marked capacity for energy absorption in the visible range of the spectrum. Light absorption of specific compounds is a very sensitive means by which such compounds may be identified and characterized. STERN and associates (STERN and DEZELIC, 1936, 1937a, b; STERN and MOLVIG, 1935, 1936a, b, 1937; STERN and WENDERLEIN, 1934, 1935, 1936a, b, c; STERN et al., 1936) extensively investigated the effect of peripheral substitution on the light absorption of porphyrins. RABINOWITCH (1944) examined visible spectra of porphyrins and related compounds and correlated their spectra with specific energy levels within the molecules. The infrared spectra has been studied by FALK and WILLIS (1951).

The Soret band of a porphyrin is the most intense band. Studies by RIMINGTON (1960) clearly show that the Soret band of porphin is more intense than that of other porphyrins with one or more of the peripheral positions substituted. The molecular extinction coefficient for the porphin Soret band in benzene is $2.64 \cdot 10^5$ l/mole/cm, whereas those for various substituted porphyrins fall in the range of 1.60–$2.17 \cdot 10^5$ l/mole/cm. In acid solutions, the porphyrins show enhanced molecular extinction coefficients with increases as great as 2.7 times. In reporting these results, RIMINGTON (1960) attributed the increased intensity of absorption to the symmetry introduced to the molecule by the protonation of the pyrrolic nitrogen atoms.

The spectrum of a typical porphyrin consists of an intense band at about 400 mμ (the Soret band) and four weaker bands at longer wavelengths. The assignment of these bands to definite electronic transitions is inherently difficult and is made more difficult by the possible presence of tautomeric forms (SIMPSON, 1949). It is thought, however, that the Soret band is due to one electronic transition which is similar for both tautomers, and that the four bands in the visible arise in pairs, two from each tautomer, from a second electronic transition which is two-fold degenerate (WILLIAMS, 1956). All four long wavelength bands move together on

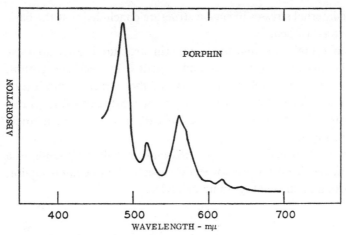

Fig.9. Spectrum of porphin. (After ROTHEMUND, 1936.)

substitution of peripheral positions of the pyrrole rings confirming the fact that they belong to the same electronic transitions, but marked differences occur in the intensities of these bands. Bands I and III (numbering from the longest wavelength positions) vary considerably by substituents, whereas II and IV are changed very little from compound to compound. The spectrum of a basic porphyrin is shown in Fig.9. This is a typical "phyllo" spectrum in which band IV is dominant. The relatively uniform spacing of the four bands, in terms of wave numbers rather than wavelength, led RABINOWITCH (1944) to conclude that they are vibrational bands corresponding to a common electronic transition and the Soret band corresponds to a different electronic excitation state. The assignment of such energy levels accordingly led to the term system for porphin as illustrated in Fig.10.

Interference in the resonance stability of a porphyrin results in a marked

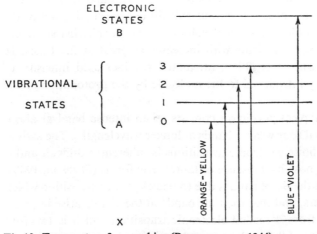

Fig.10. Term system for porphins (RABINOWITCH, 1944).

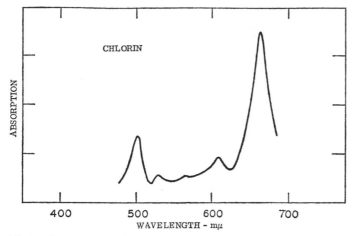

Fig.11. Spectrum of chlorin. (After RABINOWITCH, 1944.)

change in the character of the absorption spectrum. The spectrum of chlorin, a dihydroporphyrin, indicates such interference (Fig.11). The destruction of a double bond by the addition of two hydrogen atoms, as in chlorin, results in the appearance of a prominent band at about 660 mμ and a weakening and displacement toward the blue of other bands in the 500 to 700 mμ range. The position and intensity of the new band indicate that it is due to a new electronic transition. The new low-excited term was added to the term system of porphin for the term system of chlorins (RABINOWITCH, 1944) as shown in Fig.12.

A further addition to the porphin spectrum and the corresponding term system is evident in bacteriopheophytin, a tetrahydroporphyrin. The addition of two more hydrogen atoms to the porphin system, resulting in the destruction of another pyrrole double bond, causes a further weakening and displacement to

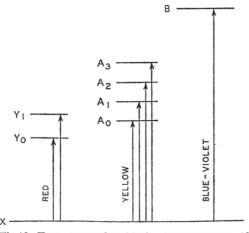

Fig.12. Term system for chlorins (RABINOWITCH, 1944).

the blue of the bands in the 500–700 mμ range. A new prominent electronic band appears near 800 mμ over-shadowing the other non-Soret bands as shown by the spectrum of bacteriopheophytin in Fig.13. The corresponding term system would therefore include a further Z term and an upward shift of the levels pertaining to the systems of A and Y as explained by RABINOWITCH (1944).

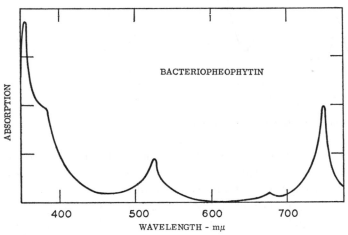

Fig.13. Spectrum of bacteriopheophytin. (After WIEGL, 1953.)

Molecular orbital investigations of the structure and spectra of porphyrins and dihydroporphyrins have been carried out by subsequent authors. MATLOW (1955) concluded that the ground state energy of the two isomers—one with the imine hydrogens on adjacent pyrrole rings and the other with the imine hydrogens on opposite nitrogens—were substantially identical. In the case of the dihydroporphyrins, the isomer having hydrogens on adjacent nitrogens was favored over the other isomers by more than 1 kcal./mole. With respect to the transition energies of porphin, Matlow came to the conclusion that the absorption bands may not be due to vibrational fine structure of a single electronic transition as proposed by RABINOWITCH (1944) but are the result of the superimposition of the electronic spectra of the two isomers, i.e., the adjacent and opposite locations for the imine hydrogens. On the other hand MATLOW (1955) agreed with Rabinowitch that the absorption bands for dihydroporphyrins were probably vibrational fine structure.

Generally, substituent groups have only minor perturbing effects on the spectra of the basic porphin compounds since they do not directly interfere with the general resonance configurations of the molecule. A discussion of classical types of spectra will include these effects.

The classical spectra already discussed are those of two types: the "phyllo" type (e.g., porphin) and the "chlorin" type (e.g., chlorin). Two other major spectral types, the "etio" and the "rhodo" types, are also observed. These differ sharply from the chlorin type but only slightly from the phyllo type, with minor changes in band intensity for the four bands in the 500 to 700 mμ range. The etio type has four bands increasing steadily in intensity from the red end of the visible spectrum to the blue, while in the rhodo type spectra the third band from the red end is predominant. Examples of these latter two spectral types are shown in Fig.14, the type compounds being etioporphyrin II and rhodoporphyrin XXI, respectively, the structures of which are shown in Fig.15. The alteration of the porphin structure by the addition of alkyl groups, as in etioporphyrin II, results in only a slight change in the spectrum with band III becoming slightly more intense than band II, whereas substitution of a carbonyl group on carbon-5 in rhodoporphyrin XXI causes an appreciable interference in the porphin structure

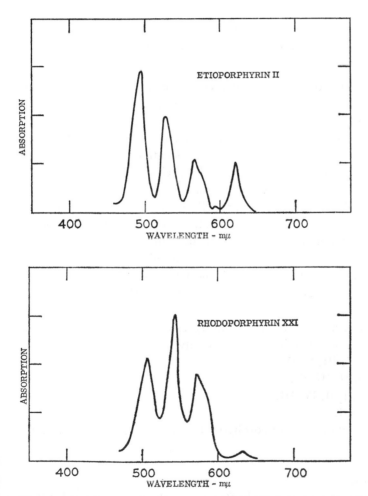

Fig.14. Etio and rhodo type spectra—etioporphyrin II and rhodoporphyrin XXI (FISCHER and ORTH, 1937).

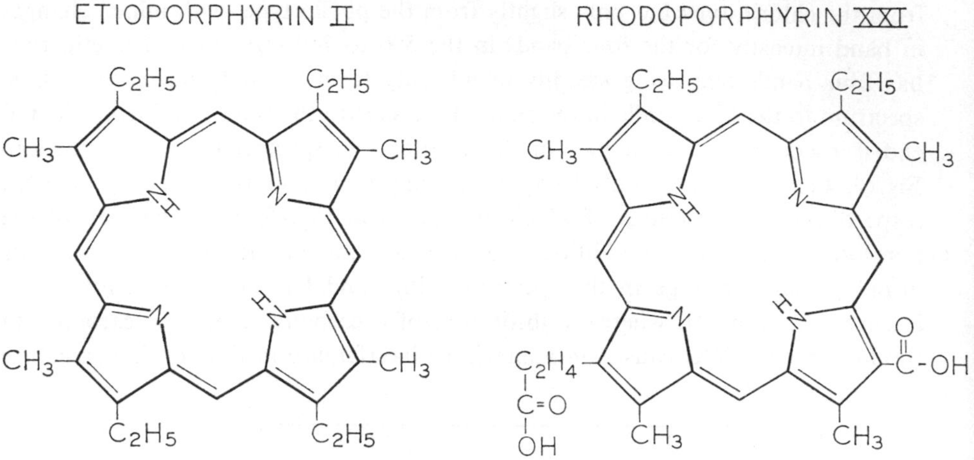

ETIOPORPHYRIN II   RHODOPORPHYRIN XXI

Fig.15. Structures of etioporphyrin II and rhodoporphyrin XXI (FISCHER and ORTH, 1937).

such that the third band from the red end becomes predominant. Undoubtedly the carbonyl group in this position influences the conjugated bond system whereas the carbonyl group of the propionic acid side chain is separated from the conjugated system, thereby having no influence on that system. The presence of substituent groups in the porphin structure tends to shift the location of the 500–700 mμ absorption bands toward the red end (STERN and associates, 1934–1937; RABINOWITCH, 1944; and ELLINGSON and CORWIN, 1946).

The spectra of chlorins differ greatly from those of porphyrins with a strong peak at about 660 mμ and wide variations in relative peak intensities. The 400 mμ peak is only moderately more intense than the major non-Soret peak, whereas in porphyrins it is commonly ten times as intense. The tetrahydroporphyrins have a greater difference in absorption spectra with the major non-Soret band shifted further toward the red, near 750 mμ and an intensity greater than that of the Soret band.

In summary there are four basic spectral types of porphyrins with relative peak height indicated in order of increasing intensity:

(a) Phyllo type: I, III, II, IV.
(b) Etio type: I, II, III, IV.
(c) Rhodo type: I, II, IV, III.
(d) Chlorin type: I.

The next important property of porphyrins to be considered is their ionization behavior.

Ionization behavior

Of the four nitrogen centres in the porphyrin nucleus, the two having substituent hydrogens are acidic in character and the other two are basic. This arrangement suggests that the molecule should be amphoteric, and indeed four species have been observed as given in Fig.16 (NEUBERGER and SCOTT, 1952). PHILLIPS (1960) assigned pK designations to the porphyrins in order of decreasing positive values. Thus pK_1 and pK_2 refer to the acidic equilibria involved in the dissociation of the two hydrogen ions and pK_3 and pK_4 refer to the two basic equilibria associated with the addition of two hydrogen ions. Accordingly, the pK values are defined by:

$$pK_1 = pH - \log_{10}(P^{2-})/(PH^-)$$
$$pK_2 = pH - \log_{10}(PH^-)/(PH_2)$$
$$pK_3 = pH - \log_{10}(PH_2)/(PH_3^+)$$
$$pK_4 = pH - \log_{10}(PH_3^+)/(PH_4^{2+})$$

Very little clarification has been obtained on establishment of the pK_1 and pK_2 acid strength values. McEwan (1946) measured the sum of these values and observed a total of about 32 for etioporphyrin I and 28–29 for its N-methyl derivative. In each case the pK_1 value was greater than the corresponding pK_2 value. These values indicate that the acidic groups are very weak. PHILLIPS (1960) also concluded that

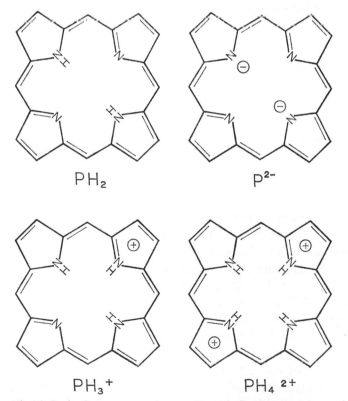

Fig.16. Ionization structures for porphin (NEUBERGER and SCOTT, 1952).

the basic groups are relatively weak, with pK_3 values falling in the range $+2$ to $+7$, and pK_4 values in the range 0 to $+4$. All values pertained to aqueous systems.

Almost all the porphyrins for which ionization data have been reported have one or more carboxyl groups. The electrostatic field effect due to the ionization of the acid side chain greatly influences the basicity of the porphyrin nucleus within the ranges reported. An intrinsic pK_3 value of $+7$ has been suggested by NEUBERGER and SCOTT (1952) but Phillips suggests a lower value, about $+5$. Little difference in basicity is noted between chlorins and porphyrins in aqueous systems but the isocyclic ring present in chlorophyll compounds is markedly base-weakening. Phillips reports that the electronegative substituents on the periphery of the porphyrin nucleus may result in a marked depression of the basicity, as indicated by the pK_3 data given in Table I.

TABLE I

THE BASICITY OF A SERIES OF PORPHYRINS IN 2.5% SODIUM DODECYL SULPHATE AT 20°C

(After PHILLIPS, 1960)

Porphyrin	Substituent in position		pK_3
	2	4	(±0.05)
Mesoporphyrin	CH_2CH_3	CH_2CH_3	5.94
Deuteroporphyrin	H	H	5.63
Coproporphyrin	$CH_2CH_2COOCH_3$	$CH_2CH_2COOCH_3$	5.58
Protoporphyrin	$CH=CH_2$	$CH=CH_2$	4.89
4-Formyl deuteroporphyrin	H	CHO	3.90
2,4-Diacetyl deuteroporphyrin	$COCH_3$	$COCH_3$	3.50
2,4-Diformyl deuteroporphyrin	CHO	CHO	2.90

Acid numbers

Acid numbers, a measure of the intrinsic acidity and basicity of porphyrins, have been widely used in the literature, particularly in older literature, to describe porphyrins and chlorins and to afford a means of separating such compounds from complex mixtures. The acid number is defined as the strength expressed as a percentage, of aqueous hydrochloric acid required to extract two-thirds of the content of a specific porphyrin from an equal volume of ether. Another measure of the basicity of a porphyrin pigment is the distribution number, defined as the percentage of porphyrin extracted by 100 ml of hydrochloric acid of stated concentration from one litre of ether solution containing three milligrams of porphyrin. Both numbers are functions of two different factors: (1) the basicity of the porphyrins and (2) the solubility partition of the pigment between the two solvents. From a listing of acid numbers, as in Table II, it is apparent that mixtures of

TABLE II

HYDROCHLORIC ACID NUMBERS OF SOME PORPHYRINS

(After LEMBERG and LEGGE, 1949)

Porphyrin	Hydrochloric acid number	
	free porphyrin	methyl ester
Porphin	1.7*	—
	3.3**	—
Isoporphin	0.5	—
Protoporphyrin	2–3	5.5
Mesoporphyrin	0.5	2.5
Deuteroporphyrin	0.3 to 0.4	2.0
Hematoporphyrin	0.1	—
Coproporphyrin	0.08	1.5
Uroporphyrin	—	ca. 7

* After FISCHER and ORTH (1937).
** After ROTHEMUND (1936).

porphyrins may be at least partially resolved on the basis of acid numbers. A refinement of simple acid number separation is the use of counter-current distribution between organic solvents and dilute acid solutions (FALK et al., 1956). A further development is the use of phosphoric acid in place of hydrochloric acid. Phosphoric acid gives a distribution which is many times more sensitive than the hydrochloric acid method (KLIEWE, 1948). Compounds which differ only slightly in acid number are very difficult to separate and recourse must be made to more sophisticated methods.

Chromatography

Chromatography for the separation of porphyrins, although known for many years, is now being extensively used for further clarification of many isomers of individual porphyrins and chlorins, as well as for separation into pure components of mixtures previously unresolvable.

The first application of chromatography more than half a century ago was in the field of chlorin pigments (TSWETT, 1906). Many reviews of the science of chromatography have been made since that time and the behavior of porphyrins and related compounds has recently been reviewed by FALK (1961). Two general forms of chromatography, paper sheet and column, have been widely used to separate porphyrins. Paper chromatography is used primarily for identification purposes and is of particular use when working with trace amounts–amounts in the range of 0.005–0.5 μg of sample. Column chromatography is used extensively for preparative purposes in which relatively large amounts of pigments are treated.

Paper chromatographs are developed with a variety of solvent systems. Lutidine-water mixtures have been used extensively, particularly with carboxylated porphyrins. The reason for this is apparent in Fig.17 in which an almost linear relationship exists between the R_F value—a measure of ease of movement of the pigment on paper—and the number of carboxyl groups on a porphyrin. Milder developing solvents are used when dealing with pigments containing few carboxyl groups, as illustrated by the work of DUNNING and CARLTON (1956) in which lutidine–petroleum ether and lutidine–hexane mixtures were used. A further variation of the paper chromatographic approach is that used by BLUMER (1956) who employed iso-octane and carbon tetrachloride for developing a mixture of petroleum porphyrins. Blumer observed that carboxylated porphyrins did not move from the starting point until they were esterified, e.g., with diazomethane. Separation of the various carboxylated porphyrins was achieved using the same solvent mixture in a direction normal to the first movement after esterification.

In column chromatography many different solid adsorbents and many variations of eluents have been utilized (FALK, 1961). The principal adsorbents used are alumina, magnesia, magnesium carbonate, calcium carbonate, silica gel, powdered sugar and cellulose fiber. The eluents consist of the majority of the common organic solvents either as pure solvents or as mixtures of two or more solvents. In many cases of column chromatography the separation depends to a considerable extent on partition chromatography, in which the solid adsorbent has been wetted with water prior to being used.

Gas chromatography has had limited application. Pyrolitic gas chromatography has been used by MORLEY et al. (1959) and LEVY et al. (1964); high-pressure gas chromatography, by KLESPER et al. (1962). Thin-layer chromatography combines some of the qualities of both paper and column chromatography. In paper chromatography small amounts of material are required but separations

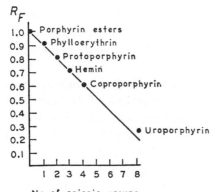

Fig.17. Chromatographic relationship between R_p value and the number of carboxyl groups on a porphyrin (FALK, 1961).

must be based only on the basic adsorptive properties of paper whereas thin-layer chromatography employs many different adsorbents as in column methods, yet retains the advantage of requiring only small amounts of material. This concept provides an almost limitless field for further expansion of detection limits of compounds previously inaccessible by more conventional methods.

In its application to porphyrinic pigments very little information has yet been published as a standard method of analysis. In a recent review of thin-layer chromatography RANDERATH (1963) mentioned application of the method to chlorins by EGGER (1962). In addition, THOMAS and BLUMER (1964) used this method for porphyrins from ancient sediments.

Fluorescence

Porphyrins and chlorins exhibit fluorescence when irradiated with light of appropriate wavelength. Although attempts have been made to explain the fluorescence on the basis of energy transitions within the molecule (STERN and MOLVIG, 1935, 1936a, b; STERN and DEZELIC, 1936; STERN and WENDERLEIN, 1935, 1936a, b, c; STERN et al., 1936; RABINOWITCH, 1944; KOSAKI, 1950), the light emission of these compounds is not well understood. In aqueous solution, the intensity of fluorescence varies with pH (FINK and HOERBURGER, 1933, 1935; RIMINGTON and SCHUSTER, 1943; JOPE and O'BRIEN, 1945), and it is very sensitive to impurities and the presence of inorganic ions (RIMINGTON, 1960). The fluorescence behavior of the pigments is directly related to the imine hydrogen atoms, and only indirectly to the other constituents of the molecule. Replacement of the imine hydrogens by other cations usually destroys the fluorescence response, and this observation is commonly used for monitoring such replacement reactions, as was done for example by O'HAGAN (1961).

Electrophoresis

Porphyrins and related pigments would be expected to be sensitive to electrophoretic processes, and E. G. LARSEN et al. (1955) have demonstrated porphyrin separations employing this method. Since electrophoresis depends on polar constituents of the molecule, the electrophoretic behavior would be governed by factors which affect the imine hydrogen atoms as well as any carboxylic acid substituent groups on the periphery of the molecule.

After the foregoing presentation of the major properties of free porphyrins, we must now consider the changes which attend the conversion of free porphyrins to metal complexes—the replacement of two imine hydrogens in the central part of the molecule with other cations.

Metal complexes of porphyrins and related compounds

The characteristics of metal complexes will be considered in a manner similar to that for the free porphyrins. In most cases comparisons between the metal complexed molecule and the free compound will be made. The main characteristics to be discussed are spectral properties, exchange and replacement of metals, and the stability of metalloporphyrins.

Structure

The porphyrin molecule is a planar structure with two hydrogens attached to adjacent or opposite nitrogens, lying outside the plane of the molecule (BARNES and DOROUGH, 1950). One or both of these hydrogens can be replaced with other cations. Evidence of mono-salt formation was obtained by ARONOFF (1958) through perchloric acid titrations of selected porphyrins. Although in general the monosalt was very unstable, an apparent dissociation constant was measured. Porphyrins also form disalts of monovalent cations, but these are unstable and break down in the presence of water (LEMBERG and LEGGE, 1949). Instability of the disalts is probably due to steric difficulties in accommodating the two large cations in the central part of the molecule. This agrees with the observation that alkali metal ions in porphyrin molecules are readily replaced by small divalent cations, by large divalent cations or by smaller alkali metal ions (BARNES and DOROUGH, 1950).

The most common metal complexes are those formed by the replacement of the two hydrogens by a relatively small divalent cation. For example, the common occurrence of nickel complexes of porphyrins is probably related to the amount of space available in the ligand pigment molecule. The distance between opposite nitrogen atoms in phthalocyanine is estimated from ROBERTSON (1936) to be 3.82 Å. The length of a Ni–N bond in NiN_3 was reported to be 1.88 Å by JUZA and SACHZE (1943), indicating ample space for the nickel atom. In fact, it suggests that the porphyrin molecule might tend to shrink toward the nickel atom. In this connection, a study made by CRUTE (1959) on nickel etioporphyrin II showed the pyrrole components of the molecule to be distorted toward the nickel atom through a reduction in the magnitude of the C–N–C angle from a value of about 108.5° to less than 100°. ROBERTSON and WOODWARD (1937) found a similar distortion for the nickel complex of phthalocyanine, the C–N–C angle becoming 99°. On the other hand, a larger metal atom, platinum, in a phthalocyanine complex, increases the size of the porphyrin structure slightly, as indicated by TONOMURA (1955). CORWIN et al. (1962), in studying porphyrin and chlorin structures with a spring analog model, produced data which indicated that the introduction of a small magnesium atom into porphyrins and chlorins caused the molecules to shrink, as in the case of the phthalocyanine compounds. In this connection, FLEISCHER (1963) reported intramolecular bond lengths for the nickel complex of etioporphyrin I which are summarized in Table III with the corresponding data for the phthalocyanines. The pyrrole carbon–carbon bonds in the porphyrin are a few per cent shorter, while the carbon–nitrogen and carbon–carbon bridging bonds are longer. The nickel–nitrogen bonds in the porphyrin are some-

TABLE III

PIGMENT BOND LENGTHS AND ANGLES

	Phthalocyanine (ROBERTSON, 1936)	Ni-phthalocyanine (ROBERTSON and WOODWARD, 1937)	Ni-etioporphyrin-II (CRUTE, 1959)	Ni-etioporphyrin-I (FLEISCHER, 1963)
Bond lengths, in Å				
C–N (pyrrole)	1.34	1.38, 1.39	1.35	1.396
C–C (pyrrole to bridge)	1.33, 1.34	1.37, 1.38	1.43	1.398
C–C (pyrrole)	1.49	1.45, 1.47	1.40	1.427
C–C (pyrrole)	1.39	1.38	1.47	1.335
C–C (pyrrole to alkyl group)	—	—	1.50	1.554
C–C (alkyl group)	—	—		1.542
N–Ni	(1.91)[1]	1.83	1.84	1.957
N–N	2.65, 2.76	2.56, 2.60	—	—
Angle, in degrees				
C–N–C (pyrrole)	108.5	99	—	104.8
N–C–C (bridging)	131	126	—	126.7
C–C–C (bridging)	115, 119	116, 118	—	—

[1] Estimated half distance between opposite nitrogen atoms in the metal free phthalocyanine.

what longer than in the phthalocyanine nickel complex. Included in the table as well are data for an isomer of the porphyrin used by Fleischer, in which the bond distances were also estimated.

It is commonly agreed that porphyrin pigment molecules are substantially planar, but deviations from planarity have been observed. FLEISCHER (1963) found that two of the pyrrole rings in nickel etioporphyrin I were bent up and two down from the plane formed by the four-corner bridging carbons. The distortion was reported to be considerable—ca. 0.25 Å. Another kind of distortion was that introduced by MCEWEN (1946) who drew attention to steric hindrances within the molecule by N-methylating a porphyrin, as well as by introducing large cations. CORWIN et al. (1962) examined the accommodation of such large units through the tilting of one or more pyrrole units of the porphyrin framework. It was concluded that such wrist-action tilting required less energy than any other modification of the porphyrin structure.

FISCHER and WENDEROTH (1939) showed that ring 4 of chlorins, because of its non-porphyrin character, is non-planar, with its substituents in a *trans* orientation (FICKEN et al., 1956).

PHILLIPS (1960) classified metal complexes of porphyrins into three groups according to their stability to acid attack: (*1*) those which were dissociated in water; (*2*) those dissociated in dilute hydrochloric acid, and (*3*) those which were dissociated only in concentrated sulfuric acid. In general, the most stable porphyrin metal complexes are those in which the complexed metal is a small divalent cation (DUNNING et al., 1953; CAUGHEY and CORWIN, 1955; and ERDMAN et al., 1957).

The fact that porphyrins and chlorins readily undergo metal complexing reactions raises the question of the nature of the bonding of the metals to the porphyrin structure. The porphyrin molecule may be regarded as a typical ligand. According to ORGEL (1960) a ligand is any ion or molecule which is directly attached to a metal ion and is regarded as being bonded to it. The most common types of ligand are monatomic or polyatomic negative ions and neutral polar molecules. The latter molecules are almost always ones which have one or more pairs of unshared electrons. Structure determinations have shown that with very few exceptions polar ligand molecules are oriented so that one unshared pair of electrons points directly at the metal ion.

The foregoing discussion suggests that a simple replacement of the hydrogens with the divalent metal would result in a type of bonding substantially the same as that for the replaced protons which may be represented by the bond configurations shown in Fig.18A. The form illustrated is, of course, only one of the contributing resonant forms. In some instances it is customary to show dotted lines joining the metal to the other pair of nitrogens thereby indicating some form of co-ordinate bonding (Fig.18B). This is in agreement with the observation that the other nitrogen atoms carry pairs of unbonded electrons which may be directed toward the central atom. Fig.18C illustrates another type of bonding which takes into consideration the electron distribution around the nitrogens. This can be considered as true covalent bonding with double bonds joining the metal to the nitrogens with pyrrole configuration and single bonds joining the metal with the remaining nitrogens. The latter is the form of presentation used by MARTELL and CALVIN (1952) in a comprehensive discussion of chelate compounds. For simplicity, the first form of representing the metal complex will be used in the present discussion, keeping in mind that there are many resonant forms which

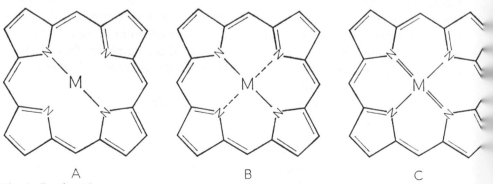

A   B   C

Fig.18. Bond configurations for metal complexes of porphyrins.

include a real bonding with the other two nitrogens. The molecular dimensions given by FLEISCHER (1963) may be taken as a guide in estimating the size of a given molecule.

A brief discussion of the modern ligand theory will help to establish a better understanding of the nature of the bonding of the metal atom within the porphyrin molecule. This can be done in one of two ways—either using the molecular orbital theory or the electrostatic field theory. While the molecular orbital theory can be used to establish the type of bonding resulting from interaction of atomic orbitals to form molecular orbitals, the same result can be obtained in considering the bond formation by studying the effect of the electrostatic field of the ligand on the atomic orbitals of the complexed atom. The electrostatic crystal field theory has been fully discussed by ORGEL (1960) and LINNETT (1960). This theory infers that the atomic orbitals of the available electrons in the complexing metal are sensitive to the presence of an external electric field, i.e., of a ligand. In the case of porphyrins, the molecule is essentially planar with the metal atom lying in the plane of the four negatively charged nitrogens. Since the external field in these ligands is essentially planar, some of the normal orbitals of the metal atom are strongly repelled and others are only mildly repelled. Thus there is a splitting of the five $3d$ orbitals (in the case of the first transition series metals). Wave-mechanics evaluations show that three of the orbitals are reduced in energy, being only mildly repelled, and the other two are increased in energy, resulting in a strong repulsion because they must lie in the plane of the nitrogens. An indication of the energy splitting is shown in Fig.19 for two spatial configurations

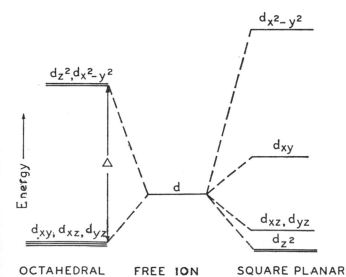

Fig.19. Electron energy level separations for 3d electrons. (After ORGEL, 1960.)

around the metal atom. One is representative of an octahedral arrangement of the ligand and the other a square planar arrangement.

The square planar arrangement may seem more obvious for porphyrins since the four nitrogen atoms lie in a common plane with the metal (CAUGHEY and CORWIN, 1955). However, considerable evidence has been reported for the existence of the octahedral arrangement with two additional ligand points lying above and below the plane of the porphyrin molecule. Generally the additional ligands are considered to be solvent molecules. This seems likely since many solvents, particularly those containing oxygen, nitrogen, or sulfur, have unbonded electrons similar to those of the porphyrin nitrogens.

Metal complexes of porphyrins and chlorins tend to form coordination compounds. McCONNEL and associates (1953) reported the addition of cyanide to cobalt porphyrin complexes, and TAYLOR (1940) reported the addition of pyridine to the manganese complex of mesoporphyrin. Further examples of solvation have been reported for porphyrins and chlorins, e.g., chlorophylls (FREED and SANCIER, 1954; and JOHNSON and KAY, 1960).

The presence of the porphyrin molecule as a complexing ligand serves to split the energy levels of the complexing atom with three of the five orbitals of $3d$ electrons being marked by a low energy level and the other two of a high energy level. Thus in the complexing reaction, $3d$ electrons readily enter the lower energy levels. If the complexing atoms are such that additional electrons must be accommodated in the upper energy levels, the resulting complex is less stable. The pairing of electrons within the available orbitals is related to the strength of the ligand field. In the case of porphyrins, the field strengths are weak, resulting in the filling of available orbitals with d electrons with little pairing until all the orbitals are

TABLE IV

IONIZATION POTENTIALS OF TRANSITION METALS OF THE FIRST TRANSITION SERIES IN ELECTRON VOLTS

(After ORGEL, 1960)

Element	First ionization potential	Second ionization potential	Third ionization potential
Sc	6.56	12.80	24.75
Ti	6.83	13.57	27.47
V	6.74	14.65	29.31
Cr	6.76	16.49	30.95
Mn	7.43	15.64	33.69
Fe	7.90	16.18	30.64
Co	7.86	17.05	33.49
Ni	7.63	18.15	35.16
Cu	7.72	20.29	36.83
Zn	9.39	17.96	39.70

TABLE V

LIGAND FIELD STABILIZATION ENERGIES

(After ORGEL, 1960)

Number of electrons	Ligand field stabilization energy[1]
0	0
1	$2/5\ E$
2	$4/5\ E$
3	$6/5\ E$
4	$3/5\ E$
5	0
6	$2/5\ E$
7	$4/5\ E$
8	$6/5\ E$
9	$3/5\ E$
10	0

[1] It is assumed that the bonding orbital is stabilized by an energy E and contains 4 electrons while the antibonding orbital is destabilized by an energy E.

half filled (ORGEL, 1960). The extent of filling of the $3d$ orbitals may be inferred from the data in Table IV in which the transition metals from scandium to zinc are listed. Orgel has given an evaluation of the ligand field stabilization energies (Table V) indicating preferential configurations of electrons in the orbitals of the complexing metals. The two metals that are predominant are those with three and eight d electrons, i.e., vanadium and nickel, respectively. In the vanadium atom, the three electrons occupy the three low-energy orbitals outlined in Fig.19. The corresponding eight nickel electrons occupy the three low-energy levels in spin-paired orbitals (six electrons) and in each of the high-energy orbitals in single assignments (two electrons). The other possibilities, those for other metals in the series, are less stable. For example, iron (II) with six d electrons having one pair of electrons spin-paired, has a stabilization energy from ligand field splitting of only one-third that of vanadium and nickel. Chromium and copper (II) similarly have a stabilization of only half that of vanadium and nickel ions.

The foregoing discussion has assumed an octahedral orientation for the complexes, but the nickel complexes are sometimes considered as being planar. If this is true the nickel complex should be relatively stable because the eight d electrons can be accommodated in the four low-energy orbitals of Fig.19. In the same manner, the chromium complex may be stable in a planar orientation since its four d electrons could also be readily accommodated in the four low-energy orbitals, but in an unpaired state.

The vanadium complex probably cannot assume a form other than an octahedral configuration due to the fact that it is not a complex of V^{2+}, but rather

VO²⁺ (ERDMAN et al., 1956b). The complex should be referred to as a vanadyl complex and not as a vanadium complex. There is no space within the plane of the molecule for accommodation of the oxygen atom; therefore it must occupy some position outside the plane—either above or below at one of the points of the octahedron. The corresponding octahedral point on the opposite side of the molecular plane could be occupied by a solvent molecule. This kind of spatial arrangement is indicated in Fig.20. Mass spectra of such complexes have been reported by MEAD and WILDE (1961).

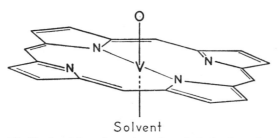

Fig.20. Spatial configuration of octahedral orientation.

An example of a transition from planar to octahedral configurations is given by the porphyrin complexes of cobalt through the addition of various groups to the metal ion (JOHNSON and KAY, 1960). Although this is not an example of solvent addition, the change to the octahedral orientation is observed spectrally as indicated in the spectra of cobaltous etioporphyrin I and its corresponding pyridinobromo addition compound (Fig.21). A similar change in the spectrum of nickel solvates has not been observed, probably because the bonding in the latter cases is much more indistinct.

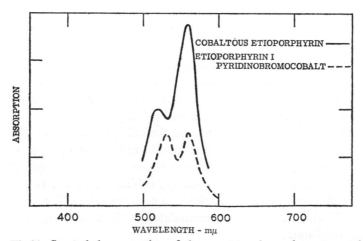

Fig.21. Spectral demonstration of the transition from planar to octahedral orientation of a porphyrin. The solid line illustrates the planar configuration, and the dotted line illustrates the octahedral configuration (JOHNSON and KAY, 1960).

Spectra

The spectra of complexes of porphyrins with monovalent cations and large divalent cations are similar to those of the free pigments as illustrated in Fig.22. On the formation of a metal porphyrin by introduction of a small divalent cation into the porphyrin, the four bands in the visible range are replaced by two bands, as indicated in Fig.23 for the spectrum of the nickel complex of deuteroporphyrin IX dimethylester. WILLIAMS (1956) ascribed this change to the absence of tautomeric forms of the metal complexes. The longer wavelength band is related to bands I and III of the free porphyrin spectra and the second band to bands II and IV. Further, the second band does not change in intensity with a change in peripheral substitution. No term system has been presented for the change in spectra as a result of metal complexing; however, these are changes to be expected if the

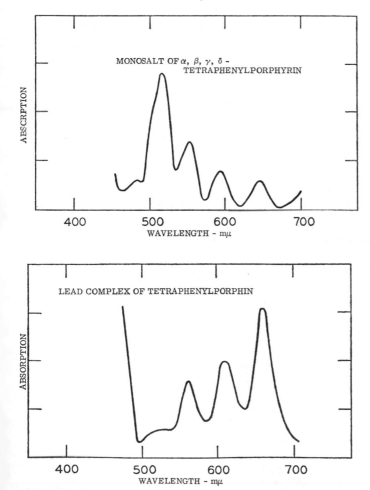

Fig.22. Spectra of a porphyrin complexed with a monosalt and with a large divalent metal cation.

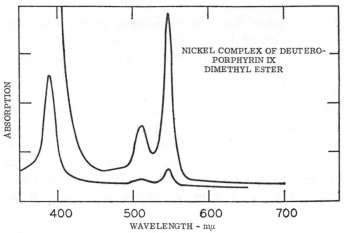

Fig.23. Spectrum of a metal complexed porphyrin—the nickel complex of deuteroporphyrin IX dimethyl ester.

formation of the metal complex of the pigment increases stability of the molecule.

Although many metal complexes of chlorins are not widely observed, complexes of one of the more important chlorins—pheophytin *a*—have been studied extensively. The magnesium complex of pheophytin *a*, i.e., chlorophyll *a*, is a very well-known, naturally occurring metal complex of a chlorin. The spectrum of chlorophyll *a* is not characteristic of metal complexes, and LEVITT (1954) reported that this pigment behaves as though it were not complexed. In contrast to this, other small divalent cations exhibit spectra which agree with the thesis that metal complexing produces marked changes in the compound, as indicated in the spectrum of the nickel complex of pheophytin *a* (Fig.24).

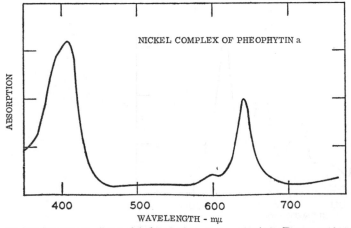

Fig.24. Spectrum of the nickel complex of pheophytin *a* (BAKER and HODGSON, 1961).

Other metal complexes of pheophytin *a* and pheophorbide *a*, including complexes with copper, zinc, iron, lead, etc., have been studied by LAMORT (1956).

From a theoretical standpoint, little or no attempt has been made to consider these metal complexes from the molecular orbital point of view even though the molecular orbital approach has been used extensively to describe the free pigments.

Having discussed the present incomplete knowledge of the bonding of the metal atom in the porphyrin molecule, the exchange reactions involving the metal porphyrin complexes will now be reviewed.

Metal complex exchange reactions

Bonding of protons and metal ions to the pigment molecule is largely covalent in character (BARNES and DOROUGH, 1950; LEMBERG and LEGGE, 1949), suggesting that the cation probably does not undergo exchange reactions with cations in solution. Isotope exchange reactions involving iron, cobalt, copper, zinc and magnesium complexes verify this with negligible rates (STRANKS and WILKINS, 1957). As would be expected the complexes of porphyrins incorporating monovalent cations show rapid exchange. Unfortunately, the exchange reactions with divalent cations were not exhaustively examined; therefore, although negative results were obtained, it is possible that metal complexes of these divalent cations may undergo exchange at low but measurable rates. The technology of replacement reactions which are related to exchange reactions has yielded more information.

The simplest replacement reaction is that of a divalent metal ion replacing the two imine hydrogens in a free pigment. For example, nickel readily enters a chlorin pigment, pheophytin *a*, in a replacement reaction characterized by an activation energy of about 24 kcal./mole (BAKER and HODGSON, 1961). This falls well within the range of 20–25 kcal./mole commonly regarded as typical of replacement or exchange reactions. A very interesting phenomenon was described by LOWE and PHILLIPS (1961) in which it was found that the addition of detergents to a metal–porphyrin complexing system facilitated the introduction of the metal to a marked degree. Generally a replacement reaction will proceed easily if the product is more stable than the starting metal complex. This was proved for porphyrin metal complexes by BARNES and DOROUGH (1950). From studies with lithium, sodium, potassium, divalent lead, mercury, copper, silver, cobalt, magnesium and tin, two rules for the replacement reactions were formulated: (*1*) the order of increasing stability is alkali metal, large divalent metal and small divalent metal; (*2*) the metal porphyrin with the smallest metal is the most stable.

Replacement of copper in chlorins and porphyrins with nickel and vanadium was possible only under considerably more severe conditions than ordinary refluxing of common solvents (HODGSON et al., 1960). A further kind of replacement reaction was that carried out by CORWIN and MELVILLE (1955) in which the magnesium complex of etiochlorin II was reacted with etioporphyrin II resulting in the formation of the magnesium complex of etioporphyrin II and the free etiochlorin II.

Stability

CAUGHEY and CORWIN (1955) reported that porphyrins are stabilized through metal complexing and cited this as a logical reason for the persistence of metal porphyrins in crude oil. MORANDI and JENSEN (1964) retorted porphyrins from oil shale at 900°F. This severe treatment changed the spectrum of the porphyrin from phyllo to an etio type but the basic porphyrin structure survived. HODGSON and BAKER (1957) measured the thermal stability of metal porphyrin complexes occurring in crude oil. The apparent activation energy for the destruction of total porphyrin in crude oil was found to be 52.5 kcal./mole, indicating a considerable stability for compounds of such complex configuration.

Another measure of stability is the magnitude of dissociation constants of metal complexes of pigments. For example, CORWIN and WEI (1962) examined the stabilities of magnesium chelates of porphyrins and chlorins by allowing them to equilibrate with magnesium phenate in phenol solutions at 100°C. Magnesium porphyrins were found to be more stable than magnesium chlorins. Further, the closure of the isocyclic ring in chlorophyll-like structures produced a warpage of the pigment system and decreases in the stability of the magnesium complex.

A more extreme test of the stability of metal complexes of pigments is that of direct acid attack. As noted earlier, mono salts of porphyrins are decomposed with very weak acids, e.g., water. CAUGHEY and CORWIN (1955) reported on the stability of several metal complexes of etioporphyrin II in relation to their cleavage by sulfuric acid. The order for increasing stability was Zn (II), Cu (II), Ni (IV) and Co (II). Further examination of the copper complex cleavage at 30°C showed the reaction to be second order with respect to the complex, and fourth order with respect to the acid in a sulfuric–acetic acid system. ERDMAN et al. (1957) extended the cleavage studies to etioporphyrin I including vanadyl complexes. The order of increasing stability to sulfuric acid attack was found to be Cu (II), Ni (II), Fe (III) and VO (II). The relative rate constants spanned a range of approximately 10^{12}. CORWIN et al. (1957) examined this further using acid demetallation procedures and observed that the porphyrins bound to vanadium and nickel are not identical. Later, DEAN and GIRDLER (1960) also used sulfuric acid procedures which were based upon the relative stabilities of vanadyl, nickel and copper complexes of etioporphyrin I. The nickel and copper complexes readily broke down to the free pigment while evidence was obtained for the formation of a stable complex of vanadyl porphyrin with a second VO^{2+} ion.

Another measure of the stability of metal complexes of porphyrins is given by the volatilization of these compounds in distillation reactions. It is generally accepted that metal porphyrins distill with hydrocarbons in refining operations, particularly in vacuum distillations, as noted by WRIGHTSON (1949) and WOODLE and CHANDLER (1952). SKINNER (1952) reported the breakdown of metal complexes at temperatures above 230 °F. A molecular still approach used by ERDMAN et al. (1956a) further demonstrated the stability of metal complexes of porphyrins under severe thermal conditions. Gamma radiation is effective in destroying porphyrins (DUNNING and MOORE, 1959; ERDMAN et al., 1963).

Only minor attention has been given to the thermal stabilities of specific portions of the porphyrin molecules. In this connection, the carboxyl group of some acid porphyrins has been noted as being particularly susceptible to thermal decomposition, leading to the commonly quoted statement that carboxylated porphyrins in petroleum and oil shales indicate a low temperature history for these substances, evidently with temperatures no higher than 200 °C, as attributed to TREIBS (1936).

In concluding this section it might be noted that the complexing of porphyrins with metal ions generally results in significant changes in the porphyrin properties. This, as indicated above, is not always the case. Even the fluorescence phenomenon does not always die out, since KOSAKI (1951) observed that diamagnetic metal porphyrins show fluorescence similar to porphyrins, whereas paramagnetic metal porphyrins do not fluoresce. Complexes of nickel, copper and vanadium with chlorins and porphyrins do not exhibit fluorescence (RIEKER, 1962). Significant changes in fluorescence result upon formation of a very stable metal complex which by virtue of its stability tends to persist for long periods of time under natural conditions.

THE OCCURRENCE OF PORPHYRINS IN PETROLEUM AND RELATED SUBSTANCES

Of the many porphyrins, chlorins and tetrahydroporphyrins arising in biological systems, only a few persist in petroleum and related substances. However, these few are very widespread in their occurrence. Porphyrins have been found in petroleum, oil shale, coal and other bituminous materials in concentrations of less than one part per million in some light crude oils and up to 0.4% in some oil shales. The porphyrins are usually found as metal complexes but free porphyrins also occur.

Free pigments

Little is known of the occurrence of free porphyrins in crude oil. This is primarily due to two factors: the content of free porphyrins is apparently very low, and the methods of analysis and detection are not well developed. Uncomplexed porphyrin pigments may be extracted from solvents such as ether with aqueous acids— this property is frequently used in resolving mixtures of porphyrin pigments. However, when this method is applied to crude oil it apparently fails. This may be due to the presence of ether-soluble materials which sharply alter the partition coefficients in favor of the organic phase. This difficulty may be partially overcome by the use of solvents in which the pigments are less soluble, or by precipitation of the interfering materials (BLUMER, 1950).

Free porphyrins have been reported in Swiss oil shales. Shales from Serpiano, which were examined by BLUMER and OMENN (1961) yielded significant quantities of deoxophylloerythroetioporphyrin, deoxophylloerythrin and mesoetioporphyrin (etioporphyrin III). These findings supported earlier reports by TREIBS (1936). These compounds are described below.

Although free porphyrins probably also exist in petroleum there is limited evidence to date that they do. BLUMER (1956) reported the presence of free deoxophylloerythroetioporphyrin and deoxophylloerythrin in crude oil. It is likely that the concentrations are small since the concentrations of free porphyrins in one sample of Serpiano oil shale was only ca. 1% of the total porphyrin content (BLUMER, 1950). The free porphyrins were found to range from C_{27} to C_{34} as indicated by mass spectrometer analysis (THOMAS and BLUMER, 1964).

Description of porphyrin pigments

The most commonly reported pigment occurring in crude oil is deoxophylloerythroetioporphyrin. The chemical structure of this compound is shown in Fig.25. It has a molecular formula of 1, 3, 5, 8-tetramethyl-2, 4, 7-triethyl-6, gamma-ethane porphin ($C_{32}H_{36}N_4$) with a molecular weight of 476. The ether solution of this pigment is deep red in color and its absorption spectrum is a typical phyllo type with maxima at 621, 610, 594, 566, 558, 532, 498, and 400 mμ as indicated in Fig.26. This spectrum is similar to that of porphin. There are distinguishing features of its structure to which attention should be drawn: the compound contains a fifth ring—an isocyclic ring joining the gamma carbon to the number 6 carbon on pyrrole ring III; and the compound does not contain carboxyl or carbonyl groups. The hydrochloric acid extraction number is 2.5. This pigment is the most abundant free porphyrin in Swiss oil shale. It is convenient to refer to compounds of this class as H_2P_p as suggested by HODGSON et al. (1963a).

Deoxophylloerythrin is the carboxylated form of deoxophylloerythroetioporphyrin, with one carboxyl group, in a propionic acid side chain on carbon-7 of pyrrole ring IV. The structure of this carboxylated pigment is also illustrated in Fig.25. Spectrally the two compounds are almost identical. The chemical properties of deoxophylloerythrin appear to differ from those of the decarboxylated compound only as they are directly related to the carboxyl group. For this reason deoxophylloerythrin is soluble in dilute alkali and its extraction number is lowered to a value between 1.5 and 2.0. Deoxophylloerythrin and similar compounds may be represented as H_2P_pCOOH.

Mesoetioporphyrin or etioporphyrin III is also illustrated in Fig.25. It does not contain the isocyclic ring as in the previous two compounds. This decarboxylat-

DEOXOPHYLLOERYTHRIN

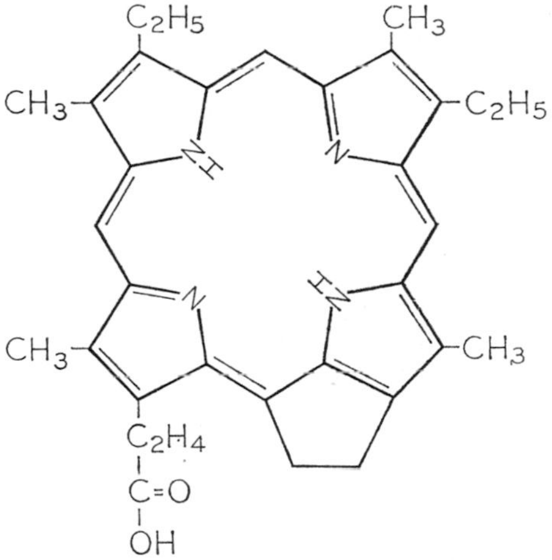

DEOXOPHYLLOERYTHROETIOPORPHYRIN

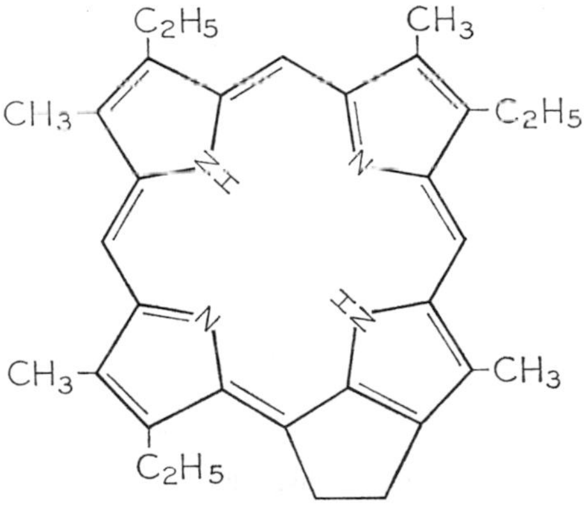

ETIOPORPHYRIN III

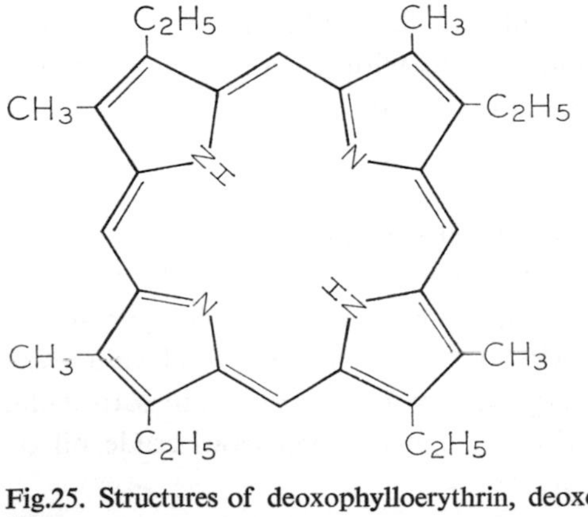

Fig.25. Structures of deoxophylloerythrin, deoxophylloerythroetioporphyrin and etioporphyrin III.

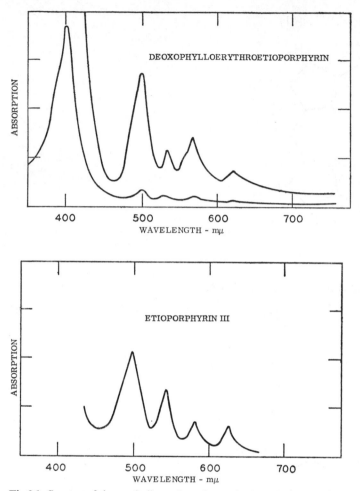

Fig.26. Spectra of deoxophylloerythroetioporphyrin and etioporphyrin III.

ed porphyrin has the molecular formula 1, 3, 5, 8-tetramethyl-2, 4, 6, 7-tetraethyl porphin ($C_{32}H_{38}N_4$) with a molecular weight of 478. Its absorption spectrum in pyridine has maxima at 625, 577, 538 and 502 mμ with a general configuration indicative of a typical etio porphyrin spectrum (Fig.26).

Metal complexes of porphyrins

Metal complexes of porphyrins are widespread in petroleum. The concentration levels of the complexes are usually quite low, generally falling in the range of 10–1,000 p.p.m. with some reported less than 1 p.p.m. In some oils, porphyrins have not been detected (DUNNING and MOORE, 1957). Some typical values are given in Table VI for concentrations of porphyrin metal complexes in petroleum.

  While metal complexes of porphyrins can be obtained from crude oil by

TABLE VI

CONCENTRATIONS OF PORPHYRIN METAL COMPLEXES IN CRUDE OILS

(After DUNNING et al., 1960)

Oil	Porphyrins	Carboxylated	Percentage of V and Ni complexed		
	(p.p.m.)	(%)	(%)	V (p.p.m.)	Ni (p.p.m.)
Bachaquero, Venezuela	380	0.2	8.5	430	53
Boscan, Venezuela	1680	—	18.7	900	66
Coleville, Canada	110	—	9.6	94	32
Lagunillas, Venezuela	170	0.1	5.1	317	41
North Belridge, Calif.	390	5.4	44.6	23	83
Rhodes, Kans.	135	0.0	8.8	133	33
Santa Maria, Calif.	300	1.8	8.1	280	130
Tatums, Okla.	165	0.0	8.4	148	71
Tia Juana, Venezuela	60	—	3.2	187	24
West Texas, Texas	12	—	4.7	23	5
Wilmington, Calif.	200	—	21.6	46	60

solvent extraction, the customary method for quantitative estimations involves cleaving the metals from the metal complexes and extracting the free porphyrins using an aqueous acid solution (TREIBS, 1934; GROENNINGS, 1953; and CO-STANTINIDES and BATTI, 1957). Many variations of the method originally used by Treibs have been developed. A typical method involves digestion of a sample of oil at 50°C for four days in a sealed container with acetic acid saturated with hydrobromic acid. The porphyrins freed from their metals by this digestion are partially drawn off with the acid phase and then with successive hydrochloric acid extractions of the oil phase to complete the separation of the porphyrins from the bulk of the crude oil. The material obtained by such a procedure is commonly referred to as the petroleum porphyrin aggregate.

As in the case of the free porphyrins in petroliferous substances, the porphyrin metal complex content of petroleum is commonly believed to consist mainly of deoxophylloerythroetioporphyrin along with smaller amounts of deoxophylloerythrin, mesoporphyrin and mesoetioporphyrin (TREIBS, 1936). One other porphyrin, with an etio type spectrum similar to deuteroporphyrin (which has been observed in coal) or pyrroetioporphyrin, has been detected in crude oil (FISHER and DUNNING, 1961). The possibility of the occurrence of other porphyrins does exist and uncertainties of identification have been noted by CORWIN and BAKER (1964). For example, several groups of porphyrins as shown in Table VII have been separated from the petroleum porphyrin aggregate of a California crude oil (DUNNING and CARLTON, 1956).

TABLE VII

TYPES OF PORPHYRINS OBSERVED IN PETROLEUM PORPHYRIN AGGREGATE OF A CALIFORNIA CRUDE OIL

(After DUNNING and CARLTON, 1956)

Group[1]	Spectral type	Percentage of total
1	etio	7.9
2	etio	16.1
3	phyllo	14.2
4	phyllo	21.6
5	phyllo	12.6
6	phyllo	16.0
7	phyllo	7.6

[1] Groups 1 and 2. These porphyrins have spectra typical of animal porphyrins and some plant porphyrins. They are similar to etioporphyrin III rather than pyrroporphyrin.

Groups 3–6. These are spectra typical of plant porphyrins. They are decarboxylated and resemble the phylloetioporphyrin or deoxophylloerythroetioporphyrin types.

Group 7. These porphyrins contain one carboxyl group and are probably deoxophylloerythrin.

The use of the ordinary acid digestion approach obscures the identity of the metal involved in the indigenous metal complexes of the oils, although a careful application of the acid demetallation process permits the step-wise demetallation of nickel and vanadyl complexes (ERDMAN et al., 1957). It is generally believed that the principal metals are vanadium and nickel, although iron was at first thought to be important (TREIBS, 1934; GLEBOVSKAYA and VOL'KENSHTEIN, 1948). Porphyrin complexes containing iron however were reported by MOORE and DUNNING (1955) for the Green River oil shales. The vanadium complexed with porphyrins in crude oil is in the vanadyl form (ERDMAN et al., 1956b). Structures for the vanadium and nickel complexes of deoxophylloerythroetioporphyrin are illustrated in Fig.27.

Difficulties created by the presence of vanadium and nickel in crude oils and especially as metal porphyrin complexes which are volatile (ERDMAN et al., 1956a) has focussed much attention in the petroleum refining industry on the occurrence of these metals (JONES and HARDY, 1952). Only a part of the total nickel and vanadium in crude oil is recognized to occur in porphyrin structures as outlined in Table VI. In general it is believed that only about 10% of the total metal in a crude oil is accommodated as porphyrin complexes (DUNNING et al., 1960), although improvements in analytical techniques as shown by a recent examination of the Boscan crude oil indicate over 40% of the vanadium and nickel are present as metal porphyrin complexes (SUGIHARA and BEAN, 1962). HODGSON and BAKER (1957) showed that there was a significant difference in behavior between the total vanadium–nickel constituent and the porphyrin constituent in crude oils, the

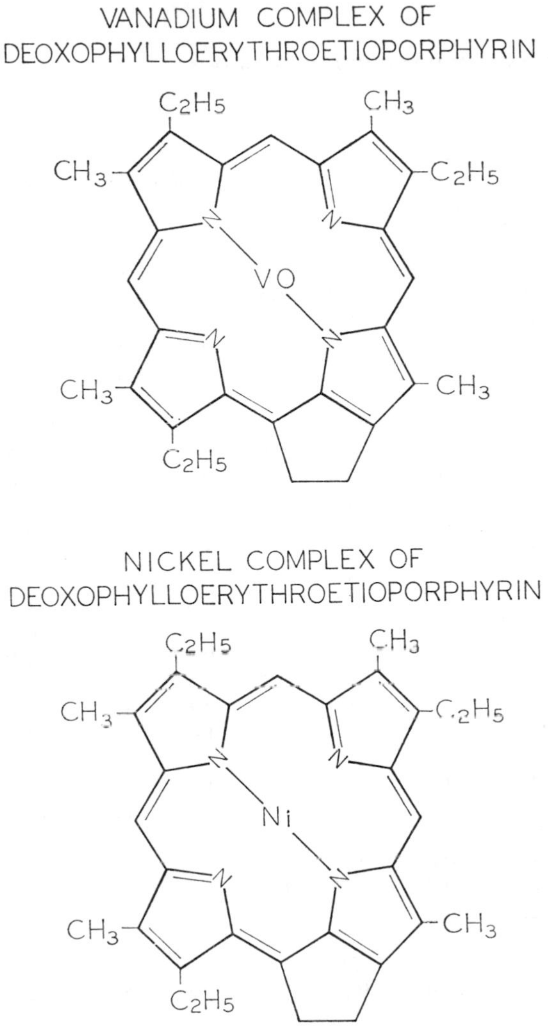

VANADIUM COMPLEX OF
DEOXOPHYLLOERYTHROETIOPORPHYRIN

NICKEL COMPLEX OF
DEOXOPHYLLOERYTHROETIOPORPHYRIN

Fig.27. Structures of the vanadium and nickel complexes of deoxophylloerythroetioporphyrin.

former being somewhat more resistant to thermal action. HOWE and WILLIAMS (1960) indicated that there are three classes of metallic complexes in crude petroleum: metallic porphyrins, metallic compounds—porphyrins which are easily decomposable by glacial acetic–hydrochloric acid mixtures, and metallic compounds—non porphyrins which are not readily decomposable by glacial acetic–hydrobromic acid mixtures. An indication of the occurrence of nickel and vanadium and other trace metals in crude oil is given in Table VIII.

A more satisfactory method of studying the metal complexes of petroleum is to recover the complexes directly with the metals intact by chromatography. CORWIN et al. (1957) and CORWIN and BAKER (1964) developed suitable methods

TABLE VIII

ANALYSES OF OIL SOLUBLE ASH IN UNITED STATES AND VENEZUELAN CRUDE OILS

(After JONES and HARDY, 1952)

Crude oil	Ash	NiO	Na$_2$O	SiO	VO	FeO	Al$_2$O$_3$	CaO	SO$_3$
	(p.p.m. of original crude oil)								
North Louisiana	44	0.7	20.4	—	1.8	1.5	—	1.2	18.9
Central Louisiana	8	0.6	3.5	—	0.8	0.5	—	—	1.8
South Louisiana	10	1.7	0.9	0.3	0.5	1.6	—	—	3.6
Southwest Louisiana	5	0.2	0.7	0.4	0.0	1.5	0.1	0.6	0.6
Louisiana–Mississippi	11	0.0	6.8	—	0.0	0.3	0.1	0.7	4.5
Heidelberg–Eucutts (Miss.)	319	7.6	52.0	—	27.0	3.5	—	—	104.0
Olla (La.)	100	7.2	35.6	—	—	1.0	—	—	59.6
Conroe (Texas)	7	—	2.9	0.5	0.0	1.2	0.2	0.9	2.0
Yates–Pecos (Texas)	22	3.3	0.9	2.6	13.9	0.2	2.7	0.2	3.6
Imogene–West Texas	66	2.2	21.8	0.5	15.2	0.1	0.2	—	20.0
East Texas	36	1.1	16.6	1.8	2.2	0.7	2.5	—	15.1
Talco (Texas)	109	3.3	24.8	—	15.8	2.9	—	—	45.8
Salt Flats (Texas)	26	1.8	1.6	1.0	14.8	2.4	3.0	—	3.4
Coastal heavy (Texas)	73	2.9	24.2	—	1.7	1.1	—	—	40.4
Refugio light (Texas)	5	0.9	0.4	0.2	1.2	0.5	0.1	—	0.5
Illinois–Indiana	75	1.7	21.4	—	6.8	1.7	—	—	35.8
Louden (Ill.)	14	0.8	2.3	0.1	2.2	0.8	0.2	1.2	5.9
Oklahoma–Kansas	49	1.0	16.6	3.4	5.3	0.5	1.6	1.4	19.0
Big Horn mixture (Wyo.)	44	4.6	1.3	1.9	28.5	1.1	1.4	—	6.4
Quiriquire (Venezuela)	236	7.6	23.6	—	55.9	2.8	5.0	78.4	74.3
San Joaquin (Venezuela)	5	0.2	1.5	0.8	0.6	0.6	0.2	—	0.8
Jusepin (Venezuela)	160	2.6	36.9	7.7	26.4	6.7	0.8	—	65.6
Lagunillas (Venezuela)	348	10.4	30.3	39.0	208.0	1.4	4.5	—	0.7
La Rosa medium (Venezuela)	394	12.6	49.6	42.1	237.0	1.2	—	—	0.8
Tia Juana (Venezuela)	388	9.7	55.5	75.0	210.0	3.5	5.0	5.8	2.7

for this and have established the occurrence of several metal complexes in Wilmington crude oil. Three vanadium complexes were recovered and the presence of several nickel complexes was demonstrated (CORWIN et al., 1957). Similarly, SUGIHARA and MCGEE (1957) were able to recover the nickel complex of the usual petroleum porphyrin, deoxophylloerythroetioporphyrin, from Utah gilsonite. HODGSON et al. (1963a, b) separated intact porphyrin complexes from a series of crude oils paying particular attention to the relative quantities of vanadium and nickel complexes present, in an attempt to relate these to the circumstances under which oil may have arisen. The method was based upon an extraction of the crude oil with methanol and a chromatography of the extract on silica gel. Elution of the adsorbed extract with 1:1 hexane–benzene removed the nickel porphyrins (NiP$_p$) and 1:1 benzene–chloroform eluted the vanadyl porphyrins (VOP$_p$). The significance of the relative abundances of vanadyl and nickel porphyrins in petroleum is not clear. Nickel porphyrins are commonly more abundant than vanadyl in light crude oils, and the reverse is generally the case for heavy crude oils (DUNNING et al., 1953; HODGSON et al., 1963a, b). Exceptions to the rule seem to be related to the sulfur content of the oil, with evidence of some kind of direct relationship between sulfur and vanadyl pigments, as noted by RADCHENKO and SHESHINA (1955) and HODGSON et al. (1963b).

As noted earlier the forming of a stable metal complex of a porphyrin greatly simplifies the absorption spectrum of a free porphyrin with a change from

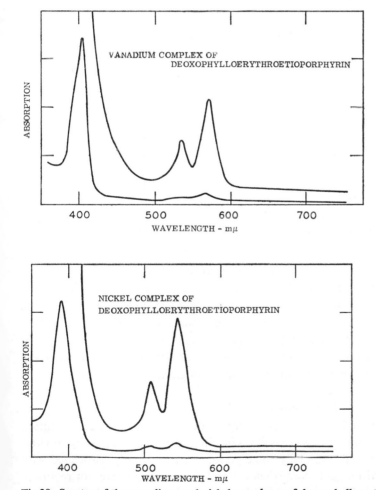

Fig.28. Spectra of the vanadium and nickel complexes of deoxophylloerythroetioporphyrin.

the typical four band spectrum to a two band spectrum. This is evident in the spectra of the vanadyl and nickel complexes of deoxophylloerythroetioporphyrin shown in Fig.28. The vanadyl complex has its major non-Soret bands occurring at longer wavelengths than those of the corresponding nickel complex. The occurrence of the absorption bands at shorter wavelengths for the nickel complex was thought to indicate a greater stability of the nickel complex over the vanadyl complex (CAUGHEY and CORWIN, 1955).

Fig.29 shows the absorption spectrum of vanadyl etioporphyrin III in dioxane; it is similar to that of the mesoporphyrin ester metal complexes. The corresponding nickel complexes of etioporphyrin III and mesoporphyrin IX are not well known.

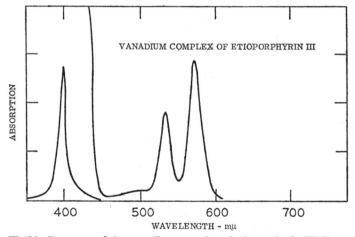

Fig.29. Spectrum of the vanadium complex of etioporphyrin III (ERDMAN et al., 1956).

Carboxylated porphyrin complexes in petroleum, MP_pCOOH, are common but not abundant. In a study of the United States and Venezuelan oils DUNNING et al. (1960) reported that carboxylated porphyrins made up less than 5% of the porphyrin material present in young oils, with an even smaller proportion in older oils. SOKOL'NIKOVA and RIZAEVA (1962) were unable to find carboxylated porphyrins in the oils from Uzbekistan. HODGSON et al. (1963a, b) reported NiP_p-COOH and VOP_pCOOH in several oils from America and Japan.

Chlorin compounds in petroleum

With porphyrins occurring in virtually every crude oil, albeit in trace quantities, it is perhaps reasonable to expect similar chlorin and tetrahydroporphyrin compounds to occur as well, especially since petroleum is normally associated with highly reducing environment. Nevertheless tetrahydro pigments are not reported, and only a few isolated occurrences of chlorin compounds are noted. In the handling of porphyrin aggregates, the occurrence of green compounds which may have been chlorins have been noted from time to time (GLEBOVSKAYA and VOL'KENSH- TEIN, 1948; GROENNINGS, 1953). Recently FISHER and DUNNING (1961) isolated a chlorin-like compound from a petroleum porphyrin aggregate. While its spectrum, shown in Fig.30, is similar to that of a chlorin, the weight of the evidence seemed to indicate that it was an oxidation product of a porphyrin, perhaps a hydroxypor- phyrin or an oxychlorin (FISHER and DUNNING, 1961). In a somewhat similar manner Howe reported the finding of chlorins in the petroleum porphyrin aggregate (HOWE, 1961), but some doubt was cast upon the interpretation of the results (BLUMER, 1961) and there is still no clear-cut case for the occurrence of chlorins or chlorin metal complexes in petroleum.

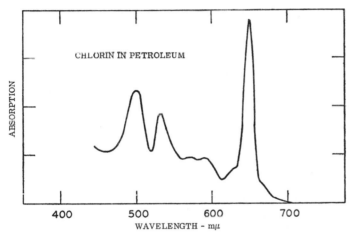

Fig.30. Spectrum of chlorin-type material isolated from petroleum porphyrin aggregate (FISCHER and DUNNING, 1961).

A further examination of oil shales by Blumer resulted in the reporting of chlorins in oil shales as dihydro-mesoetioporphyrin (etiochlorin III) and dihydro- deoxophylloerythroetioporphyrin (deoxomesoetiopyrropheophorbide *a*). Struc- tures of these compounds are illustrated in Fig.31 and the spectrum of the latter compound is shown in Fig.32. Blumer attributed the occurrence of these compounds not to the preservation of primary chlorins but rather to the formation of secondary chlorins through hydrogenation of the corresponding porphyrins under extreme reducing conditions.

Having gained some understanding of the fundamentals of porphyrin chem- istry and some knowledge of the occurrence of such compounds in petroleum, the manner in which these compounds might have arisen and become part of the petroleum substance will now be considered.

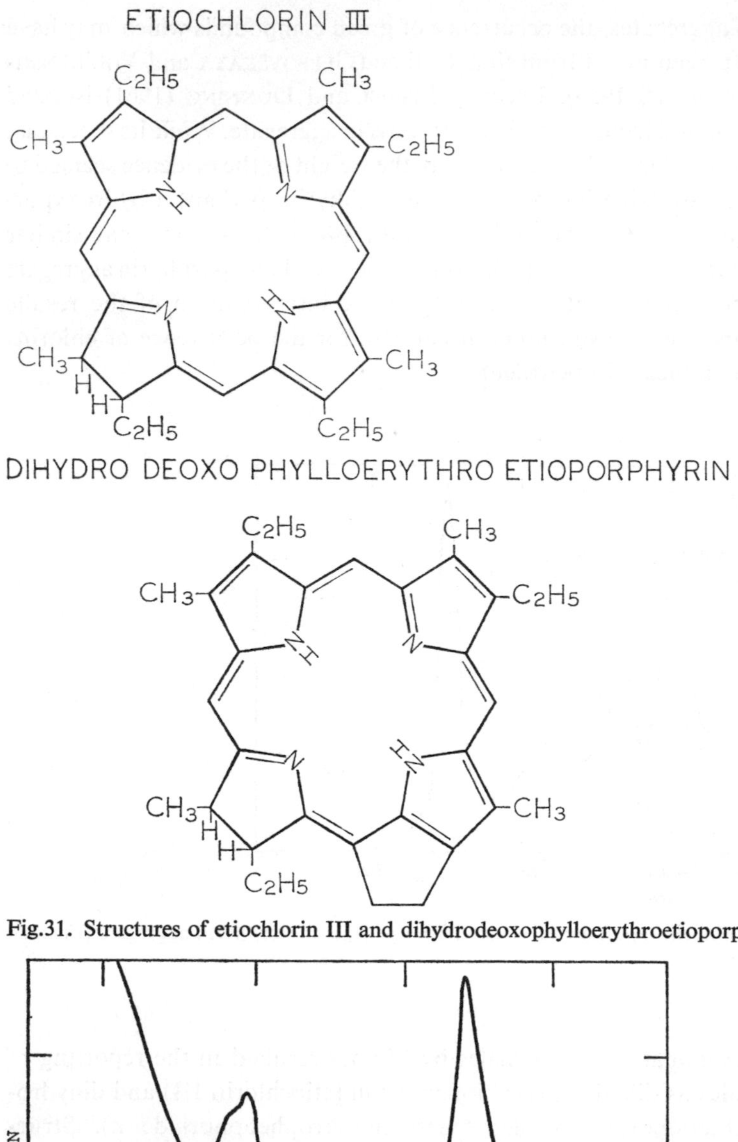

ETIOCHLORIN III

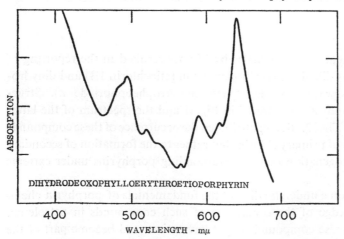

DIHYDRO DEOXO PHYLLOERYTHRO ETIOPORPHYRIN

Fig.31. Structures of etiochlorin III and dihydrodeoxophylloerythroetioporphyrin.

DIHYDRODEOXOPHYLLOERYTHROETIOPORPHYRIN

ABSORPTION

400   500   600   700

WAVELENGTH - mμ

Fig.32. Spectrum of dihydrodeoxophylloerythroetioporphyrin (BLUMER and OMENN, 1961).

THE EVOLUTION OF PETROLEUM PORPHYRINS

The most abundant porphyrins in petroleum are marked by the presence of a fifth ring, the isocyclic ring. This implies that these compounds have arisen in some manner from chlorophyll (TREIBS, 1934). At the same time some of the less abundant porphyrins do not have the isocyclic ring which accounts for a tendency to attribute these compounds to an animal origin. Hemin, a constituent of animals, may give a series of hemin-type porphyrins. Such observations tend to focus attention on the origin of petroleum porphyrins, and the purpose of the following discussion is to explore the origin of porphyrins in such a manner that some light may be shed on the general question of the origin of petroleum.

There are several groups of pigments which may be regarded as possible precursors of petroleum porphyrins. In addition to the chlorophylls and hemin, there are the bacteriochlorophylls. Further, there is evidence of other metal chlorin complexes in living matter, and it is important to include the possibilities of contributions from porphyrin enzyme systems which are common trace constituents of living matter also. Before dwelling on the contributions to be expected from specific trace pigments in organisms, attention will be directed first to the role of chlorophylls, bacteriochlorophylls and hemin as precursors to petroleum pigments.

As mentioned earlier the basic porphin structure may be synthesized from pyrrole. In fact, porphin may be regarded as a condensation product of pyrrole. This has been used as a method of synthesizing porphin by ROTHEMUND (1936), in which formaldehyde was utilized to provide the bridging methine between neighboring pyrrole components. The yield of product by this method was small, and a more effective method based on the use of a Grignard reagent and the required alpha-substituted pyrrole—2-dimethylaminomethyl pyrrole was used by EISNER and LINSTEAD (1955a). The product of this condensation is not porphin but chlorin. The chlorin is dehydrogenated with a quinone to produce porphin (EISNER and LINSTEAD, 1955b). The corresponding conversion of porphin to chlorin can be brought about by sodium reductions (SCHLESINGER et al., 1950), or by Raney nickel reduction (BLUMER and OMENN, 1961).

The chemical syntheses of porphyrins and chlorins probably have no significance insofar as the origin of such pigments in petroleum is concerned. It is of interest, however, to note that the condensation of pyrrole in nature is not impossible in in-vivo systems. UREY (1952) reported that porphyrins may have originated under reducing conditions of ultraviolet light irradiation and spark discharge of methane, ammonia, water and hydrogen. The importance of such indicated reactions is usually related to discussions concerned with the establishment of life in which light irradiation and spark discharge in a reducing atmosphere may be of considerable significance for establishing biologically active compounds (HODGSON and BAKER, 1964). Purple crystals of a porphyrin mixture were obtained by heating

pyrrole and benzaldehyde in the presence of pyridine (ARONOFF and CALVIN, 1943).
The importance of such reactions in accounting for the presence of porphyrins
in petroleum in a direct sense is undoubtedly very small.

The presence of the isocyclic ring in most petroleum porphyrins is usually
interpreted as an indication that these pigments originally came from chlorophyll.
This is clear from the structure of chlorophyll *a* as given in Fig. 33, when it is
compared with the structure of the equally ubiquitous pigment with considerable
biological importance, hemin. It is clear that the phylloporphyrins in crude oil
may be derived from chlorophylls and the etio compounds from hemin. It is easy
to reach such a conclusion, then immediately go one step further and assign the
origin of crude oil to plant and animal life in a like proportion. This surely is an
over-simplification of the origin of porphyrins and the origin of petroleum, because
two factors are overlooked: hemin-like porphyrins are known to occur in plant
material (DUNNING and MOORE, 1957); and the isocyclic ring of chlorophyll degradation products can be cleaved with amines (WELLER and LIVINGSTONE, 1954).

In the present discussion the authors will try to establish, in a general sense, an
understanding of the manner in which chlorophylls may give rise to petroleum porphyrins. Any particular discussion of this topic at this time must be arbitrary
since the starting materials have not been positively established. For example,
while it is readily accepted that chlorophylls are the starting material, the question
arises as to what variety of chlorophyll is being considered.

In photosynthetic organisms, several types of chlorophylls have been iden-

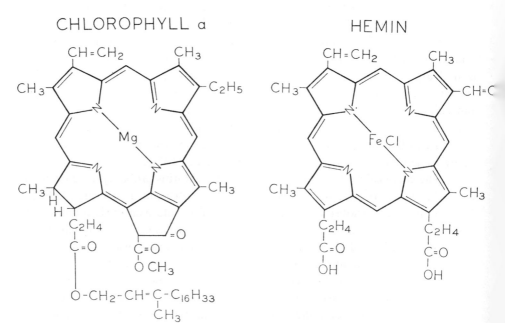

Fig.33. Structures of chlorophyll *a* and hemin.

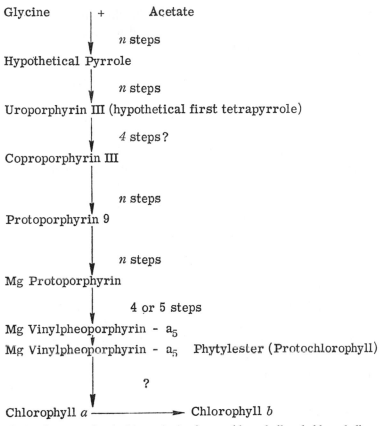

Fig.34. Sequence for the biosynthesis of protochlorophyll and chlorophyll *a*.

tified; chlorophylls (*a*, *b*, *c*, *d*, and *e*), bacteriochlorophylls (*a*, *b*, and *c*), and bacterioviridins. For a detailed study of these, the reader is referred to the work and summary by STRAIN (1949). Chlorophyll *a* is the most abundant, being common to all autotrophic organisms except the pigmented bacteria. Chlorophyll *b* is found with chlorophyll *a* in higher plants and in some algae. Chlorophylls *c*, *d* and *e* are found only in algae and associated with chlorophyll *a*. Bacteriochlorophylls are the chlorophylls of a number of purple and brown bacteria (VAN NIEL and ARNOLD, 1938). Bacterioviridins, the chlorophylls of the green bacteria (METZNER, 1922) have subsequently been given the more appropriate name — chlorobium chlorophylls (H. LARSEN, 1953). There are apparently several chlorobium chlorophylls (HUGHES and HOLT, 1962).

Chlorophylls *a* and *b* are the most abundant and their biosynthesis has been studied in some detail.

Ideas on the formation of chlorophyll have centred on concepts of genesis, nature and transformation of chlorophyll precursors. Many names have been given to this precursor by investigators including leukophyll, chlorophor, carotenoid pigments, etiolin, protophyllin, protochlorophyll, chlorophyllogen, etc. SMITH and YOUNG (1956) concluded that protochlorophyll was the best name to designate the immediate precursor of chlorophyll.

On the base of tracer studies and the compounds isolated from *Chlorella* mutants, GRANICK (1948, 1949, 1951) proposed a sequence for the biosynthesis of protochlorophyll and chlorophyll *a* (see Fig.34).

Later, SMITH (1960) reviewed protochlorophyll transformations. In very recent years considerable work has been done expanding the knowledge on biological and photosynthetic mechanisms in plants and bacteria. From the investigations already performed have come, for example, identification of new compounds (THOMAS and MARTELL, 1959; STANIER and SMITH, 1960; STANIER, 1960; OLSON and ROMANO, 1962; EIMHJELLEM et al., 1963; and JEFFREY, 1963), new ideas or mechanisms (STANIER, 1961; BOGORAD, 1963; and KARALI and PRICE, 1963), as well as improvements in methods (CALVIN, 1959; HOLDEN, 1962; SPORER et al., 1954; and HENDRICKSON et al., 1957).

It is important to note that all chlorophylls tend to degrade to either the same structure or structures which are very similar, distinguishable only through mass spectra (THOMAS and BLUMER, 1964). As a result the contributions from specific chlorophylls become obscured. An attempt will be made to show a sequence of reactions which could account for the conversion of chlorophylls to petroleum pigments in a "pure" chemical system. Following this the "pure" system will be related to those of the environment attending the formation of petroleum.

Description of possible porphyrin precursors

Chlorophyll a

Chlorophyll *a* is of widespread occurrence in plant organisms. In the pure state it is a waxy, blue-black substance very freely soluble in ether, ethyl alcohol, acetone, chloroform, carbon disulfide and benzene; it is slightly soluble in petroleum ether. The alcoholic and ether solutions are blue-green in color with a deep red fluorescence. The structure of chlorophyll *a* is given in Fig.33 and is represented by the molecular formula: the magnesium complex of 1, 3, 5, 8-tetramethyl-2-vinyl-4-ethyl-9-oxo-10-carbmethoxy-phorbin-7-propionic acid phytyl ester ($C_{55}H_{72}N_4O_5Mg$). Its molecular weight is 894 and the compound has a melting point of 117°C. Some of its important structural features are: (*1*) A vinyl group on carbon 2; (*2*) An isocyclic ring joining the gamma carbon to carbon-6; (*3*) A phytyl ester on the propionic acid side chain on carbon-7; (*4*) The magnesium atom complexed in the centre of the molecule; (*5*) The two active hydrogen atoms on carbons 7 and 8.

It is apparent that chlorophyll is a rather highly substituted naturally occurring chlorin. Although the molecule is a metal complex its spectrum in ether is similar to that of a free chlorin with absorption maxima at 660, 613, 577, 531, 498, 429 and 409 mμ (Fig.35). The fact that magnesium is very loosely bonded in

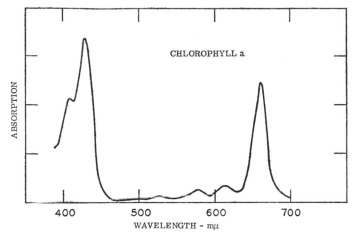

Fig.35. Spectrum of chlorophyll *a* in ether (ZSCHEILE and COMAR, 1941).

the molecule is reflected by the readiness with which it is split from the molecule with mild acids as indicated by JOSLYN and MACKINNEY (1938) in a study on the rate of conversion of chlorophyll *a* to pheophytin *a*. Acid attack (a few minutes with concentrated hydrochloric acid) will saponify the phytyl ester producing pheophorbide *a*.

The most significant advance in recent years in chlorophyll chemistry has been the synthesis of chlorophyll *a* by WOODWARD and his associates (1960). A partial synthesis of pheophorbide *a* (a prime intermediate in the formation of chlorophyll *a*) was accomplished about the same time by STRELL et al. (1960).

The content of chlorophyll in green leaves varies between about 0.05 and 0.20% fresh weight, generally consisting of 2.5 parts of chlorophyll *a* to one part of chlorophyll *b* (WILLSTATTER and STOLL, 1913). Leaves of yellow–green varieties may have a far greater relative amount of chlorophyll *a*, with the total amount of chlorophyll often being less than one-third that in green varieties of leaves. A greater proportion of chlorophyll *a* is frequently found in "shade" plants compared to "sun" plants.

Great variations in chlorophyll content occur in different classes of algae. In *chlorella*, the chlorophyll content may be as much as three times that of leaves and the chlorophyll *a*/chlorophyll *b* ratio may be as great as 3/1 whereas in many green algae it is only 1.4/1. Chlorophyll *b* is absent in brown algae, red algae, diatoms and the blue–green algae. Thus chlorophyll *a* is generally the most abundant form in all plants, and with the exception of bacteria, is common to all types of autotrophic plants. In the brown algae, diatoms and flagellates, in which the *b* component is absent, chlorophyll *c* is present in an amount about one-tenth that of the total chlorophyll content. In the marine environment, especially offshore in deeper water, chlorophyll *c* may be equally or more abundant than chlorophyll *b* (ALLEN et al., 1961). Chlorophyll *d*, which was reported to accompany chlorophyll *a* in red algae (STRAIN and MANNING, 1942a, 1942b; MANNING and STRAIN, 1943), has been found to be very sporadic in its abundance in red algae and may possibly be a pathological oxidation product of chlorophyll *a* of questionable biological significance (HOLT, 1961). RICHARDS and THOMPSON (1952) devised a method for the estimation and characterization of plankton by chlorophyll analysis. This method has been discussed and revised by PARSON and STRICKLAND (1963) and a new method devised for the determination of chlorophyll *c* (PARSON, 1963).

Chlorophyll b

Chlorophyll *b* differs from chlorophyll *a* structurally in only one respect—it has a formyl group rather than a methyl group on carbon-3 as shown in Fig.36. This seemingly minor difference in structure brings about an appreciable change in the absorption spectrum, as shown in Fig.37, with maxima at 642, 593, 545, 453 and 427 mμ (in ether). The ether solution of chlorophyll *b* has a brilliant green color with a red fluorescence.

Other chlorophylls

Chlorophylls *c* and *d* are considerably less abundant than the *a* and *b* components and are much less clearly defined. The absorption spectrum for chlorophyll *c* has

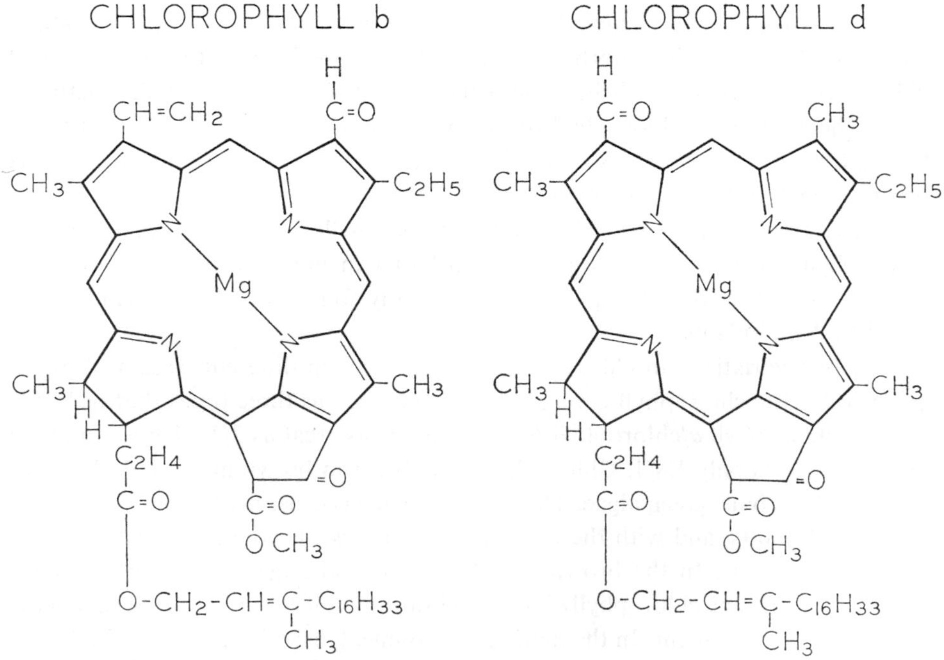

Fig.36. Structures of chlorophyll *b* and chlorophyll *d*.

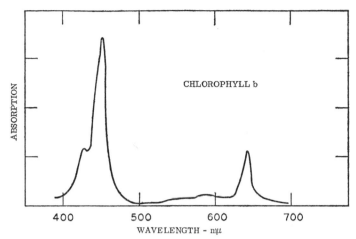

Fig.37. Spectrum of chlorophyll *b* in ether (ZSCHEILE and COMAR, 1941).

been reported by STRAIN and MANNING (1942a) with absorption maxima in methyl alcohol solution, at 635, 583 and 450 mμ.

The structure of chlorophyll *c* is not known but GRANICK (1949) suggested that it was a magnesium pheoporphyrin rather than a magnesium chlorin—based on spectra of the pheophytin. The pheophytin has an acid number of about 12 (GRANICK, 1949; JEFFREY, 1963). JEFFREY (1963) has recently reported properties based on more highly purified material. Spectral characteristics are slightly different than previously reported. Based on the magnesium content he reported a molecular weight of 1052 ± 50.

The spectrum for chlorophyll *d* in methyl alcohol has maxima at 695, 633, 460 and 400 mμ. Chlorophyll *d* in petroleum ether has a yellow–green color with deep red fluorescence and is considered to resemble chlorophyll *a* more than chlorophyll *c*. HOLT and MORLEY (1959) proposed a molecular formula for chlorophyll *d* as 2-desvinyl-2-formyl chlorophyll *a* (Fig.36).

Bacteriochlorophyll

All the foregoing chlorophylls with the exception of chlorophyll *c* are believed to be chlorin (dihydroporphyrin) pigments. Bacteriochlorophyll on the other hand is a tetrahydroporphyrin having an additional pair of "extra" hydrogens, as shown in Fig.38, on pyrrole ring II. In addition, the vinyl group on carbon-2 of chlorophyll *a* is replaced by an acetyl group. These changes in the molecule result in a further marked change in the absorption spectrum of the pigment. The spectrum of the ether solution, shown in Fig.39, is characterized by a major non-Soret band at very high wavelengths as noted earlier, the maxima being located at 772, 697, 575, 526, 391 and 358 mμ (WIEGL, 1953).

Bacteriochlorophyll is the green pigment in purple photosynthetic bacteria. The green photosynthetic bacteria contain the pigment bacterioviridin whose

structure may be intermediate between that of chlorophyll *a* and bacteriochlorophyll, and whose absorption spectrum is similar to that of chlorophyll *a* (HILL and
WHITTINGHAM, 1955).

BUDER (1919) stated that the ecological significance of bacterial purpurin,
in connection with purple bacteria, lies in its capacity for absorbing infra-red,
yellow and green light, i.e., those rays which are transmitted by chlorophyll. He
stated further that purple bacteria are therefore capable of covering the bottom
of a body of water, the surface of which is obscured by a dense mat of algae. When

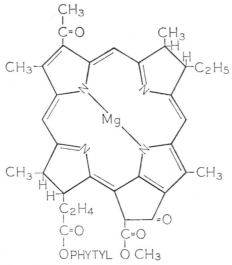

Fig.38. Structure of bacteriochlorophyll *a*.

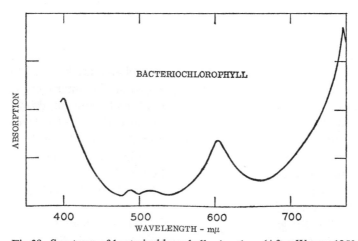

Fig.39. Spectrum of bacteriochlorophyll *a* in ether. (After WIEGL, 1953.)

the absorption spectra of living leaves is compared with that of such bacteria, a rather uniform alternation of the absorption bands of chlorophyll and bacteria is observed.

VAN NIEL (1938) and GAFFRON (1933) were able to prove the ability of red sulfur bacteria (thiocystis) and sulfur-free bacteria (rhodovibrio) to assimilate carbon dioxide in a photosynthetic manner similar to the action of chlorophyll in plants. For this reason the green pigment from these bacteria was named bacterio-chlorophyll. The sulfur bacteria are extremely broadly propagated. They require no oxygen, grow in pure inorganic nutrient medium and are capable of assimilation of carbon dioxide. They are recorded as being the oldest earth inhabitant and from this geologists conclude that the original atmosphere of the earth had no oxygen (FISCHER et al., 1938).

A number of investigators have sought clarification of the bacterio-chloro-phyll structure (NOACK and SCHNEIDER, 1933; SCHNEIDER, 1930, 1934; FISCHER and HASENKAMP, 1935a, b; and FISCHER et al., 1938). Bacteriochlorophyll has a basic porphin structure containing magnesium in complex bonding, and as in chloro-phyll a, there are two carboxyl groups of which one is esterified with a methyl group and the other with a phytyl group or another high molecular alcohol.

There are believed to be several isomers of bacteriochlorophyll. Bacterio-chlorophylls a, b, and c have been reported but their structures have not been established. There also is some uncertainty over the relative abundance of each isomer. SCHNEIDER (1934) reported a greater abundance of the b component over a than the excess of chlorophyll a over chlorophyll b in higher plants, whereas SEYBOLD and EGLE (1939) contended that there was considerable variation in the relative quantities of each but that the a component generally exceeded the b component.

SEYBOLD and EGLE (1939) reported a method for separating the three isomers. A benzene extract of thiocystis bacteria suspension was chromatographed on powdered sucrose with benzene, the steel-blue layer at the top of the column developed into two layers. Bacteriochlorophyll b was identified as the pigment making up the upper green layer and bacteriochlorophyll a made up the lower steel-blue layer. Each layer was eluted with a methyl alcohol-ether mixture. The alcohol solution from which the a and b components had been removed was treated with benzene and other reagents such that the remaining pigment passed into the benzene layer. This benzene solution was chromatographed on powdered sugar and a third component obtained which was identified as bacterio-chlorophyll c.

SEYBOLD and EGLE (1939) stated that if the bacteria suspension is extracted directly with methyl alcohol containing oxalic acid, only bacteriopheophytin a is obtained; however, both bacteriopheophytins a and b are obtained if a methyl alcohol solution of bacteriochlorophyll a is allowed to stand in the dark for several hours and then converted into bacteriopheophytin with oxalic acid; this, according to Seybold and Egle, indicates that bacteriochlorophylls *b* and *c* are not present in bacteria, in vivo, but that they are formed during handling of the extract.

Bacteriochlorophyll *a* is azure blue in ether, methyl alcohol, benzene and acetone, and does not fluoresce. Bacteriochlorophyll *b* is a dirty green–yellow in ether, somewhat similar to chlorophyll *b*. It has a red fluorescence unlike the *a* component. Bacteriochlorophyll *c* is brown in ether with a strong red fluorescence and has an absorption spectrum very similar to bacteriochlorophyll *b*.

A high degree of lability of bacteriochlorophyll *a* has been reported which is supported by a study of SEYBOLD and EGLE (1939) in which the non-fluorescing bacteriochlorophyll *a* was irradiated for only a few seconds either with sunlight or an ultra-violet lamp. Fluorescence occurred accompanied by a gradual change in color of the ether solution. The spectrum of the irradiated solution was essentially identical with that of bacteriochlorophyll *b*. The above authors, when investigating the physiology of plant pigments, chromatographed the colored materials from red sulfur bacteria (thiocystis). Accompanying bacteriochlorophyll *a* were two other green pigments whose absorption spectra were in good agreement with that of 2-acetyl chlorophyll *a*. These were labelled as bacteriochlorophylls *b* and *c* (SEYBOLD and EGLE, 1939). FISCHER et al. (1938) proved that the extremely sensitive bacteriochlorophyll *a* very quickly forms 2-acetyl chlorophyll *a* in vitro and the conclusion was reached that bacteriochlorophyll *b* was in fact 2-acetyl chlorophyll *a*. Seybold and Egle reported that Fischer's bacteriochlorophylls *b* and *c* probably existed as dehydrogenation products due to handling of the extracts. Fischer suggested a reciprocal relationship between the *a* and *b* bacteriochlorophylls according to the following scheme:

$$\text{Bacteriochlorophyll } a \underset{\text{hydrogenation}}{\overset{\text{dehydrogenation}}{\rightleftarrows}} \text{2-acetyl chlorophyll } a$$

Oxidation of bacteriochlorophyll, i.e., with $KMnO_4$, I_2, H_2O_2, oxygen of the air, etc., produces a stable molecule. This type of reaction also occurs by aging a bacteriochlorophyll solution in the light (similar to the irradiation mentioned above). A characteristic red band appears in place of the band in the yellow region of the spectrum. The occurrence of this red band makes the absorption spectrum similar to that of chlorophyll (SCHNEIDER, 1934).

Saponification of aqueous solutions of bacteriochlorophylls produces bacteriochlorophyllins (by loss of the phytyl group) which are clearly defined by their characteristic color and absorption spectra. Three bacteriochlorophyllins were observed corresponding to the three bacteriochlorophylls.

Hemin

Although it is apparent that petroleum porphyrins for the most part are derived from chlorophyll-like compounds, there are pigment compounds in petroleum which resemble another biologically important pigment—hemin. The structure of

this compound is illustrated in Fig.33 and is given by the molecular formula
1, 3, 5, 8-tetramethyl-2, 4-divinyl-6, 7-dipropionic acid ferric chloride ($C_{34}H_{32}N_4O_4$.
FeCl) with a molecular weight of 652. Hemin is a porphyrin, not a chlorin. Significant aspects of the molecule in the present discussion are: (*1*) It has no isocyclic
ring; (*2*) Iron is the complexed metal; (*3*) There is a vinyl group on carbon 4;
(*4*) The propionic acid groups on carbons 6 and 7 are not esterified.

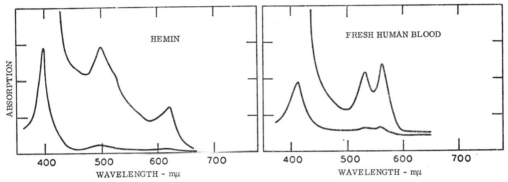

Fig.40. Spectrum of hemin in methyl alcohol and human blood.

Hemin can be obtained from the hemoglobin constituent of blood. Spectra
of hemin and of fresh human blood are given in Fig.40. CALVIN (1963) presented
evidence that hemoglobin has a "crevice" structure, with the hemin held in the
"crevice" by two ligands, rather than a "plate" structure, with the metalloporphyrin connected to the polypeptide by a single ligand.

Hemin compounds have been extensively reviewed by FALK et al., 1961.

Other naturally-occurring porphyrin and chlorin pigments

While chlorophylls and the hemin compounds are commonly regarded as likely
source pigments for petroleum porphyrins, care should be taken to include the
possibilities of significant contributions from other naturally-occurring pigments.
For example, it is well known that enzyme systems almost always contain trace
metals (BOYER et al., 1959), and contributions from these as a general class should
be considered. Porphyrins in general, whether in enzyme systems or otherwise,
are common to invertebrates as well as vertebrates as reviewed recently by RI-
MINGTON and KENNEDY (1962). Special mention might be made of porphyrin
pigments in the excreta of living organisms, since these bear on transformation of
primary compounds by biological agents. Reviews of this phase of the topic have
been published by ALLEN (1960) and RIMINGTON and KENNEDY (1962).

Origin of petroleum porphyrins

Petroleum porphyrin metal complexes are generally regarded as stable end products
of the partial breakdown of primary source material of petroleum. It is clear that

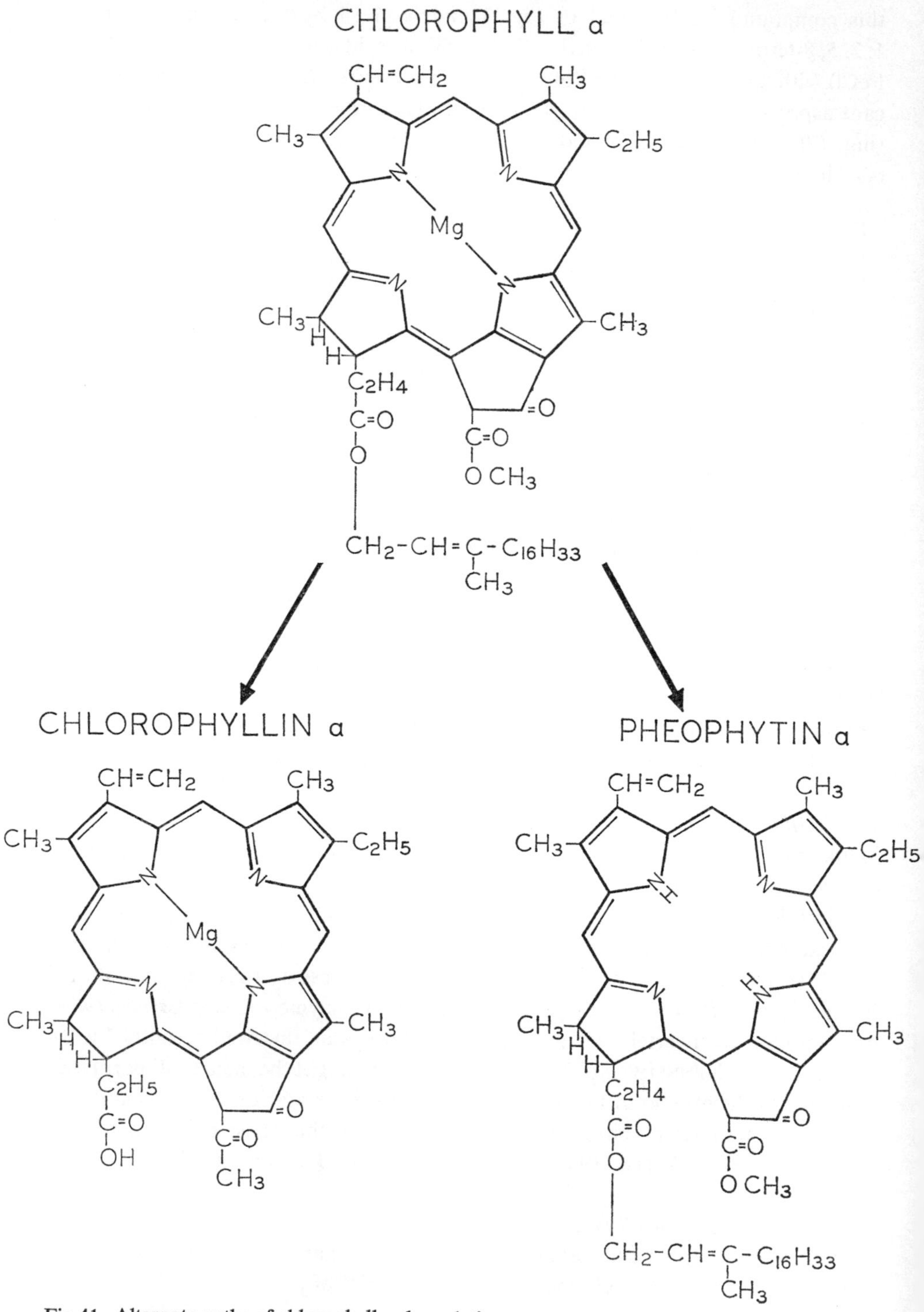

Fig.41. Alternate paths of chlorophyll *a* degradation.

many pigments of living organisms would degrade and stabilize to these pigments. It is convenient to use the chlorophylls and hemin pigments to illustrate a systematic set of reactions which might account for the production of petroleum porphyrins, but care must be taken to avoid assuming that these compounds are necessarily the initial compounds.

In the case of chlorophyll *a*, such a sequence of reactions might be set out as follows—the order of presentation is not necessarily the most likely order which the compounds would experience: (*1*) Removal of magnesium and iron; (*2*) Saponification of the esters; (*3*) Oxidation of chlorin hydrogens; (*4*) Saturation of the vinyl group(s); (*5*) Reduction of the formyl and acetyl groups; (*6*) Reduction of carbonyl groups; (*7*) Decarboxylation of the acid groups; (*8*) Complexing with vanadium or nickel.

A wide range of chemical changes is required and the object of this section is to consider how these may be accomplished chemically. Some of the indicated reactions proceed with greater difficulty than others, therefore it is necessary to select a sequence of reactions somewhat arbitrarily for illustrating the reactions.

As noted by ORR et al. (1958) the major reaction path could follow either of two possible paths depending on the timing of the loss of magnesium from the chlorophyll structure. If the magnesium were retained, it would follow a short series of chlorophyllin compounds; if the magnesium were lost immediately, the sequence would involve a series of pheo-compounds. These alternate paths are illustrated in Fig.41. The latter possibility seems to be favored because of the known lability of the magnesium atom (JOSLYN and MACKINNEY, 1938; MACKINNEY and JOSLYN, 1940, 1941; HODGSON and HITCHON, 1959). As a result attention will be directed to the development of the petroleum porphyrins starting with the latter alternative—the pheo-series—to illustrate a likely sequence of reactions leading to petroleum pigments.

Such a sequence of reactions involves both the degradation of the chlorophyll, hemin and bacteriochlorophyll starting materials and the formation of metal complexes, leading to the vanadium and nickel complexes of petroleum porphyrins. It is not known when the metal complexes arise; therefore it is convenient first to discuss the degradation reactions, and then consider the metal complexing reactions.

Conversion of precursors to petroleum porphyrins

Chlorophyll *a* in mildly acid conditions is converted to pheophytin *a* (JOSLYN and MACKINNEY, 1938; WICKLIFF and ARONOFF, 1963). This is simply a replacement of the magnesium with acid hydrogens. It may take place as a stepwise process with an intermediate compound being formed in which one hydrogen is attached but the magnesium is still closely associated with the molecule. The free chlorin formed is reasonably stable and has an absorption spectrum different

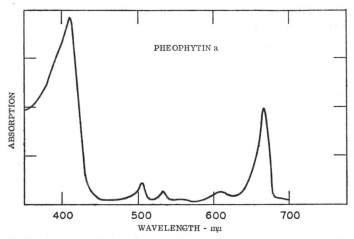

Fig.42. Spectrum of pheophytin *a* in ether (ZSCHEILE and COMAR, 1941).

from that of chlorophyll *a*. The spectrum of pheophytin *a* (Fig.42) is that of a typical chlorin. Its absorption maxima occur at 666, 608, 558, 535, 505 and 410 mμ for an ether solution (ZSCHEILE and COMAR, 1941). Like chlorophyll, it has a low water solubility. It is soluble only in concentrated acid even though basic nitrogens do exist in the molecule. Its acid extraction number is 28–29%. Pheophytin *a* is freely soluble in alcohol and petroleum ether; very slightly soluble in benzene and chloroform. Its ether solution is olive green in color and shows a red fluorescence.

    Other isomers of pheophytin are discussed by STRAIN and MANNING (1942a, b) and MANNING and STRAIN (1943). The spectra of pheophytin *b* and bacterio-pheophytin are shown in Fig.43.

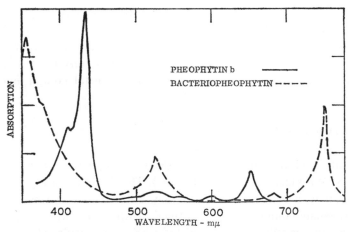

Fig.43. Spectrum of pheophytin *b* in ether (ZSCHEILE and COMAR, 1941) and bacteriopheophytin in ether. (After WIEGL, 1953.)

The most labile portion of the pheophytin molecule is probably the phytyl ester group on the propionic acid side chain on carbon-7. This is readily removed by slightly acidic or basic media giving rise to the pheophorbides. Pheophorbide *a* is a reasonably stable compound having chemical properties very similar to those of pheophytin *a*. The extraction number is lower (about 15%) than that of pheophytin, as a result of either or both of two factors: the removal of a large water-insoluble "hydrocarbon" portion of the pigment molecule, and the possibility that the free propionic acid side chain increases the basicity of the pyrrole nitrogens. Probably the former is the more powerful factor. Hydrolysis of the ester, in producing a free carboxyl group on the pigment molecule, makes the compound soluble in very dilute alkalies through the formation of alkali metal salts. The spectrum of pheophorbide *a* is almost identical with that of pheophytin *a*, differing only in that the extinction coefficient of the major non-Soret band in pheophorbide is lower than of pheophytin. The conversion of chlorophyll *a* to pheophorbide *a* is summarized in Fig.44.

Bacteriopheophorbides are formed from bacteriochlorophyll in a similar manner and have properties similar to those of the bacteriopheophytins. Since there is no ester group in the compounds of the hemin series, there is no corresponding saponification; however, these compounds exhibit the same alkali solubility characteristics due to the presence of the free propionic acid groups.

The next step in the development of petroleum porphyrins is not well established, but it appears that the next most labile groups in the molecules are the chlorin "extra" hydrogens. Removal of these hydrogens results in a major conversion to porphyrin structures. As noted earlier, the conversion of a chlorin to a porphyrin through removal of the chlorin hydrogens is basically an oxidation process and can readily be accomplished by reacting the chlorin with quinones (EISNER and LINSTEAD, 1955b). It may be better to regard the conversion as a hydrogen transfer which can be brought about by any reagent which promotes lability of such hydrogens. Such a reagent would also favor the introduction of hydrogens into areas of unsaturation in such a molecule. There has been suggested an overall reaction for the conversion of pheophorbide *a* to pheoporphyrin which involves stripping of the "extra" hydrogens from carbons-7 and 8 and a simultaneous saturation of the vinyl group on carbon-2. This can be accomplished by treating pheophorbide *a* in acetic acid with hydriodic acid for a few minutes (FISCHER and SUS, 1930). Such mild treatment tends to bear out the suggestion that this could be a next step in the development of petroleum porphyrins. This conversion is illustrated in Fig.45. Similar conversions can be envisaged for the other pheophorbides. Again there is no directly corresponding reaction for members of the hemin series except insofar as saturation of the vinyl groups on the molecule are concerned.

The compound resulting from the above reactions (pheoporphyrin) is readily recognized as a porphyrin by its spectrum with four significant non-Soret bands

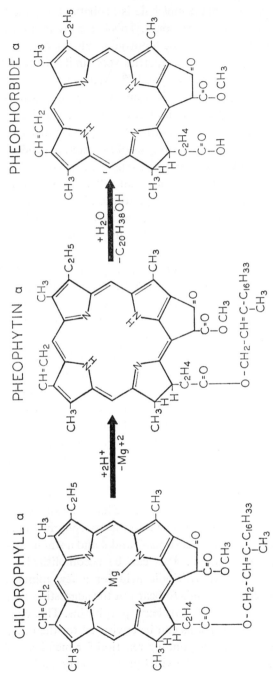

Fig.44. Structural conversion of chlorophyll *a* to pheophorbide *a*.

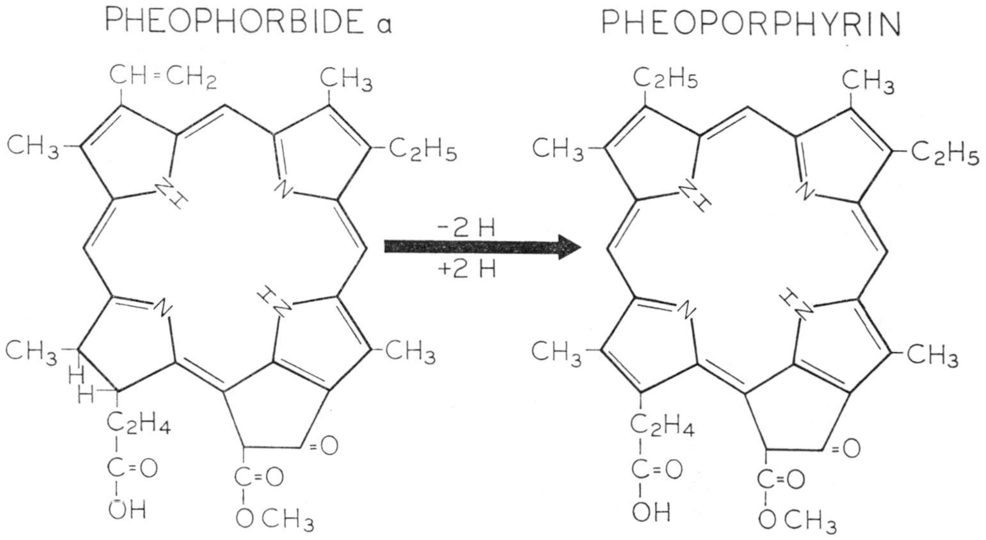

PHEOPHORBIDE a   PHEOPORPHYRIN

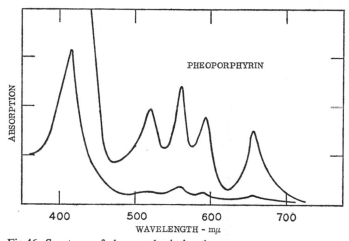

Fig.45. Structural conversion of pheophorbide *a* to pheoporphyrin.

Fig.46. Spectrum of pheoporphyrin in ether.

as illustrated in Fig.46. It has the form of a rhodo-type spectrum, with some suggestion of a chlorin residue by the prominence of the first band. This porphyrin is very soluble in chloroform and almost insoluble in methyl alcohol. Its extraction number of 9% represents a further increase in the basicity of the pyrrole nitrogens.

Pheoporphyrin is unstable and almost spontaneously degrades to phylloerythrin. This takes place through a saponification of the methyl ester of the carboxylic acid associated with the isocyclic ring, followed by decarboxylation of the resulting free acid. This type of reaction is characteristic of esters of carboxylic

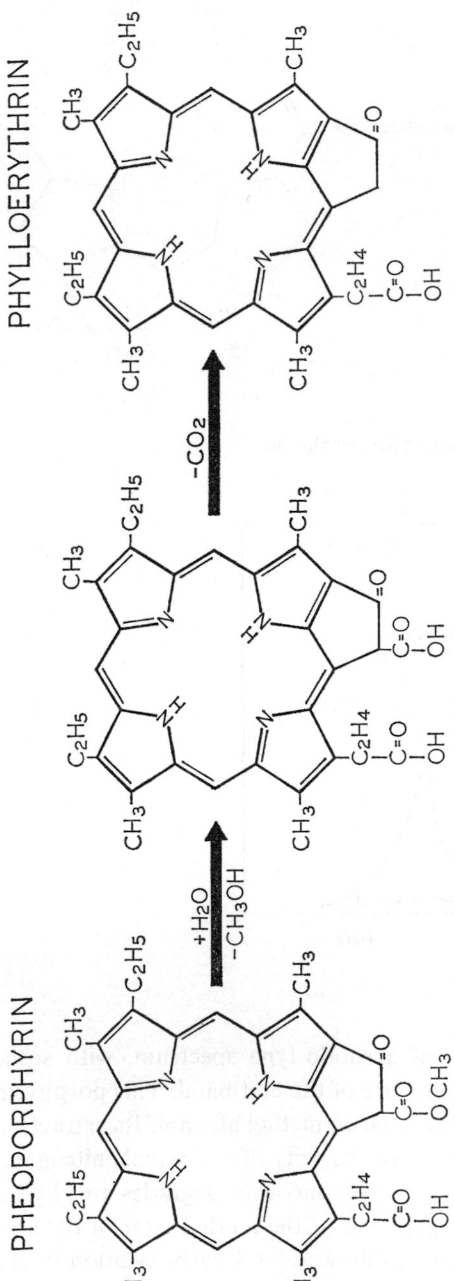

Fig.47. Structural conversion of pheoporphyrin to phylloerythrin.

acids which have a carbonyl group in a position beta to the carboxyl group. These reactions are illustrated in Fig.47 and are brought about by a further treatment of pheoporphyrin with hydriodic acid. Phylloerythrin has been observed in ox bile and feces of herbivora. These biological occurrences convinced Fischer that the hydriodic acid treatment was mild (STEELE, 1937).

Similar reactions can be postulated for the formation of pheoporphyrins from other compounds. Chlorophyll b and bacteriochlorophyll would have undergone one further reaction—the reaction required to reduce the formyl or acetyl groups.

Treatment of bacteriochlorophyll derivatives in acetic acid with hydriodic acid results in the formation of two bacteriopheoporphyrins which are analogous to the corresponding chlorophyll derivatives. They were identified by their acid extraction numbers—one being bacteriopheoporphyrin-7 and the other bacterio-pheoporphyrin-12 (SCHNEIDER, 1934).

The corresponding reactions in the chlorophyll d series would result in a phylloerythrin differing from the foregoing structure in the detail that carbon-2 would be bearing a methyl group rather than an ethyl group. This compound would be almost indistinguishable from phylloerythrin in all respects except by mass spectra.

The spectrum of phylloerythrin in the chlorophyll a series resembles that of pheoporphyrin in that it is also a rhodo type. The one significant difference is that the first peak, which was so dominant in pheoporphyrin, is reduced in intensity and shifted to shorter wavelengths so that the spectrum of phylloerythrin is that of a typical rhodo compound. The spectrum of phylloerythrin is illustrated in Fig.48.

Phylloerythrin is very similar to pheoporphyrin in chemical characteristics. Its extraction number is 7–8 %, making difficult the separation of the two compounds on the basis of acid solubility. A new technique developed by HUGHES and HOLT

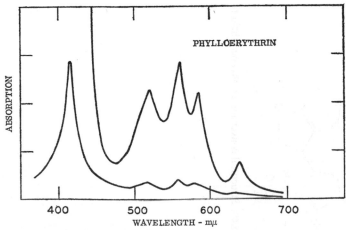

Fig.48. Spectrum of phylloerythrin in ether.

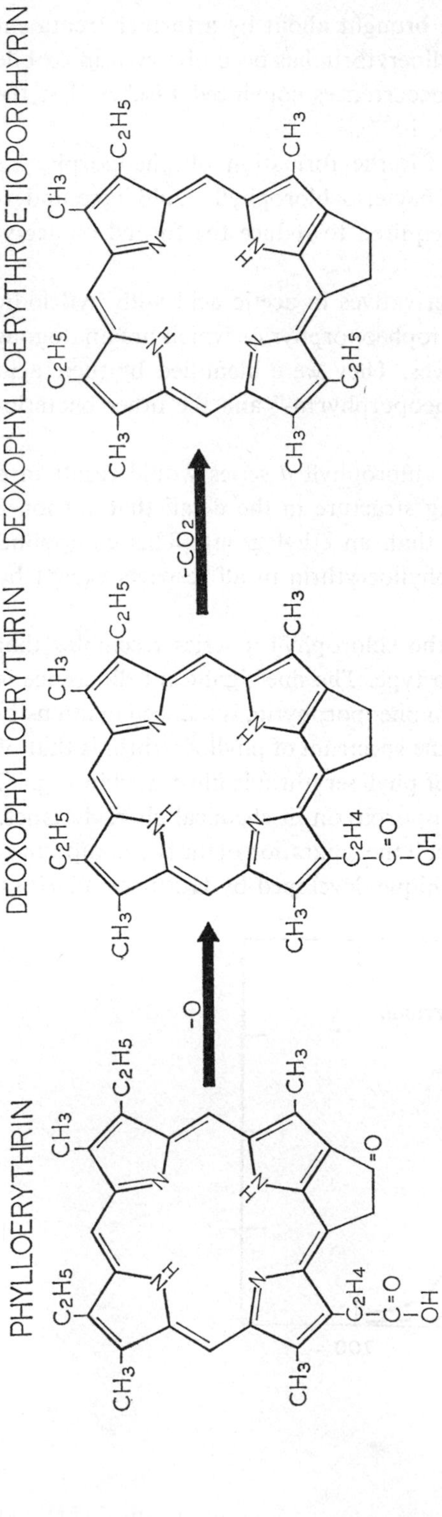

Fig. 49. Structural conversion of phylloerythrin to deoxophylloerythroetioporphyrin.

(1962) using counter-current liquid–liquid partition chromatography, for the separation of six chlorobium pheophorbides, may well be adapted to this separation.

The next major change in the developing petroleum porphyrin pigments is the reduction of the carbonyl group on the isocyclic ring. This results in the formation of deoxophylloerythrin, one of the petroleum pigments. The structural change is indicated in Fig.49 and the spectrum of the free pigment is given in Fig.50, indicating that the spectrum has now assumed the phyllo-type configuration. The significant change in spectral configuration is a graphic illustration of the effect of the carbonyl group in partial conjugation with the porphin ring structure. The reduction of the carbonyl group is accomplished with considerable difficulty— the reaction requiring treatment with hydrobromic acid in acetic acid at 180°C (FISCHER and ORTH, 1957). The pigment so formed is a still stronger base, being extractable with only 2% hydrochloric acid. The persistence of the propionic acid group on carbon-7 still accounts for the solubility of the pigment in dilute alkalies.

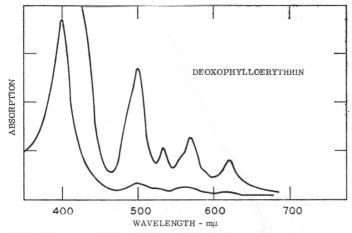

Fig.50. Spectrum of deoxophylloerythrin in ether.

The major pigment complex in petroleum is evidently deoxophylloerythro-etioporphyrin, which is formed by the decarboxylation of deoxophylloerythrin. The structure of this compound is also illustrated in Fig.49 and is substantially the same as its precursor chemically. It differs only in that it is not able to form a salt with dilute alkali and is therefore not soluble in alkali medium. Its spectrum is virtually identical with that of deoxophylloerythrin—a phyllo type spectrum. Chemically, deoxophylloerythroetioporphyrin can be prepared by decarboxylating deoxophylloerythrin, but this process requires very severe conditions (soda lime distillation at 300°C; FISCHER and ORTH, 1937). The removal of the acid group on carbon-7 alters the extraction number upward from 1.5 for deoxophylloerythrin to 2.5 for deoxophylloerythroetioporphyrin.

It is likely that the deoxo-compound from the chlorophyll *d* series under-

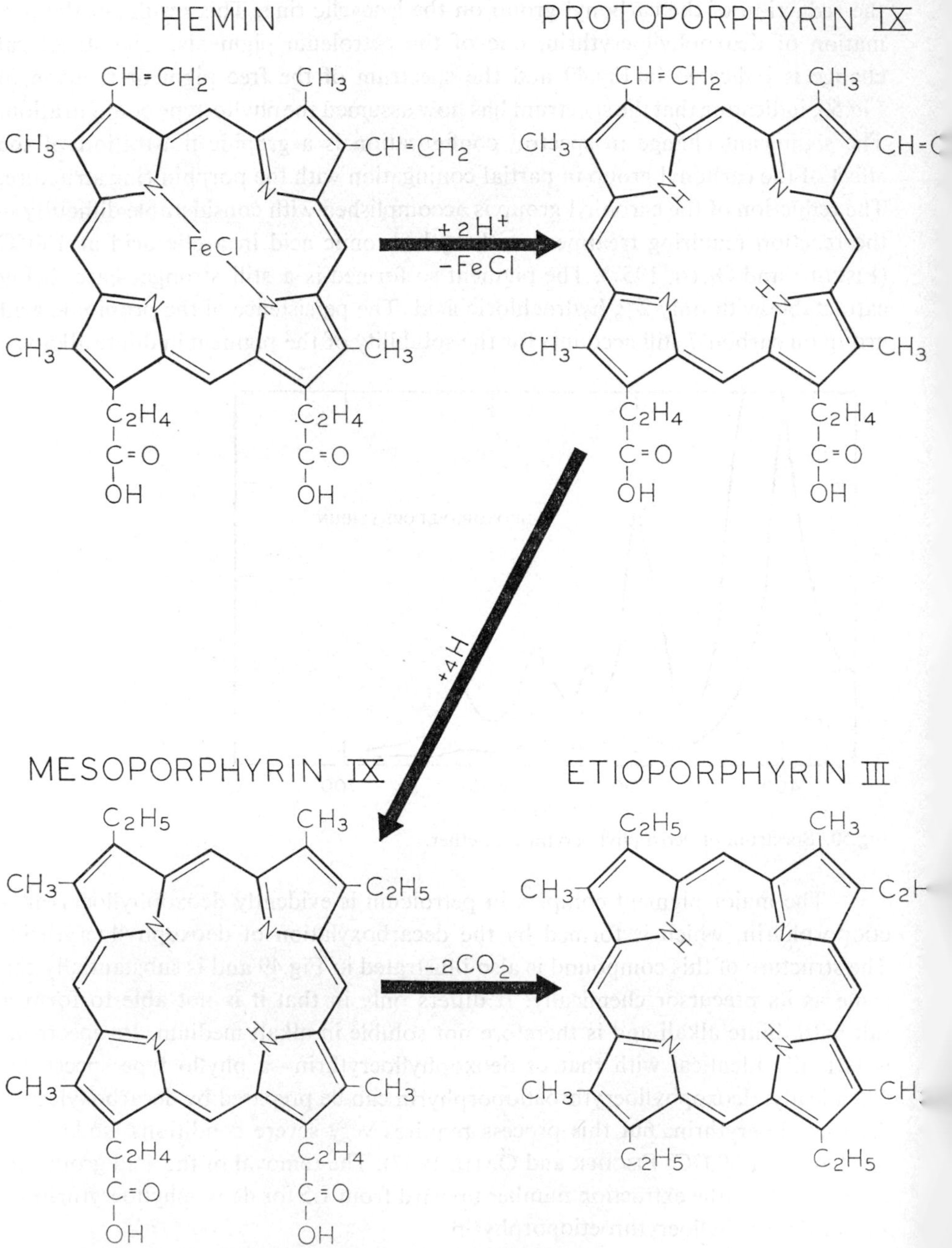

Fig.51. Structural conversion of hemin to etioporphyrin III.

goes similar decarboxylation yielding a decarboxylated pigment which is virtually indistinguishable from deoxophylloerythroetioporphyrin. In a like manner the carboxylated porphyrins from the hemin series probably are decarboxylated to porphyrins similar to, if not identical with, etioporphyrin III shown in Fig.51. Mesoporphyrin IX is synthesized by gentle reduction of hemin with hydriodic acid-acetic acid under addition of phosphonium iodide, or by heating hemin with HBr-acetic acid at 180 °C (FISCHER and ORTH, 1937).

Alkali degradation of bacteriochlorophylls at elevated temperatures produces molecules which are similar to those formed by chlorophyll degradation. Pyrroporphyrin has four methyl groups, two ethyl groups and one propionic acid group in peripheral substitution. The structure of phylloporphyrins is the same with the exception that it also has a substituent on one of the methine bridges. The carboxyl-free molecule could only be obtained by using the soda lime treatment; however, this laboratory method did not give complete decarboxylation.

Metal complexes of chlorophyll and hemin degradation products

As noted earlier, one of the major changes in the development of petroleum porphyrin pigments is the complexing of the pigments with trace metals, principally vanadium and nickel. This complexing reaction can take place with any of the intermediate products discussed above. In the chlorophyll *a* series of degradation products, it is a well-established fact that pheophytin readily undergoes complexing with a large number of divalent cations (LAMORT, 1956). Similarly each of the indicated intermediates in the same series undergoes ready complexing with vanadyl ion, nickel and copper. In fact, copper seems to complex more readily than the other two (HODGSON, 1960). Probably members of the other series react in a similar manner. Generally mild acid conditions accelerate the metal complexing reactions; however, even in neutral alcoholic media metal complexing reactions are readily accomplished, as indicated by the complexing of pheophytin *a* with nickel, with a good yield of the nickel complex of pheophytin *a* in only a few hours at 130 °C (BAKER and HODGSON, 1961). The reaction appeared to be a simple replacement reaction marked by an activation energy of about 24 kcal./ mole. The other pigments in the series varied in reaction rate. Pheophorbide appeared to react much more readily than pheophytin—this may have been due to the pH effect of the free carboxyl group of the pigment in the unbuffered alcoholic solution. In general, the ease of complexing falls in the following order (with the first metal having the fastest rate): copper, nickel and vanadyl ion. Interconversion of the metal complexes, i.e., replacement of copper by nickel, etc., appeared to be possible but there was little indication that any net gain was achieved by going through a copper intermediate in the ultimate formation of a nickel or vanadyl complex. The nickel complex could be formed just as readily from the free pigment as from the copper complex (HODGSON, 1960).

Free porphyrins are only moderately stable. Metallation increases their stability considerably (CORWIN, 1959). Evidence has been given illustrating that dehydrogenation of metallic derivatives by irradiation in the presence of quinones takes place much more readily than that of the free chlorins under the same conditions (EISNER and LINSTEAD, 1955b).

Experiments involving standard clay minerals and both vanadium and nickel complexing metal ions with several chlorin and porphyrin pigments showed that copper complexes could be directly converted to vanadium and nickel complexes (HODGSON, 1960). Upon alteration of the environment of the clay mineral system to mildly reducing conditions, reduction of the vanadium pigment was observed with ultimate conversion to the vanadium complex of deoxophylloerythrin (HODGSON and PEAKE, 1961).

In summary, a sequence of reactions may be written to demonstrate the manner in which chlorophyll and hemin-type pigments would give rise to petroleum porphyrin pigments. The petroleum metal complexes may also arise from pigments other than chlorophyll or hemin precursors, and the most likely would be chlorin or porphyrin components of enzyme systems existing in living organisms. Since most enzyme systems contain trace metal components, there is a possibility that petroleum porphyrin complexes are formed from chlorin or porphyrin components of such compounds which could join the development scheme outlined above at the appropriate points. The pigments which occur in the environments of the origin of petroleum will be examined in an attempt to establish the most likely reaction paths leading to the ultimate formation of petroleum accumulations.

Chlorin and porphyrin pigments in sediments

Laboratory investigations have shown the conversion of chlorophyll to other chlorins and to porphyrins similar to those found in petroleum. If petroleum porphyrins are derived from the pigments of living organisms it should be possible to find evidence for the stepwise conversion of the organism pigments in the environments commonly thought to be part of the oil genesis process. In the sections to follow, attention will be directed to the pigments existing in ancient sediments, formation waters, Recent sediments, ground waters, fresh- and sea-waters and in living organisms.

The methods of extracting pigments from sediments and plants are improving very rapidly. VERNON (1960) has developed a method whereby chlorophylls *a* and *b*, pheophytins *a* and *b* total chlorophyll and total pheophytin can be quantitatively determined in plant extracts. Utilizing sonic oscillation on plankton, NELSON (1960) has succeeded in obtaining greater yields of chlorophyll by acetone extraction than was previously possible.

Ancient sediments have long been known to contain porphyrin pigments, and it was in this area that the classical work of Treibs was responsible for arousing interest in the geochemistry of such pigments. Thus TREIBS (1934, 1935, 1936) reported the presence of metal complexes of porphyrins in oil shales. The pigments were principally deoxophylloerythrin, deoxophylloerythroetioporphyrin and the complexing metals were vanadium, nickel and iron (TREIBS, 1936). Green River shales of Colorado were reported by MOORE and DUNNING (1955) to contain nickel and iron complexes of similar pigments. Nickel and vanadyl porphyrins occur in a Tertiary shale of Japan (HODGSON et al., 1963a), and evidence was found of an ester of the nickel porphyrin in addition to a pigment resembling hematin. A few Cretaceous shales of Canada were examined and found to contain nickel and vanadyl porphyrins in the range of 0.001–2 p.p.m. (HODGSON et al., 1963b), and further work indicates similar compounds for the Posidonia shales of Germany (HODGSON and BAKER, 1964). A limited number of Precambrian pegmatites appeared devoid of porphyrins (HODGSON et al., 1963b), but coals have long been known to contain porphyrins, and these are commonly more closely related to the hemin series rather than the chlorophyll series of pigments (TREIBS, 1936). Evidence for porphyrin pigments has even been found in a carbonaceous meteorite (HODGSON and BAKER, 1964).

With porphyrin compounds very widespread in ancient sediments, consideration should be given to the occurrence of such compounds in formation fluids. It may be expected that the distribution of pigments would be governed by their solubility in the formation fluids. The decarboxylated compounds, i.e., the MP_p compounds, are very slightly soluble in water and quite soluble in hydrocarbons. It is not surprising therefore to find the concentration of MP_p compounds in oil to be very much greater than in water. Thus, the content in oils commonly falls in the range of 1–1,000 p.p.m., while in oil field water and non-petroliferous waters the few determinations which have been made fall below detection limits of the methods used, i.e., less than 0.000,01 p.p.m. (G. W. Hodgson, B. L. Baker and E. Peake, unpublished). Carboxylated pigments, MP_pCOOH, are more soluble in water, but have not been detected in formation waters. Porphyrins have a very low vapor pressure and would not be expected to occur to any extent in gaseous hydrocarbons. Porphyrins however have been found in tarry materials accompanying dry gas production (Hodgson et al., unpublished results) but these phenomena are probably a result of mechanical entrainment. This draws attention to mechanical entrainment of clay minerals in moving formation waters, and an interesting observation was made (HODGSON et al., 1963b) in which VOP-laden clay particles were carried out of an oil-saturated sample of unconsolidated sandstone.

Porphyrin pigments occur in Recent sediments. FOX and ANDERSON (1941) found a deep yellow–brown pigment in sediments 4,000 years old from the Gulf of California. It had absorption maxima at 575 and 553 mμ, similar to those of the VOP_p of crude oil. HODGSON et al. (1960) reported a similar pigment in Recent lake sediments, in Arctic delta sediments (HODGSON et al., 1963b), and in marine sediments (HODGSON et al., 1963a). In the latter sediments from the shores of

Japan, there was also evidence for the corresponding nickel complex. It is noted that the porphyrin pigments in the Recent sediments occurred not only at depth in the sediments, but also in the top few centimeters.

The majority of the Recent sediment porphyrins are evidently complexes of deoxophylloerythroetioporphyrin (MP_p) and deoxophylloerythrin (MP_pCOOH). A significant further observation however indicated the existence of pigments similar to the vanadyl complex of phylloerythrin (G. W. Hodgson, B. L. Baker and E. Peake, unpublished). This suggests a direct connection between the porphyrin pigments and the chlorin pigments of the sediments, since the latter may be the precursors of the former.

Chlorin pigments are very abundant in Recent sediments and have been widely reported, usually as chlorophyll degradation products or pheophytins (Fox and ANDERSON, 1941; Fox et al., 1944; SHABAROVA, 1954; VALLENTYNE, 1955; ORR and GRADY, 1957; CORCORAN, 1957; GORHAM, 1959, 1960; and HODGSON et al., 1960). Similar pigments have been found in older sediments in California (VALLENTYNE and CRASTON, 1957) and in interglacial gyttjas as old as 100,000 years (ANDERSON and GUNDERSON, 1955). In Recent sediments, pheophytins a and b and pheophorbides a and b are the most abundant individual compounds. These free chlorins have been found in quantities up to 350 p.p.m. of the dried sediments. The methyl ester of pheophorbide has also been reported.

Tetrahydroporphyrins also exist in Recent sediments, but they have been less completely studied. An indication of such compounds is given by absorption maxima in the 750 mμ region. On this basis, VALLENTYNE (1960) reported the presence of bacteriochlorophyll pigments in fresh-water sediments. Generally the identification of sediment pigments is based upon separation methods such as:

(*a*) Extraction of the pigments with aqueous acetone.

(*b*) Crude separation of the pigments with hydrochloric acid and ether.

(*c*) Further separation by chromatography.

(*d*) Identification by comparison of the chemical, spectral and chromatographic characteristics of the separated compounds with those of known compounds (CORCORAN, 1957; VALLENTYNE, 1960).

Concentrations of these pigments were expressed in one of two ways: either as sedimentary chlorophyll units defined as that amount of pigment, which when dissolved in 10 ml of solvent gave an optical density of 0.10 using a 10 mm light path (VALLENTYNE, 1955); or the absorbance was converted to pigment weight by arbitrarily assuming an extinction coefficient which was considered reasonable (ORR and GRADY, 1957). Each method has its shortcomings due to the mixture of pigments within the solutions; however, absolute accuracy is not claimed by the investigators.

Metal complexes of chlorins (MP_c, MP_cCOOH and MP_cCOOR) are much less abundant than the free chlorins (H_2P_c, H_2P_cCOOH and H_2P_cCOOR). The chlorophylls are included as metal complexes since they are magnesium complexes.

Chlorophyll *a* accompanied by chlorophyll *b* has been reported in one sample of surface sediments from the Gulf of Mexico (CORCORAN, 1957). Chlorophyll *b* has also been reported in a near-surface sediment from a lake in Ontario, Canada (VALLENTYNE, 1960), accompanied by a pigment similar to chlorophyll *c*. Chlorophyllides were also reported, suggesting that hydrolysis of the phytyl ester may occur under some circumstances more readily than the removal of the magnesium.

Other metal-chlorin complexes would be expected in Recent sediments, and evidence has been presented for the assignment of a vanadyl identity to metal chlorins found in Recent lake and marine sediments (HODGSON and PEAKE, 1961; and HODGSON et al., 1963a). The extracts of the marine sediments also exhibited pigments similar to complexes of chlorins with nickel. Almost all of the pigments in the Recent sediments contained free carboxyl groups.

Little understanding has been developed for the occurrence of chlorin and porphyrin pigments in the waters associated with Recent sediments. Waters expressed from compacting Recent sediments appear to carry chlorin pigments, but largely only in close association with suspended clay particles (G. W. Hodgson, B. L. Baker and E. Peake, unpublished). Lake waters (HODGSON et al., 1963b) also exhibit chlorin pigments, but again there is evidence that these may carry sufficient suspended matter to account for the indicated pigment content of about 0.000,1 p.p.m. The same may hold for the pigments found in spring waters at much the same level.

Living organisms contain a wealth of chlorin and porphyrin pigments. The distribution of porphyrins has recently been reviewed by RIMINGTON and KENNEDY (1962) and a series of papers edited by FALK et al. (1961) focus attention on the hematin enzymes. In the field of petroleum geochemistry little has been done to carry the understanding of the source of petroleum back beyond the Recent sediment starting point. One interesting finding however has been that the metal chlorin pigment occurring in Recent sediments, tentatively identified as a vanadyl chlorin similar to vanadyl pheophytin, evidently exists in at least some plant organisms and may account for the metal-complexing step in the formation of petroleum vanadyl porphyrins (HODGSON et al., 1963a).

GEOCHEMICAL SIGNIFICANCE OF PORPHYRINS AND RELATED COMPOUNDS

To aid in assessing the significance of petroleum porphyrins in the general topic of the origin of oil, the discussions up to this point are now summarized. Porphyrins are large organic compounds of remarkable stability and ready recognition. While a very large number of porphyrins are structurally possible, crude oil contains only a few porphyrin compounds. And while porphyrins may be formed directly from pyrroles under extreme conditions, it is generally agreed that petroleum porphyrins are of biogenic origin.

The geochemical significance of petroleum porphyrins has long been recognized, TREIBS (1934) having been the first to draw attention to this point; DUNNING (1963) has made a recent publication on this topic. Treibs and his associates including DHERE and HRADIL (1934) and KREJCI-GRAF (1935) recognized some connection between the pigments of bituminous substances and the pigments of petroleum source material. In addition the thermal decarboxylation of mesoporphyrin was examined (TREIBS, 1935), giving rise to the oft-quoted 200 °C limit on the environmental temperature for developing petroleums. It was generally agreed that porphyrin pigments were markers for tracing the history of bituminous substances. TREIBS (1936) outlined the processes for the pigment formation from chlorophyll to be:

(1) Magnesium cleavage.

(2) Saponification of the ester group.

(3) Hydrogenation of the vinyl group to an ethyl group.

(4) Dehydrogenation of the green chlorin system to the red porphyrin system.

(5) Reduction of the carbonyl group to CH_2.

(6) Decarboxylation.

(7) Complex formation.

All of the reactions were regarded as readily accomplished except the decarboxylation step which may have to be a biochemical reaction. TREIBS (1936) also noted chromatographic effects which would be expected as a result of migration of a developing oil. In the years since the original work of Treibs much further consideration has been given to the geochemical principles involved in the genesis of crude oil but surprisingly little real progress is evident.

Petroleum porphyrins are generally attributed to the chlorophyll of the source organisms and the possibility of contributions from special trace pigments in organisms is admitted, although contributions from vanadium-containing compounds of special organisms such as the ascidians (BERTRAND, 1941) is largely discounted.

Much emphasis has been placed upon the generation of petroleum porphyrins in Recent sediments in keeping with the attention directed to this environment in connection with the source of hydrocarbons which ultimately may become petroleum. Thus, the abundance of chlorins in Recent sediments indicates conditions favorable for their preservation. The stability of the degradation products has been attributed to four factors: the water insolubility of the pigments in their natural state, and the lack of light, oxygen and heat in subsurface sediments (VALLENTYNE, 1960). The first factor provides a mechanism by which the pigments reach the sediments. In all probability water soluble pigments would never reach these sediments in significant quantities. The other three factors—lack of light and oxygen and low temperatures—tend to preserve the chlorins.

Investigations of Recent sediments have revealed conditions which tend to preserve rather than destroy the chlorins. The temperature varies between 4 and

10 °C (VALLENTYNE and CRASTON, 1957), E_h values are negative to slightly positive indicating weakly reducing conditions, and the acid-base conditions correspond to a pH range between 6 and 9 (HODGSON et al., 1960).

Experiments have been carried out to determine the extent of preservation and conversion of chlorophyll to pheophytin under simulated petroleum source rock conditions (HODGSON and HITCHON, 1959). The pH was found to be the controlling factor. The chlorophylls were extensively destroyed in a high pH environment.

It is important to examine the whole topic of porphyrin geochemistry to avoid the errors which might creep in through unjustified assumptions. For example, the source of the pigment material must be considered as the organisms in which the pigment was synthesized. The fate of the pigment from this point might be considered systematically, and it is immediately obvious that the Recent sediment environment is far removed from the source of the pigments and by implication far removed from the source of the hydrocarbons. The pigments occurring in organisms are reasonably well known, except for the trace pigments. The fate of the pigments in metabolic processes is also reasonably well known, at least so far as the higher organisms are concerned (RIMINGTON and KENNEDY, 1962). Generally the question is a matter of the chlorins being converted to porphyrins, and the porphyrins being converted further to more stable porphyrins. Oxidizing conditions usually appear to result in polycarboxylic porphyrin structures, rather than the reduced porphyrin side chains characteristic of oil environments.

It appears therefore that the source of the pigments includes chlorophylls, hemins, enzymatic porphyrin and chlorin pigments, metabolic products of these and other less clearly defined naturally occurring pigments. The dominance of phyllotype porphyrins in crude oil focusses attention on the chlorophyll-like starting pigments, but it would be unwise to neglect the role of the other pigments at this stage. The source pigments, so defined, are incorporated into the soil, if the growth of the source organisms occurs on land. The pigments are then subjected to the chemical and biochemical environment of the soil until they are leached out by circulating ground waters or are carried out with the soil substance through the normal course of erosion. Very little is known of these processes insofar as the pigments are concerned. Circulating groundwaters contain virtually no pigment as indicated by values less than 0.000,1 p.p.m., and this pigment may have been accommodated on particulate material suspended in river water, which pertained to the erosion of soils and the transportation of the eroded material toward the sea (HODGSON et al., 1963b). The pigment content was appreciable, about 10 p.p.m. of the solids, and was composed of chlorins principally with a small amount of porphyrin material as well. Such material is moved along in river streams and ultimately reaches the river mouth where it may accumulate in deltaic deposits before reaching open water. Deltaic deposits contain both chlorins and porphyrins therefore derived from the terrigenous sources, augmented by pigments from organic material generated in the river system. As the pigments are moved along with the sedimentary material from the fresh-water to the marine environment, additional organic matter is incorporated into it from that generated in the marine waters. The relative proportions of the marine and non-marine contributions are quite variable, of course, and Recent marine sediments so formed therefore contain variable amounts of land- and sea-derived chlorins and porphyrins.

Recent sediments, both fresh water and marine, contain both chlorins and porphyrins. The porphyrins occur in the surface layers of sediment, as well as at depth, and may be an expression of the deposition of porphyrins from the land-derived reworked sediments, as well as from rapid formation of porphyrins from chlorins deposited from the land- and sea-generated organic matter. The porphyrins are generally of the deoxophylloerythrin type, in either nickel or vanadyl complex form. The occurrence in fresh-water sediments of an apparent precursor of the vanadyl pigment suggests that a systematic conversion of the pigments might be involved, drawing attention to the fact that evidently only carboxylated pigments exist in Recent sediments, and further that only one additional step, that of decarboxylation, is required, for the porphyrin pigment in Recent sediments to assume a form essentially identical with that occurring in crude oil. This indicates that by the time the organic matter reaches the sediments the chemical conditions within the prior environments must have been such as to bring about, at least to some degree, the reactions required to convert pigments to the immediate precursors of petroleum porphyrins, leaving only the final decarboxylation as the remaining step. This seems to be consistent with the views of BAKER (1959) and MEINSCHEIN (1961) who drew attention to the simple preservation of hydrocarbons of living organisms as a possible source of crude oil hydrocarbons, augmented by those hydrocarbons formed by the reduction of alcohols and decarboxylation of organic acids. BREGER (1960) in this connection drew attention to the origin of aliphatic, alicyclic and aromatic compounds from unsaturated lipids. The final decarboxylation step however seems to present a significant obstacle, although COOPER and BRAY (1963) have suggested a novel mechanism for accomplishing it. TREIBS (1936) recognized the difficulty in accounting for decarboxylations in geochemical processes involving fatty acid structures, and while biological agents have been prevailed upon, such a biological pathway is not immediately apparent. Chemical conditions for this reaction are very severe (TREIBS, 1936), and yet the reaction evidently takes place, as indicated by the fact that while Recent sediments contain almost solely carboxylated pigments, ancient sediments and crude oils contain pigments which have been almost completely decarboxylated. This would suggest that organic matter undergoes two stages of diagenesis: one in which the early environments including the source organisms themselves, bring about demetallation, hydrogen transfer, metallation, hydrolysis reduction, etc., to the final decarboxylated stage; and the other, in which a very slow further development takes place including such difficult processes as decarboxylation. HODGSON et al.

(1963a), in terms of petroleum geochemistry, suggested that this process might well take place during the migration phases and might be directly responsible for the release of the petroleum hydrocarbons from the migrating aqueous system.

Another factor relating to porphyrins in petroleum depends on a secondary introduction of these pigments into the crude oil. RADCHENKO and SHESHINA (1955) have drawn attention to the relationship which exists between vanadyl porphyrins and sulfur in crude oils. The conclusion has been that the vanadyl porphyrins were introduced in some manner concomitantly with the sulfur, probably through the action of microbiological agents, and at some time subsequent to the initial formation of the crude oil. In this manner the vanadyl porphyrins and the sulfur might be regarded as secondary components of the oil.

Evidence has been produced by PARK and DUNNING (1961) through carbon isotope studies to discount the possibility of such secondary introduction of vanadyl porphyrins, but the fact remains that there is some relation between sulfur in crude oil and the vanadyl porphyrin content. This is particularly striking in the case of the Utah and Madagascar oil sand deposits (HODGSON et al., 1963b) in which very heavy crude oils are found with a very low sulfur content—less than 0.5%—and with a correspondingly low vanadyl content—about 15 p.p.m. compared with say 5% and 500 p.p.m., respectively, for heavy oils such as the Athabasca oil-sand oil. It is well known that sulfur and vanadium compounds are very important factors in redox systems—possibly this could account for the simultaneous entry of the two substances into crude oil. This would seem to place the occurrence of vanadium in crude oil into some sort of special category distinct from that for nickel which does not have the same strong interaction with sulfur in a redox system. Some support for these suggestions is given by recent work on the synthesis of petroleum porphyrins from chlorophyll (HODGSON and PEAKE, 1961) in which it was noted that a sulfide reducing system was effective in converting a vanadyl chlorin complex to a porphyrin complex.

This topic has considerable bearing on the relative occurrence of vanadium and nickel in crude oils. Attempts have been made in the past to relate relative abundances of these two trace metals to the age of the oil, and while trends have been demonstrated (KATCHENKOV, 1949; HODGSON, 1954; and BALL et al., 1960), they have tended to be contradictory. It now appears that the relative abundances are not related to age or thermal history of the oil (HODGSON and BAKER, 1957) but rather to the source sediment environment. In this connection it is noted that the vanadium and nickel content of crude oil is very much lower than the magnesium content of the original source material (BAKER and HODGSON, 1959).

To explain further the relative abundances of the vanadium and nickel in crude oil, some attention has been directed to the possibility of intermediate metal complexes—complexes which form initially with the free chlorins, pheophytin and pheophorbide, and then undergo exchange or replacement reactions with vanadium and nickel (HODGSON et al., 1960). Copper for example, complexes very readily with a wide variety of chlorins and porphyrins and yet does not appear as a major trace metal in crude oil. The spectra of such complexes are very similar to those of vanadium and nickel as shown in Fig.52. The question is still unresolved because it appears that while copper is replaced from chlorin complexes by both nickel and vanadium it does not have any expected "catalytic" effect in the formation of nickel or vanadyl complexes, nor have copper complexes of chlorins and porphyrins been found in source environments.

In summary, there is much support for attributing the origin of porphyrins in crude oil to the wide variety of chlorophyll and hemin-like compounds in living organisms. From these through a series of chemical transformations, the chlorins are converted to metal complexes which subsequently become metal porphyrins.

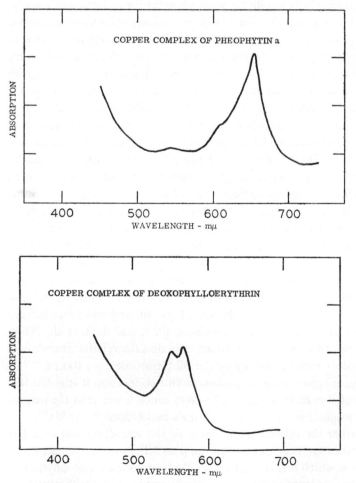

Fig.52. Spectra of copper complexes of a chlorin (pheophytin *a*) and a porphyrin (deoxophylloerythrin).

Vanadyl chlorins in plants may be a significant source of vanadyl porphyrins. Further, the possibility of the existence and preservation of petroleum porphyrins in the living organisms cannot be completely dismissed.

Chlorins and porphyrins in the initial migration of hydrocarbons

It is generally accepted that petroleum hydrocarbons are derived from trace hydrocarbons or compounds closely related to hydrocarbons existing in living organisms. Processes of crude oil formation call for a separation of these substances from the great mass of organic matter in the source sediments. Evidence is growing to support the theory of BAKER (1959) that solubilizers are the key to the initial migration of hydrocarbons from the sediments. Many different kinds of solubilizers exist, notably among them are carboxylated organic compounds. All of the pigments in the indicated sequence between pheophytin and deoxophylloerythroetioporphyrin of crude oil have free carboxyl groups and may therefore be regarded as potential surfactants. In addition, the abundance of carboxylated pigments in source sediments is high relative to the trace hydrocarbons. Thus, there is adequate solubilizer present in the form of pigments to solubilize the hydrocarbons. In this connection a study of bitumens of the Volga–Ural region in source rocks and reservoir rocks by NERUCHEV (1962) found that, in the main, only the oil fractions of the bitumen migrate from the source rocks. The so-called bitumen is enriched in hydrocarbons and is similar to crude oil in its composition. This material is considered to be true petroleum, the migration of which results in the formation of oil deposits.

There is a strong feeling that the hydrocarbons move out of the source sediment in the continuous water phase and travel with it as a "contaminant" until conditions change and the hydrocarbon can no longer be held in the water phase. The most obvious change would be for the surfactant agent to cease being a solubilizer through a decarboxylation reaction. If this were to happen, the pigment surfactant would become an etioporphyrin complex (in the extreme case) and would be representative of the bulk of pigments found in petroleum. The hydrocarbons would tend to collect into droplets and globules and would begin to assume the form of crude oil.

Chlorins and porphyrins in the final migration of crude oil

It is now of interest to consider the position of petroleum pigments in the migration of crude oil. It is generally recognized that crude oil does migrate, and several attempts have been made to relate such migration to systematic variations in oil characteristics. Noteworthy in this regard is the work of BONHAM (1956) who noted changes in the character of crude oil across the Seminole area, and attributed these systematic changes to migration of the oil within the field reservoir. During the migration a natural chromatographic process was envisaged in which metal-containing compounds were selectively adsorbed from the migrating system. A similar picture was drawn for a group of oil fields in western Canada (HODGSON and BAKER, 1959), and THOMPSON (1961), COLOMBO and SIRONI (1961) and COLOMBO et al., (1963) presented further results dealing with the migration of oil and its effect upon the character of the oil. The entire topic was examined by NAGY (1958), but the role of natural chromatography in controlling or effecting the porphyrin content of crude oils is still not clear. Porphyrin metal complexes occur primarily in the asphaltic fraction of crude oil although there is a considerable porphyrin content in some of the middle fractions. A large percentage of the vanadium in crude oil is also associated with the asphaltene fractions, and a substantial amount of such vanadium is not in porphyrin complexes (ERDMAN and HARJU, 1962; Table IX). Accordingly, if natural chromatography is a real factor in the migration of crude oil, one could expect it to have some influence on the porphyrin and trace metal content since these would be most subject to adsorption on mineral surfaces, particularly as a result of their association with the asphaltic components.

An interesting reversal of this postulated chromatographic behaviour was given by LOUIS (1963) in which the metal-containing fractions of the oil appeared to migrate the furthest, again drawing attention to the nature of the migrating system as a continuous aqueous phase tending to retain the very polar components of the dispersed hydrocarbon phase.

Porphyrin complexes are subject to attack by other agents during migration.

TABLE IX

VANADIUM CONTENT OF CRUDE OIL PORPHYRINS

(After ERDMAN and HARJU, 1962)

		Boscan	LaLuna	Baxterville	Belridge
Present as porphyrin	Crude oil	350	56	46.7	17
complex (p.p.m.)	Asphaltenes	868	200	230	180
	Resin	622	460	73	31
	Oil	21.6	9.05	0.56	2.7
Present as non-	Crude oil	784	152	0	15
porphyrin complex	Asphaltene	3612	2740	0	95
(p.p.m.)	Resin	439	370	0	58.7
	Oil	9.8	3.3	0.2	0
Percent of total	Crude oil	69	73	0	47
vanadium, as non-	Asphaltene	81	93	0	35
porphyrin complex	Resin		45	0	65
	Oil		27		0

For example, porphyrin metal complexes may be destroyed to some extent through oxidation if the migrating oil should come in contact with oxygenated ground waters. It is difficult to assess the magnitude of this possibility since few data are available. COSTANTINIDES and BATTI (1957) reported that 90% of the porphyrin complexes in an oil were destroyed in a few hours at about 200°C under mild oxidizing conditions, but obviously it is difficult to interpret these data in terms of migration conditions.

For the same reason it is difficult to assess the degree of destruction of porphyrin metal complexes under the influence of natural gamma radiation. This is further complicated by the fact that the porphyrins are apparently protected by the hydrocarbon components of the crude oil, as shown by DUNNING and MOORE (1959).

REFERENCES

ALLEN, M. B., FRENCH, C. S. and BROWN, J. S., 1961. Nature of extractable forms of chlorophyll in various algae groups. In: M. B. ALLEN (Editor), *Comparative Biochemistry of Photoreactive Systems*. Acad. Press, New York, N.Y., pp. 33–52.

ANDERSON, S. and GUNDERSON, K., 1955. Ether soluble pigments in interglacial gyttja. *Experimentia*, 11: 345–348.

ARONOFF, S., 1958. Perchloric acid titrations of porphyrins in nitrobenzene. *J. Phys. Chem.*, 62: 428–431.

ARONOFF, S. and CALVIN, M., 1943. Porphyrinlike products of the reaction of pyrrole with benzaldehyde. *J. Org. Chem.*, 8: 205–223.

BAK, B., CHRISTENSEN, D., HANSEN, L. and RASTRUP-ANDERSEN, J., 1956. Microwave determination of the structure of pyrrole. *J. Chem. Phys.*, 24: 720–725.

BAKER, B. L. and HODGSON, G. W., 1959. Magnesium in crude oils of western Canada. *Bull. Am. Assoc. Petrol. Geologists*, 43: 472–476.

BAKER, B. L. and HODGSON, G. W., 1961. Rate of formation of the nickel complex of pheophytin a. *J. Phys. Chem.*, 65: 1078–1079.

BAKER, E. G., 1959. Origin and migration of oil. *Science*, 129: 871–874.

BALL, J. S., WENGER, W. J., HORR, C. A. and MYERS, A. T., 1960. Metal content of twenty-four petroleums. *J. Chem. Eng. Data*, 5: 553–557.

BARNARD, J. R. and JACKMAN, L. M., 1956. Theoretical studies of the macrocyclic pigments, I. The structure of bacteriochlorophyll. *J. Chem. Soc.*, 1956: 1172–1178.

BARNES, J. W. and DOROUGH, G. D., 1950. Fundamental properties of porphyrin systems, II. Exchange and replacement reactions of α, β, γ, δ-tetraphenylporphyrins. *J. Am. Chem. Soc.*, 72: 4045–4050.

BERTRAND, D., 1941. Vanadium in ascidians. *Bull. Soc. Chim. Biol.*, 25: 39–43.

BLUMER, M., 1950. Porphyrinfarbstoffe und Porphyrin-Metallkomplexe in Schweizerischen Bitumina. *Helv. Chim. Acta*, 33: 1627–1637.

BLUMER, M., 1956. Separation of porphyrins by paper chromatography. *Anal. Chem.*, 28: 1640–1644.

BLUMER, M., 1961. Improved chromatographic analysis of petroleum porphyrin aggregate and quantitative measurement by integral absorption by W. Warren Howe. *Anal. Chem.*, 33: 1288–1289.

BLUMER, M. and OMENN, G. S., 1961. Fossil porphyrins: Uncomplexed chlorins in a triassic sediment. *Geochim. Cosmochim. Acta*, 25: 81–90.

BOGORAD, L., 1963. Enzymatic mechanisms in porphyrin synthesis. Possible enzymatic blocks in porphyries. *Ann. N.Y. Acad. Sci.*, 104: 676–688.

BONHAM, L. C., 1956. Geochemical investigations of crude oils. *Bull. Am. Assoc. Petrol. Geologists,* 40: 897–908.

BOYER, P. D., LARDY, H. A. and MYRBACK, K., 1959. *Enzymes,* 2nd ed. Acad. Press, New York, N.Y., pp. 3–103.

BREGER, I. A., 1960. Diagenesis of metabolites and a discussion of the origin of petroleum hydrocarbons. *Geochim. Cosmochim. Acta,* 19: 297–308.

BUDER, J., 1919. Biology of bacterial porphyrins and purple bacteria. *Jahrb. Wiss. Botan.,* 58: 525–568.

CALVIN, M., 1959. The evolution of enzymes and the photosynthetic apparatus. *Science,* 130: 1170–1174.

CALVIN, M., 1963. More evidence supports crevice concept. *Chem. Eng. News,* 41 (48): 42.

CAUGHEY, W. S. and CORWIN, A. H., 1955. The stability of metalloetioporphyrins toward acids. *J. Am. Chem. Soc.,* 77: 1509–1513.

COLOMBO, U. and SIRONI, G., 1961. Geochemical analyses of Italian oils and asphalts. *Geochim. Cosmochim. Acta,* 25: 24–51.

COLOMBO, U., DENTI, E. and SIRONI, G., 1963. Radiation effects on hydrocarbons—a geochemical study. *World Petrol. Congr., Proc., 6th, Frankfurt,* 1 (28): 15 pp.

COOPER, J. E. and BRAY, E. E., 1963. A postulated role of fatty acids in petroleum formation. *Geochim. Cosmochim. Acta,* 27: 1113–1127.

CORCORAN, E. F., 1957. *Quantitative Studies of Organic Matter and Associated Biochromes in Marine Sediments.* Thesis, Univ. Calif., Los Angeles, Calif., 142 pp.

CORWIN, A. H., 1959. Petroporphyrins. *World Petrol. Congr., Proc., 5th, New York,* 5: 119–129.

CORWIN, A. H. and BAKER, E. W., 1964. Structure studies on petroporphyrins. *Am. Chem. Soc., Div. Petrol. Chem., Preprints,* 9 (1): 19–24.

CORWIN, A. H. and MELVILLE, M. H., 1955. Relative stabilities of chelate compounds of pyrrole pigments. *J. Am. Chem. Soc.* 77: 2755–2759.

CORWIN, A. H. and WEI, P. E., 1962. Stabilities of magnesium chelates of porphyrins and chlorins. *J. Org. Chem.,* 27: 4285–4290.

CORWIN, A. H., CAUGHEY, W. S., LEONE, A. M., DANIELEY, J. E. and BAGLI, J. F., 1957. Petroporphyrins. *Am. Chem. Soc., Div. Petrol. Chem., Preprints,* 2 (4): A35–A39.

CORWIN, A. H., WALTER, J. A. and SINGH, R., 1962. An analog computer for pyrrole, porphyrins and chlorophyll strains. *J. Org. Chem.,* 27: 4280–4285.

COSTANTINIDES, G. and BATTI, P., 1957. Oxidation behaviour of bitumen porphyrins. *Chem. Ind. (Milan),* 39: 96–100.

CRUTE, M. B., 1959. The crystal structure of nickel etioporphyrin II. *Acta Cryst.,* 12: 24–28.

DEAN, R. A. and GIRDLER, R. B., 1960. Reaction of metal etioporphyrins on dissolution in sulphuric acid. *Chem. Ind. (London),* 1960: 100–101.

DHERE, C. and HRADIL, G., 1934. Spectroscopic investigation of the fluorescence of oil shales. *Schweiz. Mineral. Petrog. Mitt.,* 14: 279–295.

DOROUGH, G. D. and SHEN, K. T., 1950. Fundamental properties of porphyrin systems, I. A spectroscopic study of N-H isomerism in porphyrin free bases. *J. Am. Chem. Soc.,* 72: 3939–3944.

DUNNING, H. N., 1963. Geochemistry of organic pigments. In: I. A. BREGER (Editor), *Organic Geochemistry.* Pergamon, London, pp. 367–430.

DUNNING, H. N. and CARLTON, J. K., 1956. Paper chromatography of a petroleum porphyrin aggregate. *Anal. Chem.,* 28: 1362–1366.

DUNNING, H. N. and MOORE, J. W., 1957. Porphyrin research and origin of petroleum. *Bull. Am. Assoc. Petrol. Geologists,* 41: 2403–2412.

DUNNING, H. N. and MOORE, J. W., 1959. Decomposition of metal porphyrin complexes by γ-irradiation. *Ind. Eng. Chem.,* 51: 161–164.

DUNNING, H. N., MOORE, J. W. and DENEKAS, M. O., 1953. Interfacial activities and porphyrin contents of petroleum extracts. *Ind. Eng. Chem.,* 45: 1759–1765.

DUNNING, H. N., MOORE, J. W., BIEBER, H. and WILLIAMS, R. B., 1960. Porphyrins, nickel, vanadium and nitrogen in petroleum. *J. Chem. Eng. Data,* 5: 546–549.

EGGER, K., 1962. Thin layer chromatography of the pigments of plastids. *Planta,* 58: 664–667.

EIMHJELLEM, K. E., AASMUNDRUD, O. and JENSEN, A., 1963. A new bacterial chlorophyll. *Biochem. Biophys. Res. Commun.*, 10: 232–236.

EISNER, U. and LINSTEAD, R. P., 1955a. Chlorophyll and related substances, I. The synthesis of chlorin. *J. Chem. Soc.*, 1955: 3742–3749.

EISNER, U. and LINSTEAD, R. P., 1955b. Chlorophyll and related substances, II. The dehydrogenation of chlorin to porphin and the number of extra hydrogen atoms in the chlorins. *J. Chem. Soc.*, 1955: 3749–3754.

ELLINGSON, R. C. and CORWIN, A. H., 1946. Pyrrole studies, 16. Further studies on steric deformation. *J. Am. Chem. Soc.*, 68: 1112–1115.

ERDMAN, J. G. and HARJU, P. H., 1962. The capacity of petroleum asphaltenes to complex heavy metals. *Am. Chem. Soc., Div. Petrol. Chem., Gen. Papers*, 7 (1): 43–56.

ERDMAN, J. G., RAMSEY, V. G. and HANSON, W. E., 1956a. Volatility of metalloporphyrin complexes. *Science*, 123: 502.

ERDMAN, J. G., RAMSEY, V. G., KALENDA, N. W. and HANSON, W. E., 1956b. Synthesis and properties of porphyrin vanadium complexes. *J. Am. Chem. Soc.*, 78: 5844–5847.

ERDMAN, J. G., WALTER, J. W. and HANSON, W. E., 1957. The stability of porphyrin metallo complexes. *Am. Chem. Soc., Div. Petrol. Chem., Preprints*, 2 (1): 259–267.

ERDMAN, J. G., PARK, A. and WRIGHT, J. H., 1963. Irradiation destruction of complexes. *U.S. Patent 3,100,182.*

FALK, J. E., 1961. Chromatography of porphyrins and metalloporphyrins. *J. Chromatog.*, 5: 277–299.

FALK, J. E., 1964. *Porphyrins and Metalloporphyrins.* Elsevier, London, 266 pp.

FALK, J. E. and WILLIS, J. B., 1951. Infra red spectra of porphyrins and their iron complexes. *Australian J. Sci. Res.*, A4: 579–594.

FALK, J. E., DRESEL, E. I. B., BENSON, A. and KNIGHT, B. C., 1956. Nature of porphyrins formed on incubation of chicken erythrocyte preparations with NH_2CH_2COOH, δ-aminolevulinic acid or porphobilinogen. *Geochem. J.*, 63: 87–94.

FALK, J. E., LEMBERG, R. and MORTON, R. K. (Editors), 1961. *Haematin Enzymes.* Pergamon, London, 666 pp.

FICKEN, G. E., JOHNS, R. B. and LINSTEAD, R. P., 1956. Chlorophyll and related compounds, 4. The position of the extra hydrogens in chlorophyll. The oxidation of pyropheophorbide *a. J. Chem. Soc.*, 1956: 2272–2280.

FINK, H. and HOERBURGER, W., 1933. A contribution to the fluorescence of porphyrins, 1. *Z. Physiol. Chem.*, 218: 181–201.

FINK, H. and HOERBURGER, W., 1935. Fluorescence of porphyrins, 4. *Z. Physiol. Chem.*, 232: 28–35.

FISCHER, H. and HASENKAMP, J., 1935a. Chlorophyll, 52. Constitution of the dye of purple bacteria. 9-hydroxydesoxopheoporphyrin-a_5. *Justus Liebigs Annal. Chem.*, 515: 148–164.

FISCHER, H. and HASENKAMP, J., 1935b. Chlorophyll, 59. Transformation of the vinyl group of chlorophyll and its derivatives into the hydroxyethyl residue; ketopyrroporphyrins. *Justus Liebigs Annal. Chem.*, 519: 42–58.

FISCHER, H. and ORTH, H., 1937. *Die Chemie des Pyrrols.* Leipzig Akad. Verlag, Leipzig, 2 (I): 720 pp.

FISCHER, H. and SUS, O., 1930. Chlorophyll, 14. Transformation of pheophorbides into phylloerythrin. *Justus Liebigs Annal. Chem.*, 482: 225–232.

FISCHER, H. and WENDEROTH, H., 1939. Chlorophyll, 84. *Justus Liebigs Annal. Chem.*, 537: 170–177.

FISCHER, H., LAMBRECHT, R. and MITTENZWEI, H., 1938. Bacteriochlorophyll II. *Z. Physiol. Chem.*, 253: 1–39.

FISCHER, L. R. and DUNNING, H. N., 1961. Chromatographic resolution of petroleum porphyrin aggregates. *U.S., Bur. Mines, Rept. Invest.*, 5844, 19 pp.

FLEISCHER, E. G., 1963. The structure of nickel etioporphyrin I. *J. Am. Chem. Soc.*, 85: 146–148.

FOX, D. L. and ANDERSON, L. J., 1941. Pigments from marine muds. *Proc. Natl. Acad. Sci. U.S.*, 27: 333–337.

FOX, D. L., UPDEGRAFF, D. M. and NOVELLI, D. G., 1944. Carotenoid pigments in the ocean floor. *Arch. Biochem.*, 5: 1–23.

FREED, S. and SANCIER, K. M., 1954. Solvates of chlorophylls and related substances and their equilibria. *J. Am. Chem. Soc.*, 76: 198–205.

GAFFRON, H., 1933. Metabolism of sulphur-free purple bacteria. *Biochem. Z.*, 260: 1–17.

GLEBOVSKAYA, E. A. and VOL'KENSHTEIN, M. V., 1948. Spectra of porphyrins in petroleum and bitumens. *Zh. Obshch. Khim.*, 18: 1440–1451.

GORHAM, E., 1959. Chlorophyll derivatives in woodland soils. *Soil Science*, 87: 258–261.

GORHAM, E., 1960. Chlorophyll derivatives in surface muds from English lakes. *Limnol. Oceanog.*, 5: 29–33.

GRANICK, S., 1948. Protoporphyrin-9 as a precursor of chlorophyll. *J. Biol. Chem.*, 172: 717–727.

GRANICK, S., 1949. Pheoporphyrin nature of chlorophyll *c*. *J. Biol. Chem.*, 179: 505.

GRANICK, S., 1951. Biosynthesis of chlorophyll and related pigments. *Ann. Rev. Plant Physiology*, 2: 115–144.

GROENNINGS, S., 1953. Determination of the porphyrin aggregate in petroleum. *Anal. Chem.*, 25: 938–941.

HENDRICKSON, M. J., BERUEFFY, R. R. and McINTYRE, A. R., 1957. Radial paper chromatography. Application to analysis of mixtures of chlorophyll derivatives. *Anal. Chem.*, 29: 1810–1815.

HILL, R. and WHITTINGHAM, C. P., 1955. *Photosynthesis*. Wiley, New York, N.Y., 1965 pp.

HODGSON, G. W., 1954. Vanadium, nickel and iron trace metals in crude oils of western Canada. *Bull. Am. Assoc. Petrol. Geologists*, 38: 2537–2554.

HODGSON, G. W., 1960. Copper complexes of chlorophyll derivatives in the formation of petroleum porphyrins. *Geochem. Soc., 5th Ann. Meeting, Oct. 31, Nov. 1–2, Denver, Colo.*, 10 pp.

HODGSON, G. W. and BAKER, B. L., 1957. Vanadium, nickel and porphyrins in the thermal geochemistry of petroleum. *Bull. Am. Assoc. Petrol. Geologists*, 41: 2413–2426.

HODGSON, G. W. and BAKER, B. L., 1959. Geochemical aspects of petroleum migration in Pembina, Redwater, Joffre, and Lloydminster oil fields of Alberta and Saskatchewan, Canada. *Bull. Am. Assoc. Petrol. Geologists*, 43: 311–328.

HODGSON, G. W. and BAKER, B. L., 1964. Evidence for porphyrins in the Orgueil meteorite. *Nature*, 202: 125–131.

HODGSON, G. W. and HITCHON, B., 1959. Primary degradation of chlorophyll under simulated petroleum source rock sedimentation conditions. *Bull. Am. Assoc. Petrol. Geologists*, 43: 2481–2492.

HODGSON, G. W. and PEAKE, E., 1961. Metal chlorin complexes in recent sediments as initial precursors to petroleum porphyrin pigments. *Nature*, 191: 766–767.

HODGSON, G. W., HITCHON, B., ELOFSON, R. M., BAKER, B. L. and PEAKE, E., 1960. Petroleum pigments from recent fresh water sediments. *Geochim. Cosmochim. Acta*, 19: 272–288.

HODGSON, G. W., USHIJIMA, N., TAGUCHI, K. and SHIMADA, I., 1963a. The origin of petroleum porphyrins. Pigments in some crude oils, marine sediments and plant material of Japan. *Sci. Rept. Tohoku Univ., Ser. 3*, 8: 483–513.

HODGSON, G. W., BAKER, B. L. and PEAKE, E., 1963b. The origin of petroleum porphyrins; the position of the Athabasca oil sands. In: M. A. CARRIGY (Editor), *K. A. Clark Volume— Athabasca Oil Sands—Res. Council Alberta, Inform. Ser.*, 45: 75–100.

HOLDEN, M., 1962. Separation by paper chromatography of chlorophylls *a* and *b* and some of their breakdown products. *Biochim. Biophys. Acta*, 56: 378–379.

HOLT, A. S., 1961. Further evidence of the relation between 2-desvinyl-2-formyl-chlorophyll *a* and chlorophyll *d*. *Can. J. Botany*, 39: 327–331.

HOLT, A. S. and MORLEY, H. V., 1959. Proposed structure for chlorophyll *d*. *Can. J. Chem.*, 37: 507–514.

HOWE, W. W., 1961. Improved chromatographic analysis of petroleum porphyrin aggregate and quantitative measurement by integral absorption. *Anal. Chem.*, 33: 255–260; 1289–1290.

HOWE, W. W. and WILLIAMS, A. R., 1960. Classes of metallic complexes in petroleum. *J. Chem. Eng. Data*, 5: 106–110.

HUGHES, D. W. and HOLT, A. S., 1962. Chlorobium chlorophylls, 4. Preparative liquid–liquid partition chromatography of porphyrins and chlorophyll derivatives and its use to resolve chlorobium pheophorbide (650) into six components. *Can. J. Chem.*, 40: 171–176.

JEFFREY, S. W., 1963. Purification and properties of chlorophyll *c* from Sargassum flavicans. *Biochem. J.*, 86: 313–318.

JOHNSON, A. W. and KAY, I. T., 1960. The preparation of some cobalt porphyrin complexes. *J. Chem. Soc.*, 1960: 2979–2983.

JONES, M. C. K. and HARDY, R. L., 1952. Petroleum ash components and their effect on refractories. *Ind. Eng. Chem.*, 44: 2615–2619.

JOPE, E. M. and O'BRIEN, J. R. P., 1945. Spectral absorption and fluorescence of coproporphyrin isomers I and III and the melting points of their methyl esters. *Biochem. J.*, 39: 239–244.

JOSLYN, M. A. and MACKINNEY, G., 1938. The rate of conversion of chlorophyll to pheophytin. *J. Am. Chem. Soc.*, 60: 1132–1136.

JUZA, R. and SACHZE, W., 1943. Metal amides and metal nitrides, 12. The system Ni–N. *Z. Anorg. Allgem. Chem.*, 251: 201–212.

KARALI, E. F. and PRICE, C. A., 1963. Iron, porphyrin and chlorophyll. *Nature*, 198: 708.

KATCHENKOV, S. M., 1949. Correlation of petroleum by microelements. *Dokl. Akad. Nauk S.S.S.R.*, 67: 503–505.

KLESPER, E., CORWIN, A. H. and TURNER, D. A., 1962. Porphyrin studies, 20. High pressure gas chromatography above critical temperatures. *J. Org. Chem.*, 27: 700–701.

KLIEWE, H., 1948. Use of phosphoric acid in the fluorimetric characterization of porphyrins. *Z. Ges. Inn. Med. Ihre Grenzgebiete*, 3: 543–545.

KOSAKI, T., 1950. Porphyrins and metalloporphyrins. *Mie Med. J.*, 1: 85–104.

KOSAKI, T., 1951. Porphyrins and metalloporphyrins. *Mie Med. J.*, 2: 85–174.

KREJCI-GRAF, K., 1935. The origin of petroleum. *Naturwissenschaften*, 23: 599–605.

LAMORT, C., 1956. Spectrographic study of *a* and *b* chlorophylls and the influence of different physical and chemical agents. *Rev. Ferment. Ind. Aliment.*, 11: 34–45; 84–105.

LARSEN, E. G., MELCER, I. and ORTEN, J. M., 1955. Biogenesis of porphyrins employing paper electrophoresis. *Federation Proc.*, 14: 440.

LARSEN, H., 1953. Microbiology and biochemistry of the photosynthetic green bacteria. *Kgl. Norske Videnskab. Selskabs., Skrifter*, 1953: 1–205.

LEMBERG, R. and LEGGE, J. W., 1949. *Hematin Compounds and Bile Pigments*. Interscience, New York, N.Y., 775 pp.

LEVITT, L. S., 1954. The role of magnesium in photosynthesis. *Science*, 120: 33–35.

LEVY, R. L., GESSER, H., HALEVI, E. A. and SAIDMAN, S., 1964. Pyrolysis gas chromatography of porphyrins. *J. Gas Chromatog.*, in press.

LINNETT, J. W., 1960. *Wave Mechanics and Valency*. Wiley, New York, N.Y., 184 pp.

LOUIS, M., 1963. Société des Pétroles d'Afrique Équatoriale et Institut Français Pétrole, 1963. Géologie et géochimie du Champ de Tchengue. *World Petrol. Congr., Proc., 6th, Frankfurt*, 1 (12): 17 pp.

LOWE, M. B. and PHILLIPS, J. N., 1961. Catalysis of metalloporphyrin formation. Possible enzyme model for hem iron incorporation. *Nature*, 190: 262–263.

MACKINNEY, G. and JOSLYN, M. A., 1940. Conversion of chlorophyll to pheophytin. *J. Am. Chem. Soc.*, 62: 231–232.

MACKINNEY, G. and JOSLYN, M. A., 1941. Chlorophyll–pheophytin: temperature coefficient of the rate of pheophytin formation. *J. Am. Chem. Soc.*, 63: 2530–2531.

MANNING, W. M. and STRAIN, H. H., 1943. Chlorophyll *d*, a green pigment of red algae. *J. Biol. Chem.*, 151: 1–19.

MARTELL, A. E. and CALVIN, M., 1952. *Chemistry of the Chelate Compounds*. Prentice-Hall, New York, N.Y., 580 pp.

MATLOW, S. L., 1955. LCAOMO study of the phenomenon of thermochromism. *J. Chem. Phys.*, 23: 152–154.

MCCONNEL, R. J., OVERELL, B. G., PETROW, V. and STURGEON, B., 1953. Chemistry of antipernicious anemia factors, 11. Preparation and properties of some cobalt porphyrins. *J. Pharm. Pharmacol.*, 5: 179–195.

MCEWEN, W. K., 1946. Steric deformation. The synthesis of N-methyl etioporphyrin I. *J. Am. Chem. Soc.*, 68: 711–713.

MEAD, W. L. and WILDE, A. J., 1961. Mass spectrum of vanadyl etioporphyrin I. *Chem. Ind.*, 1961: 1315–1316.

MEINSCHEIN, W. G., 1961. Significance of hydrocarbons in sediments and petroleum. *Geochim. Cosmochim. Acta*, 22: 58–64.

METZNER, P., 1922. The coloring matter of green bacteria. *Ber. Botan. Ges.*, 40: 125–129.

MOORE, J. W. and DUNNING, H. N., 1955. Interfacial activities and porphyrin contents of oil shale
    extracts. *Ind. Eng. Chem.*, 47: 1440–1444.
MOORE, J. W. and DUNNING, H. N., 1957. Metal porphyrin complexes in an asphaltic mid-
    continent crude oil. *U.S., Bur. Mines, Rept. Invest.*, 5370, 24 pp.
MORANDI, J. R. and JENSEN, H. B., 1964. Porphyrin skeleton survives retorting. *Chem. Eng.
    News*, 42 (16): 48.
MORLEY, H. V., COOPER, F. P. and HOLT, A. S., 1959. Separation and identification of degradation
    products of porphyrins by gas-liquid partition chromatography. *Chem. Ind.*, 1959: 1018.
NAGY, B., 1958. Fundamentals of geochemistry. *Oil Gas J.*, 56 (26): 126–128; 56 (28): 155–158;
    56 (30): 265–269; 56 (32): 146–151; 56 (34): 132–140.
NELSON, D. J., 1960. Improved chlorophyll extraction method. *Science*, 132: 351.
NERUCHEV, S. G., 1962. On the composition of bitumens migrating from the organic material
    of mother rocks and on the processes of their accumulation in traps. *Dokl. Akad. Nauk
    S.S.S.R.*, 143: 191–193.
NEUBERGER, A. and SCOTT, J. J., 1952. Basicity of nitrogen atoms in the porphyrin nucleus. *Proc.
    Roy. Soc. (London)*, A 213: 307–326.
NOACK, K. and SCHNEIDER, E., 1933. A chlorophyll-like bacterial pigment. *Naturwissenschaften*,
    21: 835.
O'HAGAN, J. E., 1961. The heme-globin linkage, 3. The relationship between molecular structure
    and physiological activity of hemoglobins. In: J. E. FALK, R. LEMBERG and R. K. MORTON
    (Editors), *Haematin Enzymes*. Pergamon, London, pp.173–193.
OLSON, J. M. and ROMANO, C. A., 1962. A new chlorophyll from green bacteria. *Biochim. Biophys.
    Acta*, 59: 726–728.
ORGEL, L. E., 1960. *An Introduction to Transition Metal Chemistry. Ligand Field Theory*. Wiley,
    New York, N.Y., 180 pp.
ORR, W. L. and GRADY, J. R., 1957. Determination of chlorophyll derivatives in marine sediments.
    Deep-Sea Res., 4: 263–271.
ORR, W. L., EMERY, K. O. and GRADY, J. R., 1958. Preservation of chlorophyll derivatives in
    sediments off Southern California. *Bull. Am. Assoc. Petrol. Geologists*, 42: 925–962.
PARK, R. and DUNNING, H. N., 1961. Stable carbon isotope studies of crude oils and their por-
    phyrin aggregates. *Geochim. Cosmochim. Acta*, 22: 99–105.
PARSON, T. R., 1963. A new method for the microdetermination of chlorophyll *c* in sea water.
    J. Marine Res., 21 (3): 164–171.
PARSON, T. R. and STRICKLAND, J. D. H., 1963. Discussion of spectrophotometric determination
    of marine-plant pigments, with revised equations for ascertaining chlorophylls and
    carotenoids. *J. Marine Res.*, 21 (3): 155–163.
PHILLIPS, J. N., 1960. Ionization and coordination behaviour of porphyrins. *Rev. Pure Appl.
    Chem.*, 310: 35–60.
RABINOWITCH, E., 1944. Spectra of porphyrins and chlorophyll. *Rev. Mod. Phys.*, 16: 226–235.
RADCHENKO, O. A. and SHESHINA, L. S., 1955. Origin of porphyrins in petroleum. *Dokl. Akad.
    Nauk S.S.S.R.*, 105: 1285–1288.
RANDERATH, K., 1963. *Thin Layer Chromatography*. Acad. Press, New York, N.Y., 250 pp.
    (translation).
RICHARDS, F. A. and THOMPSON, T. G., 1952. The estimations and characterization of plankton
    populations by pigment analysis. *J. Marine Res.*, 11: 156–172.
RIEKER, R. E., 1962. Hydrocarbon fluorescence and migration of petroleum. *Bull. Am. Assoc.
    Petrol. Geologists*, 46: 60–75.
RIMINGTON, C., 1960. Spectral absorption coefficients of some porphyrins in the Soret band
    region. *Biochem. J.*, 75: 620–623.
RIMINGTON, C. and KENNEDY, G. Y., 1962. Porphyrins; structure, distribution and metabolism.
    In: M. FLORKIN and H. S. MASON (Editors), *Comparative Biochemistry*. Acad. Press, New
    York, N.Y., 4: 557–614.
RIMINGTON, C. and SCHUSTER, E., 1943. A simple fluorescence comparator and its application to
    the determination of porphyrins. *Biochem. J.*, 37: 137–142.
ROBERTSON, J. M., 1936. An X-ray study of the phthalocyanines, 2. Structure determination of the
    metal-free compound. *J. Chem. Soc.*, 1936: 1195–1209.

ROBERTSON, J. M. and WOODWARD, I., 1937. An X-ray study of phthalocyanines, 3. Quantitative structure determination of nickel phthalocyanines. *J. Chem. Soc.*, 1937: 219–230.

ROTHEMUND, P., 1936. Porphyrin studies, 2. The synthesis of porphin. *J. Am. Chem. Soc.*, 58: 625–627.

SCHLESINGER, W., CORWIN, A. H. and SARGENT, L. J., 1950. Porphyrin studies, 9. Synthetic chlorins and dihydrochlorins. *J. Am. Chem. Soc.*, 72: 2867–2871.

SCHNEIDER, E., 1930. Physiology of the pigments of purple bacteria, 1. Pure cultures of rhodobacillus pallustris Molisch and the obtaining of its pigments. *Beitr. Biol. Pflanz.*, 18: 81–115.

SCHNEIDER, E., 1934. Physiology of the pigments of purple bacteria, 2. The bacteriochlorophyll of purple bacteria. *Z. Physiol. Chem.*, 226: 221–254.

SEYBOLD, A. and EGLE, K., 1939. Chlorophyll, 2. Bacteriochlorophyll. *Sitzber. Heidelberg. Akad. Wiss., Math. Naturw. Kl.*, 1939: 7–17.

SHABAROVA, N. T., 1954. Determination of chlorophyll in sea plants and in sea deposits of recent origin. *Biokhimiya*, 19: 156–160.

SIMPSON, W. T., 1949. The theory of π-electron systems in porphines. *J. Chem. Phys.*, 17: 1218–1221.

SKINNER, D. A., 1952. The chemical state of vanadium in Santa Maria valley crude oil. *Ind. Eng. Chem.*, 44: 1159–1165.

SMITH, J. H. C., 1960. Protochlorophyll transformations. In: M. B. ALLEN (Editor), *Comparative Biochemistry*. Acad. Press, New York, N.Y., 257–277.

SMITH, J. H. C. and YOUNG, V. M. K., 1956. Chlorophyll formation and accumulation in plants. In: R. LUMRY and H. EYRING (Editors), *Radiation Biology*. McGraw-Hill, New York, N.Y., pp. 393–442.

SOKOL'NIKOVA, M. D. and RIZAEVA, M., 1962. Porphyrins in oils of Uzbekistan. *Issled. Mineral'n. i Rast. Syr'ya Uzbekistana, Akad. Nauk Uz. S.S.R., Inst. Khim.*, 1962: 121–127.

SPORER, A. H., FREED, S. and SANCIER, K. M., 1954. Paper chromatography of chlorophylls. *Science*, 119: 68–69.

STANIER, G. Y., 1960. On the existence of two chlorophylls in green bacteria. In: M. B. ALLEN (Editor), *Comparative Biochemistry*. Acad. Press, New York, N.Y., pp.69–72.

STANIER, G. Y., 1961. Photosynthetic mechanism in bacteria and plants—development of a unitary concept. *Bacterial Rev.*, 25: 1–17.

STANIER, G. Y. and SMITH, J. H. C., 1960. Chlorophylls of green bacteria. *Biochim. Biophys. Acta*, 41: 478–484.

STEELE, C. C., 1937. Recent progress in determining the structure of chlorophyll. *Chem. Rev.*, 20: 1–39.

STERN, A. and DEZELIC, M., 1936. Fluorescence of the porphyrins, 3. *Z. Physikal. Chem.*, 176: 347–357.

STERN, A. and DEZELIC, M., 1937a. The light absorption of porphyrins, 11. *Z. Physikal. Chem.*, 179: 275–294.

STERN, A. and DEZELIC, M., 1937b. The light absorption of porphyrins, 12. Metal Complexes. *Z. Physikal. Chem.*, 180: 131–138.

STERN, A. and MOLVIG, H., 1935. Fluorescence of porphyrins. *Z. Physikal. Chem.*, 175: 38–62.

STERN, A. and MOLVIG, H., 1936a. Fluorescence of the porphyrins, 2. *Z. Physikal. Chem.*, 176: 209–225.

STERN, A. and MOLVIG, H., 1936b. The light absorption of porphyrins, 8. *Z. Physikal. Chem.*, 177: 365–386.

STERN, A. and MOLVIG, H., 1937. The light absorption of porphyrins, 10. *Z. Physikal. Chem.*, 178: 161–183.

STERN, A. and WENDERLEIN, H., 1934. The light absorption of porphyrins, 1. *Z. Physikal. Chem.*, 170: 337–350.

STERN, A. and WENDERLEIN, H., 1935. The light absorption of porphyrins, 2. *Z. Physikal. Chem.*, 174: 81–103.

STERN, A. and WENDERLEIN, H., 1936a. The light absorption of porphyrins, 4. *Z. Physikal. Chem.*, 175: 405–437.

STERN, A. and WENDERLEIN, H., 1936b. The light absorption of porphyrins, 5. *Z. Physikal. Chem.*, 176: 81–124.

STERN, A. and WENDERLEIN, H., 1936c. The light absorption of porphyrins, 7. Z. Physikal. Chem., 177: 165–192.

STERN, A., WENDERLEIN, H. and MOLVIG, H., 1936. The light absorption of porphyrins, 6. Z. Physikal. Chem., 177: 40–81.

STRAIN, H. H., 1949. Functions and properties of the chloroplast pigments. In: J. FRANCK and W. E. LOOMIS (Editors), Photosynthesis in Plants. Iowa State Coll. Press, Ames, Ia., pp.133–178.

STRAIN, H. H. and MANNING, W. M., 1942a. Chlorofucine (chlorophyll c), a green pigment of diatoms and brown algae. J. Biol. Chem., 144: 625–636.

STRAIN, H. H. and MANNING, W. M., 1942b. Isomerization of chlorophylls a and b. J. Biol. Chem., 146: 275–276.

STRANKS, D. R. and WILKINS, R. G., 1957. Isotopic tracer investigations of mechanisms and structure in inorganic chemistry. Chem. Rev., 57: 743–866.

STRELL, M., KALOJANOFF, A. and KOLLER, H., 1960. Partial synthesis of pheophorbide a, the key intermediate of chlorophyll a. Angew. Chem., 72: 169–170.

SUGIHARA, J. M. and BEAN, R. M., 1962. Direct determination of metalloporphyrins in Boscan crude oil. J. Chem. Eng. Data, 7: 269–271.

SUGIHARA, J. M. and McGEE, L. R., 1957. Porphyrins in gilsonite. J. Org. Chem., 22: 795–798.

TAYLOR, J. F., 1940. Metalloporphyrins, 2. Cobalt and manganese mesoporphyrins in coordination with nitrogenous bases. J. Biol. Chem., 135: 569–595.

THOMAS, D. W. and BLUMER, M., 1964. Porphyrin pigments of a triassic sediment. Geochim. Cosmochim. Acta, 28: 1147–1154.

THOMAS, D. W. and MARTELL, A. E., 1959. Metal chelates of tetraphenylporphine and some of their p-substituted derivatives. J. Am. Chem. Soc., 81: 5111–5119.

THOMPSON, R. R., 1961. Chromatographic effects of sedimentary minerals in regard to certain petroleum constituents. Geochem. Soc., Cincinnati, Ohio, 6th Ann. Meeting, Abstr., 160A.

TONOMURA, S., 1955. Metal complexes of chlorophyll derivatives. Chem. Chem. Ind. (Japan), 8: 505–509.

TREIBS, A., 1934. The occurrence of chlorophyll derivatives in an oil shale of the Upper Triassic. Justus Liebigs Annal. Chem., 509: 103–114.

TREIBS, A., 1935. Chlorophyll and hemin derivatives in bituminous rocks, petroleums, coals and phosphate rocks. Justus Liebigs Annal. Chem., 517: 172–196.

TREIBS, A., 1936. Chlorophyll and hemin derivatives in organic materials. Angew. Chem., 49: 682–686.

TSWETT, M., 1906. Physical-chemical studies on chlorophyll. Ber. Deut. Botan. Ges., 24: 316.

UREY, H. C., 1952. On the early chemical history of the earth and the origin of life. Proc. Natl. Acad. Sci. U.S., 38: 351–363.

VALLENTYNE, J. R., 1955. Sedimentary chlorophyll determination as a paleobotanical method. Can. J. Bot., 33: 304–313.

VALLENTYNE, J. R., 1960. Fossil pigments. In: M. B. ALLEN (Editor), Comparative Biochemistry of Photoreactive Systems. Acad. Press, New York, N.Y., 83–105.

VALLENTYNE, J. R. and CRASTON, D. F., 1957. Sedimentary chlorophyll degradation products in surface muds from Connecticut lakes. Can. J. Bot., 35: 35–42.

VAN NIEL, C. B. and ARNOLD, W., 1938. Quantitative estimation of bacteriochlorophyll. Enzymologia, 5: 244–250.

VERNON, P. L., 1960. Spectrophotometric determination of chlorophylls and pheophytins in plant extracts. Anal. Chem., 32: 1144–1150.

WELLER, A. and LIVINGSTONE, R., 1954. Reaction of chlorophyll in amines. J. Am. Chem. Soc., 76: 1575–1578.

WICKLIFF, J. L. and ARONOFF, S., 1963. Degradation of chlorophyll a to pheophytin a, pheophorbide a, and pyrroporphine XV for tracer studies. Anal. Biochem., 6: 39–46.

WIEGL, J. W., 1953. Absorption spectra of bacteriochlorophyll. J. Am. Chem. Soc., 75: 999–1000.

WILLIAMS, R. J. P., 1956. Absorption spectra and stability of complex ions. J. Chem. Soc., 1956: 8–15.

WILLSTATTER, R. and STOLL, A., 1913. Investigations on Chlorophyll; Methods and Results. Sci. Prees, Lancaster, Pa., 385 pp.

WOODLE, R. A. and CHANDLER JR., W. B., 1952. Mechanism of occurrence of metals in petroleum distillates. *Ind. Eng. Chem.*, 44: 2591–2596.

WOODWARD, R. B., AYER, W. A., BEATON, J. M., BICKELHAUPT, F., BONNETT, R., BUCHSCHACHER, P., CLOSS, G. L., DUTLER, H., HANNAH, J., HAUCK, F. P., ITO, S., LANGEMANN, A., LEGOFF, E., LEIMGRUBER, W., LWOWSKI, W., SAUER, J., VALENTA, Z. and VOLZ, H., 1960. The total synthesis of chlorophyll. *J. Am. Chem. Soc.*, 82: 3800–3802.

WRIGHTSON, F. M., 1949. Determination of traces of iron, nickel and vanadium in petroleum oils. *Anal. Chem.*, 21: 1543–1545.

ZSCHEILE, F. P. and COMAR, C. L., 1941. Influence of preparative procedures on the purity of chlorophyll components as shown by absorption spectra. *Botan. Gaz.*, 102: 463–481.

Chapter 6

THE ASPHALTIC COMPONENTS OF PETROLEUM

P. A. WITHERSPOON AND R. S. WINNIFORD

University of California, Berkeley, Calif. (U.S.A.)
Whitworth College, Spokane, Wash. (U.S.A.)

INTRODUCTION

The asphaltic components of petroleum consist of aggregates of a large number of compounds that contain the highest molecular weight fractions and have the most complicated structure of any of the compounds that make up this fluid. They are in the general classification of non-hydrocarbons because, in addition to hydrogen and carbon, they contain significant amounts of nitrogen, sulfur and oxygen.

In considering the role of these complex compounds in the geochemistry of petroleum, one must keep in mind that petroleum is made up of a mixture of hydrocarbons and non-hydrocarbons. The hydrocarbons are composed of many different paraffins, naphthenes, and aromatics ranging in complexity from the simplest methane molecule to complicated ring systems with numerous alkyl side chains. The array of hydrocarbons that makes up the naphtha and gas-oil fractions of petroleum is fairly well known, but knowledge of the non-hydrocarbons is far from complete. In recent years, considerable data have been obtained on the lower molecular weight, sulfur-containing and nitrogen-containing compounds, but much remains to be learned of the asphaltic components.

A knowledge of the nature of these asphaltic components, which may be present in any concentration up to about half of the crude oil, is important from several standpoints. As will be discussed below, these components differ significantly from the other constituents in petroleum, not only in their chemical composition and structure, but also because they exist in petroleum as colloidal particles.

In early studies on the asphaltic components in petroleum, there was some confusion as to whether colloidal particles existed in petroleum or not. For example, in an early symposium on colloid chemistry, DUNSTAN (1931) mentioned as evidence of the colloidal nature of petroleum the waxes that are known to be associated with paraffinic oils, the coagulation of bituminous materials from asphaltic oils, the optical heterogeneity of oil, and the ability of certain adsorbents such as Fuller's earth to decolorize petroleum oils. MORELL and EGLOFF (1931) in this same symposium reiterated Dunstan's views and summarized their thinking with the statement: "It is quite obvious to one with even superficial knowledge of the subject that petroleum . . ., especially the asphaltic base types, is a colloid system".

On the other hand, GURWITSCH (1931), who attended this same symposium, presented different views. He stated that the scattering of light by oil is only weakly polarized, and therefore the reported optical effects (as of 1931) are due to the well-known fluorescence of petroleum rather than scattering by colloidal particles. With regard to the precipitation of asphaltic materials from crude oil, Gurwitsch pointed out that large proportions of solvent are necessary, so that the effect may simply be one of a change in solvent with resultant ordinary precipitation. In discussing the reported presence of colloidal wax in petroleum, he stated that from his own observations, a number of paraffin-base oils of widely different origin "show an abundance of paraffin crystals when examined microscopically in polarized light".

After discussing the meager work that had been done on osmosis, diffusion, and cataphoresis of oil, Gurwitsch concluded that the properties generally characteristic of the colloidal state are only very indefinitely developed in petroleum. In a later review, FREUNDLICH (1938) supported the viewpoint of Gurwitsch, although he was inclined to suspect that colloidal particles are present in petroleum but are too elusive to be found.

Although the above reported research failed to find colloidal-sized particles in crude oils, a large majority of the asphalt investigators have considered asphalt to be a colloidal system. One of the first elaborate colloid-chemical investigations on asphaltic bitumen was reported by NELLENSTEYN (1923). At atmospheric temperatures, asphalts are highly viscous and sometimes apparently solid. There has been an intensive study of the rheological properties of such substances as a literature survey by NEPPE (1952) reveals. Such studies have shown that bitumens may behave like Newtonian or non-Newtonian fluids and may also exhibit thixotropic, dilatant, and pseudoplastic phenomena. Although the rheological properties of asphalts vary considerably, such studies have led to the conclusion that asphalt is a colloidal system (TRAXLER and COOMBS, 1936; EILERS, 1949).

Ultracentrifuge studies have definitely proven that the asphaltic components can exist as colloidal particles in petroleum as well as in a variety of other solvents (WITHERSPOON, 1957, 1962; WINNIFORD, 1963; WALES and VAN DER WAARDEN, 1964). Such particles are intimately involved with the many other petroleum constituents, and by the very nature of colloidal systems, one would expect the physical and chemical properties of crude oils to be influenced significantly. For example, these colloidal fractions are likely to contain the more complex and polar compounds. The presence of such compounds in petroleum has already been established, as will be discussed later. Such compounds will tend to concentrate at interfaces, thereby affecting the wettability of the solid phase as well as the interfacial phenomena between oil and water phases. Because of the very large internal surface area of sedimentary rocks, interfacial forces are magnified in their effect and may therefore be expected to play an important part in the multiphase flow of oil and water through porous media. This would effect both the migration and accumulation of petroleum as well as its economic exploitation.

Another problem where a knowledge of the nature of the asphaltic constituents must not be overlooked is the intriguing question of the origin of petroleum. Many investigators have studied petroleum genesis, but the complicated nature of crude oil and the fact that the point of entrapment may be at some distance from the point of origin have raised a number of difficult questions. Because geologically younger crude oils are often more asphaltic than the older oils, some workers have proposed that the transformations of the organic matter involve a youthful stage of heavy asphaltic oils (BARTON, 1937; KARIMOV, 1955) which are further altered by low-temperature physico-chemical processes (MCNAB et al., 1952) to a mature paraffinic stage. Other workers have proposed that hydrocarbons are transported in aqueous solutions (BAKER, 1960) and the final accumulation is dependent on the solubility characteristics of the various hydrocarbons that make up petroleum. Many other theories for petroleum genesis have been formulated, but whatever processes may be proposed, the final product must have the properties of petroleum as we find it in nature. If the asphaltic fractions are present as colloidal particles, the proposed processes for the origin of petroleum must be consistent with that fact, and these processes must also be consistent with the known facts concerning the chemical nature of the asphaltic fractions.

The asphalt workers have published a voluminous literature on the science and technology of asphalt and the methods of adapting refinery residuums to a variety of commercial uses. Several books have been published that include comprehensive reviews of the literature (PFEIFFER, 1950; ABRAHAM, 1960; TRAXLER, 1961; BARTH, 1962). In their fundamental investigations, the asphalt workers have published much valuable data that is important to consider in developing a concept of the chemical and physical nature of the asphaltic substances in petroleum. The authors have drawn upon this wealth of information keeping in mind that the frame of reference in this discussion is that of understanding natural petroleum rather than commercial asphalt.

CHEMICAL COMPOSITION

The asphaltic fraction of crude oil is broadly defined as the residue after a nondestructive distillation has removed all the hydrocarbons that will distill over. The temperature of the oil being distilled is generally kept at or below 350°C (662°F). In specifying tests for refined petroleum products, the A.S.T.M. D86-61 procedure recommends temperature up to 371°C (700°F) or until a decomposition point is observed. Since an excess of propane added to crude oil at ambient temperatures causes essentially the same fraction to be precipitated, this procedure has also been used as a method of separation (SKINNER, 1952; DUNNING et al., 1953). SACHANEN (1945) summarizes a number of other methods that have been used in isolating asphaltic substances. In the process of asphalt manufacture, various procedures are used depending on the gravity and type of crude feedstock, and there is a considerable variation in the properties of the end products even though the term "asphalt" is applied to all.

As might be expected from such a broad definition, the asphaltic fraction will vary in composition over a considerable range depending on the source of the crude oil. For purposes of study, some further subdivision is desirable, and one of the most convenient procedures is to separate this fraction into two parts based on its solubility in light petroleum hydrocarbons, especially normal pentane. The soluble portion known as *petrolenes* (or maltenes) is usually a viscous liquid that can be further subdivided into "resins" and "oils". The insoluble portion is known as *asphaltenes* and is a brown or black powdery solid that when heated decomposes and finally sinters together. According to SACHANEN (1945), the total content of asphaltic compounds in crude oils varies within very broad limits, from 1 to 40% by weight, and the asphaltenes from 0 to 15%. WITHERSPOON et al. (1961) have reported some investigations on a California crude oil containing 21% asphaltenes.

A more complete method of fractionating the asphaltic components has been proposed by KLEINSCHMIDT (1955). After precipitating the asphaltenes with *n*-pentane, the petrolenes are chromatographically separated over a column of Fuller's earth. Successive elutions with *n*-pentane, methylene chloride, methyl–ethyl ketone, and a mixture of acetone and chloroform produce colorless and dark oils, respectively, in the first two eluates and resins in the latter two. TRAXLER and SCHWEYER (1953) have proposed a scheme for fractionating asphalts based on solubility in *n*-butanol and acetone. The *n*-butanol insoluble fraction, which contains most of the asphaltenes is called "asphaltics". The acetone soluble portion is called "cyclics" and the acetone insoluble portion "saturates"; however, it is not to be inferred that these names do more than suggest important chemical classes which are considered to be present. Certainly both fractions contain cyclic compounds.

LOUIS (1951) and coworkers (BIENNER et al., 1955) have proposed a somewhat different scheme using boiling ethyl acetate to separate the petrolenes from an insoluble fraction. The petrolenes are further separated into the oily constituents and resins by adsorption on Fuller's earth and Soxhlet extraction of the adsorbent with light petroleum ether. The insoluble fraction is leached with CCl_4 to remove the asphaltenes and leave an insoluble residue called *carbenes*. This latter term was first proposed by RICHARDSON (1905) to denote those fractions in manufactured asphalt produced by overheating or cracking. This fraction is normally not separated from the asphaltenes in petroleum because the carbene content of crude oil is usually negligible. In analyzing 32 different oils from Italy and Sicily, COLOMBO and SIRONI (1959) found the carbene content to range from 0 to only 1% and it exceeded 0.3% in only four of their samples.

Because the molecular weights of the materials that make up the asphalt fraction vary from 300 to 5,000 or more, GRIFFIN et al. (1959) used molecular distillation as a means of separating this fraction according to molecular size. Each molecular weight fraction was further separated chromatographically over silica gel using successive elutions of isopentane, benzene, and an ethanol–benzene mixture to produce three fractions which they called saturates, aromatics, and resins, respectively. The residue from the molecular distillation was separated into an oil fraction and asphaltenes by solvent precipitation using isopentane. The oil fraction was either further molecularly distilled or separated by the same chromatographic procedure.

COLOMBO and SIRONI (1959) have analyzed the asphaltic components of several Italian oils and asphalts using both the Kleinschmidt and Louis methods of separation. They found that the combined oils of the Kleinschmidt method were essentially the same amount as the oily fraction obtained by the Louis method, and the only difference noted was that the colorless oils were practically free of oxygenated compounds. Similarly, they found that when the two resin fractions obtained by the Kleinschmidt method were combined, they were equivalent to the resins of the Louis method.

Elemental analyses of the asphaltic components of a crude oil of Triassic age from Ragusa, Sicily are given in Table I from the work of COLOMBO and SIRONI (1959) to demonstrate the differences in composition of the fractions obtained by the Kleinschmidt method. Similar analyses from their work on a natural asphalt of Triassic age from Gela, Sicily are given in Table II. It will be noted that only a trace of nitrogen is reported for the resins and asphaltenes in these results. Ordinarily 1–2% nitrogen is found, but the analysis for nitrogen in these compounds is known to be difficult.

The C/H ratio is included in these tables because this ratio is often used to characterize petroleum constituents. Aliphatic hydrocarbons have a ratio approaching 0.5; benzene has a ratio of 1.0; and naphthalene, 1.25. The increasing values of the C/H ratios on Table I and II show how the fractions change from the relatively aliphatic colorless oils to the highly aromatic asphaltenes.

TABLE I

ELEMENTAL ANALYSES OF ASPHALTIC COMPONENTS IN RAGUSA CRUDE OIL

Element	Colorless oils	Dark oils	Resins	Asphaltenes
C%	86.56	82.95	79.84	81.32
H%	11.97	10.19	9.73	8.54
N%	trace	trace	trace	trace
S%	1.45	3.07	3.26	5.22
O%	0.02	3.79	7.17	4.92
C/H	0.60	0.68	0.68	0.79
% of sample	44.50	24.06	16.52	13.99

TABLE II

ELEMENTAL ANALYSES OF ASPHALTIC COMPONENTS IN GELA ASPHALT

Element	Colorless oils	Dark oils	Resins	Asphaltenes
C%	83.39	77.98	71.08	78.86
H%	11.69	9.51	8.75	7.82
N%	trace	trace	trace	trace
S%	4.88	8.67	7.09	10.27
O%	0.04	3.84	13.08	3.05
C/H	0.59	0.68	0.68	0.84
% of sample	26.25	14.31	13.70	38.24

The petrolene fraction of a typical mid-continent asphalt has been studied intensively by GARDNER et al. (1959) using a thermal diffusion process to separate the compounds according to molecular shape. Ten different fractions of equal volume having widely different properties were produced. Table III summarizes elemental composition and molecular weights (determined ebullioscopically). Temperatures ranged from 185 °F to 225 °F; thus, the possibility of cracking is eliminated. It will be noted that there is a greater range in the C/H ratios (0.51–0.76) than was observed for the petrolenes that were separated by the Kleinschmidt method (see Table I and II). This indicates a considerably wider variation in the type of molecules that make up this heterogeneous fraction. As will be discussed later, GARDNER et al. (1959) were able to characterize these compounds as ranging from simple alkyl naphthenes in fraction 1 to highly condensed, aromatic-naphthenic structures in fraction 10.

TABLE III

ELEMENTAL ANALYSES AND MOLECULAR WEIGHTS OF THERMAL DIFFUSION FRACTIONS OF PETROLENES FROM MIDCONTINENT ASPHALT

Fraction	Carbon (%)	Hydrogen (%)	N.S.O. by diff. (%)	C/H ratio	Molecular weight
1	85.31	13.99	0.70	0.51	1070
2	85.11	12.65	2.24	0.56	950
3	85.37	12.66	1.97	0.56	1150
4	86.77	11.60	1.63	0.62	1560
5	87.30	11.40	1.30	0.64	1695
6	86.59	11.25	2.16	0.64	760
7	86.87	10.98	2.16	0.66	1160
8	86.41	10.73	2.86	0.67	—
9	86.96	10.41	2.69	0.70	3000
10	86.37	9.52	4.11	0.76	3800

Elemental analyses of the asphaltene fractions that were extracted from a group of widely distributed crude oils are given in Table IV. Excepting those from the Salem, Illinois crude oil, which was ultracentrifuged to produce an asphaltene sediment (WITHERSPOON, 1957), the other asphaltenes were all precipitated with normal pentane (ERDMAN and RAMSEY, 1961). The range in C/H ratios from 0.77 to 0.95 indicates that the asphaltene fraction of petroleum is by no means a well-defined system. This fraction has the highest degree of aromaticity of the various asphaltic components in petroleum, and apparently, it is a complex mixture of compounds whose composition may vary significantly from one crude to the next.

TABLE IV

ELEMENTAL ANALYSES OF ASPHALTENES FROM VARIOUS CRUDE OILS

Crude oil and source	Carbon (%)	Hydrogen (%)	Nitrogen (%)	Sulfur (%)	Oxygen (%)	C/H ratio
Baxterville, Miss., U.S.A.	84.5	7.4	0.80	5.60	1.7	0.95
Burgan, Kuwait	82.2	8.0	1.70	7.60	0.6	0.86
Lagunillas, Venezuela	84.2	7.9	2.00	4.50	1.6	0.89
Mara, Venezuela	83.5	8.3	0.98	2.68	1.5	0.81
Ragusa, Sicily	81.7	8.8	1.47	6.31	1.8	0.77
Salem, Ill., U.S.A.	88.2	8.1	1.71	0.62	1.3*	0.91
Wafra, Neutral Zone	81.8	8.1	1.03	7.80	1.5	0.84

* By difference.

The separation of petrolenes from asphaltenes on the basis of their pentane solubility does not mean they are unrelated. Petrolenes are rather easily converted to asphaltenes, and thus it seems likely that the pentane fractionation may only separate related compounds of lower molecular weight and polarity (petrolenes) from those of higher molecular weight and polarity (asphaltenes). The wide variation in the properties of the petrolene fractions that were separated by thermal diffusion (GARDNER et al., 1959) would certainly seem to support this viewpoint. One may note on Table III that the C/H ratio for petrolene fraction 10 (0.76) is as high as values obtained on certain asphaltenes (see Table IV).

MOLECULAR WEIGHT DETERMINATIONS

The molecular weight of the asphaltic components in petroleum is a problem that has not been completely resolved. This is especially true of the asphaltenes. FLINN et al. (1961) have given a good review of the asphaltene molecular weight problem, and in an earlier study of this problem by viscosity methods, ECKERT and WEETMAN (1947) have reviewed asphaltene molecular weight measurements conducted prior to that time.

A great variety of molecular weights have been reported for asphaltenes depending on the methods employed. The problem has been summarized by WINNIFORD (1963) and WALES and VAN DER WAARDEN (1964). The data of Table V illustrate the situation.

Boiling-point molecular weights give values of a few thousand, and in addition vary with the solvent employed. Freezing-point molecular weights yield some surprisingly low values, even below 1,000. Both methods give number-average molecular weights and are therefore sensitive to low molecular weight impurities. Viscosity molecular weights give values from about 900 up to 4,000. These depend, however, upon assumptions that may not be valid for asphaltenes. The viscosity methods were developed for highly voluminous chain polymers and may not be applicable to the more condensed asphaltene structures. Furthermore, the relationship of viscosity to molecular weight must be established by correlation with independent molecular weight data, and therefore, the viscosity molecular weights are subject to all of the errors inherent in the calibrating molecular weights.

WINNIFORD (1963) proposed that the high molecular weight values were given by methods where shearing was minimal or absent, so that large asphaltene aggregates were built up. The low values were obtained where shearing or vigorous agitation was part of the method. WALES and VAN DER WAARDEN (1964) have shown that the ultracentrifuge molecular weights are temperature dependent, and they concluded, in accord with Winniford, that asphaltene molecular weights were dependent on the amount of association remaining between asphaltene molecules under the conditions of the experiment.

TABLE V

MOLECULAR WEIGHTS FOR ASPHALTENES AS DETERMINED BY VARIOUS METHODS

	Number averages	Weight averages
Undisturbed systems		
osmotic pressure	42,000–80,000[1,2]	
ultracentrifuge		19,000– 46,000[3]
film balance		80,000–140,000[4]
Agitated or hot systems		
boiling point	2,500– 5,000[5]	
freezing point	600– 4,000[1]	
viscosity		900– 4,000[6,7]

[1] LABOUT (1950)
[2] ZARRELLA and HANSON (1960)
[3] RAY et al. (1957)
[4] PFEIFFER and SAAL (1940)
[5] GRIFFIN et al. (1959)
[6] FISCHER and SCHRAM (1959)
[7] ECKERT and WEETMAN (1947)

Wales and Van der Waarden also point out that if one excludes the viscosity molecular weights and the osmotic-pressure molecular weights, then the high values of Table V are given by the weight-average molecular weights and the low values by the number-average molecular weights. The viscosity molecular weights are suspect for the reasons already mentioned. In the case of osmotic-pressure results, it is possible that low molecular weight material may diffuse through the osmotic membrane, and thus give rise to molecular weights much higher than those of the other number average methods. In this connection, ECKERT and WEET-MAN (1947) pointed out that much of an asphaltene sample will diffuse through a collodion membrane. Weight-average molecular weights of non-homogenous substances are always significantly higher than the number-average values; thus, the difference between weight-average and number-average molecular weights is undoubtedly responsible for at least a part of the divergence of molecular-weight values that have been reported.

It appears at present that the average size of the asphaltene molecules is probably between 1,000 and 10,000. It is also recognized that asphaltenes are not homogeneous and, therefore, may consist of significantly larger molecules as well as much smaller ones, which are in the asphaltene solubility class because of their high polarity. The high polarity causes the smaller molecules to be insoluble in the media used for the separation of asphaltenes.

Asphaltene association definitely plays an important role in those methods which yield molecular weights in tens and hundreds of thousands. These systems certainly consist of aggregates or clusters of asphaltenes.

STRUCTURAL INVESTIGATIONS

Many methods have been employed in an effort to obtain a clear picture of the chemical structure of the asphaltic components in petroleum. While a complete picture has not yet been worked out, a number of significant details has been gathered over the years. Most of this work has concentrated on the asphaltenes, and the following is a resume of the knowledge thas has been gained from these various investigations.

Oxidation and hydrogenation

Combustion analyses are an oxidation procedure that has provided most of the data on the quantities of various elements contained in the asphaltic constituents of petroleum. Combustion analyses of asphaltenes from various sources are compiled in Table IV. It is seen that the asphaltenes vary in the percentage of each element. In general, they contain 82–88% carbon and 7–9% hydrogen. Sulfur is often a significant component (7% for certain Venezuelan and California coastal crude oils) but may fall as low as 1 % in the case of certain oils from the San Joaquin valley area of California. Nitrogen may be present in amounts up to 4 % in shale oil bitumen, but in most petroleum asphaltenes, it does not exceed 2 %. The oxygen content is likewise variable, but makes up about 1 % of the weight of most asphaltenes. Where the petroleum has been exposed to air, as in tar pits, oxidation has progressed, and the asphaltenes from these sources can have oxygen contents in excess of 5 %.

From this chemical composition, the problem has been to determine how all these elements are arranged in the asphaltene structure. In some pioneering studies, NELLENSTEYN (1923) obtained mellitic acid (hexacarboxybenzene) from an intensive oxidation of asphaltenes. Since the same product is obtained by the oxidation of graphite, he concluded that asphaltenes consist of a graphitic core surrounded by progressively less carbonaceous material.

ERDMAN and RAMSEY (1961) have reported studies on the oxidation of asphaltenes derived from petroleum sources in comparison to those obtained from coals and other bitumens. The degree of oxidation was measured in terms of the consumption of potassium permanganate, but the nature of the oxidation products was not studied. However, they found significant differences in the oxidation rates of coal versus petroleum asphaltenes. The petroleum asphaltenes were difficult to oxidize, whereas coal and oil shale bitumens were oxidized rapidly. Black carbonaceous material from non-marine shale was found to oxidize at a rate similar to that of the coal asphaltenes; whereas the material from a marine limestone oxidized at a rate approximately the same as that of the petroleum asphaltenes. These results suggest a marine origin for the particular oils studied.

Infrared spectra of asphaltenes recovered from oxidized asphalt show carbonyl bands at 6.0 μ as well as the usual bands in the region of 5.85 μ. These bands are interpreted as evidence of aromatic acids, that is, those acids having the carbonyl double bond conjugated with the aromatic ring system. This evidence indicates an aromatic character for asphaltenes.

The reaction of asphalts with oxygen in the air has been used for many years to introduce desired rheological properties. The reaction produces marked non-Newtonian character with significant elastic behavior as well as increased hardness. The viscosity under small stresses becomes very high so that resistence to spontaneous flow is markedly increased.

The oxidation reaction is carried out at temperatures of about 500 °F. and is known to consist primarily of dehydrogenation processes and polymerization. Water, carbon dioxide, and low-molecular weight oxygenated species are found in the oxidation products. At lower temperatures (263 °F) a significant amount of oxygen is retained in the "air-blown" material, whereas very little is retained at the usual air-blowing temperature (HUGHES, 1960). The carbonyl groupings in these oxygenated asphaltenes are readily apparent in the infrared spectra. The asphaltene content of the material is increased. It is, of course, recognized that the asphaltenes formed in this air-blowing process are often significantly different from those which were originally present in the crude oil.

Hydrogenation experiments have also provided useful information on the chemical nature of asphaltenes. The asphaltenes quickly poison the hydrogenation catalysts. The mechanism of the poisoning is in part a deposition of coke on the catalyst surface (FLINN et al., 1961). In order to hydrogenate these molecules, it is necessary to add fresh catalyst in large quantities repeatedly. The hydrogenation process converts asphaltenes to less complex species. The asphaltene content is reduced and petroleum oils and resins are formed. SERGIENKO and PUSTIL'NIKOVA (1959) found that the sulfur and oxygen content of the asphaltenes was reduced and that the molecular weight was also reduced. They concluded that sulfur and oxygen linkages existed between segments of asphaltene molecules. It must be borne in mind, however, that apparent molecular weights on asphaltenes may reflect changes in a state of association as well as changes in molecular size. This topic was discussed earlier in this chapter.

FISCHER and SCHRAM (1959) also conducted hydrogenation experiments on asphaltenes and arrived at similar conclusions. Hydrogenation of asphaltenes under a variety of conditions has been reported by BESTOUGEFF and GENDREL (1964). Oily products similar to those found in the crude oils were produced, and a high-melting asphaltene remained.

Other chemical behavior

Asphaltenes react with bromine and iodine compounds used in the common unsaturation tests (GREENFELD, 1960). The high iodine and bromine numbers obtained are thought to be due in large measure to substitution reactions or the oxidation of sulfides or other highly labile groupings. It is doubted that they should be considered as measures of olefinic double bonds in these compounds.

Asphaltenes can be alkylated by paraffinic hydrocarbons (ILLMAN, 1961). They can be easily sulfonated to form water-soluble derivatives, both sulfonates and sulfonic acid esters (HILLMAN and BARNETT, 1937), but containing 5–6% nitrogen. According to BARTH (1962), these products are of the nature of phenyl-nitromethane.

Molecular complexes are formed with ferric chloride, mercuric bromide, and copper sulfate. Aluminum chloride promotes further ring condensation (BARTH, 1962).

Reactions of halogens with asphalts are discussed by LABOUT (1950). Halogen acids are liberated and more asphaltenes are formed; however, it is not clear which of the asphaltic components is primarily responsible for the reactions. Heating asphalts with halogen containing organic compounds such as carbon tetrachloride and hexachlorethane results in evolution of hydrogen chloride and formation of more asphaltenes. Again, it is not established which of the asphaltic components reacted.

Asphaltenes do not combine or react with diazo compounds (BARTH, 1962). They do react with formaldehyde and other carbonyl compounds to form insoluble derivatives (GORDON et al., 1959). Alkalis produce an emulsification of asphalts. The ease of emulsification is related to the content of carboxylic acids in the bitumen.

While the above chemical behavior does not contribute significantly to an exposition of the chemical structure of the asphaltenes, many of the reactions suggest an aromatic character. Carboxylic acids and sulfides are also indicated as configurations that are often present.

Infrared and ultraviolet spectroscopy

Studies of asphalts using infrared and ultraviolet spectroscopy have been reported by SCHWEYER (1958) and more recently by HIDALGO and VALERO (1963). The most extensive use of infrared spectra to date has been made by the asphalt workers at the National Bureau of Standards (STEWART, 1957; BEITCHMAN, 1959; GREEN-FELD and WRIGHT, 1962; WRIGHT and CAMPBELL, 1962; CAMPBELL et al., 1962; and CAMPBELL and WRIGHT, 1964). This group has made much use of the changes in infrared spectra of roofing asphalts. The roofing asphalts contain significant quantities of synthetic asphaltenes in addition to those native to the crude oil that was the source of the asphalt. These synthetic asphaltenes are produced by air blowing the residuum; thus, they represent a more highly polymerized and more oxygenated asphaltene than that which occurs naturally. Although the studies do not deal primarily with natural asphaltenes, they do indicate possible con-figurations for the oxygen containing functional groups in those asphaltenes which show significant oxidation as obtained from the virgin crude oil. Examples of oils containing oxygenated asphaltenes are the Kern, Oxnard, and the San Ardo crude oils of California.

CAMPBELL and WRIGHT (1964) show that aldehydes, ketones, and organic acids can account for most of the oxygen containing functional groups. They discount the significance of ester groups which are proposed by GOPPEL and KNOTNERUS (1955) as the principal oxygen-containing group produced in the high-temperature commercial air-oxidation processes. Ester groups, if present, probably have structures wherein the carbonyl group is conjugated with the aromat-ic ring system. Such structures do not appear to be ruled out by the studies of CAMPBELL and WRIGHT (1964).

The activating influence of aromatic ring systems on the alpha or benzylic carbon is well known. In a reaction with oxygen, it is logical that the attack of the oxygen should be on those hydrogens attached to the alpha carbons, and that the resulting carbonyl group should be found attached to these alpha carbons. It should also be noted that SERGIENKO and GARBALINSKII (1963) report that esters are formed in this process.

In addition to the carbonyl-containing structures, infrared data also show a strong CH band at 3.4 μ, peaks characteristic of CH_2 groups at 6.8 μ, and peaks for methyl groups at 7.25 μ. The group of three bands at 11.5, 12.2, and 13.3 μ, which generally are of similar intensity, are believed due to substituted aromatic ring structures. The aromatic ring band at 6.25 μ is well marked. The broad and strong absorbance between 7.5 and 9 μ is believed due to oxygen-containing species (STEWART, 1957). Peaks at 7.7 and 8.8 μ have been attributed to sulfur-oxygen bonds (STEWART, 1957; BROWN and KNOBLOCH, 1957). A characteristic peak at 9.6 μ has not been accounted for. The band at 13.8 μ which is attributed to CH_2 chains of four or more units in length is usually observed and varies in intensity with the source of the asphalt. Infrared spectra taken from FISCHER and SCHRAM (1959) are shown in Fig.1. The carbonyl, aromatic carbon, and methylene chain carbon absorptions are identified by the dashed lines at wave numbers of 1,700 cm^{-1}, (5.85 μ), 1,610 cm^{-1} (6.25 μ) and 7,20 cm^{-1} (13.8 μ).

Traxler and coworkers (CHELTON and TRAXLER, 1959; ROMBERG et al., 1959) used infrared data to deduce the percentages of carbon in methyl, methylene, naphthenic ring and aromatic ring configurations. Their data for the fraction which they call "asphaltics" (butanol insoluble, principally asphaltenes) is given in Table VI.

The infrared study of asphaltenes made by YEN and ERDMAN (1962) indicates a different type of ring condensation for petroleum asphaltenes than that found in coals. The asphaltenes are primarily peri-condensed, like phenanthrene, while the coals are kata-condensed, like anthracene. Condensed naphthenic structures

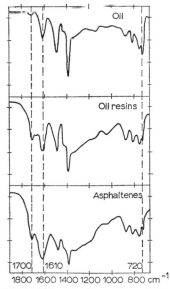

Fig.1. Infrared absorption of the oil, resin and asphaltene fractions isolated from petroleum bitumen. (The spectra are taken in decalin as a solvent. The spectrum of the solvent is suppressed by compensation). (After FISCHER and SCHRAM, 1959.)

TABLE VI

CARBON TYPES IN ASPHALTENES FROM ASPHALTS OF DIFFERENT RHEOLOGICAL TYPE

Carbon type	Percentage of each carbon type[1]		
	gel	sol-gel	sol
Aromatic ring	58	39	60
Methyl groups	9	7	9
Methylene chains	30	25	26
Other carbon types	3	29	5

[1] Gel, sol-gel and sol refer to the rheological and colloidal nature of the asphalts.

are also indicated, and the proportions of aromatic, naphthenic and methyl carbon are estimated.

The ultraviolet spectra of asphaltenes are rather lacking in character. The intensity of absorbance increases regularly with shorter wavelength, but no peaks emerge unless the particular asphaltene fraction is rich in porphyrins (for detailed discussion of porphyrins see Chapter VI). The UV spectra also indicate that highly condensed aromatic ring systems are present in the asphaltenes (ROSENBAUM, 1958).

X-ray diffraction studies

X-ray diffraction studies by WILLIFORD (1943) showed a very slight evidence of crystallinity in asphaltenes prepared for use in road paving. As shown by BARTH (1962), however, the most pronounced diffraction patterns in asphalt are produced by large quantities of wax in the system. Data by ALEXANIAN and LOUIS (1950) indicated that natural asphaltenes freed from the solvency of resinous constituents showed much crystallinity and some evidence of chain orientation.

YEN et al. (1961b) found that the X-ray diffraction patterns obtained with natural asphaltenes could be matched by simple mixtures of graphite and polyethylene. From their data, YEN et al. (1961b) reported that the X-ray diffraction pattern of asphaltenes that had been precipitated from petroleum could be explained on the basis of polynuclear aromatic sheets of 9–15 Å diameter, spaced about 3.6 Å units apart. A package consisting of about four sheets could be stacked up before the natural heterogenity of asphaltenes prevented further accumulation on a particular nucleus. Further accumulation on other nuclei was still possible because the asphaltene "molecules" were considered to contain two or more of the polynuclear aromatic sheets bonded together by aliphatic carbon linkages. Crystallinity was also indicated in the X-ray diffraction patterns resulting from the chain orientation of aliphatic groups. These were spaced about 5.7 Å apart in the manner of a saturated carbon chain or loose net of naphthenic rings. Their concept of the precipitated asphaltenes is presented in Fig.2.

This picture of asphaltenes can be conveniently extrapolated to explain the colloidal character of asphaltic constituents in petroleum. The solvency of petroleum hydrocarbons is generally not high enough to prevent this association among

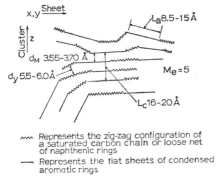

— Represents the zig-zag configuration of
   a saturated carbon chain or loose net
   of naphthenic rings
— Represents the flat sheets of condensed
   aromatic rings

Fig.2. Cross-sectional view of an asphaltene model. (After YEN et al., 1961.)

the polynuclear aromatic segments of the asphaltene molecules, hence these groups may assemble into micelles. Aromatic species may be readily included between the aromatic sheets of asphaltenes in the micelle. This region also provides a pseudophase of higher polarity and thus a region where the more polar species, the so-called resins, may be concentrated. The solubility characteristics of sulfur compounds indicate a higher concentration of these substances in the asphaltene micelle also. The region outside the micelle then consists of the less aromatic and polar components, primarily aliphatic and naphthenic hydrocarbons. The aliphatic sections of the asphaltene molecules serve to provide a transition between the polar and non-polar regions in the petroleum and to prevent the assembly of polar aggregates so large as to be non-dispersible in the crude oil.

Mass spectroscopy

CLERC and O'NEAL (1961) conducted a mass-spectrometric analysis of an asphalt produced by molecular distillation and propane deasphalting of a West-Texas crude oil. The asphalt was not further fractionated and thus should have contained asphaltenes and petrolenes. A number of fragments were observed in the high-mass spectrometer, and possible configurations could be assigned to some of these as shown in Fig.3. These fragments were deduced to be condensed aromatic and heterocyclic ring systems. Structures isomeric with these are, of course, possible.

Clerc and O'Neal volatized the asphalt at low pressure (50 μ) off a heater mounted in the ionizing region of the instrument. Because they did not find light hydrocarbon gases in the spectra, which would be characteristic of cracking, they

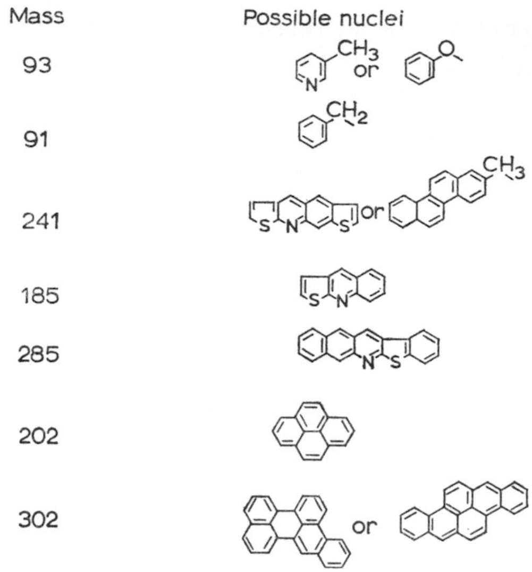

Mass   Possible nuclei

93

91

241

185

285

202

302

Fig.3. Assignment of fragment peaks in the mass spectrum of asphalt. (After CLERC and O'NEAL, 1961.)

concluded that the asphalt molecules were vaporized without decomposition. No evidence of a carbon residue was found on the heater; thus they further concluded that all of the asphalt had vaporized. An average molecular weight for the particles of about 900 was obtained. They also concluded that insignificant quantities of material with a mass above 1900 was present in that sample.

Although Clerc and O'Neal concluded that thermal degradation had not occurred in their experiment, the ease with which such decomposition can occur in asphaltenes is well-known. Commercial processing of residua where temperatures reach 750–800 °F often result in changes in the nature of the asphaltenes. Thus the possibility remains that thermal degradation may have occurred in the volatilization from the hot wire.

Earlier studies by O'Neal and coworkers (CARLSON and O'NEAL, 1958; HOOD et al., 1959), on high molecular weight petroleum distillates indicated that these compounds consisted principally of condensed ring structures, both aromatic and cyclic, to which one long chain was attached. If two ring systems were found in a molecule, they were indicated to be located at the opposite ends of a long chain. Branching attached to the rings was believed to be limited to methyl and ethyl groups. These molecules are very probably the principle components of the so-called resin fraction in petroleum and asphalt.

Thermal diffusion

One of the difficulties in structure work on the asphaltic components of petroleum is due to the complexity of the mixture of chemical compounds present in the system. Thermal diffusion is a relatively new and very effective method for fractionating complex mixtures of viscous materials. In thermal diffusion, the molecules are separated primarily on the basis of shape. Those which can migrate fastest under a temperature gradient are separated from the slower moving molecules. Thermal diffusion was applied by JONES (1958) and by MELPOLDER et al. (1958) to high-boiling petroleum distillates. It was also applied by CHELTON and TRAXLER (1959) to petrolene fractionation, and these fractions were classified as to ring types by infrared analysis (see Table VI).

GARDNER et al. (1959) used thermal diffusion to separate petrolenes obtained by pentane extraction from a blend of Oklahoma and Illinois crude oil residua into ten fractions. The thermal diffusion fractions were characterized by infrared analysis, viscosities, molecular weight determination (ebullioscopic), carbon–hydrogen analyses nuclear magnetic resonance, and electron spin resonance.

Analytical data obtained on the ten fractions are presented in Table IV. Carbon–hydrogen ratios are seen to range steadily higher beginning with 0.51 at fraction 1, the most fluid fraction, up to 0.76 for fraction 10, which had the viscosity characteristic of a hard paving asphalt. A C/H ratio of 0.5 is characteristic of a good grade of lubricating oil and such a material is not an asphaltic component in the usual sense. Asphaltenes ordinarily have C/H ratios exceeding 0.80, but otherwise the fraction-10 material is very like an asphaltene. Asphaltic resins ordinarily have C/H ratios of about 0.75, and thus are, on the average, slightly more aromatic than thermal diffusion fraction 5, for which a C/H ratio of 0.64 was obtained. It appears then that fractions 1–4 are oils, fractions 5–9 are representative of resins, and fraction 10 is very nearly an asphaltene.

GARDNER et al. (1959) have constructed a most helpful set of hypothetical molecules representing their first, middle, and last fractions. These are reproduced in Fig.4. They concluded that these ten fractions range in composition from fairly simple alkyl naphthenes at the one extreme (fraction 1) to highly condensed, aromatic-naphthenic structures at the other (fraction 10).

Data obtained from high-mass spectrometer studies (CARLSON and O'NEAL, 1958) on the high molecular weight fractions of petroleum, suggests that the condensed rings of petrolene molecules may be primarily collected at the ends of the molecules. The degree of condensation, however, and the quantity of the various types of ring systems are probably more as shown by GARDNER et al. (1959). This work represents an important step forward in understanding the nature of the asphaltic components of petroleum.

Electron spin and nuclear magnetic resonance

With the advent of electron spin resonance (E.S.R.), also called electron paramagnetic resonance (E.P.R.), it was found that most crude oils showed the absorption of electromagnetic energy characteristic of unpaired electrons. This ob-

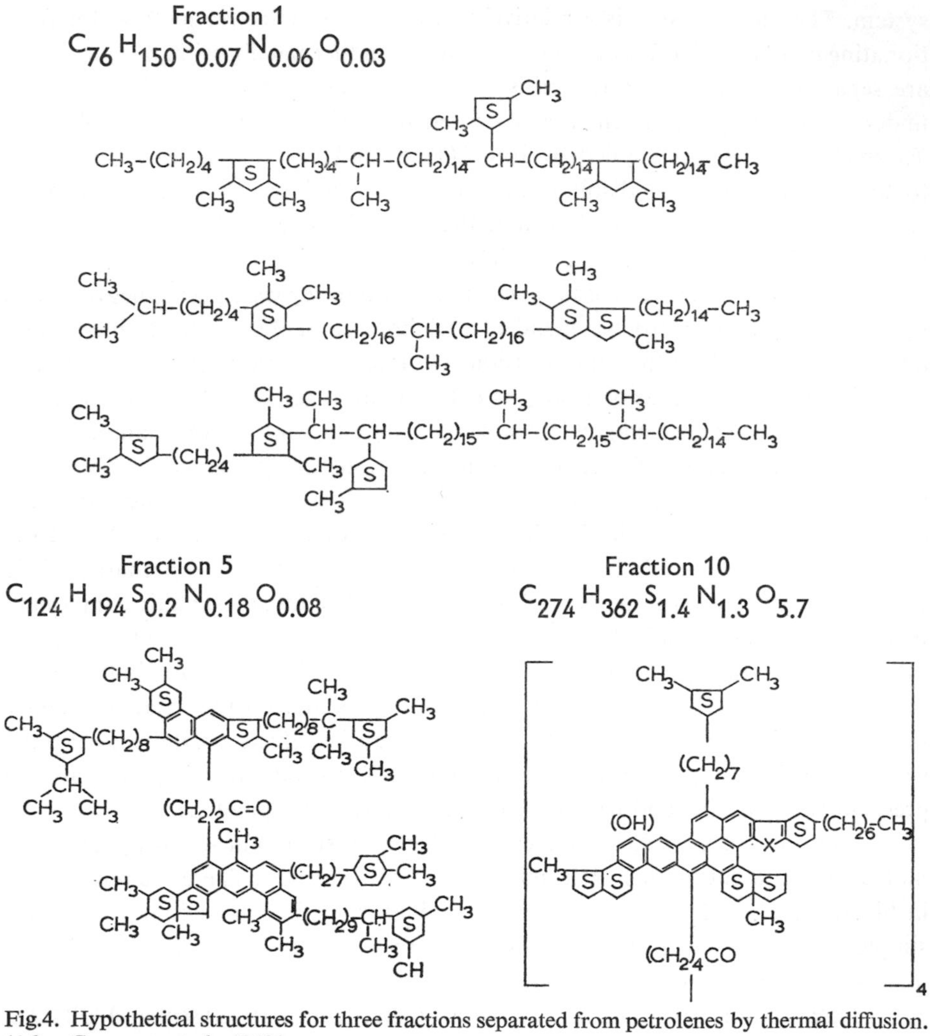

Fig.4. Hypothetical structures for three fractions separated from petrolenes by thermal diffusion. (After GARDNER et al., 1959.)

servation was first reported by GARIFIANOV and KOZYREV (1956) for a crude oil and a petroleum asphalt. GUTOWSKY et al. (1958) reported that these unpaired electrons (free radicals) were associated with the asphaltene fraction. O'REILLEY (1958) showed that at least a part of the free radical signal was due to etioporphyrin-vanadium complexes, and the signal was later used as the basis for an analytical method for vanadium in crude oil (SARCENO et al., 1961). WILLIAMS and SAUNDERS (1959a) showed that the free radical signal can also be used as a measure of the asphaltene content of petroleum hydrocarbons.

FLINN et al. (1961) also discussed the asphaltene-free radicals. They reported 2 to 4 · 10^{18} free radicals per gram or about one per hundred asphaltene molecules, assuming a molecular weight of about 2,000 for the asphaltenes. They made the reasonable postulate that the free radicals contribute to the tendency toward micelle formation in the asphaltenes. The free radicals were essentially confined to the asphaltene fraction. The resins contained only 2% of the total free radicals present.

YEN et al. (1962) found that the nature of the asphaltene-free radical signal was most closely approximated by certain neutral radicals of carbon and nitrogen. The signal is closer to that of an aromatic hydrocarbon radical ion than to a semiquinone radical ion, which is thought to be present in coals (GIVEN, 1959).

The free radical signal is partly removed by reduction processes and is increased by oxidation processes. YEN et al. (1962) conclude that the free electron is associated with a resonating π-electron system. Hetero-atoms of nitrogen, sulfur and oxygen, in the asphaltenes, increase the probability that a stable unpaired electron will be found in the molecule. Possible free-electron sites are shown in Fig.5 taken from the paper by YEN et al. (1962).

Nuclear magnetic resonance (N.M.R.), in which microwave energy is absorbed by protons in molecules of organic compounds, has provided a new tool which has also been utilized in studying the structure of the asphaltic components of petroleum. In a pioneering study, WILLIAMS (1958) deduced the amounts of aromatic carbon, aliphatic carbon, and carbon adjacent to aromatic rings from nuclear magnetic resonance (N.M.R.) data on West Texas asphaltenes and resins. In a subsequent paper, GARDNER et al. (1959) used N.M.R. methods in studying the structures of a series of fractions obtained by the thermal diffusion of petrolenes.

WINNIFORD and BERSOHN (1962) have proposed possible structures for asphaltenes from San Joaquin Valley, California and Venezuelan crude oils as well as asphaltenes produced by thermal cracking and the airblowing process using N.M.R.

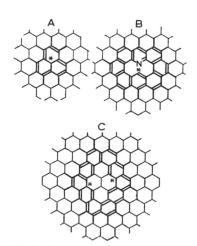

Fig.5. Structures of the type which may be the sites of the free electrons in petroleum asphaltenes. (After YEN et al., 1962.)

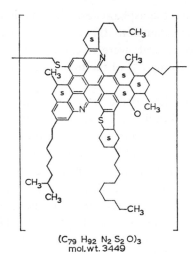

$(C_{79} H_{92} N_2 S_2 O)_3$
mol. wt. 3449

Hydrogen distribution ratios		Composition	
Methylene	1.00	%C=	82.5
Methyl	0.40	%H=	8.0
Benzylic	0.28	%N=	2.5
Aromatic	0.06	%O=	1.4
		%S=	5.6
		C/H ratio= 0.86	

Fig.6. Hypothetical structure for asphaltene from Venezuelan crude oil. (After WINNIFORD and BERSOHN, 1962.)

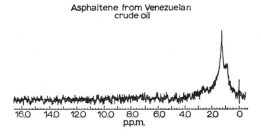

Asphaltene from Venezuelan
crude oil

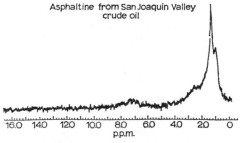

Asphaltine from San Joaquin Valley
crude oil

Fig.7. Nuclear magnetic resonance spectra for asphaltenes from Venezuelan and San Joaquin Valley crude oils. (After WINNIFORD and BERSOHN, 1962.)

data plus other information. They also discussed other structures that had been proposed earlier in the literature. Fig.6 shows their hypothetical structure for an asphaltene taken from the Venezuelan crude oil.

The N.M.R. spectra of Winniford and Bersohn are shown in Fig.7. These data show that approximately 50% of the hydrogen in natural asphaltenes is in methylene groups. Aliphatic methyl hydrogens are second in abundance to the methylene hydrogens followed by benzylic hydrogens, and lastly, the aromatic hydrogens. These results are in clear contrast to those obtained on coal asphaltenes where the hydrogens are found to be principally attached to aromatic rings (DEWALT and MORGAN, 1962). The relative lack of aromatic and benzylic hydrogen in petroleum asphaltenes argues for condensed polynuclear aromatic ring systems in contrast to structures which contain large amounts of benzene and naphthalene rings. These latter require large amounts of aromatic and benzylic hydrogen, which the nuclear resonance data indicate to be present in much smaller quantities.

The N.M.R. results also lead to the kind of structures suggested by YEN et al. (1961b) from their X-ray diffraction studies of precipitated asphaltenes (see Fig.2). Thus, it is the interpretation that the structure of asphaltenes consists of polynuclear aromatic ring systems that are composed of 10–20 fused rings and carry aliphatic and naphthenic side chains. It must, of course, be emphasized that this picture is by no means fully established, but it is believed that it presents an attractive working hypothesis that explains much of the observed behavior of the asphaltic components.

PHYSICO-CHEMICAL INVESTIGATIONS

In addition to the structural investigations discussed above, a considerable amount of research has been aimed at gaining a better understanding of the physical and chemical behavior of the asphaltic components in petroleum. Much of this work has focussed on the colloidal nature of petroleum because it has been found that the asphaltic components exist in petroleum as colloidal particles of considerable dimensions. It has therefore been important to investigate the properties of these particles and the role they play in controlling the overall behavior of petroleum.

Electron microscopy

With the advent of the electron microscope about thirty years ago, it was postulated that direct observation of crude oils under high magnification might reveal the presence of colloidal-sized particles. In the first of these studies, PRECKSHOT et al. (1943) reported that when untreated crude oil was placed directly in the microscope for examination, no particles could be seen. If some solvent such as benzene or petroleum ether were added to the oil before placing it in the microscope, particles as small as 100 Å appeared, which Preckshot et al. attributed to a precipitation phenomenon caused by the solvent. Similar negative results have been reported by others (DYKSTRA et al., 1944; KATZ and BEU, 1945; SKINNER, 1952). After examining a large number of samples from crude oil as well as asphalt, KATZ and BEU (1945) concluded that if asphaltic materials exist as colloidal particles in petroleum, they must be less than 65 Å in size. In checking the resolving power of their electron microscope, Katz and Beu concluded that particles as small as 32 Å could be seen.

An attempt to avoid particle aggregation was made by WITHERSPOON (1957) using a replica technique. In these studies a platinum replica was prepared of an asphaltic sediment that had been centrifuged from an Illinois crude oil. When the replica was examined with the electron microscope, numerous particles of the order of 50 to 100 Å in size could be seen. A typical example at high magnification is shown in Fig.8.

By shadowing the original material with platinum at an angle of approximately 15°, the replicated specimen showed an interesting accumulation of particles which may be seen on the right-hand side of Fig.8. This prominent accumulation, which resembles the head of a housefly, is about 0.8 μ (8,000 Å) in diameter, and judging from the length of its shadow, it is about 80 Å high. Inside the accumulation,

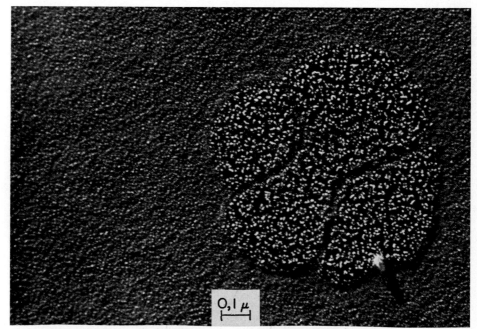

Fig.8. Electron micrograph of asphaltic sediment centrifuged from Illinois crude oil. (Replica obtained by platinum shadow backed up with carbon film.) (After WITHERSPOON, 1957.)

the particles are somewhat larger than outside and average around 100 Å in size. It may be noted that many of the larger particles appear to be clusters of several smaller particles.

Particles of observable size have also been reported by WINNIFORD (1963), who examined dilute benzene solutions (0.1%) of asphaltenes that had been obtained from two crude oils, one from Venezuela and one from California. Asphaltenes were taken from steam-refined residua of each crude oil and also from the product of air-blowing each of the residue. Aggregation in varying degrees was observed and was more pronounced for the airblown asphaltenes. The size of the aggregates varied with the source of the asphaltene and ranged from 50 to 150 Å. In the case of the steam-refined California asphaltenes, however, nothing could be seen at the maximum magnification of this study (75,000 ×).

FREUND and VAJTA (1958) were able to observe particle aggregation taking place in an asphalt during the course of an air-blowing process. Although the initial residuum showed little evidence of such particles, electron micrographs revealed the formation of particles more and more clearly with increasing air treatment.

In all of these studies, it is evident that unless the asphaltic materials were removed from their natural environment or changed in some way, they could not be seen. Two explanations for this have been proposed. Either the colloidal particles are too small to be seen with the resolving power of an electron microscope, or the transition in chemical character from the petroleum through the more aliphatic portions of the asphaltene micelles to the aromatic central portion is too gradual. In the latter case, there is no definite interface to provide a reflecting surface to beams of light or electrons (FREUNDLICH, 1938; SKINNER, 1952). As will be discussed below, ultracentrifuge investigations indicate that the size of these colloidal particles is large enough that they should be visible in the electron microscope. The fact that large particles are not visible in the electron microscope is compatible with the type of micelle that has been proposed (see the section on X-ray diffraction).

Ultracentrifugation

If asphaltic substances exist in petroleum as particles of colloidal dimensions, the question arises of whether or not such particles are big enough to move appreciably under the influence of the high gravitational fields that can be developed in an ultracentrifuge. The driving force that will cause such motion is dependent on the difference in density between the asphalt particle and the crude oil, the size of the particles, and the magnitude of the imposed gravitational field. The specific gravity of most crude oils ranges from 0.8 to 0.95 whereas the density of asphaltenes is much higher, exceeding 1.0 g/ml (SACHANEN, 1945). The size of the asphaltene molecule has not been clearly established, but from the data of Table V, it would appear that we must consider particles whose molecular (or particle) weight can range from as low as 1,000 to as high as 140,000.

From theoretical considerations, WITHERSPOON and MUNIR (1960) have shown that if asphaltenes exist in crude oil as discrete molecules with a molecular weight of 1,000, then the application of an ultracentrifuge force field of 80,000 g will cause only a slight rearrangement in the distribution of particles without causing any sediment to be thrown out of the system. On the other hand, if the particles have a molecular weight of 100,000, they are so large that for all practical purposes they would all be driven out of the oil and deposited as a sediment. Similar calculations for molecular weights of 10,000 and 20,000 indicated that these are probably the minimum sizes that can be sedimented out of a crude oil under the assumed conditions.

To check on these calculations, Witherspoon and Munir examined a number of crude oils from the mid-continent, Gulf Coast, and Rocky Mountain regions using a force field of 80,000 g. These oils ranged in gravity from 18° to 46° A.P.I., and in general, a well-defined sediment was centrifuged from each oil whose A.P.I. gravity was 30° or more. Crude oils, whose gravities were less than 30° showed a distinct collection of asphaltic materials in the bottom layers of the centrifuge cell, but usually the viscosity in this region was increased so much that no clean separation of oil from sediment was possible. In many cases, an oil that originally was black in color took on a distinctly greenish color as the asphaltic substances were driven out. It is clearly evident that asphaltic particles of considerable size are commonly present in petroleum.

ELDIB et al. (1960) have also found that asphaltenes and non-hydrocarbons are concentrated toward the bottom of the oil column during ultracentrifugation. When they centrifuged a de-asphalted oil, however, no sedimentation of asphaltenes was observed, which they interpret as an indication that the colloidal-sized particles were removed by the de-asphalting.

Using analytical ultracentrifuge methods WITHERSPOON (1957) examined the sediment that had been centrifuged from an Illinois crude oil. In this work, the sediment, which was primarily composed of asphaltenes, was first dispersed in benzene and the rate of sedimentation measured. Then the material was dispersed in carbon tetrachloride and instead of sedimenting, it floated, i.e., the material moved toward the center of rotation because its density was less than that of the solvent. The results of these investigations with asphaltenes dispersed in benzene, carbon tetrachloride, and two different mixtures of these solvents at 23°C are given in Fig.9. The sedimentation coefficients have been corrected for the differences in viscosity and the compressibility effects of the two solvents (WITHERSPOON, 1957). On the basis of these results and the assumption of a spherical shape, it was determined that the particle diameter was about 40 Å. Since Fig.9 indicates the density of the dispersed asphaltenes was 1.22 g/ml, the molecular weight was found to be approximately 30,000.

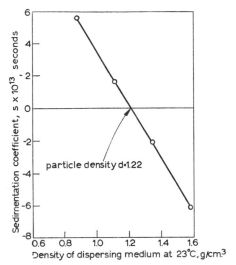

Fig.9. Corrected sedimentation coefficients for asphaltenes dispersed in solvents of different density. (After WITHERSPOON, 1957.)

WINNIFORD (1963) obtained similar sedimentation coefficients at 25°C when he used the ultracentrifuge approach to study asphaltenes that were separated from air-blown and steam-refined asphalts. However, voluminosities as given by viscosity data suggested that the asphaltene particles are solvated. Solvation reduces the effective density of the sedimenting particle; thus, higher molecular or particle weights were calculated. Using benzene solutions, particle weights ranging from 40,000 to 500,000 were obtained, but when normal butylamine was used as a solvent, the values were only one third as large.

More recently, WALES and VAN DER WAARDEN (1964) have used a combination of ultracentrifuge, diffusion, and intrinsic viscosity data at 25°C to investigate the particle size of asphaltenes extracted from asphalt from a California valley crude oil. They report a molecular weight of 39,000 by using sedimentation and viscosity data and 48,500 by using sedimentation and diffusion data. If a spherical shape is assumed, the particles would have a diameter of 68 Å. They question the concept that solvation should be assumed for these particles, but if the intrinsic viscosity data is interpreted in terms of solvation, then they obtained a "dry" molecular weight of 48,000.

It will be noted on Fig.9 that a linear relationship was obtained between the sedimentation coefficient and the density of the various dispersing agents used in the ultracentrifuge work. It has been shown by others (SHARP et al., 1944; SCHACHMAN and LAUFFER, 1949) that such a straight line relationship will be obtained if the dispersing medium has no effect on the size and shape. In other words, the state of aggregation of the asphaltic particles was not affected by the different solvents used. The same results have been reported by WINNIFORD (1963) and also by WALES and VAN DER WAARDEN (1964).

Rheology

If the size of asphaltene particles in petroleum is as large as is indicated by the above ultracentrifuge results, one would anticipate that such particles are likely to have a profound effect on viscosity. Investigations on the non-Newtonian behavior of oils have been confined largely to various refined products. However, WITHERSPOON et al. (1961) have reported the effect of asphaltic materials on the viscosity of five California crude oils ranging in gravity from 15° to 25° A.P.I.

Although crude oils are generally considered to be Newtonian fluids, the asphaltic oils of this investigation exhibited pronounced pseudoplastic, non-Newtonian behavior which became more apparent with increasing concentration of asphaltenes. The highest concentration found in this study was 21% asphaltenes, by weight, and the results of viscosity measurements on this crude oil are shown in Fig.10. The non-Newtonian characteristic of a decreasing viscosity with increasing rate of shear is evident at all temperatures but is most obvious at 25°C.

To investigate the effect of asphaltene concentration, WITHERSPOON et al. (1961) made a series of measurements on this same crude oil with different amounts of asphaltenes. The asphaltic substances were first removed from the sample by *n*-pentane precipitation and then added back to the residual oil to produce several different concentration so it was found that the viscosity of the mixture increased exponentially with asphaltene concentration demonstrating the profound effect

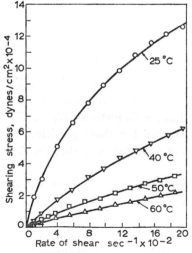

Fig.10. Viscosity measurements on a California crude oil containing 21% asphaltenes. (After WITHERSPOON et al., 1961.)

that asphaltic components have on the viscous behavior of crude oil. The results of this study also indicated that crude oils with an asphaltene content in excess of about 5% are likely to exhibit non-Newtonian behavior.

Where the asphaltic components are concentrated, as in commercial asphalts, the rheological behavior is highly complex. Researchers in the asphalt industry have studied this rheology extensively (SAAL and LABOUT, 1940; ROMBERG and TRAXLER, 1947; NEPPE, 1952; VAN DER POEL, 1954; BROWN et al., 1957; GRIFFIN et al., 1959; WINNIFORD, 1960). Surveys of asphalt rheology are given by BARTH (1962) and TRAXLER (1961) in their books on asphalt technology. The cited references are only a small part of the literature on asphalt rheology. In general, the behavior is interpreted as that of a colloidal system. However, some references show that the rheology can also be discussed in terms of the behavior of chain polymers (GASKINS et al., 1960).

Systems rich in asphaltenes show elastic behavior as well as non-Newtonian flow. They also show thixotropic behavior in that the viscosity is reduced by active shearing and increases again as the system is allowed to stand or is sheared less vigorously.

The highest degree of non-Newtonian flow is obtained when the asphaltenes are dispersed in media of low solvent power. Essentially Newtonian flow is observed at low asphaltene contents in media of high solvent power and at low shear rates. Raising the temperature leads to more Newtonian flow, except that very hard asphalts show increased thixotropy when they are softened slightly by warming.

The rheological behavior of asphalts can be interpreted in terms of clusters of asphaltenes which are deformed by shearing stresses. The size of these clusters depends upon the dispersing power of the medium in which they are found and upon the temperature. FISCHER and SCHRAM (1959) deduced from viscosity and molecular weight data that the asphaltenes form rheological units consisting of about 1,000,000 asphaltene units at low temperatures in certain asphalts, and that this number drops to about one asphaltene molecule per flow unit at high temperatures in media of good solvent power.

Surface active constituents

A considerable amount of work has been devoted to isolating surface active components from petroleum. The first evidence that such components must be present in crude oil was the ease with which many crudes form emulsions in the presence of water. In an early study, LOTTERMOSER and CALANTAR (1929) reported that asphaltic materials lead to the formation of stable water-in-oil emulsions. MORRELL and EGLOFF (1931) and UREN (1939) also name the asphaltic components as the emulsifying agents responsible for the formation of water-in-oil emulsions.

BARTELL and NIEDERHAUSER (1949) were probably the first to attempt to

isolate the surface active materials from a number of crude oils. They were successful in isolating such materials from one California crude oil, but could not re-
produce their results when they studied a group of other oils in the absence of air.
They, therefore, concluded that the isolated substances were formed by an oxidation
process during sampling and are not present in the normal fluids of an oil reservoir.
Others, however, have demonstrated that surface active materials do indeed exist
in petroleum, especially in the more asphaltic crude oils.

In a series of papers from the U.S. Bureau of Mines, DENEKAS et al. (1951);
DODD et al. (1952); DUNNING (1953); and DUNNING et al. (1953, 1954, 1956)
showed that surface active materials could be isolated from crude oils of Oklahoma
and California. They found that the surface-active constituents had a high metal
content, and they also established that vanadium and nickel porphyrin complexes
were the major contributors to the interfacial activity and film-forming tendencies
exhibited by their samples.

In studying the displacement of crude oil by water in saturated cores, REIS-
BERG and DOSCHER (1956) have reported that oil recovery was dependent on over-
coming rigid interfacial films that developed at oil-water interfaces and caused
the oil to adhere to a water-wetted, hydrophilic surface. The interfacially active
materials were found to be asphaltic. DODD (1960) has been able to demonstrate
the high viscosity and non-Newtonian behavior of a film formed at a crude oil-
water interface. LAWRENCE and KILLNER (1948) and BLAKEY and LAWRENCE (1954)
showed that emulsions of sea water in fuel oil were stabilized by strong asphaltic
films.

GREENLEE (1960), however, has reported that the content of the asphaltic
components in an oil does not correlate with the observed surface activity. No
single group of compounds, including the porphyrins, showed sufficient surface
activity that it might be said to control the observed phenomena. Greenlee proposed
that the greatest film forming power is present when the asphaltenes are in a
state of incipient flocculation. Water droplets induce the flocculation and are thus
encased in a film of precipitated asphaltenes and resins. Greenlee noted that asphaltenes which had been precipitated from an oil and then added back to the
oil do not show this surface activity; incipient precipitation that can be induced
by water droplets is required. VAN DER WAARDEN (1958) has demonstrated the
stability of water-in-oil emulsions and the film forming role played by asphaltenes
that are near a condition of incipient flocculation.

Peptization

In his pioneering colloid-chemical investigations, NELLENSTEYN (1931) studied the
peptizing properties of the asphaltic components. He demonstrated the peptizing
power of an asphaltic oil by showing that a stable dispersion of carbon could be
produced in a distillate from the oil. The carbon could not be effectively dispersed
in a paraffin oil.

PFEIFFER and SAAL (1940) have proposed the concept of an asphalt micelle that consists of a central core of asphaltenes surrounded by peptizing layers of petrolenes. The peptizing layers become progressively less aromatic as the distance of the layer from the asphaltene core increases, and the whole structure is essentially spherical in shape. HÖPPLER (1941) has also postulated a spherical shape for these micelles, although EILERS (1949) believes that deviations from a sphere occur with increasing concentration. The concept of peptizing layers is called the "onion skin" theory by asphalt workers.

According to this concept, the asphaltenes are fully peptized when the system contains enough petrolenes for the formation of the outer regions of the micelle. The micelles are then able to move about as freely as the viscosity of the matrix permits. If there is a shortage of the petrolene fractions, however, not all of the adsorptive forces that cause the micelle are satisfied. The asphaltene micelles then interact and the system can attain the rheological character of a gel (TRAXLER and COOMBS, 1936; PFEIFFER and SAAL, 1940; HÖPPLER, 1941).

VAN KERKVOORT et al. (1952) have developed a direct measure of what they call the "state of peptization" of fuel oil blends. Although numerical quantities for the "peptizability" of the asphaltenes and the "peptizing power" of the continuum are calculated by Van Kerkvoort et al., it is recognized that the observed phenomena need not actually involve peptization in the usual sense, wherein an adsorbed species prevents the further growth of the colloidal micelle. Changes in solvent power of the continuum will also yield the same results.

MERTENS (1960) and HEITHAUS (1960) have applied the approach of VAN KERKVOORT et al. (1952) to asphalts. In these experiments, the system containing asphaltenes is progressively diluted with a non-solvent for asphaltenes (heptane or cetane) until the first evidence of asphaltene precipitation can be detected. The relative quantities of asphaltene solvent and non-solvent used in the experiments yield the values for "peptizability" of the asphaltenes and "peptizing power" of the medium in which the asphaltenes were suspended. The phenomena could be described as well in terms of solvent power and solubility, and it is probable that in the highly aromatic and resinous asphalt systems, solubility plays as important a role as peptization in these experiments. The tests show, however, the ease with which asphaltenes can be precipitated from any given medium, and they should be useful to the petroleum chemist or engineer who is concerned with the colloidal stability of petroleum.

BRIANT (1963) has studied the factors that cause flocculation and precipitation of asphaltenes from a Sahara crude oil (Hassi-Messaoud). He found that the addition of metallic chlorides, particularly ferric chloride, causes a rapid flocculation of the asphaltenes. The amount of precipitate obtained with any given concentration of $FeCl_3$ was about doubled when the temperature increased from 20° to 80°C as shown in Fig.11. Conversely, an increase in pressure on the system reduced the amount of asphaltenes precipitated by the ferric chloride.

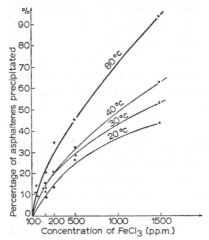

Fig.11. Effect of temperature and concentration of FeCl₃ on precipitation of asphaltenes from Hassi-Messaoud crude oil. (After BRIANT, 1963.)

Electrophoretic mobility

In colloidal systems it is often found that the dispersed particles are stabilized by virtue of the electrical charge that they carry, and such charge stabilized colloids are found to move in an electric field, i.e., they exhibit electrophoretic mobility (GLASSTONE, 1946). A number of investigations have concentrated on this aspect of the asphaltic components in petroleum, and hydrocarbon systems that contain asphaltenes have been found to have well-developed electrical properties. Thus, a patent has been issued to WILLIAMS and SAUNDERS (1959) on a process for using the conductivity of refining streams as a measure of the asphaltene content of such streams.

PRECKSHOT et al. (1943) were probably the first to study the electro-deposition of asphaltenes from crude oil. They subjected an asphaltic oil to a potential difference of 300 V and observed deposition on both the negative and positive electrodes. The material on the positive electrode adhered firmly and was largely insoluble in pentane, so it was assumed to be asphaltenes. The material on the negative electrode was pentane soluble.

In contrast to the above, CSANYI and BASSI (1958) obtained the opposite result when they electrolyzed solutions of asphaltenes in various mixtures of solvents (methanol and benzene, methanol and carbon tetrachloride, acetic acid-pyridine and carbon tetrachloride). They found that most of the deposition occurred on the negative electrode, indicating a positive charge on the asphaltenes. In a few cases, they did observe deposition on the positive electrode. More recently, WRIGHT and MINESINGER (1963) suspended asphaltenes with a particle size of 5 μ in nitromethane and observed their migration under low potential

(6 V) toward the negative electrode. The asphaltenes were extracted from airblown asphalts, however, which may have altered the electrical character of the material.

ELDIB (1962) has reported that the charge on the asphaltenes depends on the potential imposed on the system. When asphaltenes in nitrobenzene were placed in an electrophoresis apparatus at 500 V, their direction of migration indicated they were negatively charged. When 3,000 V were used, the particles became positively charged.

BRIANT (1963) has studied the electrophoretic mobility of asphaltenes that were extracted from a Sahara crude oil (Hassi-Messaoud) and dissolved in tetralin to which increasing amounts of squalane were added. He observed that the sign of the charge on the asphaltene particles was reversed by the addition of squalane, and this was followed by precipitation. If ferric chloride were added to the same tetralin solution, the electrophoretic movement dropped to a negligible amount due to flocculation of the asphaltene particles.

The results suggest that the electrical character of asphaltenes is easily modified by external forces and that these complex particles can be made to carry either positive or negative charge. The chemical system seems capable of accommodating itself to temporary excesses as well as deficiencies of electrons. Apparently, the large polynuclear aromatic portion of the molecules is capable of acting either as an electron source or an electron sink.

Association

As mentioned previously, early work on the rheological properties of asphalt led to the conclusion that asphalt is a colloidal system (TRAXLER and COOMBS, 1936; EILERS, 1949). As the chemistry of polymers developed, however, it became apparent that the rheological properties that had been interpreted as evidence of the colloidal character of asphalts could also be explained in terms of a polymer hypothesis. The polymer hypothesis was supported by the high molecular weights of the order of 100,000 for asphaltenes that had been obtained by film balance and osmotic pressure methods. At the same time, the low molecular weight values of a few thousand that have been obtained by many other methods (see Table V) were a stumbling block to the proponents of this hypothesis.

WINNIFORD (1963) therefore proposed from a combination of electron microscope, ultracentrifuge, and viscosity studies that asphaltenes associate readily even in supposedly good solvents such as benzene and carbon tetrachloride. When he investigated asphaltenes in benzene solutions of different concentration by ultracentrifuge methods, he found a sharp decrease in the apparent rate of sedimentation with increasing concentration, which he interpreted as evidence of a loose particle to particle association of low overall density. From viscosity data on different concentrations of asphaltenes in benzene, he concluded that the asphaltenes were relatively low molecular weight materials, associated through weak bonds into aggregates that were stable only at low shear rates, as in the ultracentrifuge or in osmosis experiments.

Recently, WALES and VAN DER WAARDEN (1964) have presented what is probably the most convincing evidence for this association. They report molecular weight data on asphaltenes that were extracted from asphalt obtained from a California valley crude oil. They used toluene solutions of this material at temperatures ranging from 25° to 85°C and computed molecular weights from a combination of ultracentrifuge sedimentation data and intrinsic viscosity measurements. Their results are summarized in Table VII.

TABLE VII

EFFECT OF TEMPERATURE ON MOLECULAR WEIGHTS OF ASPHALTENES

Temperature (°C)	Sedimentation coefficient $S \cdot 10^{13}$ (sec)	Intrinsic viscosity (N)	Molecular weight (M)
25	3.54	0.0513	49,500
45	3.35	0.0558	32,600
65	3.05	0.0421	17,300
85	3.13	0.0361	12,300

The very considerable drop in molecular weight is definite evidence of asphaltene particles that tend to disaggregate into smaller sizes with increasing temperature. Wales and Van der Waarden also found that the low molecular weight value increased with time if the temperature was reduced indicating that the process of disaggregation is to some degree reversible. They concluded, in agreement with WINNIFORD (1963) that asphaltenes are most certainly associated in solution.

When Wales and Van der Waarden used ebullioscopic methods on these same asphaltenes, they obtained a molecular weight of 2,570. They suggest that the large difference between ebulliscopic methods, which give a number average molecular weight, and sedimentation methods, which give a weight average molecular weight, might actually be a real difference wherein the state of aggregation depends mainly on the temperature, rather than on the shearing forces. They point out that if one considers particles containing one "A" site and an indefinite number of "B" sites, where A and B may react or join together, the resulting particle size distribution after aggregation through A–B linkages can be extra-ordinarily broad. They do not suggest however, the nature of their "A" or "B" sites. Wales and Van der Waarden, therefore suggest that both ebullioscopic and sedimentation measurements give valid answers for their respective experimental conditions.

It seems to the authors that the mechanism of asphaltene association is probably the plate to plate condensation of the polynuclear aromatic units as has been suggested by YEN, ERDMAN, and POLLACK (1961) from their X-ray diffraction studies. Those aromatic nucleii that have the greatest polarity and polarizability are postulated as the central molecules of the complex. Situated further from the center of the complex are those molecules of lesser polarity that are progressively more displaced from the aggregate by an energy input, either in the form of shear or through a temperature increase. The solvent power of the surrounding medium for this polynuclear aromatic complex must, of course, be a factor governing the ultimate size of the associated aggregates. Thus, the less polar aromatic molecules of the petrolene fraction can be part of the association complex, but because of their lower polarizability, they do not readily transmit the internal attractive forces of the asphaltene core and hinder the growth of the micelle. This then, may be the mechanism of the peptizing action of the petrolenes. Since the association complex can carry an electrical charge, apparently either positive or negative, it is probable that this charge aids in stabilizing the colloidal particles.

REFERENCES

ABRAHAM, H., 1960. *Asphalts and Allied Substances*, 6th ed. Van Nostrand, New York, N.Y., 1695 pp.

ALEXANIAN, C. and LOUIS, M., 1950. Contribution à la connaissance des asphaltènes. *Compt. Rend.*, 231 (22): 1233–1234.

BAKER, E. G., 1960. A hypothesis concerning the accumulation of sediment hydrocarbons to form crude oil. *Geochim. Cosmochim. Acta*, 19 (4): 309–317.

BARTELL, F. E. and NIEDERHAUSER, D. O., 1949. Film-forming constituents of crude petroleum oils. In: *Fundamental Research on Occurrence and Recovery of Petroleum, 1946–1947*. Am. Petrol. Inst., New York, N.Y., pp. 57–80.

BARTH, E. J., 1962. *Asphalt Science and Technology*. Gordon and Breach, New York, N.Y., 700 pp.

BARTON, D. C., 1937. Evolution of Gulf Coast crude oil. *Bull. Am. Assoc. Petrol. Geologists*, 21 (7): 914–946.

BEITCHMAN, B. D., 1959. Infrared spectra of asphalts. *J. Res. Natl. Bur. Std., A*, 63 (2): 189–192.

BESTOUGEFF, M. A. and GENDREL, P., 1964. Study on the structure of asphaltenic constituents by combined physical and chemical methods. *Am. Chem. Soc., Div. Petrol. Chem., Preprints*, 9 (2): B51–B68.

BIENNER, F., BONNARD, E., BURGER, J. J., GAYRAL, R., LEVY, R., LOUIS, M., METROT, R. and SALLE, C., 1955. Contribution de la géochimie à l'étude de l'évolution des huiles brutes dans les bassins sedimentaires. *World Petrol. Congr., Proc. 4th, Rome, 1955*, 1: 337–357.

BLAKEY, B. C. and LAWRENCE, A. S. C., 1954. The surface and interfacial viscosity of adsorbed films of asphalt. *J. Inst. Petrol.*, 40 (367): 203–205.

BRIANT, J., 1963. Sur quelques facteurs influençant la formation de certains dépots (paraffines, asphaltènes) dans les installations de production. *Rév. Inst. Franç. Pétrole Ann. Combust. Liquides*, 18: 1–16.

BROWN, A. B. and KNOBLOCH, J. O., 1957. The composition of petroleum distillates as revealed by their sulfonates, *Am. Soc. Testing Mater., Spec. Tech. Publ.*, 1957 (224): 213–226.

BROWN, A. B., SPARKS, J. and SMITH, J., 1957. Viscoelastic properties of a high-consistency asphalt. *J. Colloid Sci.*, 12 (3): 283–293.

CAMPBELL, P. G. and WRIGHT, J. R., 1964. Infrared spectra of asphalts: some aspects of the changes caused by Photooxidation. *Div. Petrol., Chem., Am. Chem. Soc., Preprints*, 9 (2): B89–B97.

CAMPBELL, P. G., WRIGHT, J. R. and BOWMAN, P. B., 1962. The effect of temperature and humidity on the oxidation of air-blown asphalts. *Mater. Res. Std.*, 2 (12): 988–995.

CARLSON, E. G. and O'NEAL, M. J., 1958. Analysis of petroleum oils by mass spectroscopy. *Am. Soc. Testing Mater., Spec. Tech. Publ.*, 1958 (224): 151–166.

CHELTON, H. M. and TRAXLER, R. N., 1959. Composition of chromatographic and thermal diffusion fractions of typical asphalts. *World Petrol. Congr., Proc., 5th, N.Y., 1959*, 5 (19): 247–257.

CLERC, R. J. and O'NEAL, M. J., 1961. The mass spectrometric analysis of asphalt, a preliminary investigation. *Anal. Chem.*, 33 (3): 380–382.

COLOMBO, U. and SIRONI, G., 1959. Geochemical analysis of Italian oils and asphalts. *World Petrol. Congr., Proc., 5th, N.Y.*, 1: 177–205.

CSANYI, L. H. and BASSI, B. S., 1958. Analysis of asphalts by electrical means. *Proc. Assoc. Asphalt Paving Technologists*, 27: 52–73.

DENEKAS, M. O., CARLSON, F. T., MOORE, J. W. and DODD, C. G., 1951. Materials adsorbed at crude petroleum–water interfaces. *Ind. Eng. Chem.*, 43 (5): 1165–1168.

DEWALT, C. W. and MORGAN, M. S., 1962. Proton magnetic resonance spectrometry in the characterization of coal-tar pitches. *Symp. Tars, Pitches, Asphalts, Am. Chem. Soc., Div. Fuel Chem., Preprints*, 1962: 33–45.

DODD, C. G., 1960. The rheological properties of films at crude petroleum–water interfaces. *J. Phys. Chem.*, 64 (5): 544–550.

DODD, C. G., MOORE, J. W. and DENEKAS, M. O., 1952. Metalliferous substances adsorbed at crude petroleum–water interfaces. *Ind. Eng. Chem.*, 44 (11): 2585–2590.

DUNNING, H. N., 1953. The interfacial activity of mesoporphyrin IX and some derivatives. *J. Colloid Sci.*, 8 (3): 279–287.

DUNNING, H. N. and RABON, N. A., 1956. Porphyrin-metal complexes in petroleum stocks. *Ind. Eng. Chem.*, 48 (5): 951–955.

DUNNING, H. N., MOORE, J. W. and DENEKAS, M. O., 1953. Interfacial activities and porphyrin contents of petroleum extracts. *Ind. Eng. Chem.*, 45 (8): 1759–1765.

DUNNING, H. N., MOORE, J. W. and MEYERS, A. T., 1954. Properties of porphyrins in petroleum. *Ind. Eng. Chem.*, 46 (9): 2000–2007.

DUNSTAN, A. E., 1931. Colloidal chemistry of petroleum. In: J. ALEXANDER (Editor), *Colloidal Chemistry*. Chemical Catalog Co., New York, N.Y., 3: 491–502.

DYKSTRA, H., BEU, K. and KATZ, D. L., 1944. Precipitation of asphalt from crude oil by flow through silica. *Oil Gas J.*, 43 (21): 79–102.

ECKERT, G. W. and WEETMAN, B., 1947. Mean molecular weights of asphalts and their constituents. *Ind. Eng. Chem.*, 39 (11): 1512–1516.

EILERS, H., 1949. The colloidal structure of asphalt. *J. Phys. Colloid Chem.*, 53 (8): 1195–1211.

ELDIB, I. A., 1962. The solvation, ionic and electrophoretic properties of colloidal asphaltenes in petroleum. *Div. Petrol. Chem., Am. Chem. Soc., Preprints*, 7 (1): 31–41.

ELDIB, I. A., DUNNING, H. N. and BOLEN, R. J., 1960. The nature of colloidal materials in petroleum. *Div. Petrol. Chem., Am. Chem. Soc., Preprints*, 5 (1): 31–41.

ERDMAN, J. G. and RAMSEY, V. G., 1961. Rates of oxidation of petroleum asphaltenes and other bitumens by alkaline permanganate. *Geochim. Cosmochim. Acta*, 25 (3): 175–188.

FISCHER, K. A. and SCHRAM, A., 1959. The constitution of asphaltic bitumen. *World Petrol. Congr., Proc., 5th, N.Y., 1959*, 5 (20): 259–271.

FLINN, R. A., BENTHER, H. and SCHMID, B. K., 1961. Now you can improve residue treating. *Petrol. Refiner*, 40 (4): 139–144.

FREUND, M. and VAJTA, S., 1958. Untersuchung der Bitumenstruktur mit dem Electronenmikroskop. *Erdöl Kohle*, 11 (1): 13–18.

FREUNDLICH, H., 1938. Colloidal and capillary chemistry of petroleum. In: A. E. DUNSTAN, A. W. NASH, B. T. BROOKS and H. TIZARD (Editors), *The Science of Petroleum*, 2. Oxford Univ. Press, London, pp. 1057–1067.

GARDNER, R. A., HARDMAN, H. F., JONES, A. L. and WILLIAMS, R. B., 1959. Characterization of thermal diffusion fractions of petrolenes from a mid-continent asphalt. *J. Chem. Eng. Data*, 4 (2): 155–159.

GARIFIANOV, N. S. and KOZYREV, B. M., 1956. Paramagnetic resonance in anthracite and other carbonaceous substances. *J. Exptl. Theoret. Phys.*, 30 (2) 255–263.

GASKINS, F. H., BRODNYAN, J. G., PHILIPPOFF, W. and THELEN, E., 1960. The rheology of asphalt, 2. Flow characteristics of asphalt. *Trans. Soc. Rheol.*, 4: 265–278.

GIVEN, P. H., 1959. Structure of bituminous coals: evidence from distribution of hydrogen. *Nature*, 184 (4691): 980–981.

GLASSTONE, S., 1946. *Textbook of Physical Chemistry*. Van Nostrand, New York, N.Y., 1320 pp.

GOPPEL, J. M. and KNOTERUS, J., 1955. Fundamentals of bitumen blowing. *World Petrol. Congr., Proc., 4th, Rome, 1955*, 3: 399–415.

GORDON, L. B., MAY, P. D. and LEE, R. J., 1959. Converting aromatics to useful resins. *Ind. Eng. Chem.*, 51 (10): 1275–1278.

GREENFELD, S. H., 1960. Chemical changes occurring during the weathering of two coating-grade asphalts. *Am. Chem. Soc., Div. Petrol. Chem., Preprints*, 5 (4): A89–A106.

GREENFELD, S. H. and WRIGHT, J. R., 1962. Four methods for predicting the durability of roofing asphalts. *Mater. Res. Std.*, 2 (9): 738–745.

GREENLEE, R. W., 1960. Factors in the stability of petroleum emulsions. *Am. Chem. Soc., Div. Petrol. Chem., Preprints* 5 (3): 133–140.

GRIFFIN, R. L., SIMPSON, W. C. and MILES, T. K., 1959. Influence of composition of paving asphalt on viscosity, viscosity–temperature susceptibility, and durability. *J. Chem. Eng. Data.*, 4 (4): 349–354.

GURWITSCH, L., 1931. Colloidal chemistry in petroleum. In: J. ALEXANDER (Editor), *Colloidal Chemistry*. Chemical Catalog Co., New York, N.Y., 3: 523–526.

GUTOWSKY, H. S., RAY, B. R., RUTLEDGE, R. L. and UNTERBERGER, R. R., 1958. Carbonaceous-free radicals in crude petroleum. *J. Chem. Phys.*, 28: 744–745.

HEITHAUS, J. J., 1960. Measurement and significance of asphaltene peptization. *Am. Chem. Soc., Div. Petrol. Chem., Preprints*, 5 (4): A23–A37.

HIDALGO, A. and VALERO, L., 1963. Study of bitumen by infrared spectra. *Ann. Real Soc. Espan. Fis. Quim. (Madrid)*, Ser. B. 59 (4): 315–320.

HILLMAN, E. S. and BARNETT, B., 1937. The constitution of cracked and uncracked asphalts. *Proc. Am. Soc. Testing Mater.*, 37 (2): 558–568.

HOOD, A. R., CLERK, J. and O'NEAL, M. J., JR., 1959. The molecular structure of heavy petroleum compounds. *J. Inst. Petrol.*, 45 (426): 168–173.

HÖPPLER, F., 1941. Viscosität, Plastizität, Elastizität und Kolloidik der Bitumina. *Öl Kohle*, 37 (48): 995–1009.

HUGHES, F. J., 1960. Kinetics of asphalt oxidation. *Am. Chem. Soc., Div. Petrol. Chem., Preprints*, 5 (4): A63–A69.

HUGHES, R. H. and MARTIN, R. J., 1958. Determination of methylene, and alkylbenzene group types by infrared absorption. *Am. Soc. Testing Mater., Spec. Tech. Publ., 1958* (224): 127–149.

ILLMAN, J. C., 1961. U.S. Patent No. 2,970,099.

JONES, A. L., 1958. New thermal diffusion techniques applicable to high-boiling petroleum fractions. *Am. Soc. Testing Mater., Spec. Tech. Publ., 1958* (224): 83–93.

KARIMOV, A. K., 1955. Petroleum conversion in nature. *Neft. Khoz.*, 33 (12): 52–54 (in Russian).

KATZ, D. L. and BEU, K. E., 1945. Nature of asphaltic substances. *Ind. Eng. Chem.*, 37 (2): 195–200.

KLEINSCHMIDT, L. R., 1955. Chromatographic method for the fractionation of asphalt into distinctive groups of components. *J. Res. Natl. Bur. Std.*, 54 (3): 163–166.

LABOUT, J. W. A., 1950. Chemical reactivity of asphaltic bitumen. In: J. PH. PFEIFFER, (Editor), *Properties of Asphaltic Bitumen*. Elsevier, Amsterdam, pp.109–120.

LAWRENCE, A. S. C. and KILLNER, W., 1948. Emulsions of seawater in Admiralty fuel oil with special reference to their demulsification. *J. Inst. Petrol.*, 34 (299): 821–856.

LOTTERMOSER, A. and CALANTAR, N., 1929. Die Kolloidchemischen Faktoren bei der Bildung und Entmischung der Rohölemulsionen. *Kolloid Z.*, 48 (4): 362–376.

LOUIS, M., 1951. Étude des indices de Pétrole. *Rév. Inst. Franç. Pétrole*, 6: 20–31.

MARCUSSON, J., BURCHATRZ, H. und WILKE, P., 1931. *Die Natürlichen und Künstlichen Asphalte*, 2. Aufl. Englemann, Leipzig, 254 pp.

MCNAB, J. G., SMITH, P. V. and BETTS, R. L., 1952. The evolution of petroleum. *Ind. Eng. Chem.*, 44 (11): 2556–2563.

MELPOLDER, F. W., SAUER, R. W. and MARSHALL, T. A., 1958. The separation of high-boiling petroleum oils by thermal diffusion. *Am. Soc. Testing Mater., Spec. Tech. Publ.*, 1958 (224): 94–104.

MERTENS, E. W., 1960. Predicting weatherability of coating grade asphalts from asphaltene characteristics. *Am. Soc. Testing Mater., Spec. Tech. Publ.*, 1960 (250): 40–44.

MORRELL, J. C. and EGLOFF, G., 1931. Colloidal chemistry of petroleum. In: J. ALEXANDER (Editor), *Colloid Chemistry*, Chemical Catalog Co., New York, N.Y., pp. 503–522.

NELLENSTEYN, F. J., 1923. *Bereiding en Constitutie van Asphalt*. Thesis, Technische Hogeschool, Delft.

NELLENSTEYN, F. J., 1931. Asphalt. In: J. ALEXANDER (Editor), *Colloidal Chemistry*. Chemical Catalog Co., New York, N.Y., pp. 535–546.

NEPPE, S. L., 1952. The concept and derivation of viscosity number and other related new indices – experimental work for the study of rheological properties. *J. Inst. Petrol.*, 38 (340): 257–280.

O'REILLY, D. E., 1958. Paramagnetic resonance of vanadyl etioporphyrin I. *J. Chem. Phys.*, 29: 1188–1189.

PFEIFFER, J. PH., 1950. *The Properties of Asphaltic Bitumen*. Elsevier, Amsterdam, 285 pp.

PFEIFFER, J. PH. and SAAL, R. N. J., 1940. Asphaltic bitumen as a colloid system. *J. Phys. Chem.*, 44 (2): 139–149.

PRECKSHOT, G. W., DELISLE, N. G., COTTRELL, C. E. and KATZ, D. L., 1943. Asphaltic substances in crude oil, *Am. Inst. Mining Engrs., Trans.*, 151: 188–205.

RAY, B. R., WITHERSPOON, P. A. and GRIM, R. E., 1957. A study of the colloidal characteristics of petroleum using the ultracentrifuge. *J. Phys. Chem.*, 61 (10): 1296–1302.

REISBERG, J. and DOSCHER, T. M., 1956. Interfacial phenomena in crude-oil–water systems. *Producers Monthly*, 21 (1): 43–50.

RICHARDSON, C. and FORREST, C. N., 1905. Carbon tetrachloride and its uses as a solvent for differentiating bitumens. *J. Soc. Chem. Ind. (London)*, 24 (7): 310–311.

ROMBERG, J. W. and TRAXLER, R. N., 1947. Rheology of asphalt. *J. Colloid Sci.*, 2: 33–47.

ROMBERG, J. W., NESMITH, S. D. and TRAXLER, R. N., 1959. Some chemical aspects of the components of asphalt. *J. Chem. Eng. Data*, 4 (2): 159–161.

ROSENBAUM, E. J., 1958. Introduction to session II—Spectroscopic methods. *Am. Soc. Testing Mater., Spec. Tech. Publ.*, 1958 (224): 125–126.

SAAL, R. N. J. and LABOUT, J. W. A., 1940. Rheological properties of asphaltic bitumens. *J. Phys. Chem.*, 44 (2): 149–165.

SACHANEN, A. N., 1945. *The Chemical Constituents of Petroleum*. Rheinhold, New York, N.Y., 451 pp.

SARCENO, A. J., FANALE, D. T. and COGGESHALL, N. D., 1961. An electron paramagnetic resonance investigation of vanadium in petroleum oils. *Anal. Chem.*, 33 (4): 500–505.

SCHACHMAN, H. K. and LAUFFER, M. A., 1949. The hydration, size, and shape of tobacco mosaic virus. *J. Am. Chem. Soc.*, 71 (2): 536–541.

SCHWEYER, H. E., 1958. Spectral adsorption of asphaltic materials. *Anal. Chem.*, 30 (2): 205–209.

SERGIENKO, S. R. and GARBALINSKII, V. A., 1963. Chemistry of formation of brown asphaltic bitumens. *Acta Chim. Acad. Sci. Hung.*, 37 (2): 213–225.

SERGIENKO, S. R. and PUSTIL'NIKOVA, S. D., 1959. Chemical U.S.S.R. nature of petroleum asphaltenes. *J. Appl. Chem. (U.S.S.R.)*, 32, 12: 2892–2895.

SHARP, D. J., TAYLOR, A. R., MCLEAN, I. W., BEARD, D. and BEARD, J. W., 1944. Density and size of influenza virus (PR8 strain) in solution. *Science*, 100 (2590): 151–153.

SKINNER, D. A., 1952. Chemical state of vanadium in Santa Maria Valley crude oil. *Ind. Eng. Chem.*, 44 (5): 1159–1165.

STEWART, J. E., 1957. Infrared spectra of chromatographically fractionated asphalts. *J. Res. Natl. Bur. Std.*, 58: 265–269.

TRAXLER, R. N., 1961. *Asphalt, Its Composition, Properties, and Uses*. Rheinhold, New York, N.Y., 294 pp.

TRAXLER, R. N. and COOMBS, C. E., 1936. The colloidal nature of asphalt as shown by its flow properties. *J. Phys. Chem.*, 40 (9): 1133–1147.

TRAXLER, R. N. and SCHWEYER, H. E., 1953. How to make component analysis. *Oil Gas J.*, 52 (19): 158.

UREN, L. C., 1939. *Petroleum Production Engineering—Oil Field Exploration*, McGraw-Hill. New York, N.Y., 756 pp.

VAN DER POEL, C., 1954. A general system describing the Viscoelastic properties of bitumens and its relation to routine test data. *J. Appl. Chem. (London)*, (5): 221–236.

VAN DER WAARDEN, M., 1958. Stability of emulsions of water in mineral oils containing asphaltenes. *Kolloid Z.*, 156, (2): 116–122.

VAN KERKVOORT, W. J., NIEUWSTAD, J. J. J. et VAN DER WAARDEN, M., 1952. Le comportement des systèmes hydrocabures-asphaltènes. Un facteur important pour la stabilité et la compatibilité des fuel-oils residuels. Congr. *Intern. Chauffage Ind.*, 4e, Paris, 1952, *Preprint*, 1952 (220): 1–8.

WALES, M., and VAN DER WAARDEN, M., 1964. Molecular weights of asphaltenes by ultracentrifugation. *Div. Petrol. Chem., Am. Chem. Soc., Preprints*, 9 (2): B21–B38.

WILLIAMS, R. B., 1958. Characterization of hydrocarbons in petroleum by nuclear magnetic resonance spectroscopy. *Am. Soc. Testing Mater., Spec. Tech. Publ.*, 1958 (224): 168–194.

WILLIAMS, R. B. and SAUNDERS, R. K., 1959a. U.S. Patent No. 2,909,482.

WILLIAMS, R. B. and SAUNDERS, R. K., 1959b. U.S. Patent No. 2,909,483.

WILLIFORD, C., 1943. X-ray studies of paving asphalts. *Texas Agr. Exp. Sta., Bull.*, 73: 7–70.

WINNIFORD, R. S., 1960. The influence of asphalt composition on its rheology. *Am. Soc. Testing Mater., Spec. Tech. Publ.*, 1960 (294): 31–50.

WINNIFORD, R. S., 1963. The evidence for association of asphaltenes in dilute solutions. *J. Inst. Petrol.*, 49 (475): 215–221.

WINNIFORD, R. S. and BERSOHN, M., 1962. The structure of petroleum asphaltenes as indicated by proton magnetic resonance. *Symp. Tars, Pitches, Asphalts, Am. Chem. Soc., Div. Fuel Chem., Preprints*, 1962: 21–32.

WITHERSPOON, P. A., 1957. *Studies on Petroleum with the Ultracentrifuge*. Thesis, Univ of Illinois; Illinois State Geol. Surv., Rept. Invest., 206: 82 pp.

WITHERSPOON, P. A., 1962. Colloidal nature of petroleum. *Frans. N.Y. Acad. Sci.*, 24 (4): 344–361.

WITHERSPOON, P. A. and MUNIR, Z. A., 1960. Size and shape of asphaltic particles in petroleum. *Producers Monthly*, 24 (10): 20–31.

WITHERSPOON, P. A., DATTA, P. and NAGY, D., 1961. The effect of asphaltic materials on the viscosity and non-newtonian behavior of crude oil. *Am. Inst. Mining Engrs Soc., Petrol. Engrs. Meeting, Spec. Papers*, SPE-234, 1961: 13 pp.

WRIGHT, J. R. and CAMPBELL, P. G., 1962. Determination of oxidation rates of air-blown asphalts by infrared spectroscopy. *J. Appl. Chem. (London)* 12 (6): 256–266.

WRIGHT, J. R. and CAMPBELL, P. G., 1964. Oxidation of asphalt in the presence of ozone. *Am. Chem. Soc., Div. Petrol. Chem., Preprints*, 9 (2): B99–B105.

WRIGHT, J. R. and MINESINGER, R. R., 1963. The electrophoretic mobility of asphaltenes in nitromethane. *J. Colloid Sci.*, 18 (3): 223–236.

WRIGHT, J. R., CAMPBELL, P. G. and FRIDINGER, T. L., 1964. The effect of carbon arc intensity on asphalt oxidation. *J. Appl. Chem. (London)*, 14 (1): 30–35.

YEN, T. F. and ERDMAN, J. G., 1962. Investigation of the structure of petroleum asphaltenes and related substances by infrared analysis. *Am. Chem. Soc., Div. Petrol. Chem., Preprints*, 7 (1): 5–17.

YEN, T. F., ERDMAN, J. G. and HANSON, W. E., 1961a. Reinvestigation of densiometric methods of ring analysis. *J. Chem. Eng. Data*, 6 (3): 443–448.

YEN, T. F., ERDMAN, J. G. and POLLACK, S. S., 1961b. Investigation of the structure of petroleum asphaltenes by X-ray diffraction. *Anal. Chem.*, 33 (11): 1587–1594.

YEN, T. F., ERDMAN, J. G. and SARCENO, A. J., 1962. Investigation of the nature of free radicals in petroleum asphaltenes and related substances by electron spin resonance. *Anal. Chem.*, 34 (6): 694–700.

ZARRELLA, W. M. and HANSON, W. E., 1960. Molecular weight distribution in a petroleum asphaltene. *Geol. Soc. Am., Abstr. Ann. Meeting*, 1960: 240.

Chapter 7

A GEOCHEMICAL EVALUATION OF PETROLEUM MIGRATION AND ACCUMULATION

E. G. BAKER

Esso Research and Engineering Company, Linden, N. J. (U.S.A.)

INTRODUCTION

There is widespread belief that petroleum deposits represent accumulations of hydrocarbons that at one time were only trace constituents of the sedimentary basin. As ordinarily conceived, oil is formed in fine-grained sediments and subsequently transferred to more porous and permeable strata wherein it may become pooled, if suitable traps are present. The movement of petroleum from source to reservoir rock is termed primary migration, whereas the segregation of petroleum into pools within the reservoir rock involves secondary migration (ROOF and RUTHERFORD, 1958). This description of the oil-forming processes focuses attention on three distinct stages of petroleum evolution, as enumerated by D. R. BAKER (1962): (*1*) the origin of petroleum hydrocarbons; (*2*) the primary migration of these hydrocarbons; and (*3*) their final accumulation in the reservoir rock.

It is commonly assumed that a requisite to the genesis of petroleum in commercial quantities is a depositional environment favorable to the accumulation of abundant organic matter of a suitable nature under conditions allowing preservation and diagenetic transformation to petroleum. In other words, the belief is that oil is formed in fine-grained sediments and, thus, the problem of petroleum migration is the problem of moving oil out of the source sediments and gathering it in the reservoir rock. The idea that oil is formed at the source and moves essentially inviolate from there to the trap has greatly influenced the approach to the migration problem. It has prompted many petroleum geologists to suggest the movement of a discrete oil phase at saturations completely disallowed by the field and laboratory experiences of the reservoir engineer. It is significant, however, that D. R. BAKER (1962) found no gradient in the hydrocarbon content of the Cherokee shale in the direction of the reservoir sands. Such a gradient would be expected if there really was primary migration of an oil phase into the contiguous reservoir rock. Even in the more permeable water-wet sandstone and limestone reservoirs it is unlikely that the capillary pressure of the oil–water interface ever exceeds the displacement pressure of oil from the larger openings or capillaries between the pores. Indeed, G. A. Hill, as discussed by LEVORSEN (1954), has calculated that forces several thousand times greater than those produced by normal hydrodynamic gradients would be needed to cause migration of isolated oil globules in a typical reservoir rock.

In view of these difficulties, the various migration theories that essentially depend on the movement of oil along with water that has been set in motion by the compaction of fine-grained sediments (primary migration) or by the force of gravity in reservoir rock (secondary migration) will not be discussed in this chapter and the reader is referred to the reviews of these concepts by RUSSEL (1960).

The present dilemma is occasioned by the belief that oil is generated in fine-grained sediments, or source rocks. From the time of Berthelot, the origin of petroleum and of hydrocarbons have been considered synonomous (MEINSCHEIN, 1965). Suppose, however, that one distinguishes between oil and the hydrocarbons which ultimately comprise the major portion of the oil. This distinction may be significant because the way one states a problem greatly influences the investigation of it. For example, one may postulate that it is the gathering of widely disseminated hydrocarbons that results in the origin of oil; and, further, one may postulate that this gathering is independent of the generation of hydrocarbons within a particular source section. It may occur whether or not any significant alteration of sedimentary organic matter takes place. This view contrasts with the belief that it is the generation of oil within a source that is the primary cause of the existence of oil pools.

As discussed by MEINSCHEIN (1959) and DVALI (1964), the task of separating hydrocarbons from the sedimental organic matter and of gathering them in reservoirs as crude oil deposits may be of much greater significance to the genesis of petroleum in commercial quantities than is the formation of hydrocarbons in the first place. In this light, the problem of petroleum migration is the problem of the origin of oil.

The purpose of this chapter is to outline a possible mechanism of petroleum migration (oil origin) as viewed by the author in a way which employs certain likely physico-chemical processes. It is also the purpose of this chapter to examine some of the published data on hydrocarbon and organic carbon occurrence and of crude oil composition which collectively suggest that the process outlined may take place.

A "MINERAL-LIKE" ORIGIN OF OIL

For a number of years investigators at the Esso Research and Engineering Company studied the water solubility of gasoline-range and higher molecular weight hydrocarbons in order to evaluate the possible importance of water movement in the transport of dissolved petroleum hydrocarbons. The original emphasis was on primary migration, i.e., on the transfer of hydrocarbons from fine-grained sediments to the more porous and permeable carrier beds. If the water that is inevitably expelled from compressible sediments with increasing depth of burial acts as the vehicle for introducing hydrocarbons into reservoir rocks, then the productiveness of a carrier bed would be understandable in terms of the role it played in leading off the waters expelled during the early and most active stages of compaction (E. G. BAKER, 1959).

The fact that young sediments, such as those of the Pliocene and Miocene, have the highest incidence of proved oil occurrence per unit volume of sediments (WEEKS, 1960) is consistent with the postulated importance of water movement. As HEDBERG (1964) stated: "The combination of (1) the sedimentation of fine-grained inorganic matter resulting in an initially highly porous water-filled deposit, with (2) the subsequent expression of a large part of the contained water from this sediment through compaction, appears to be a critically essential accompaniment to the formation of substantial petroleum accumulations. Both are simple, well substantiated, directly observable, and almost inevitable physical processes so that nothing hypothetical is called for in assuming their operation."

If geologically significant quantities of petroleum hydrocarbons move in compaction water, one has to understand the conditions under which the hydrocarbons would be released from solution in the mobile formation water (HOBSON, 1961). Presumably there is also the problem of secondary migration, i.e., the mechanism by which precipitated hydrocarbons are concentrated, or pooled within the reservoir rock. Let one suppose, however, that the hydrocarbons are *first* *precipitated* at places coincident with adequate trapping facilities, i.e., in locally high structures, or in porosity wedges. In this event there would be no vital concern with secondary migration, nor with the problem of explaining why oil does not usually leave traces of its movement through carrier beds (WALTERS, 1960). In those relatively porous and permeable rocks where oil stains are clearly evident, one might imagine that the mechanism of hydrocarbon release has produced only miniature, widely-scattered oil deposits. What might this mechanism of hydrocarbon release be that usually operates, however, only at places where commercially important storage facilities exist? A salting-out mechanism is one process that comes to mind.

According to the membrane theory of brine concentration (DESITTER, 1947), the continual leakage of water through the confining layers of porosity traps would lead to considerable localized salt enrichment in the aquifer. A marked change in the ionic strength of the formation waters could initiate hydrocarbon release and the resultant oil body might grow in place simply by acting as a "sink" for other hydrocarbons brought to the site during the long-term circulation of water in the aquifer system. The suggestion is simply that oil deposits, like certain minerals (NOBLE, 1963), develop from an "aqueous mother liquor" which may be identified as the mobile water in a pressurized aquifer system.

An in situ, "mineral-like" origin of oil based on the exclusion of salt from water re-entering fine-grained sediments may help explain the absence of oil in many suitable reservoirs and structurally effective traps that are enclosed by rocks of presumably the same physical character and organic content as those that enclose commercially important crude oil deposits. The existence of oil trends ("mineral veins") notwithstanding, it is the absence of oil where oil ought to be that is the greatest puzzle of petroleum migration. A typical example of the seemingly random emplacement of oil is presented in Fig.1.

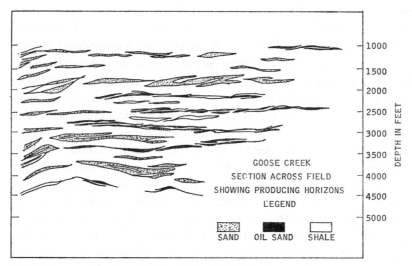

GOOSE CREEK

SECTION ACROSS FIELD

SHOWING PRODUCING HORIZONS

LEGEND

SAND   OIL SAND   SHALE

Fig.1. Cross-section through Goose Creek oil field, Texas. (After MINOR, 1926, p.553.)

GEOLOGICALLY REQUIRED OIL SOLUBILITY

In order to assess the possible importance of water as a vehicle for petroleum hydrocarbon migration, it is necessary to know the extent which hydrocarbons can be accommodated as solutes in formation waters. This value may be compared with the minimum concentration of oil in water that could yield the oil deposits, assuming efficient release and retention of the hydrocarbon solutes. As direct as the solubility criterion appears, it is difficult to apply. It is difficult to establish the geologic requirement of oil solubility using data that are currently at hand. The establishment of a minimum oil solubility for a particular sedimentary basin requires knowledge of the total volume of oil pooled within the basin and knowledge of the amounts of water, and hence, volumes of sediments, that were involved in supplying the hydrocarbons.

Detailed field and reservoir data might provide adequate estimates of the total oil in place, but it would be extremely hazardous to estimate the volume of water involved in the transport process from generalized porosity–depth relationships (HOBSON, 1943), even if the volume of sediments which participated was known, or, equally important, agreed upon. For example, the circulation of water in the aquifer system could be significantly modified by cross-formational flow due to osmosis as shown in Fig.2. HILL and WALTON (1958) have discovered many anomalies in formation pressures and water salinities which appear to be caused by the adjacent shales acting as salt filters. Although geologic osmosis may only be important in the latter stages of basin lithification, a quantitative description of the outward movement of water during periods of subsidence and deposition must await detailed reconstruction of the history of the sedimentary basin. The question is: how did the basin drain during compaction? The answer to this question is of paramount importance since the present mechanism of in situ oil origin points to producing formations as having played major roles, over long periods of time, in leading off the waters expelled during compaction.

HODGSON et al. (1964) examined some of these questions in considerable detail and have concluded that hydrocarbons would need to be mobilized to the total extent of at least one part per million (p.p.m.). This is probably the lower limit of solubility required for geologically significant hydrocarbon transport by bulk water movement. In a discussion of the distribution of hydrocarbons in sedimentary basins of the world, HUNT (1961) estimated that the ratio of the volume of dispersed hydrocarbons to reservoired oil hydrocarbons was approximately 27/1. This suggests that only about 3.6% of the hydrocarbons dispersed in the sediments become collected as crude oil. If the typical sediments which contribute hydrocarbons to crude oil deposits contain about 50 p.p.m. of hydrocarbons, only about 1.8 p.p.m. need actually be transported from source sediments to reservoir rock (on the average) to produce the known crude oil accumulations. This conclusion is consistent with Hodgson's estimate of the minimum required hydrocarbon mobility, conservatively assuming the weight of water involved was at least as great as that of the rock matrix. It is helpful to realize that a solubility of 1 p.p.m. amounts to more than one barrel of oil in 100 acre-ft. of water.

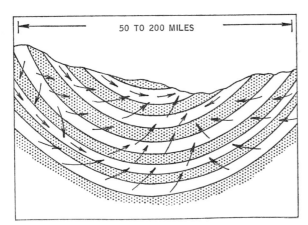

50 TO 200 MILES

Fig.2. Diagrammatic illustration of one of many regional water flow patterns possible in a structural basin in which the osmotic "salt filtering" of the cross-formational flow can lead to the buildup of anomalous salinity concentrations. (After HILL and WATSON, 1958, p.62.)

POSSIBLE EVIDENCE OF EARLY IN SITU OIL ORIGIN

In a study of petroleum migration in the early stages of compaction, KIDWELL and HUNT (1958) analyzed water samples produced from various sands at Pedernales, Venezuela. They deduced an upper limit of about 16 p.p.m. for the hydrocarbon concentration of the fluids in the sediments, and stated: "In this low concentration, the oil would almost have to be present either in solution or as an extremely dilute colloidal dispersion." Equally important, Kidwell and Hunt noted: "All sands open to the surface contained approximately the same hydrocarbon concentration as clays of corresponding depth. One lenticular sand about 110 ft. deep, however, was found to have hydrocarbon concentrations four to five times greater than those in the open sands and clays. This indicates that oil is accumulating in the closed sand but not in the open sands." KIDWELL and HUNT concluded: "It is inferred from these data that in the lenticular sands hydrocarbons are being filtered out of the moving stream of water by capillary action. This is not true of the continuous sands that are open to the surface."

Although Kidwell and Hunt may have found field evidence of the early in situ origin of oil, as shown in Fig.3, the actual hydrocarbon release mechanism remains obscure. The authors mentioned *capillary action*, but this seems insufficient regarding the possibility that migration takes place either in solution or as an extremely dilute colloidal dispersion. It seems clear, however, that some kind of filtering mechanism was operative. Unfortunately, the salinity of the formation fluid within the sand lens was not recorded.

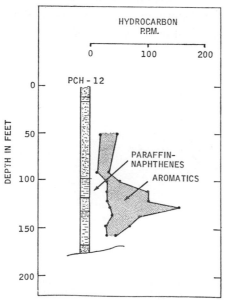

Fig.3. Hydrocarbons in Pedernales sand trap. (After KIDWELL and HUNT, 1958, p.810.)

THE SOLUBILITY REQUIRED OF INDIVIDUAL HYDROCARBONS

It is difficult, if not impossible, to measure directly the solubility of oil in water. Crude oil is a collection of various kinds of compounds which distribute themselves differently between the two immiscible phases, oil and water. Different hydrocarbons have different partition coefficients, and as a consequence, the composition of oil in the aqueous phase will differ from the composition of the oil saturating the water. It would be incorrect to identify the total equilibrium hydrocarbon solute concentration as the solubility of the saturating oil phase, for the water would contain a disproportionate amount of the more water soluble aromatic hydrocarbons.

Although the two are intimately related, the main concern is not so much regarding individual hydrocarbon solubility as it is the amount of hydrocarbons that leaves water to participate in the growth of the oil body. For example, if the in situ mechanism takes place, the concentration of an individual hydrocarbon in crude oil, C_i, would be proportional to the decrease in the concentration in water, δS_i, upon flow past the growing oil "mineral deposit".

Thus, the simple equation:

$$C_i = K_p \delta S_i \tag{1}$$

where $\delta S_i \leqslant S_i =$ the water solubility, ought to provide a means for expressing the geologically required oil solubility in terms of the necessary individual hydrocarbon solubilities. It is apparent that the reciprocal of the proportionality constant, K_p, in eq. 1 has the dimensions of "oil solubility" and that δS_i reflects the minimum amount of an individual hydrocarbon that must be accommodated by the water. With the aid of eq.1 one can understand why the concentrations of, say, toluene and n-octadecane can be nearly identical in a crude oil, even though the individual solubilities differ by a factor of 10^5. The amount of each hydrocarbon released from solution could be comparable and need not reflect the total concentration in the "aqueous mother liquor." E. G. BAKER (1959) has identified δS_i with hydrocarbon micellar solubility. His equation:

$$C_i = k(S_i - mS_i^\circ) \qquad m \geqslant 1 \tag{2}$$

where C_i is the volume ratio of the ith hydrocarbon in petroleum, S_i and S_i° are the volume ratio solubilities of the ith hydrocarbon in the colloidal electrolyte solution and in pure water, respectively, and k and m are constants for a given petroleum and colloidal electrolyte solution, identifies the amount of a hydrocarbon that leaves the water solution with the amount that was solubilized in soap micelles ($m = 1$), with allowance for perturbation by various processes, e.g., water leaching or molecular diffusion, that would systematically remove hydrocarbons from the precipitated oil in proportion to their water solubilities ($m > 1$).

Baker used eq.2 to relate measured micellar solubilities with the observed concentrations of various hydrocarbons in a representative crude oil. For at least one crude oil-colloidal electrolyte system, he deduced $k = 1.42 \cdot 10^6$ and $m = 1$. Thus, the inferred total oil solubility, $k^{-1} = 0.70 \cdot 10^{-6}$, is of the order of 1 p.p.m. This again is consistent with the estimate of HODGSON et al. (1964) of the minimum level of hydrocarbon content in water required to account for the known oil accumulations in a typical basin.

If the composition of a crude oil is largely governed by the amount of hydrocarbons released from aqueous solution at the point of entrapment, then, provided the composition (C_i) of the oil is known and the geologically required oil solubility is specified (K_p^{-1}), eq.1 may be used to calculate the minimum hydrocarbon solubility that must be obtained in a water solution. For example, Table I shows what the minimum solubilities of n-decane (C_{10}), n-octadecane (C_{18}) and n-hexatriacontane (C_{36}) have to be if the representative petroleum of API Research Project No.6 had a water solubility 1, 10, or 50 p.p.m. If geological considerations indicate that the solubility of the representative petroleum had to be, for instance, ten parts per million in order to account for the accumulation, then the amounts of C_{10}, C_{18}, and C_{36} hydrocarbons released from water would have had to be 180, 50, and 6 p.p.b. (v/v), respectively. These concentrations are the minimum solubilities that must be obtained in water in the presence of other hydrocarbons. E. G. BAKER (1958) found such concentrations are readily accommodated by dilute sodium naphthenate solutions saturated with crude oil, which is to say, in the presence of other hydrocarbons.

PEAKE and HODGSON (1965), in a study of the water solubility of C_{20}–C_{33} n-alkanes, concluded "under some conditions water has the capacity to accommodate, and possibly transport, the vast quantities of hydrocarbons involved in oil field formation and the distribution of n-alkanes accommodated in distilled

TABLE I

OIL–HYDROCARBON SOLUBILITY RELATIONSHIPS ($C_1 = K_p \, \delta \, S_1$)

Supposed solubility *A.P.I. Research Project No. 6* *(p.p.m.)*	*Resulting minimum solubility*[1] *(p.p.b., v/v)*[2]		
	n-decane (1.8)[3]	*n*-octadecane (0.5)[3]	*n*-hexatriacontane (0.06)[3]
1	18.0	5.0	0.6
10	180	50	6
50	900	250	30

[1] In water in the presence of other hydrocarbons.
[2] Volume-ratio solubilities, v/v.
[3] Concentration in petroleum, in vol. %.

water is remarkably similar to that of alkanes in API Research Project 6 crude oil and an oil field water." These workers also noted: "It is pertinent to observe that the foregoing data are in agreement with one of the major requirements for oil field formation, that of selective mobilization. The accommodation of given alkanes in distilled water is evidently a function of the properties of the alkane, rather than of the supply of the alkane. That is, odd carbon preference in the source material would not persist into the mobilizing water." These conclusions and observations are in agreement with those enumerated by E. G. BAKER (1959, 1960).

To summarize, the individual hydrocarbons that are present in crude oil in excess of 0.10 vol. % (such as the long chain n-paraffin hydrocarbons in many instances) must be able to dissolve in water at least to the extent of one p.p.b., if significant migration in aqueous solution is to take place. As will become evident, this is no trivial requirement.

THE SOURCE OF THE HYDROCARBONS

Many years ago the API Research Project 6 investigated the hydrocarbons from widely different petroleums. As summarized by ROSSINI and MAIR (1959), a detailed study of the gasoline fractions of these petroleums led to the following conclusions:

(*1*) All petroleums contain substantially the same hydrocarbon compounds.

(*2*) Within a given class of hydrocarbons, for example, the alkyl aromatics or the structurally isomeric paraffins, the individual hydrocarbons occur in proportions which are usually of the same order of magnitude for different petroleums.

(*3*) Approximately 46% of a representative petroleum has been accounted for in terms of 169 individual hydrocarbons isolated from fractions of this petroleum.

The "mineral-like" origin of oil is quite possibly reflected in these conclusions. For, is it not true that a limited range of composition is one of the most remarkable features in mineralogy? Indeed, cognitive mineral assemblages depend on it.

If a mechanism of in situ oil origin is operative, the relatively small number of different hydrocarbons in crude oil deposits ("mineral bodies") would require that there were only a limited number of different hydrocarbons available in the sediments for collection. Moreover, the relatively uniform composition within a given class of hydrocarbons must reflect a widely operative physical process by which the dispersed hydrocarbons become concentrated without undergoing significant differentiation, or fractionation. In turn, this implies that the relative abundance of homologous and isomeric hydrocarbons in the dispersed state does not vary widely and is translated essentially intact to the reservoir. MEINSCHEIN (1959) has obtained evidence of this as far as the higher boiling components of crude oil are concerned. For example, Fig.4, which is based on Meinschein's data, shows the very similar distributions of tetracyclic saturated hydrocarbons in sediments and crude oil.

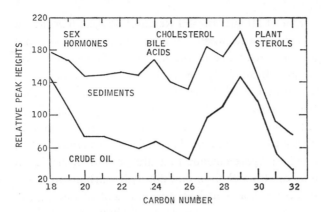

Fig.4. Distribution of tetracyclic hydrocarbons in sediments and crude oil.

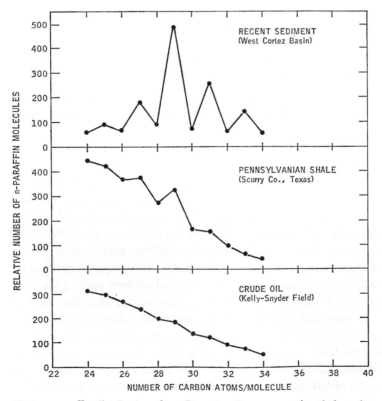

Fig.5. *n*-paraffin distributions for a Recent sediment, a marine shale and a crude oil.

Significantly, however, the distribution of *n*-paraffin hydrocarbons in crude oil is often quite different from these in the fine-grained sediments (STEVENS, 1956). Some typical *n*-paraffin distributions for a Recent sediment, an ancient sediment, and a crude oil are reproduced in Fig.5 from the work of BRAY and EVANS (1961). MEINSCHEIN (1961) has shown that crude oils and the sediments being deposited today contain many identical kinds of hydrocarbons. He has demonstrated that a close relationship exists between certain high-boiling saturated hydrocarbons present in both sediments and crude oils and some organic compounds which comprise part of the lipid fraction derived from living organisms. This is illustrated in Fig.6 for the distribution of pentacyclic saturated and sterane (tetracyclic saturated) hydrocarbons in Recent sediments, a crude oil, and butter. As another example, the tetracyclic hydrocarbons present in sediments and in crude oils (Fig.4) have carbon-number distributions that are almost identical to that in sex hormones, bile acids, cholesterol, and plant sterols. It appears that many of the hydrocarbons in petroleum are derived from plant and animal lipids.

The identification by BENDORAITUS et al. (1962) of individual isoprenoid hydrocarbons in crude oils, such as pristane (2, 6, 10, 14-tetramethylhexadecane) is remarkable in light of the fact that over 366,319 different hydrocarbons could

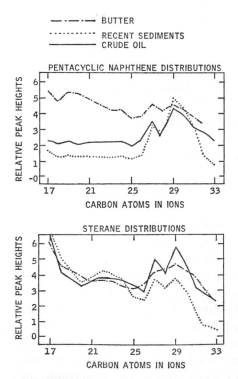

Fig.6. Distributions of hydrocarbons in Recent sediments, crude oil and butter. (After MEIN-SCHEIN, 1961.)

theoretically result from just the rearrangement of eicosane (C_{20}) as noted by FRANCIS (1947). Hence, when it is demonstrated that complex crude oil hydrocarbons, such as phytane and pristane, are also important constituents of biological and sedimental lipids (MEINSCHEIN et al., 1964), it is no wonder that the suggestion of WHITMORE (1943), that oil formation may involve the selective accumulation of hydrocarbons produced by living organisms, is considered by several geochemists. Moreover, the presence of biological-type alkanes in rocks that are more than 2.7 billion years old (BELSKY et al., 1965) attests to the surprising stability of hydrocarbons in the geological environment. There appears to be little compelling provocation for postulating important modifications in the composition of crude oil (maturation) because of the inherent thermodynamic instability of complex hydrocarbons with respect to methane or graphitic carbon. In fact, the narrow range of carbon isotope composition of crude oils, regardless of age, environment, etc., suggests that little chemical modification occurs after the oil body is once established (SILVERMAN and EPSTEIN, 1958; SILVERMAN, 1960, 1964).

It is possible that the seemingly systematic change in oil composition with increasing geologic storage time attends the fact that not all of the hydrocarbons which ultimately constitute crude oil are present in the sediments during the early stages of compaction. Although many indigenous liquid hydrocarbons are present in Recent sediments, as first disclosed by SMITH, (1952), those which comprise the gasoline fraction of crude oils are conspicuous by their absence. The absence in Recent sediments of hydrocarbons of low carbon number and their presence in older sediments has been confirmed by many investigators. In particular, ERDMAN et al. (1958) have shown the absence of low-molecular weight hydrocarbons in Recent sediments as compared with older sediments, and KVENVOLDEN (1962) has reported the absence of n-paraffins of intermediate molecular weight (C_8–C_{13}) in Recent sediments from San Francisco Bay. It is evident that additional hydrocarbons must be formed with time from the organic matter incorporated in Recent sediments (DUNTON and HUNT, 1962).

If the growth of a crude oil deposit depends on the long term circulation of formation water (which may be sporadic because of interrupted deposition or episodic subsidence), it appears that hydrocarbons of low carbon number could not be incorporated in the oil body until a relatively late stage of compaction is reached. Different times of arrival of the hydrocarbon constituents, because of different times of formation, may explain why young sediments contain relatively heavy, naphthenic constituents, whereas older sediments tend to produce a more paraffinic, lighter oil. The situation may be further complicated by traps nearer the deposition center becoming effective only in the later stages of compaction.

There are many apparent exceptions to the above generalization; for example, in the Rocky Mountains, Permian and Pensylvanian oils are heavier and darker than those of the younger Mesozoic (WEEKS, 1960). Nonetheless, temperature and time-dependent maturation processes are frequently called upon to explain systematic changes in the character of oil with the age of the formation, changes which may only reflect variations in the availability of hydrocarbons and their selective accumulation.

As noted by WEEKS (1960), the usual pattern of oil occurrence in a basin is that of increasing A.P.I. gravity basinward in any one horizon or oil system. This is a different problem than the one discussed above; here one clearly sees the effects of fractionation with respect to hydrocarbon-type occasioned by preferential release of the less water-compatible solutes. The accumulation of many billions of barrels of heavy oil, enriched in the more water-soluble compounds that contain oxygen, nitrogen, and sulfur atoms, is to be expected near the edges of sedimentary basins. So-called "tar mats" may simply arise from the complete release of residual organic solutes. One can scarcely imagine a more effective organic compound release mechanism than the evaporation of water at the sediment-air interface. The Athabasca oil sands, for instance, must reflect the focused drainage of large volumes of sediments over long periods of time (Pow et al., 1963).

It is important to distinguish between changes in the composition of oil due to sequential hydrocarbon release in a given water drainage system, i.e., oil system, from compositional differences occasioned by different times of hydrocarbon appearances in the dispersed state. Evidence (Fig.3) of the latter phenomenon was obtained by KIDWELL and HUNT (1958) in Pedernales, Venezuela. These authors wrote: "Because aromatic hydrocarbons are being initially trapped in the Pedernales sand, there must be an increase in the trapping of paraffinic hydrocarbons with time . . .," and further, "A later increase in the accumulation of paraffins receives further support from the fact that few oils have a high concentration of aromatic hydrocarbons."

In addition to the apparent fractionation resulting from the initial scarcity of low boiling hydrocarbons in fine-grained sediment, there must be some fractionation which attends the solution, migration, and release of these hydrocarbons from the water vehicle. At the present one can only mention some logical tar-mat effects which identify the farthest migrated compounds as the most soluble ones, and thus, may account for the gross differences observed in the hydrocarbon-type composition of crude oils within a given oil system.

THE WATER SOLUBILITY OF n-PARAFFIN HYDROCARBONS

It has been found that, as far as the mobility of the major constituents of crude oil is concerned, the solubilities of individual hydrocarbons in water must be of the order of parts per billion. This requirement applies, of course, to the higher carbon number n-paraffins through n-hexatriacontane (C_{36}); these straight-chain alkanes may account for as much as 0.2 vol. % of the total crude oil (MARTIN et al., 1963). Because the long chain n-paraffin hydrocarbons represent the least water-soluble components of crude oil, a study of their accommodation by water is especially definitive for assessing the possible role of compaction water in transporting hydrocarbon solutes to the site of accumulation.

In connection with studies of oil migration in aqueous solution, E. G. BAKER (1959) reported the volume-ratio solubilities of n-decane, n-octadecane, and n-hexatriacontane in distilled water at 25 °C as 22.0, 7.75, and 2.09 p.p.b., respectively. These are surprisingly large solubilities compared to the values expected from the behavior of the lower molecular weight homologues. Indeed, it is the unexpected, relatively large water solubility of high molecular weight n-paraffins that suggests the possible geological importance of hydrocarbon migration in aqueous solution (E. G. BAKER, 1956).

Recently MCAULIFFE (1963) reported values for the room temperature solubility in water of many gasoline-range hydrocarbons, including n-pentane, n-hexane, n-heptane, and n-octane. These data are recorded in Table II, together with the results CLAUSSEN and POLGLASE (1952) obtained for ethane, propane, and n-butane. The latter solubility data, originally reported in units of a, i.e., as the

TABLE II

WATER SOLUBILITY OF n-PARAFFIN HYDROCARBONS AT 25 °C

(Data of CLAUSSEN and POLGLASE, 1952)

Hydrocarbon	a^1	Vapor Pressure (atm.)	Mole fraction Solubility, $X_1°$
Methane	0.0320	> P_{crit}	—
Ethane	0.0420	38.537	$1.31 \cdot 10^{-3}$
Propane	0.0350	9.336	$2.64 \cdot 10^{-4}$
n-Butane	0.0276	2.399	$5.34 \cdot 10^{-5}$

[1] Interpolated from plots of $\ln a$ vs. $1/T$. a is the volume of gas at 0° and 760 mm dissolved in 1 vol. water at 760 mm hydrocarbon pressure.

(Data of MCAULIFFE, 1963)

Hydrocarbon	$S_i°$ (p.p.m.)[2]	Mole fraction Solubility, $X_i°$
n-Pentane	38.5 ± 2.0	$9.61 \cdot 10^{-6}$
n-Hexane	9.5 ± 1.3	$1.99 \cdot 10^{-6}$
n-Heptane	2.93 ± 0.20	$5.27 \cdot 10^{-7}$
n-Octane	0.66 ± 0.06	$1.04 \cdot 10^{-7}$

[2] Weight-ratio solubilities, w/w.

volume of gas at 0 °C and 760 mm (STP) which dissolves in one volume of water at one atmosphere hydrocarbon pressure, were used to calculate the mole fraction solubilities, $X_i°$, at the different activities (vapor pressures) possessed by the hydrocarbons at 25 °C. By so doing, the solubilities of both gaseous and condensed phase hydrocarbons can be used to demonstrate the remarkably constant and proportionate decrease in solubility with increasing carbon number.

The mole fraction water solubilities $(X_i°)$ of the paraffin hydrocarbons from ethane through n-hexane can be summarized with the following equation:

$$\ln X_i° = -3.393 - (1.622) i \tag{3}$$

where i is the number of carbon atoms per molecule.

Eq.3 can be used to calculate the solubility of the higher homologues. As evident in Table III, agreement between the experimentally determined weight-ratio solubilities and the calculated values is quite good through n-decane. Beyond n-decane, however, the hydrocarbons are much more soluble than anticipated. This is illustrated in Fig. 7 which clearly shows the discontinuity at about n-decane.

The unexpectedly large solubilities of the higher molecular weight n-paraffins has recently been confirmed by F. FRANKS (personal communication, 1965). In fact, his results for dodecane, tetradecane, and hexadecane, 10.6, 8.74, and 7.06 p.p.b., respectively, are included in Fig.7; the agreement with Baker's data is excellent. Franks writes: "It appears as though the discontinuity at C_{10} is very real, and this is brought out in a startling manner by considering a common standard state for the hydrocarbons, e.g., gas at 1 mm fugacity."

One might interpret the break in the plot of solubility versus carbon number at n-decane (C_{10}) to reflect intermolecular association ("micelle" formation) on the part of the long chain paraffin molecules. In this event, the n-paraffin hydro-

TABLE III

COMPARISON OF PREDICTED AND OBSERVED n-PARAFFIN SOLUBILITIES AT 25 °C

Hydrocarbon	Solubility (w/w) predicted	observed
n-pentane	40.0 $\cdot 10^{-6}$	38.5 $\cdot 10^{-6}$
n-hexane	9.52 $\cdot 10^{-6}$	9.5 $\cdot 10^{-6}$
n-heptane	2.19 $\cdot 10^{-6}$	2.93 $\cdot 10^{-6}$
n-octane	0.493 $\cdot 10^{-6}$	0.66 $\cdot 10^{-6}$
n-decane	23.9 $\cdot 10^{-9}$	16.0 $\cdot 10^{-9}$
n-octadecane	9.94 $\cdot 10^{-14}$	6.0 $\cdot 10^{-9}$
n-hexatriacontane	4.14 $\cdot 10^{-26}$	1.7 $\cdot 10^{-9}$

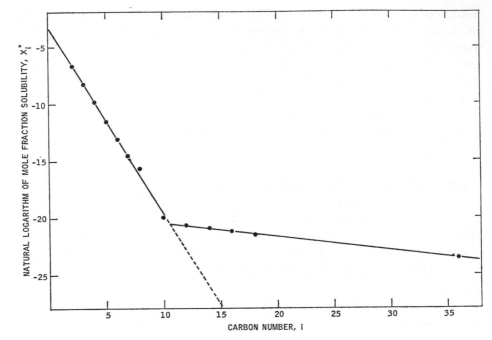

Fig.7. Dependence of *n*-paraffin water solubility on chain length at 25°C.

carbons would not exist in water solution as isolated solute molecules, but as larger clusters, or aggregates, comparable to the micelles formed in dilute solutions of colloidal electrolytes, or soap solutions (PRESTON, 1948). Apparently at least 10 carbon atoms in the chain are needed for association to take place in aqueous solution.

It is not within the scope of this chapter to consider, as have MCBAIN and HUTCHINSON (1955), the physical chemistry of micelle formation in detail, but it should be noted that possession of a net charge is not necessary to micelle stability, since many non-ionic, micelle forming detergents are known (ADAMSON, 1960). Indeed, the absence of negative charges on the *n*-paraffin molecules would facilitate aggregation at much lower concentrations than are needed in fatty acid soap solutions, for example.

PEAKE and HODGSON (1965) also found unexpectedly large solubilities in a study of the mode of accommodation of the *n*-alkanes in water. They wrote: "It is clear that hydrocarbons in the C_{20}–C_{30} range are accommodated in distilled water in amounts much greater than would be expected by simple solubility considerations, and that millipore filtration reduces the degree of accommodation in a systematic fashion while maintaining a clear-cut relation between alkane content and carbon number."

The marked effect of membrane pore size on the alkane effluent concentrations reported by E. G. BAKER (1956) and recognized by PEAKE and HODGSON (1965) is consistent with the existence of n-paraffin micelles in aqueous solution.

It is well known that the presence of colloidal electrolyte micelles in water increases the water solubility of hydrocarbons by providing hydrocarbon-like regions in which other hydrocarbon solutes can preferentially and selectively dissolve. Using ^{14}C-labeled hydrocarbons and tritiated sodium naphthenate solutions, E. G. BAKER (1962) investigated the effect of micelle type and size on hydrocarbon solubility. He found that the lognormal distributions of individual hydrocarbons in petroleum seemed to reflect certain details of their similarly distributed micellar solubilities in dilute soap solutions.

It may be that some of the "natural solubilizers" which Baker claims play an important role in petroleum migration are, in fact, the n-paraffin hydrocarbons. Certainly the paraffin aggregates might provide preferred sites for other hydro-carbon solutes, much as do the surfaces and interiors of colloidal electrolyte micelles. Moreover, long-chain paraffin micelles may well be needed to enable interstitial waters to compete successfully with the organic matter for a certain share (at least one part per million) of the hydrocarbon component.

It is interesting to note that PEAKE and HODGSON (1965) from studies of the filterability of simple aqueous alkane solutions, also found evidence of "a micellar type of accommodation—which would fit the concept of two types of micelles put forward by Baker who discussed small ionic micelles of mean size 6.4 mμ and large neutral micelles of 500 mμ mean size." The two kinds of micelles, originally postulated by McBAIN and JENKINS (1922) and emphasized by E. G. BAKER (1962), are shown schematically in Fig.8. This figure might also represent n-paraffin micelles if the negatively charged carboxylic acid groups (portrayed as open circles) were removed.

The association of long-chain paraffin hydrocarbons in aqueous solution may well explain why the distribution of these compounds in crude oil differs so markedly, unlike other hydrocarbon-types, from their distribution in sediments, especially before significant hydrocarbon redistribution has taken place therein.

SPHERICAL   LAMELLAR

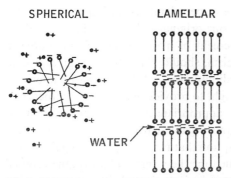

WATER

Fig.8. Two proposed structures of soap micelles.

If the *n*-paraffin micelles are not of uniform size in water solution, then their movement with compaction waters through the fine-grained sediments could result in a sieving action, such as accompanies ultrafiltration of these solutions in the laboratory. If there are two dominant micelle families involved, the bimodal lognormal distribution of high molecular weight *n*-paraffin hydrocarbons shown in Fig.9 is easily understood.

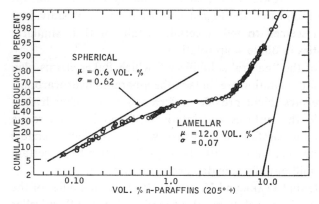

Fig.9. The bimodal lognormal distribution of high molecular weight paraffins in 121 oils from Maracaibo Basin may reflect two kinds of micelles.

In the light of the possible solubilizing action of such diverse molecules as paraffin hydrocarbons and organic acid salts, it would be unwise to overemphasize any one family of compounds as "the solubilizer." As MEINSCHEIN (1959) has pointed out, the oxygen-, sulfur-, and nitrogen-containing compounds may generally have pronounced effect on the solubility of hydrocarbons.

PETROLEUM EVOLUTION AS A REDISTRIBUTION PROCESS

Evolution may be defined as the history of a system undergoing irreversible change. The important irreversible change in petroleum evolution is the concentration in reservoir rock of the hydrocarbons originally dispersed in fine-grained sediments. The process involves the movement of hydrocarbons from source to reservoir and, no matter what the mechanism, should perturb the original hydrocarbon-organic matter relationship. Accordingly, study of the organic composition of fine-grained sediments (source-rocks) ought to provide evidence of hydrocarbon mobility. It is a question of detecting the appropriate change in the original, or inherited, pattern of hydrocarbon (HC) and organic carbon (OC) occurrence.

If one makes the fundamental assumption that the sediments being deposited today are similar to ancient sediments at the time they were laid down, the original hydrocarbon-organic matter relationship can be investigated, i.e., one can define

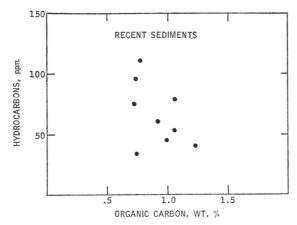

Fig.10. Variation of hydrocarbon with organic carbon content in Pedernales, Venezuela. (Data from KIDWELL and HUNT, 1958, p.796.)

the initial state of the system. For example, Fig.10 shows how the hydrocarbon content (HC) of Recent argillaceous sediments from Pedernales, Venezuela, varies with the organic carbon content (OC). The data of KIDWELL and HUNT (1958) used to construct this scatter diagram were obtained with samples taken from a single core; the depth below the sediment–water interface ranged between 15 and 155 ft. It is evident that no obvious functional relationship exists between the associated pairs of hydrocarbon and organic carbon contents. This may simply be a consequence of the non-selective incorporation in sediments of organic debris from a variety of organisms having different lipid, and, hence, different hydrocarbon masses per unit weight of organic carbon.

If hydrocarbons are formed from organic matter with the passage of time, as is apparently true of the gasoline boiling range hydrocarbons, one might anticipate closer conformance to the equation:

$$(HC) = k(OC) \tag{4}$$

in ancient sediments than in Recent ones, provided, of course, the lower carbon number hydrocarbons are included in the assessment of (HC). Analyses of the organic matter of ancient sediments usually record only hydrocarbons having more than 15 carbon atoms per molecule. The lower molecular weight components are not routinely recovered when solvent is removed prior to the chromatographic separation of hydrocarbons from the total extractable material. Nevertheless, ancient sediments often show a somewhat better correlation between hydrocarbon and organic carbon content, as illustrated in Fig.11 for ancient argillaceous sediments from southeastern Kansas. Again, the data of D. R. BAKER (1962) used to construct the scatter diagram were obtained from a single vertical core located 2,664 ft. below the sediment–air interface. The samples analyzed were drawn from a uniform lithology described as "gray shale" by D. R. Baker.

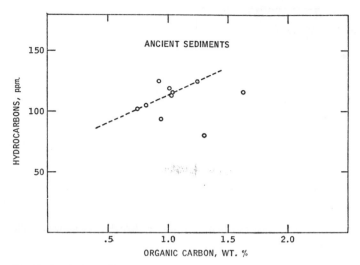

Fig.11. Variation of hydrocarbon with organic carbon content in Cherokee group. (Data from D. R. BAKER, 1962, p.1635.)

The somewhat better conformance to eq.4 shown in Fig.11 is consistent with D. R. Baker's conclusion: "Clearly there is a positive relationship between hydrocarbon content and organic carbon. As has been suggested by PHILIPPI (1957), this relationship may indicate that the hydrocarbons are an indigenous part of the sedimentary rock from which they are extracted. In other words, it is suggested that the hydrocarbons were derived directly from, and in proportion to, the amount of organic matter trapped in the sediment." D. R. Baker also cautioned: "On the other hand, it is possible that the empirical relationship between hydrocarbons and organic carbon is a consequence of some altogether different process or processes. For example, an alternate interpretation is that the extractable hydrocarbons are of migrated origin and have been picked up and retained in the rocks chiefly by highly absorptive and adsorptive organic matter, and hence, occur in amounts proportional to the organic carbon in the rocks."

In a sense, eq.4 summarizes the view of investigators who suggest transformation by saying: "... hydrocarbons were derived directly from, and in proportion to, the amount of organic matter trapped in the sediment." It follows that the ratio of hydrocarbon to organic carbon would be a constant, k, especially if a significant amount of organic matter is ultimately converted into petroleum. (It must be remembered that relative to the hydrocarbons, organic matter is always present in considerable excess in argillaceous sediments.) However, in sediments that have yielded hydrocarbons as a discrete oil phase to a reservoir rock, for example by the "filter pressing" mechanism described by GUSSOW (1954), the hydrocarbon/organic carbon ratio ought to increase with increasing concentration of organic matter. More generally, the retentivity of a sediment for the constituents of petroleum during compaction is generally believed to be a function of the amount of solid carbonaceous matter present, since the latter tends to adsorb the constituents of petroleum. As a consequence of such chromatographic behavior, it is not at all unreasonable to anticipate higher (HC)/(OC) ratios with increasing (OC). The suggestion is simply that organic-rich sediments would tend to acquire additional hydrocarbons that pass their way. The less carbonaceous sediments would not be as retentive toward the hydrocarbons; indeed, they should become relatively depleted in hydrocarbons.

On the other hand, one may assume that some of the hydrocarbons are expelled from the compacting sediments as solutes in the interstitial waters. In this event the hydrocarbon content that is measured (HC) would include contributions from both the water and the organic matter component of the mineral phase. Accordingly, in a unit volume of sediment characterized by the bulk density, ϱ_b, and volume fraction porosity, σ, the total hydrocarbon inventory, ΣHC, would be:

$$\Sigma HC = (1 - \sigma)\varrho_b \frac{g_{HC}}{g_{rock}} + \sigma\varrho_{H_2O}\frac{g_{HC}}{g_{water}} \tag{5}$$

Likewise, the total organic carbon inventory, Σ_{OC}, provided one ignores the hydrocarbons present in aqueous solution, would be:

$$\Sigma_{OC} = (1 - \sigma)\varrho_b \frac{g_{OC}}{g_{rock}} = (1 - \sigma)\varrho_b(OC) \tag{6}$$

Dividing eq.5 by eq.6, the observed ratio of hydrocarbons to organic carbon, (HC/OC)$_{obs}$, becomes:

$$(HC/OC)_{obs.} = (HC/OC)_{rock} + \frac{\sigma}{1-\sigma}\frac{\varrho_{H_2O}}{\varrho_b}\frac{\Sigma Si}{(OC)} \tag{7}$$

where the concentration of hydrocarbons in the formation waters (g_{HC}/g_{H_2O}) has been replaced by the sum of the individual hydrocarbon weight–ratio solubilities, ΣSi.

Using eq.4 and replacing the coefficient of (OC)$^{-1}$ in eq.7 by j, one obtains:

$$(HC/OC)_{obs.} = k + j/(OC) \tag{8}$$

As before, k is the (HC/OC) ratio of the indigenous organic matter, whereas j depends on hydrocarbon solubility.

Eq.8 might be regarded as a mathematical expression of the view of investigators who suggest migration since not all of the hydrocarbons are required to be associated with organic carbon even in fine-grained sediments. Because j is a positive constant, it follows from eq.8 that the observed hydrocarbon/organic carbon ratio ought to decrease with increasing organic carbon content, provided the hydrocarbons can redistribute themselves between the solid organic matrix and the mobile water phase. As previously pointed out, however, chromatographic effects, if extensive, could reverse this relationship.

Fig.12 and 13 show plots of the hydrocarbon/organic carbon ratio as a function of the total organic content for Recent sediments and ancient sediments, respectively. Negative correlations are apparent in both cases. As one might anticipate, conformance to eq.8 is more pronounced in ancient than in Recent sediments. Nonetheless, hydrocarbon dissolution appears to have taken place relatively early in the compaction of the Pedernales sediments. This is in accord with the previous description of the Pedernales structure as a possible site of early in-situ oil origin. Evidence of hydrocarbon dissolution, and hence, mobility, is quite pronounced in the ancient sediments from the Cherokee Group (Fig.13);

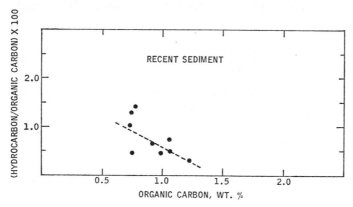

Fig.12. Variation of hydrocarbon/organic carbon ratio with organic carbon content. (Computed from data of KIDWELL and HUNT, 1958, p.796.)

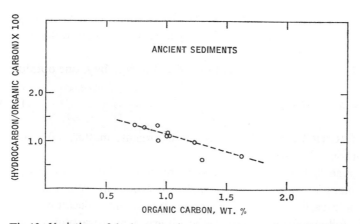

Fig.13. Variation of hydrocarbon/organic carbon ratio with organic carbon content. (After D. R. BAKER, 1962, p.1635.)

these sediments are commonly regarded as having supplied hydrocarbons to crude oil deposits which occur in the interbedded sands.

The above assessment of hydrocarbon mobility is quite independent of the present hydrocarbon inventory. Indeed, knowledge that a particular group of sediments contain an average of 40 p.p.m. HC, or 400 p.p.m. HC tells little about the mobility of hydrocarbons, i.e., whether the sediments have acted as true "source rocks of oil." Conversely PHILIPPI (1957) defines source rock quality "as the amount of hydrocarbons generated per unit weight of dry rock." Interestingly enough, however, he differentiates between indigenous and migrated hydrocarbons by whether or not there is a correlation between hydrocarbons and the non-extractable organic matter of the rock. If the amount of extractable "petroleum" correlates with the amount of residual organic matter, he concludes that the "petroleum" is indigenous; if there is no consistent relation, he assumes it is of migratory origin. The sediments with indigenous oil are considered as possible source beds. Guided by the above reasoning, one would conclude that the argillaceous sediments of Pedernales, Venezuela (Fig.10), contain migrated hydrocarbons, but are not source rocks of oil. It is difficult to know what conclusion might be drawn from the data for gray shales in the Cherokee Group (Fig.11).

It seems reasonable to emphasize that hydrocarbon mobility is the most important indicator of the role fine-grained sediments play in supplying hydrocarbons to crude oil deposits. Nonetheless it is to be anticipated that "dark, bituminous shales" will continue to be popularly regarded as source rocks of oil for a long time to come, even though in the author's opinion they may contain no convincing evidence of significant hydrocarbon redistribution, or hydrocarbon mobility. This situation arises because the "dark bituminous shales" are usually identified as source rocks after oil has been found in their close vicinity. The probability that the hydrocarbons which built the oil body were supplied by the drainage of sediments hundreds of miles away is seldom considered.

Recognition of the events which take place in fine-grained sediments is important, nonetheless, for an adequate understanding of petroleum evolution. It has been suggested that the inverse dependence of hydrocarbon/organic carbon ratio on organic carbon content reflects hydrocarbon dissolution in the associated formation water. According to USPENSKII (1962), such a relationship ought generally to be anticipated. Uspenskii, in a discussion of primary oil migration, wrote: "As the beds become more deeply buried, waters saturated with hydrocarbons are given off, and the hydrocarbons are redistributed;" and further: "the *lower* the total content of organic matter in a source rock the *higher* is the bitumen content of the organic matter." At the present state of knowledge, it is difficult to decide whether the relationship illustrated in Fig.12 and 13, and emphasized by Uspenskii, is actually due to hydrocarbon mobility. However, when the sediments having high hydrocarbon/organic carbon ratios at low levels of organic carbon are sandstones, the presence of migrated petroleum is readily acknowledged (D. R. BAKER, 1962). USPENSKII (1962) has remarked: "An increase in the bituminous content of the organic matter as the overall organic content decreases is considered by some investigators as a primary feature of organic matter due to the residual accumulation of the most highly resistant lipoid elements," and further, "There is no doubt that it [the selective preservation of lipids] takes place, or that together with the secondary processes of redistribution, it must affect the concentration ratios of the bituminous substances in the deposits." As recognized by USPENSKII, the empirical hydrocarbon mobility law suggested by eq.8 has inevitably an integral character, and it is not always possible to define clearly the role of each factor.

It appears that knowledge of the "source rocks of oil" may be of little help in finding the deposits, especially if the "mineral-like" origin concept is correct. As already mentioned, the growth of an oil body could occur hundreds of miles removed from the active source; also, no essential hydrocarbon release may have taken place in the network draining sediments that have extensively and continuously extruded water containing the ubiquitous hydrocarbons.

HYDROCARBON RELEASE FROM SUBSURFACE WATERS

Perhaps the most critical and selective step in the evolution of petroleum is the initial formation of an oil phase. Once established, however, the oil body could continue to grow simply by incorporating other hydrocarbons made available during the long-term percolation of water through the accumulation domain. Spontaneous growth of the oil "mineral deposit" might result from the fact that, compared with water, petroleum provides a highly hospitable environment for hydrocarbons. The proportionality constant, K_p, in eq.1 may be used to estimate the magnitude of the partition coefficients involved; as previously noted, K_p is of the order of 10^6, with the oil greatly favored.

Continuity in the development of an oil body would depend on continuity in the drainage pattern. The paleo-drainage patterns could be extremely complicated, as illustrated in some detail by ROBERTS (1962). For example, after a certain stage of growth is attained, saltingout and growth at previously ineffective sites might take place because of changes in artesian circulation and pressure distribution within the fine-grained sediments. As pointed out by Roberts, the drainage pattern in a basin is governed not only by the stratigraphic geometry, but also by the overall orientation of the basin. Fluid patterns apparently conform rather readily to tectonic adjustments of the basin. With respect to Fig.14, Roberts comments: "In the history of a basin fluid system, the influence of compaction pressures must gradually give way to the influence of artesian pressures, although some influence of both may always exist. The net result is a more or less blended pressure system. The system is never dead, even in the most quiescent basin. There is always fluid exchange occurring between the subsurface and the atmosphere and/or hydrosphere. Any equilibrium attained is always dynamic and vulnerable to the strengthening or weakening of any part of the system. Significant lateral and vertical pressure gradients have been observed even in the most stable basins of the world where data are available. The operation of this dynamic fluid system within the connected porosity of a basin is certain to have continuous influence over the evolution of petroleum."

Visualization of oil "mineral deposit" growth as a highly complex and selective affair, with constant shifting from a trap and then back to it, as adjustments in the fluid pressure pattern are made, might help one to understand complicated patterns of oil occurrence, as exemplified by the cross section through the Goose Creek oil field in Texas, reproduced in Fig. 1.

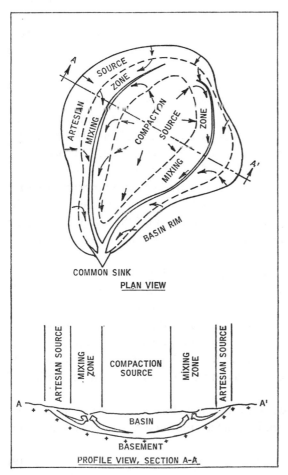

Fig.14. Confluence of hydrodynamic flow jointly energized by internal compaction and external artesian forces in a basin. (After ROBERTS, 1962.)

It is suggested that the in situ origin of oil is initiated by the exclusion of salt from water re-entering the fine-grained sediments. One can only surmise whether or not such a hydrocarbon release mechanism would be selective enough to account for the small fraction of the total sediment hydrocarbon inventory that exists in the form of crude oil deposits. However, some evidence that such a mechanism can be operative is provided by the frequent appearance of evaporites in the rocks capping oil accumulations. One might expect the water co-produced with crude oil to be more saline than that produced below the "oil–water interface". At oil saturations in excess of 25–30%, the associated water would be immobilized and its character might well be retained through geologic time.

BREDEHOEFT et al. (1963) suggest that salt filtering will occur if the hydrodynamic conditions are such that water moves through argillaceous confining layers. The logical places where water might re-enter the fine-grained sediments are provided, of course, by locally high structures (anticlines) and porosity wedges (stratigraphic traps). Bredehoeft et al. used the membrane theory of brine concentration to explain, in detail, the observed salinites of subsurface waters in the Illinois Basin where appeal to soluble saline evaporates, or brine encroachment from adjacent sources, could not be made. Their paper elaborates the suggestion of DESITTER (1947) that confining layers between more permeable formations may act as semi-permeable membranes that allow water to pass out of the formations while retarding the passage of salt ions. Bredehoeft et al. explain: "Under certain hydrodynamic conditions, long-term water movement occurs between permeable formations separated by less permeable confining formations. Layers of clay minerals in the confining formations serve as negatively charged membranes that restrict the passage of anions, and these anions hold the cations in order to maintain electrical and chemical neutrality. Such a process continued through long geologic periods of time could explain some of the very high brine concentrations observed in subsurface formations."

The effect of inorganic salts on the water solubility of non-electrolytes (non-polar hydrocarbons and their polar oxygen, nitrogen, and sulfur derivatives) is a very complex phenomenon of both fundamental and applied interest. Salt effect studies can provide considerable information about the complex interactions of ions and neutral molecules and about the nature of water as a solvent. The data also have a practical bearing on the separation of non-electrolytes from water solution by salting-out processes, such as might take place in the evolution of petroleum.

As a rule, the ability of water to accommodate hydrocarbon solutes decreases with increasing salt concentration. In fact, the SETSCHENOW (1889) equation:

$$1n \frac{S_i^\circ}{S_i} = K_s C_s \qquad (9)$$

where S_i° and S_i are the molar solubilities of the ith hydrocarbon in water and salt solution, respectively, and C_s is the molarity of the salt solution, and K_s is a parameter dependent on the particular salt present in the solution, summarizes a variety of data up to salt concentrations of 234,000 p.p.m. NaCl (McDevitt and Long, 1952a, b). The proportionately constant, K_s, in eq.9 is commonly known as the salting-out parameter. Although hydrocarbons are generally salted-out, even though to markedly varying degrees by different inorganic electrolytes, there are some salts (in addition to the colloidal electrolytes, or soaps) which actually salt-in nonelectrolytes such as benzene. In such cases, K_s in eq.9 is a negative number. Although K_s is usually referred to as an "ion-non-electrolyte" interaction parameter, molecular interactions between the salt and water, and especially the nonelectrolyte and water, are equally important in determining its magnitude and sign. For the present purpose, it is sufficient to note that in aqueous sodium chloride solutions, K_s is generally positive for a variety of non-polar and polar hydrocarbons. Indeed, the precipitation of non-electrolytes from water solution by the addition of salt is widely recognized and exploited by organic chemists. There is little doubt that hydrocarbons will be released from subsurface waters at those places where water is able to re-enter the argillaceous sediments.

Analysis of the water co-produced with crude oils should clearly show the salt effect. For a given concentration of the hydrocarbons in oil, their concentration in the water phase should be smaller, the greater the total solids content of the water. In the vicinity of salt domes or other water soluble evaporite deposits, one does not need, of course, to invoke salt-filtering to understand the nucleation of crude oil, or for that matter, natural gas deposits. One might argue, however, that the outward diffusive transport of ions from soluble salt bodies, or regions of active salt-filtration, would negate the in situ development of the oil "mineral deposit", and perhaps occasion the need for secondary migration processes after all.

Bredehoeft et al. (1963) have explained that the mass transfer of ions (and hydrocarbon solutes) by either diffusion or fluid circulation is dependent upon the geometry of the basin. However, making reasonable assumptions about the geologic and hydrologic dimensions, these workers concluded that relative to the rate of fluid transport, the outward diffusive transport of ions is negligible. The same conclusions must apply to the hydrocarbons, for if molecular diffusion played a significant role in hydrocarbon redistribution, or transport, the oil accumulations would be retained only with great difficulty over protracted periods of time. As mentioned by Berry (1965): "They would tend to disperse themselves by diffusion rates equivalent to those responsible for the primary migration. Such thinking leads to the incorrect conclusion that few older rocks (older than five million years) should contain petroleum."

Indeed, is not the gathering in reservoir rock of the hydrocarbons originally dispersed in fine-grained sediments the very antithesis of molecular diffusion?

CONCLUSIONS

In a recent review of the geologic aspects of the origin of petroleum, HEDBERG (1964) assembled many of the arguments ordinarily used to argue against an in situ origin of oil. It is appropriate to discuss them now.

Hedberg noted: "... for most major accumulations this [in situ origin] appears to be conclusively negated by the world-wide evidence of gravity control in the trapping of petroleum, which would require the unlikely coincidence of the original localization of petroleum or petroleum source material at the same points where structural traps in reservoir beds happened to be formed perhaps millions of years after deposition of these beds. Moreover, the lack of substantial solid organic residues in reservoir rocks at the site of petroleum accumulations would be explained only by complete conversion into petroleum which would not be compatible with the survival of organic residues in adjacent fine-grained sediments." Indeed, it must be agreed that a residue-less, localized conversion of organic matter into petroleum in reservoir rock is unlikely. Perhaps it is also unlikely to postulate that the transformation of organic matter to petroleum takes place out-side the reservoir rock, in the near-by shales, for this idea implies one more, in the author's opinion, unsubstantiated step—that of primary migration of an oil phase. Although there is evidence of early in situ oil origin, the process outlined in this chapter depends basically on the directed long-term circulation of compaction and artesion waters. The coincidence of oil accumulations in suitable traps may be the result of localized salt enrichment within the aquifer at those places where water re-enters the contiguous shales. Anticlines and stratigraphic traps provide the logical places where salt-filtering would take place. Equally important, the absence of oil in structurally suitable anticlinal and porosity traps can be under-stood in terms of (1) the lack of concerted water movements through them or (2) the lack of hydrocarbon nucleation because of relatively impermeable confining sediments.

HEDBERG further commented: "If it was assumed that the petroleum had come out of solution to form the accumulation, the quantity of solvent water present in the reservoir rock at the site of accumulation could not possibly have been large enough to contain the amount of petroleum present." The size of the oil deposit would depend, however, on the *integrated volume flow* past the site of accumulation. Solubility studies suggest that compaction water, if properly focused, could transport the necessary amounts of hydrocarbons if the decrease in hydro-carbon solute concentration in water upon flow past the site of active accumulation was of the order of parts per million.

Finally, it was pointed out: "Many large petroleum accumulations, of which those in isolated reef reservoirs are a prime example, are in rocks which were formed in an oxidizing environment inimical to petroleum genesis." Of course one might also ask: just how isolated from the drainage pattern were the reefs?

In summary, HEDBERG (1964) considered (*1*) oil origin from organic materials deposited at the location where the accumulation is now found, and (*2*) origin from materials deposited in the reservoir rock only, but subsequently concentrated in that rock. It is noteworthy that Hedberg considers the water supply inadequate in both of these cases without calling heavily on water from outside sources, such as water derived from compaction or from artesian circulation.

It will be apparent to the reader that the main objection to an in-situ oil origin centers about the classic need of an environment suitable for transforming organic matter into petroleum. However, if the critical need in petroleum genesis is the focused drainage of compaction waters through suitable aquifers, the classic view may be misplacing, both in time and space, the true nature of the origin of oil. Undoubtedly, petroleum migration and accumulation is not yet fully understood and further research is required to clarify the process.

REFERENCES

ADAMSON, A. W., 1960. *Physical Chemistry of Surfaces.* Interscience, New York, N.Y., 629 pp.

BAKER, D. R., 1962. Organic geochemistry of Cherokee Groups in southeastern Kansas and northeastern Oklahoma. *Bull. Am. Petrol. Geologists,* 46 (9): 1621–1642.

BAKER, E. G., 1956. Oil migration in aqueous solution—a study of the solubility of *n*-octadecane. In: *A Symposium on Chemistry in the Exploration and Production of Petroleum—Am. Chem. Soc., Div. Petrol. Chem., Preprints—Symposia,* 1 (2): 5–17.

BAKER, E. G., 1958. Crude oil composition and hydrocarbon solubility. In: *A Symposium on the Chemical Aspects of the Origin, Migration, and Accumulation of Oil—Am. Chem. Soc., Div. Petrol. Chem., Preprints,* 3 (4C): 61–68.

BAKER, E. G., 1959. Origin and migration of oil. *Science,* 129 (3353): 871–874.

BAKER, E. G., 1960. A hypothesis concerning the accumulation of sediment hydrocarbons to form crude oil. *Geochim. Cosmochim. Acta,* 19: 309–317.

BAKER, E. G., 1962. Distribution of hydrocarbons in petroleum. *Bull. Am. Assoc. Petrol. Geologists,* 46 (1): 76–84.

BELSKY, T., JOHNS, R. B., McCARTHY, E. D., BURLINGAME, A. L., RICHTER, W. and CALVIN, M., 1965. Evidence of life processes in a sediment two and a half billion years old. *Nature,* 206: 446–448.

BENDORAITUS, J. G., BROWN, B. L. and HEPNER, R. S., 1962. Isoprenoid hydrocarbons in petroleum. *Anal. Chem.,* 34: 49–53.

BRAY, E. E. and EVANS, E. D., 1961. Distribution of *n*-paraffins as a clue to recognition of source beds. *Geochim. Cosmochim. Acta,* 22: 2–15.

BREDEHOEFT, J. D., BLYTH, C. R., WHITE, W. A. and MAXEY, G. B., 1963. Possible mechanism for concentration of brines in subsurface formations. *Bull. Am. Assoc. Petrol. Geologists,* 47 (2): 257–269.

CLAUSSEN, W. F. and POLGLASE, M. F., 1952. Solubilities and structures in aqueous aliphatic hydrocarbon solutions. *J. Am. Chem. Soc.,* 74: 4817–4819.

DeSITTER, L. U., 1947. Diagenesis of oil-field brines. *Bull. Am. Assoc. Petrol. Geologists,* 31: 2030–2040.

DUNTON, M. L. and HUNT, J. M., 1962. Distribution of low molecular-weight hydrocarbons in recent and ancient sediments. *Bull. Am. Assoc. Petrol. Geologists,* 46 (12): 2246–2258.

DVALI, M. F., 1964. Trends in theoretical studies on the geology of oil and gas. *Intern. Geol. Rev.* 6 (1): 68–74.

ERDMAN, J. G., MARLETT, E. M. and HANSON, W. E., 1958. The occurrence and distribution of low molecular weight aromatic hydrocarbons in recent and ancient carbonaceous sediments. *Am. Chem. Soc., 134th Meeting, Chicago, Ill., 1958, Paper*, C-39–C-49.

FRANCIS, A. W., 1947. Numbers of isomeric alkylbenzenes. *J. Am. Chem. Soc.*, 69: 1536–1537.

GUSSOW, W. C., 1954. Differential entrapment of oil and gas; a fundamental principle. *Bull. Am. Assoc. Petrol. Geologists*, 38, (5): 816–853.

HEDBERG, H. D., 1964. Geologic aspects of origin of petroleum. *Bull. Am. Assoc. Petrol. Geologists*, 48 (11): 1755–1803.

HILL, G. A. and WALTON, H. F., 1958. *Principles of Osmosis Applicable to Oil Hydrology.* Petrol. Res. Corporation, Denver, Colo. 66 pp.

HOBSON, G. D., 1943. Compaction and some oil field features. *J. Inst. Petrol.*, 29 (230): 37–54.

HOBSON, G. D., 1961. Problems associated with the migration of oil in "solution". *J. Inst. Petrol.*, 47 (449): 170–173.

HODGSON, G. W., HITCHON, B. and TAGUCHI, K., 1964. The water and hydrocarbon cycles in the formation of oil accumulations. In: Y. MIYAKE and T. KOYAMER (Editors), *Recent Researches in the Fields of Hydrosphere, Atmosphere, and Nuclear Geochemistry.* Maruzen, Tokyo, pp.217–242.

HUNT, J. M., 1961. Distribution of hydrocarbons in sedimentary rocks. *Geochim. Cosmochim. Acta*, 22: 37–49.

KIDWELL, A. L. and HUNT, J. M., 1958. Migration of oil in recent sediments of Pedernales, Venezuela. In: *Habitat of oil.* Am. Assoc. Petrol. Geologists, Tulsa, Texas, pp. 790–817.

KVENVOLDEN, K. A., 1962. Normal paraffin hydrocarbons in sediments from San Francisco Bay, California. *Bull. Am. Assoc. Petrol. Geologists,* 46 (9): 1643–1652.

LEVORSEN, A. I., 1954. *Geology of Petroleum.* Freeman, San Francisco, Calif., 703 pp.

MARTIN, R. L., WINTERS, J. C. and WILLIAMS, J. A., 1963. Distribution of *n*-paraffins in crude oils and their implications to origin of petroleum. *Nature*, 199: 110–113.

MCAULIFFE, C., 1963. Solubility in water of C_1–C_9 hydrocarbons. *Nature*, 200: 1092–1093.

MCBAIN, J. W. and JENKINS, R. W., 1922. The ultrafiltration of soap solutions; sodium oleate and potassium laurate. *J. Chem. Soc.*, 12: 2327.

MCBAIN, M. E. L. and HUTCHINSON, E., 1955. *Solubilization and Related Phenomena.* Acad. Press New York, N.Y., 259 pp.

MCDEVITT, W. F. and LONG, F. A. 1952a. The activity coefficients of benzene in aqueous salt solutions. *J. Am. Chem. Soc.*, 74: 1773–1777.

MCDEVITT, W. F. and LONG, F. A., 1952b. Activity coefficients of nonelectric solutes in aqueous salt solutions. *Chem. Rev.*, 51: 119–169.

MEINSCHEIN, W. G., 1959. Origin of petroleum. *Bull. Am. Assoc. Petrol. Geologists,* 43 (5): 925–943.

MEINSCHEIN, W. G., 1961. Significance of hydrocarbons in sediments and petroleum. *Geochim. Cosmochim. Acta*, 22: 58–64.

MEINSCHEIN, W. G., 1965. Origin of petroleum. In: *Enciclopedia del Petrolio, E. Der Gas Naturali.* Inst. Chim., Univ. Roma, Roma, in press.

MEINSCHEIN, W. G., BARGHORN, E. S. and SCHOPF, J. W., 1964. Biological remnants in a Precambrian sediment. *Science*, 145: 262–263.

MINOR, H. E., 1926. Goose Creek oil field, Harris County, Texas, In: *Geology of Salt Dome Oil Fields.* Am. Assoc. Petrol. Geologists, Tulsa, Okla.

NOBLE, E. A., 1963. Formation of ore deposits by water or compaction. *Econ. Geol.,* 58: 1145–1156.

PEAKE, E. and HODGSON, G. W., 1965. Alkanes in natural aqueous systems; accommodation of C_{20}–C_{33} n-alkanes in distilled water and occurrence in natural water systems. *Am. Oil Chemists Soc., 56th Ann. Spring Meeting, Houston, Texas, 1965, Paper.* Also *J. Am Oil Chemists Sos.*, 43(4): 215–222.

PHILIPPI, G. T., 1957. Identification of oil source beds by chemical means. *Intern. Geol. Congr., 20th, Mexico, 1956, Rept.*, 3: 25–38.

POW, J. R., FAIRBANKS, G. H. and ZAMORA, W. J., 1963. Descriptions and reserve estimates of the oil sands of Alberta. In: *K. A. Clark Volume.* Res. Council Alberta, Edmonton, Alta.

PRESTON, W. C., 1948. Some correlating principles of detergent action. *J. Phys. Colloid Chem.*, 52: 84–97.

ROBERTS, W. H., III, 1962. Hydrodynamic analysis in petroleum exploration. Unpublished.

ROOF, J. G. and RUTHERFORD, W. M., 1958. Rate of migration of petroleum by proposed mechanisms. *Bull. Am. Assoc. Petrol. Geologists*, 42 (5): 963–980.

ROSSINI, F. D. and MAIR, B. J., 1959. The work of the A.P.I. Research Project 6 on the composition of petroleum. *World Petrol. Congr., Proc., 5th, N.Y., 1959*, 5: 1–21.

RUSSELL, W. L., 1960. *Principles of Petroleum Geology*. McGraw-Hill, New York, N.Y., 508 pp.

SETSCHENOW, J., 1889. Über die Constitution der Salzlösung auf Grund ihres Verhaltens zu Kohlensäuren. *Z. Phys. Chem.*, 4: 117.

SILVERMAN, S. R., 1960. Carbon isotopic evidence on mechanisms of petroleum maturation. *Bull. Am. Assoc. Petrol. Geologists*, 44: 1256.

SILVERMAN, S. R., 1964. Investigation of petroleum origin and evolution mechanisms by carbon isotope studies. In: H. CRAIG, S. L. MILLER and G. J. WASSERBURG (Editors), *Isotopic and Cosmic Chemistry*. North-Holland, Amsterdam, pp. 92–102.

SILVERMAN, S. R. and EPSTEIN, S., 1958. Carbon isotopic compositions of petroleums and other sedimentary organic materials. *Bull. Am. Assoc. Petrol. Geologists*, 42: 998–1012.

SMITH, P. V., JR., 1952. The occurrence of hydrocarbons in Recent sediments from the Gulf of Mexico. *Science*, 116 (3017): 437–439.

STEVENS, N. P., 1956. Origin of petroleum—a review. *Bull. Am. Assoc. Petrol. Geologists*, 40 (1): 51–61.

USPENSKII, V. A., 1962. The geochemistry of processes of primary oil migration. *Geokhimiya*, 1962 (12): 1027–1045.

WALTERS, R. P., 1960. Relation of oil occurrences at Surani, Rumania, to origin and migration of oil. *Bull. Am. Assoc. Petrol. Geologists*, 44 (10): 1704–1705.

WEEKS, L. G., 1960. Some principles of petroleum occurrence. *Shale Shaker*, 10, (6): 17–28.

WHITMORE, F. C., 1943. Transformation of organic material into petroleum-chemical and biochemical phases: Fundamental research on occurrence and recovery of petroleum. *Proc., Am. Petrol Inst.*, 1943: 124.

WRATHER, W. E. and LAKIE, F. H. (Editors), 1934. *Problems of Petroleum Geology*. Am. Assoc. Petrol. Geologists, Tulsa, Okla., 1073 pp.

Chapter 8

ORIGIN AND EVOLUTION OF PETROLEUM

UMBERTO COLOMBO

Instituto di Ricerche "G. Donegani", Montecatini–Edison, Novara, (Italy)

INTRODUCTION

Man has thought about the origin of petroleum since he first saw it and used it. Over hundreds of years many hypotheses have been developed to account for the occurrences and accumulations of crude oil. Only in recent years, however, have the combined considerations of geologists, organic chemists, physical chemists, biochemists, and geochemists, each contributing a share of the overall knowledge, been able to achieve a more generalized and intelligent picture of the subject. As a result, there are at present many good ideas that are generally accepted, and many good ideas still in the process of being tested. This chapter represents an attempt to summarize some of the more significant aspects of the problem without, however, trying to present a historical or chronological discussion of the subject.

DEFINITION OF PETROLEUM AND ITS CHEMICAL COMPOSITION

Petroleum is one of the most complex and diversified materials of geologic interest. Its physical state may be gaseous, liquid or solid, depending on the nature and on the proportions of the different compounds of which it is constituted, and also on the existing conditions of temperature and pressure. Therefore, when accumulated in commercial amounts, petroleum may form deposits of natural gas, crude oil or asphalt.

Chemically, petroleum is defined as a mixture of hydrocarbons containing small quantities of oxygen-, nitrogen- and sulfur-bearing compounds, and traces of metallic constituents. The non-hydrocarbon components are usually concentrated in the higher-boiling fractions of the crude oils: they may constitute as much as 50% of heavy crude oils, such as those from Mexico, Mississippi or Sicily, or as little as 2—3% of lighter crude oils, such as those from Pennsylvania and Oklahoma.

Until recently, the determination of the molecular constitution of petroleum was an extremely difficult task because of the serious limitations imposed by the available analytical techniques and equipment. Nevertheless, in the 1920's the American Petroleum Institute (A.P.I.) sponsored a specific research project (No. 6— MAIR, 1964), aiming at the "Separation, identification and determination of the chemical constituents of commercial petroleum fractions". A hydrocarbon-rich crude oil, produced near Ponca City, Oklahoma, was selected as the standard petroleum sample for this project, and a thorough investigation of its chemical constitution was undertaken. More recently, other research projects have been organized by the A.P.I. with the purpose of isolating and determining the sulfur compounds (Project 48—BALL et al., 1952) and the nitrogen compounds (Project 52—BALL and RALL, 1962) in petroleum. The results of these investigations have been indeed remarkable, during the last 15 years, as a consequence of the adoption of new separation and identification techniques, such as gas-liquid chromatography, mass spectrometry, nuclear magnetic resonance, infrared and ultraviolet spectroscopy.

By mid-1965 the work of A.P.I. Project 6 had led to the identification and isolation of as many as 264 individual compounds (256 being hydrocarbons), with boiling points ranging from $-161.5\,°C$ (methane) to $+475\,°C$ (n-tritriacontane). Table I illustrates the class distribution of the different compounds that have been

TABLE I

DISTRIBUTION, BY CLASS AND CARBON NUMBER, OF THE COMPOUNDS ISOLATED FROM THE PONCA CITY CRUDE OIL BY INVESTIGATORS WORKING FOR A.P.I. PROJECT 6

(After MAIR, 1965)

Compounds	Carbon No.															Total
	4	5	6	7	8	9	10	11	12	13	14	15	16	17	18	
Branched paraffins	1	1	4	6	15	7	5	—	—	—	1	1	—	—	—	41
Alkyl cyclopentanes	—	1	1	5	13	3	—	—	—	—	—	—	—	—	—	23
Alkyl cyclohexanes	—	—	1	1	8	8	2	—	—	—	—	—	—	—	—	20
Alkyl cycloheptanes	—	—	—	1	—	—	—	—	—	—	—	—	—	—	—	1
Bicycloparaffins	—	—	—	—	3	8	5	1	—	—	—	—	—	—	—	17
Tricycloparaffins	—	—	—	—	—	—	1	—	—	—	—	—	—	—	—	1
Alkylbenzenes	—	—	1	1	4	8	22	4	—	—	—	—	—	—	—	40
Aromatic cycloparaffins	—	—	—	—	—	1	4	3	—	1	—	—	—	2	1	12
Fluorenes	—	—	—	—	—	—	—	—	—	1	1	2	3	1	—	8
Dinuclear aromatics	—	—	—	—	—	—	1	2	12	15	14	5	1	—	—	50
Trinuclear aromatics	—	—	—	—	—	—	—	—	—	—	1	4	1	1	—	7
Tetranuclear aromatics	—	—	—	—	—	—	—	—	—	—	—	—	1	1	1	3
Sulfur compounds	—	—	—	—	—	—	—	—	—	1	1	—	1	1	—	4
Oxygen compounds	—	—	—	—	—	—	—	—	—	3	1	—	—	—	—	4
Total	1	2	7	14	43	35	40	10	12	21	19	12	7	6	2	233
Normal paraffins C_1 to C_{33}	—	—	—	—	—	—	—	—	—	—	—	—	—	—	—	33
Grand total	—	—	—	—	—	—	—	—	—	—	—	—	—	—	—	264

isolated (MAIR, 1965). It should be noted that all the compounds thus far isolated from the original Ponca City oil represent approximately 60% by weight of the crude petroleum.

WHITEHEAD and BREGER (1963) have listed approximately 400 compounds that have been isolated from various crude oils. Considering compounds isolated more recently, it is estimated that about 450 individual compounds are now known to occur in natural petroleum, not including metal–organic compounds and porphyrin complexes. About 200 of the compounds already identified are non-hydrocarbons, but most of the non-hydrocarbon compounds are present in the oils in relatively small concentrations.

The lower-boiling fractions of petroleum, up to and including the gasoline range, are best known from the analytical point of view. As observed by MAIR (1960), nearly all the hydrocarbons theoretically possible in the paraffin, cyclopentane, cyclohexane and benzene series (a total of about 500) are believed to be actually present, at least in small amounts, in the gasoline fraction below boiling point 132°C (and 180°C for the aromatics). Only a few possible branched paraffins and alkyl-cyclopentanes were not found in the standard oil, but they may have been present in concentrations below the limit of detection. The conclusion of Mair is that most probably the same situation exists for the higher-boiling fractions of the gasoline, and that all possible isomers of all possible classes may actually be present, at least in small amounts.

IMPLICATIONS CONCERNING THE ORIGIN OF PETROLEUM BASED ON ANALYTICAL DATA

As noted below, the analytical data on petroleum, some of which are discussed above, lead to remarkable geochemical conclusions:

(1) The molecular composition of petroleum, at least in the gasoline range, does not reflect the existence of thermodynamic equilibrium. An example of this divergency from chemical equilibrium is shown in Table II (MARTIN et al., 1963b) for certain isomeric groups in the gasoline fraction of an average crude oil.

(2) Crude oils are, in general, optically active. Inasmuch as this property is believed to be confined to biologically derived compounds, the optical activity of petroleum has been taken as evidence of the biogenic origin of oil. It should be noted, however, that the optical activity of petroleum is primarily confined to the C_{14}–C_{18} and C_{27}–C_{30} carbon number ranges (HULME, 1938; MAIR, WILLINGHAM and STREIFF, 1938). This suggests that sterols could be the parent substances of such optically active components.

(3) Petroleum contains some individual compounds that have strong structural similarities to organic substances isolated from animals or plants. Among such components are the porphyrin complexes and certain isoprenoid hydrocarbons. In Fig.1 (BENDORAITIS et al., 1963) the structural similarity between pristane and

TABLE II

EQUILIBRIUM VERSUS OBSERVED DISTRIBUTIONS IN AVERAGE CRUDE OIL[1]

(After MARTIN et al., 1963b)

	Observed distribution	Equilibrium at 65°C and 200 atm.
1,2-dimethylbenzene	32	20
1,3-dimethylbenzene	49	57
1,4-dimethylbenzene	19	23
1-methyl-2-ethylbenzene	25	11
1-methyl-3-ethylbenzene	48	49
1-methyl-4-ethylbenzene	27	40
1,2,3-trimethylbenzene	25	8
1,2,4-trimethylbenzene	59	60
1,3,5-trimethylbenzene	16	32
2-methylpentane	57	72
3-methylpentane	43	28
2-methylhexane	42	59
3-methylhexane	58	41
1,cis-2-dimethylcyclopentane	7	5
1,trans-2-dimethylcyclopentane	42	46
1,cis-3-dimethylcyclopentane	27	33
1,trans-3-dimethylcyclopentane	24	16

[1] Data are normalized to 100% in each group.

phytane (both of which have been isolated from petroleum) and phytol, a hydrolytic product of the degradation of chlorophyll, is shown.

(4) Certain components of petroleum, including porphyrin complexes, are unstable at temperatures in the range of 250–300°C. Elemental sulfur, the presence of which has been established in several crude oils, is also known to react rapidly with hydrocarbons at temperatures as low as 150°C with formation of H_2S and of cyclic sulfur compounds (see the chapter "Non-hydrocarbons in petroleum" of this volume). The occurrence of both porphyrins and free sulfur, therefore, suggests that the geochemical history of petroleum, at least from the moment in which such thermo-labile structures became part of it, must have been characterized by relatively low temperatures.

(5) The $^{13}C/^{12}C$ ratios in petroleum are more similar to those of living organic matter than to those of atmospheric CO_2 and carbonate rocks. This is shown in Fig.2 (SILVERMAN, 1964a) where it may also be noted that petroleums of

non-marine origin exhibit a greater ^{12}C enrichment than those of marine origin. It should be noted that the $^{13}C/^{12}C$ ratios in petroleum are approximately in the same ranges as those of the lipid fraction from non-marine and marine plants. This, besides providing additional evidence in favor of the organic origin of petroleum, points to the potential importance of the lipid fraction of biologic organisms as a source of petroleum.

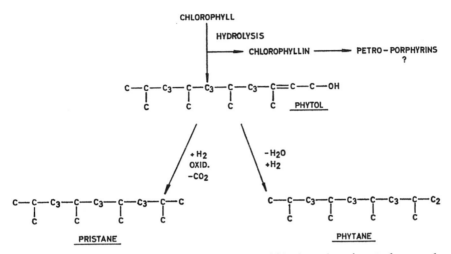

Fig.1. The structural similarity between two isoprenoid hydrocarbons in petroleum, and a well-known hydrolitic product of chlorophyll suggest the biologic origin of pristane and phytane. (After BENDORAITTIS et al., 1963.)

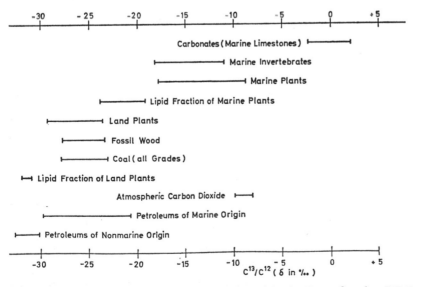

Fig.2. $^{13}C/^{12}C$ ranges in natural carbonaceous materials (δ values referred to P.D.B. standard). (Data from SILVERMAN, 1964.)

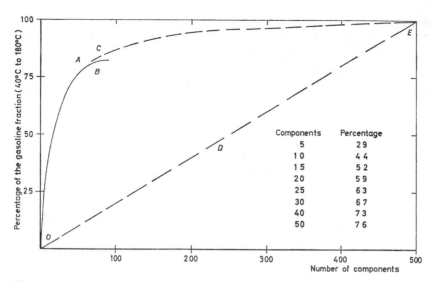

Fig.3. Number of components, counted in order of decreasing abundance, and the percentage of the gasoline fraction constituted by them. Curve *OAB* gives the results so far obtained for the Ponca crude; *OACE* the expected shape of the curve for the (approximately) 500 components which are possible; *ODE* gives the results which would be obtained if each of the 500 components occurred in equal amount. (After MAIR, 1960.)

(*6*) The bulk of petroleum, at least in the lower-boiling fractions, consists of relatively few compounds. This is illustrated by Fig.3 (MAIR, 1960) which shows that 20 individual compounds represent as much as 59% by weight of the entire gasoline fraction of the Ponca City crude oil.

(*7*) The normal paraffins are among the main constituents of petroleum. MARTIN et al., (1963) have shown that the *n*-paraffins represent typically about 15–20% of the total petroleum, and that in some cases they may comprise more than 30% of the total crude oil.

(*8*) Some crude oils exhibit a detectable predominance of *n*-paraffins with odd numbers of carbon atoms over those with an even number of carbon atoms. This is shown in Fig.4, where three of the four crudes studied exhibit a more or less pronounced predominance of odd-numbered *n*-paraffins (MARTIN et al., 1963b). This is not only an evidence for the biogenic origin of petroleum, but also suggests that the decarboxylation of fatty acids might be the mechanism by which the normal paraffins are generated. This subject will be discussed in some detail in the following pages.

(*9*) The branched-chain, cyclo-alkane and aromatic constituents that are abundant in petroleum correspond to those which might be expected to arise from various well known transformations of the *n*-paraffins (ROBINSON, 1963). Less branched structures are more common than highly branched ones. With increase in boiling range, the content of polynuclear aromatics and polycycloparaffins increases. It also appears that most of the cycloparaffins are related to cyclopentane and cyclohexane.

(*10*) Olefins, or other easily reducible substances, are as a rule absent from petroleum. This suggests that petroleum was formed (and remained) under a strongly reducing environment.

(*11*) With very few exceptions, crude oils do not contain more than 0.5% nitrogen and 1.0% oxygen. As noted by WHITEHEAD and BREGER (1963) it also appears that, with the exclusion of porphyrins (which contain both nitrogen and oxygen), no individual compound containing more than one hetero-atom (N, O, S) has been isolated to date from petroleum.

The chemical evidence in favor of an organic origin of petroleum should not be regarded as a definite indication that all petroleum has originated biogenically. On the contrary, there is chemical evidence that abiogenic hydrocarbons exist, both in the earth and in the extra-terrestrial space (MUELLER, 1963; SYLVESTER-BRADLEY and KING, 1963).

ROBINSON (1963), looking at the problem of the origin of oil primarily from a chemical point of view, suggested that petroleum has a dual origin, being composed of both abiotically and biologically produced components. According to him, the first hydrocarbons were produced on the earth by non-biological processes long before the appearance of life on earth, perhaps three billion years ago. Methane was probably formed first from metallic carbides and water (according to the theory proposed already in 1877 by MENDELÉYEF), and then it underwent reaction with steam producing carbon monoxide and hydrogen. The next stage might have been an anticipation of the Fischer–Tropsch process. Such Fischer–

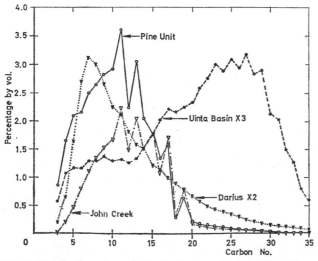

Fig.4. Distribution of *n*-paraffins in four crude oils. (After MARTIN et al., 1963b.)

Tropsch hydrocarbons (STORCH et al., 1951) would have gone through a natural hydroforming process in the reducing atmosphere which is known to have been present on the primordial earth. The abiotic oil thus formed was probably used as a source of carbon and hydrogen by primitive organisms; these became associated with the oil, their biochemistry evolved and their remains contributed components to the total petroleum which is presently found.

The value of the hypothesis on the duplex origins of petroleum is highest in connection with the problem of the origin of life on earth. As far as naphthogenesis is concerned, this hypothesis offers a reasonable explanation on how the first petroleum could have originated. It should not be assumed, however, that inorganically produced hydrocarbons constitute *now* a quantitatively important fraction of petroleum. As pointed out by KREJCI-GRAF (1963), the origin of petroleum should be regarded primarily as a geological problem. It is not sufficient to point out chemical possibilities, therefore, but these have to be reconciled with geological evidence.

From a geological point of view, the evidence in favor of an organic origin of petroleum is overwhelming. First of all, the predominant association of petroleum with sedimentary rocks should be recognized. It has been calculated (KNEBEL and RODRIGUEZ-ERASO, 1956) that over 99% of the petroleum produced to date has come from sedimentary rocks. Moreover, in those few cases where petroleum has been produced commercially from igneous or metamorphic rocks, there is evidence of the nearby occurrence of sedimentary strata which could well have been the source of the gas, oil or asphalt found in adjacent non-sedimentary strata. This geological association of petroleum with sedimentary strata that contain or have contained organic material of animal or plant origin, has led nearly all geologists to reject as absolutely inadequate the old theories of a 100% inorganic genesis of oil. This, of course, does not deny the existence of inorganic hydrocarbons, which are known to occur in several instances (although never in commercial quantities) in volcanic gases (TAZIEFF, 1963) as well as in magmatic rocks (GOGUEL, 1963).

Other geologic considerations for the biological origin of petroleum are:

(*a*) Many crude oils contain identifiable remains of ancient plants or animals.

(*b*) Large petroleum accumulations are common in those sedimentary basins which have deep strata of particular ages when life processes were quite active.

(*c*) Traces of hydrocarbons have been found in nearly all Recent sediments.

The conclusions in favor of a biological origin of petroleum are based on quantitative rather than qualitative factors, with the idea that any theory on naphthogenesis should explain the occurrence of the immense petroleum accumulations actually found in the petroliferous regions of the world, and should give reason of the known geographic and geologic distribution of petroleum. An excellent discussion on this point has been presented by VASSOJEVICH (1962).

COX, in a timely paper in 1946, suggested a "geological fence" representing the physical and geological conditions required for the generation of petroleum. These were: (*1*) biological origin; (*2*) marine environment; (*3*) temperatures below about 200°C; (*4*) overburden pressures of at least 5,000 ft.; (*5*) time ranging from Cambrian to Pliocene.

HEDBERG (1964) in a geological review of the subject, concludes that the "corner posts" of the original fence are substantially correct, although they should be somewhat shifted in the light of more recent findings. The biological origin is confirmed, although admittedly there may be a small contribution from abiogenic hydrocarbons. The question of marine environment is rather controversial, since some major petroleum occurrences are almost unquestionably of non-marine origin. This has been confirmed by the isotopic data of SILVERMAN (1964a), which indicated the close similarity of $^{13}C/^{12}C$ ratios in non-marine petroleum to those of the lipid fraction of land plants (see Fig.2). The upper limiting temperature for the formation of petroleum, as indicated by the presence of porphyrin compounds, has been raised to 300°C, but it should be recognized that most petroleums have originated at temperatures below 100°C. The minimum overburden pressure values are now considered to be as low as 3,000 ft. or even lower. Finally, the time range of terrestrial oil is now known to extend from far back into the Precambrian to well along the Pleistocene. In the same paper, HEDBERG (1964) lists a number of environmental factors ("sedimentational setting") which are essential for the genesis of oil. They are: (*1*) abundant production of organic matter of right kind. Whether this organic matter is predominantly animal or plant, marine or terrestrial, is still to be clarified; (*2*) early development of anaerobic conditions and reducing environment; (*3*) absence of destructive organisms; (*4*) active and rapid deposition of fine-grained sediments, which provide a cover for preservation of organic matter from decay, as well as a water-rich matrix for the diagenetic processes of the organic matter; (*5*) availability of reservoir space, even during the compaction of the sediments. In addition to these factors, Hedberg stressed the importance of restricted basins with little fluid circulation. In such basins the generation of petroleum might very well be favored by the same conditions required for the formation of evaporites. This would explain why very many of the largest petroleum accumulations in the world are associated with evaporites (MOODY, 1959).

THE SOURCE MATERIAL OF PETROLEUM

Although most geochemists agree on the biological origin of petroleum, the chemistry of its formation, as well as the nature of the source material, are still debated.

An approach to the problem of identifying the source material of petroleum is the study of chemical similarities between crude oils and known biogenic compounds. Examples of this type have already been mentioned in preceeding

TABLE III

C4 TO C8 HYDROCARBONS IN SEDIMENTS, p.p.m.

(After DUNTON and HUNT, 1962)

Hydrocarbon type	Venezuela (Recent)	Texas (Recent)	Cuba (Recent)	Norway (Recent)	Venezuela (Miocene)	Venezuela (Eocene)	Wyoming (Cretaceous)	Utah (Triassic)	Oklahoma (Mississippian)	Alberta (Devonian)	Ontario (Silurian)	Oklahoma (Ordovician)	Michigan (Precambrian)
C_4 paraffins	—	—	—	—	0.10	3.77	6.43	0.03	33.78	0.15	11.44	1.05	0.42
C_5 paraffins	—	—	—	—	0.14	4.60	9.46	0.11	46.01	0.35	7.38	0.67	0.17
Cyclo C_6	—	—	—	—	0.38	5.33	20.84	0.29	46.82	0.89	2.86	0.92	0.07
C_6 paraffins	—	—	—	—	0.22	4.33	7.96	0.11	31.11	1.07	5.02	0.56	0.13
Cyclo C_7	—	—	—	—	0.44	2.19	4.23	0.31	23.01	1.70	1.83	0.24	0.11
C_7 paraffins	—	—	—	—	0.60	2.87	6.19	0.12	19.01	1.68	3.19	0.20	0.02
C_8 paraffins	—	—	—	—	0.44	2.54	6.43	0.79	15.45	2.80	2.86	0.24	0.27
Total	—	—	—	—	2.32	25.63	61.54	1.76	215.19	8.64	34.58	3.88	1.19
Total organic matter in rock in weight %	3.4	1.2	2.9	1.8	1.77	2.2	1.99	0.02	7.2	0.16	0.61	0.12	0.95

sections (porphyrins and chlorophyll, isoprenoid hydrocarbons and phytol). An important question to answer is that of the similarity of current biochemistry with past biochemistry, which is the basic assumption one has to make when using the chemical analysis of today's organisms and sediments to evaluate the nature of the organic material deposited throughout geologic times. ABELSON (1959, 1963), ABELSON and HOERING (1961) and ABELSON and PARKER (1962) have provided convincing evidence for the suggestion that the basic biochemistry of today is practically identical with that of Cambrian time. Such evidence includes the similarity of porphyrins from different ages, as well as carbon isotope work showing that the biochemical steps employed in carbon fixation and lipid synthesis have remained virtually unchanged since before Cambrian time.

Hydrocarbons themselves are widely distributed, although in minor amounts, in living flora and fauna of all types. Recognizing their importance, WHITMORE (1943) proposed that such biogenic hydrocarbons constitute a quantitatively important fraction of the total accumulated petroleum. This hypothesis was at first rejected on the assumption that bacterial attack destroys biogenically produced hydrocarbons shortly after they are incorporated into sediments with the remains of organisms. Whitmore's hypothesis was again brought to light when SMITH (1954) reported the isolation of hydrocarbons, which ^{14}C analysis showed to be of recent origin, in a variety of Recent sediments. MEINSCHEIN subsequently (1959) proposed that petroleum can be explained as being simply the accumulation of hydrocarbons already present in Recent sediments, without the need for a chemical conversion of organic matter into petroleum with time and depth of burial. A somewhat similar hypothesis was advanced by the Soviet hydrogeologists, AL'TOVSKII et al. (1958). However, it was soon realized that crude oils contain substances that are neither present in living organisms nor formed in Recent sediments. For example, ERDMAN et al. (1958) have shown that aromatic hydrocarbons, from benzene through the xylenes, are not present in Recent sediments. DUNTON and HUNT (1962), ERDMAN (1962), KVENVOLDEN (1962), also reported the absence of some light hydrocarbons in Recent sediments. DUNTON and HUNT (1962) compared the quantity of the light hydrocarbons in typical Recent and ancient sediments to see if the results would indicate that light hydrocarbons form with time and depth of burial. Their results, reported in Table III, indicate that no hydrocarbons in the C_4–C_8 range were present in all Recent sediments analyzed, while they were present in crude oils from reservoirs of ages ranging from Precambrian to Tertiary. Furthermore, the results showed that the total concentration of such light hydrocarbons was roughly proportional to the amount of organic matter in the rock samples, which led to the suggestion that some of the hydrocarbons actually present were formed from the organic matter by long-term chemical processes.

Many different substances have been regarded as possible sources for petroleum. The great majority of the organic compounds in living plants and animals can be considered as belonging to any of the following classes: carbohydrates, proteins, lignins and lipids.

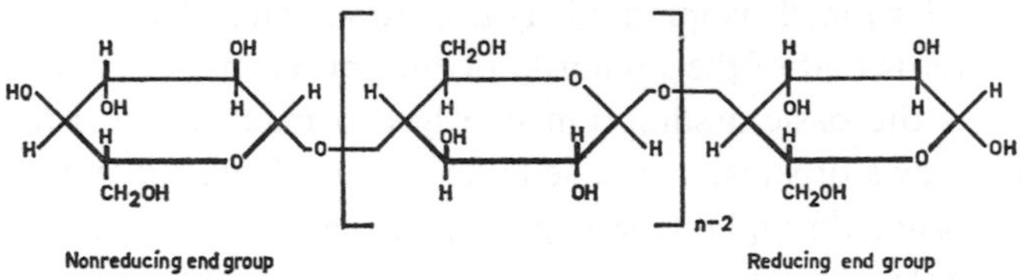

Fig.5. Structure of cellulose.

The carbohydrates are mainly pentoses and hexoses. The structure of cellulose, composed of six-carbon monosaccharides, is shown in Fig.5. In order to convert a substance of this type into hydrocarbons, one should visualize a thorough reduction with elimination of all hydroxyl groups, plus the breaking of the ether linkages and further reduction. This complex sequence of chemical reactions is believed to be most difficult to achieve under sedimentary conditions. This opinion, on the other hand, is not shared by some organic chemists including GILLET (1959), who suggested a purely hypothetical mechanism through which, by reduction and dismutation or hydroxyl exchange, cellulose would be converted into hydrocarbons. However, it is well known that the simpler water-soluble carbohydrates form an ideal substrate for bacteria and are easily destroyed by microorganisms with formation primarily of carbon dioxide and water. Moreover in swamp environments, where carbohydrates are initially quite abundant, there is a tendency for the formation of coal-like materials rather than of petroleum.

The structure of a typical protein molecule is shown in Fig.6. Proteins are macro-molecules derived from aminoacids connected by peptide bonds. They can be easily hydrolyzed by alkali or acid to yield smaller water-soluble products, which in turn are readily destroyed by microorganisms. Proteolytic processes as a rule convert proteinaceous matter into simple products such as carbon dioxide, water, ammonia, nitrogen and hydrogen sulphide. Therefore, it can be said that, in general, proteins and carbohydrates should not be considered important progenitors of petroleum. This does not mean, however, that such biological compounds are completely extraneous to the origin of petroleum. On the contrary, it should be mentioned that J. G. Erdman (personal communication, 1963) has suggested, on the basis of experimental work carried out in his laboratories by Stephan, that when soluble sugars and amino acids come in contact under conditions existing

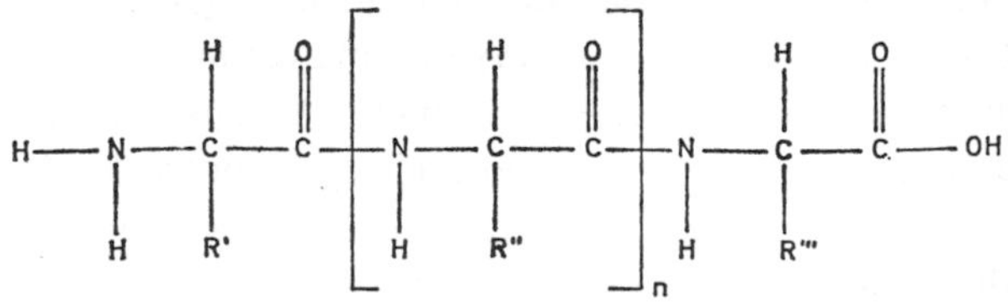

Fig.6. Schematic structure of a protein.

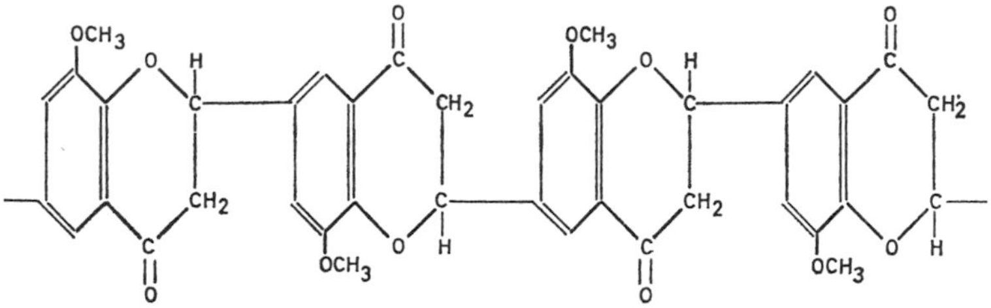

Fig.7. Schematic formula of lignin. (After RUSSELL, 1948.)

in sediments, they could react according to the Maillard reaction followed by an Amadori-type rearrangement and decarboxylation. The final products observed by Erdman and Stephan were the so called "dark polymers", which are normally considered to be part of the "resin" fraction of crude oils.

Lignin, which forms the cell wall structure of plants, can be considered to be an aromatic substance, derivative of phenylpropane (see Fig.7). In sediments lignin is often found associated as a complex with protein and carbohydrate molecules. The degradation of lignin structures under sedimentary conditions, as pointed out by BREGER (1960), kerogen is a more likely product than petroleum.

Lipids, from both plants and animals, are composed mainly of the ether-, benzene-, or chloroform-soluble oils, fats and waxes. Chemically, oils and fats are esters of fatty acids and glycerol, while waxes are composed of esters of fatty acids and alcohols, as well as of unesterified alcohols. The unsaponifiable lipids contain a mixture of steroids, isoprenoids and other hydrocarbons. The formulas of several different types of components of the lipid fraction are shown in Fig.8. As pointed out by MEINSCHEIN (1959), all these lipid components are structurally similar to naturally occurring hydrocarbons.

Fatty acids are derived biologically from carbohydrates and amino acids via a two-carbon radical mechanism that gives rise to even-numbered carbon chains. There is, therefore, a marked predominance of even carbon-numbered fatty acids

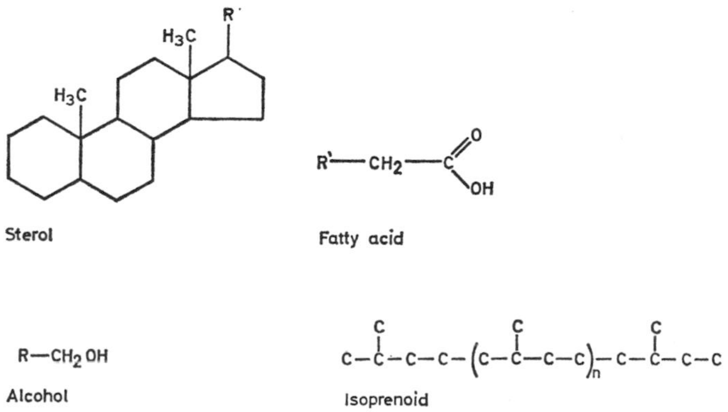

Sterol

Fatty acid

R—CH$_2$OH

Alcohol

Isoprenoid

Fig.8. Examples of several lipids.

in lipids. The acids with 14, 16, 18 and 20 carbon atoms per molecule are, in effect, particularly abundant. Simple decarboxylation of such acids to form straight-chain hydrocarbons would yield large amounts of products with 13, 15, 17 and 19 carbon atoms. Yet, in petroleum, particularly in the larger molecules, such a great predominance of odd-carbon numbered hydrocarbons is not found, and, contrarily, hydrocarbons with 7, 8, 9 or 10 carbon atoms, which should be present

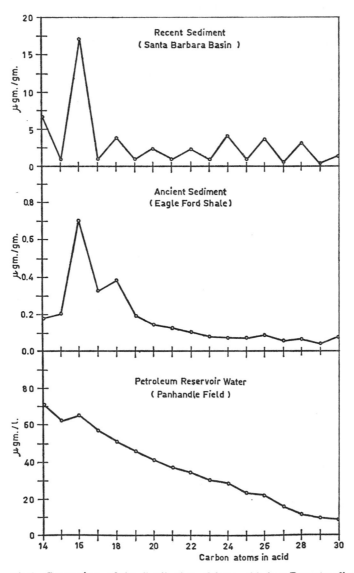

Fig.9. Comparison of the distribution of fatty acids in a Recent sediment, an ancient sediment, and in water from a petroleum reservoir. (After COOPER, 1962.)

in relatively low amounts if they were formed by simple decarboxylation of the corresponding fatty acids, are quite abundant.

To date, there is no definite evidence for the direct biochemical decarboxylation of fatty acids to yield hydrocarbons. This decarboxylation, which seems very likely in naphthogenesis, is, therefore, believed to occur through a non-biochemical process, perhaps of thermal or catalytic nature. In order to give the similarity of odd and even carbon numbers noted in crude oils, simple decarboxylation is not adequate, and one must invoke also the breakage of C–C bonds. COOPER (1962) has shown that the distribution of fatty acids in sediments varies according to the age of deposition (see Fig.9), and that the relative abundance of odd-numbered acids increases in going from Recent sediments to ancient sediments and from these to the formation waters of petroleum reservoirs. COOPER and BRAY (1963) offered a possible explanation of this change in distribution, showing that each fatty acid in sediments can lose carbon dioxide to form an intermediate radical which may react to give two products, an *n*-paraffin and a fatty acid, each of these products containing one carbon atom less than the original acid. The new acid produced would undergo the same reaction to form a new paraffin and a new acid. Such a process would continue in the sediment until, for all practical purposes, there is no preference between even- or odd-carbon numbered paraffins or acids. The scheme of the reaction mechanism for the decarboxylation of fatty acids, as proposed by Cooper and Bray, is shown in Fig.10.

$$RCH_2 \overset{\overset{\displaystyle O}{\|}}{C}-OH \longrightarrow RCH_2^{\bullet} + CO_2 + H^{\bullet} \quad (1)$$

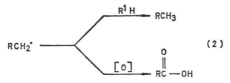

$$RCH_2^{\bullet} \begin{cases} \xrightarrow{R^1 H} RCH_3 \\ \xrightarrow{[O]} RC \overset{\overset{\displaystyle O}{\|}}{}-OH \end{cases} \quad (2)$$

Fig.10. Mechanism suggested by COOPER and BRAY (1963) for the decarboxylation of fatty acids. The radical formed in reaction 1 would undergo reaction with a donor of hydrogen atoms to form a paraffin, and with an oxidizing reagent to form a fatty acid with one carbon atom less than the original acid.

Fatty acids have been suggested as sources, not only of aliphatic hydrocarbons, but also of cyclic hydrocarbons. BREGER (1960) has proposed that cyclic structures of both naphthenic and aromatic type could be originated from the partially unsaturated ring compounds resulting from Diels–Alder reaction, by hydrogenation and dehydrogenation processes which both may occur in sediments (Fig.11).

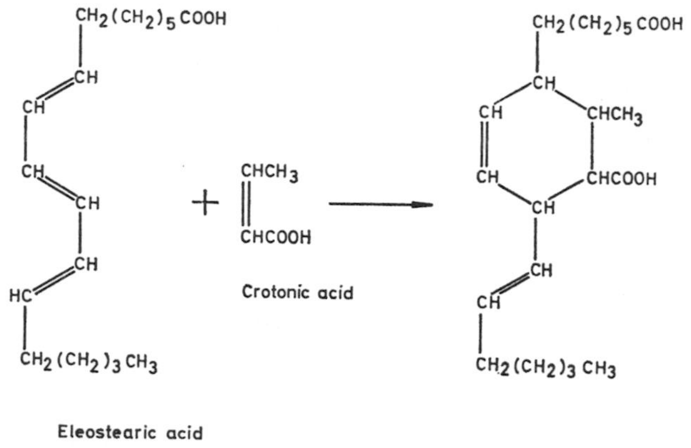

CH$_2$(CH$_2$)$_5$COOH

CH

CH

CH

CH

CH

HC

CH$_2$(CH$_2$)$_3$CH$_3$

Eleostearic acid

+

CHCH$_3$

CHCOOH

Crotonic acid

⟶

CH$_2$(CH$_2$)$_5$COOH

CH

CH   CHCH$_3$

CH   CHCOOH

CH

CH

CH

CH$_2$(CH$_2$)$_3$CH$_3$

Fig.11. Example of a Diels–Alder reaction showing one of several possible products obtainable from eleostearic and crotonic acids. (After BREGER, 1960.)

Summing up, it may be stated that lipids are probably the most important contributors to the formation of petroleum. The various possibilities of interaction of the different saturated and unsaturated compounds in this class could lead to a very complex mixture of open-chain and cyclic hydrocarbons. For this reason, sapropels (the organic sediments formed, as the products of putrification, in water free from oxygen), and more specifically plankton, which is known to be very rich in lipids, have been suggested by many authors, including KREJCI-GRAF (1963) as the most likely parent substances of petroleum.

Several different energy sources have been considered for the generation of hydrocarbons. Bacterial activity was first suggested by CUNNINGHAM-CRAIG (1914, 1923) and later investigated by ZOBELL (1943, 1945) and KUZNETSOV (1950). Radioactivity was proposed by LIND and BARDWELL (1926) and later by SOKOLOV (1937) and TIRATSOO (1941); its limitations were pointed out by SHEPPARD and WHITEHEAD (1946), BREGER and WHITEHEAD (1951), and lately by COLOMBO et al. (1964a). Catalytic activity by clay minerals was suggested by various investigators and mainly supported by the work of BROOKS (1948, 1949, 1952, 1959). Thermal processes were invoked as early as in 1888 by ENGLER and reproposed by SEYER (1933), BARTON (1934), MCNAB et al. (1952), ABELSON (1963).

THE "SOURCE BED" AND "SOURCE ROCK" CONCEPTS

The "source bed" concept has been used extensively, by geologists and geochemists, during the past one hundred years, as a working hypothesis. This concept was introduced by A. Winchell (AMERICAN GEOLOGICAL INSTITUTE, 1960 p.274) as early as 1865, and later refined by many others.

The use of this concept arises from the belief that petroleum, in general, is not indigenous to the reservoir rock where it is found, but must have migrated into the reservoir from other beds where it was formed. It is, therefore, assumed that in each sedimentary basin there are some beds which either have yielded or will yield petroleum, while other beds have not in the past and never will yield petroleum. The geologic formations in which oil or gas are generated are named "source rocks" of petroleum.

The organic content of a sedimentary rock, according to the supporters of the "source rock" concept, is not directly related to the rock's ability to serve as a source of petroleum. However, it is recognized that source rocks should contain a relatively large amount of residual organic matter, including the oil which has not been expelled, the by-products of its formation and, perhaps, substantially un-altered organic matter. In this picture of source rocks it is implied that the trans-formation of the organic matter into a sort of petroleum takes place within the source rock itself, and that subsequently this petroleum migrates as such from the source to the reservoir where it is eventually found. In other words, migration is pictured here as a step in the formation of petroleum deposits, completely distinct, as far as time is concerned, from the preceding step of naphthogenesis.

This idea has led petroleum geologists and geochemists to conclude that the identification of source rocks within a sedimentary basin is of paramount im-portance for the exploration of petroleum in a basin. The belief was that once the source rocks were found, it would be much easier to reconstruct the paths of migration and thereby locate the traps where oil has accumulated. In 1928, the Romanian geologist Macovei (quoted in LOUIS, 1965) stated that "the question to be posed when one tries to understand the formation of oil deposits is that of source rocks. Only when the source rocks have been identified beyond doubt, is solution of the basic problem approached". Although not explicitly stated, it is implied here that source rocks of petroleum are rather peculiar sediments, restricted to limited areas, otherwise their identification would not be so important.

The important works by TRASK (1932) and TRASK and PATNODE (1942) led to the availability of extremely valuable information on the physical and chemical properties of a great number of sediments of various ages. The attempts of Trask to find some unequivocal indices for characterizing source beds of petroleum were not very successful, although there was an indication that the reducing power of sediments, and more specifically the ratio between the residual nitrogen content and the reducing power (determined by the chromic acid tech-nique), differed between hypothetical source beds and non-source beds. The intro-duction of nitrogen as a criterion for the recognition of source rocks was questioned by LOUIS (1965), who found that certain diatomites and limestones, which allegedly are source rocks of petroleum, being characterized by a high nitrogen content, would not, according to Trask, present a favorable source rock index.

KHALIFEH and LOUIS (1961), on the basis of a statistical study on the oxi-dation of the organic matter in sedimentary rocks under mild laboratory con-

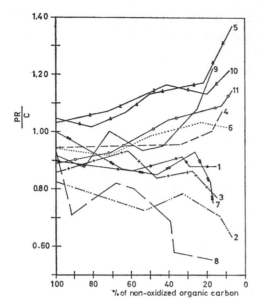

Fig.12. Partial oxidation curves used to identify source rocks of petroleum. Curves *1* and *2* were obtained with Recent sediments, curves *6, 7, 8* with probable non-source rocks, curves *4, 5, 6, 9, 10, 11* with alleged source rocks. (After KHALIFEH and LOUIS, 1961.)

ditions, proposed the use, for the identification of source rocks, of the ratio of reducing power (PR) to total carbon (C). By plotting this ratio against the amount of non-oxidized organic carbon for consecutive partial oxidation stages, they found that alleged source rocks are characterized by ascending curves, and Recent sediments by more or less horizontal lines. Probable non-source rocks, instead, give rise to descending curves (Fig.12). The same authors, however, concluded that, in spite of the significance of their work, there was no reliable way of identifying beyond doubt the source character of sedimentary rocks.

According to PHILIPPI (1957), the source quality of a given sedimentary rock can be established on the basis of the amount of residual hydrocarbons generated per unit weight of dry rock. It is, however, very difficult to prove that the "residual" hydrocarbons in a rock are actually indigenous to the rock itself, and did not migrate there, at least in part, some time after the deposition of the sediments.

BRENNEMAN and SMITH (1958) reported the results of a comparative geochemical study of crude oils and organic extracts from their alleged source-rocks. The most significant conclusion of this geochemical work was that no unique property was found that linked all the crude oil-source rock pairs examined.

Recently an effort was made by BREGER and BROWN (1962, 1963) to differentiate the types of organic matter of which the kerogen in the Chattanooga Shale is composed. They reported that, although the Chattanooga Shale has all the attributes of a source bed, it has produced no oil because the organic matter is related to coal derived from terrestrial sources. It was concluded that organic matter of aquatic origin is necessary for the generation of oil.

BRAY and EVANS (1965) pointed out that the problem of the search for source beds of petroleum is complicated by the great variability of organic material in sediments, and stressed the importance of the collaboration between geologists and geochemists for the organization and guidance of sampling programs. They found that the carbon preference index (C.P.I.), defined as the ratio of odd-carbon to even-carbon numbered n-paraffins in the samples, could be assumed to be an indication of the capacity of the rocks to generate petroleum. Such C.P.I. values were found to vary inversely with the proportion of hydrocarbons in the organic material of shales and mudstones and, therefore, they were believed to be indicative of the conversion of organic material into hydrocarbons (Fig.13).

HEDBERG (1964), recognizing the difficulty in establishing the source quality of sedimentary rocks, concluded that one of the most reliable means of identifying good source rocks in a general way is through a study of the geologic association of specific rocks with specific petroleum accumulations. He agreed that source rocks, which are specifically and rather definitely identifiable on geologic grounds, may be not too common, but that where such evidence is strong, they do furnish a basis for study, which may yield clues of value in investigating more doubtful source candidates.

COLOMBO (1965), in a critical evaluation of the source rock concept, attributed to the term "source rock" a substantially quantitative value, therefore recognizing that it is practically impossible to draw a definite borderline between hypothetical

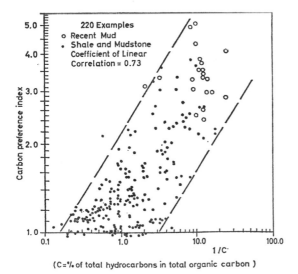

(C = % of total hydrocarbons in total organic carbon)

Fig.13. Positive relation between carbon preference index (C.P.I.) and reciprocal concentration of hydrocarbons. (After BRAY and EVANS, 1965.)

source rocks and non-source rocks. This is equivalent to recognizing that all sedimentary rocks may, in effect, have contributed to a greater or smaller extent
in the generation of hydrocarbons which eventually will be accumulated in a
reservoir. HODGSON and HITCHON (1965), after pointing out that "an almost
magic character" has been attributed to source beds, concluded that the "source
sediment" and "source rock" terminology has led to unnecessary limitations which
seriously restrict objective considerations of the genesis of petroleum. They suggested, therefore, that the term "source" should be referred to the processes through
which hydrocarbons are generated, rather than to a specific connotation of
locality.

THE GEOCHEMICAL EVOLUTION OF PETROLEUM

The idea of an "evolution" of petroleum is practically as old as that of source
rocks. Geologists during the last century tried to interpret the chemical and
physical differences among crude oils in terms of the more general concept of
regional metamorphism. Reiterating in a broader aspect an older hypothesis by
ROGERS (1860), WHITE proposed his famous carbon-ratio theory in 1915, based on
the statistical rule that in any area where oils and coals are both present, the
specific gravity of the oils varies inversely with the ratio of fixed carbon to total
carbon in related coals. Since this "carbon ratio" was known to increase with
temperature, as a result of the elimination of volatile constituents from coals, it
was logical to assume that metamorphism does play an important role in the
natural transformation of petroleum. Later studies showed that the validity of the
carbon-ratio theory was substantially qualitative, and that the carbon-ratio value
could be used as an index of the local metamorphic intensity, which in turn is of
help in predicting the likelihood of finding commercial accumulations of petroleum (THOM, 1934).

A clear reference to the evolution of petroleum after its accumulation in the
reservoirs was made by BARTON (1934) in his famous paper on the natural history
of the Gulf Coast crude oil. Barton had noticed that in the Gulf Coast, as well as
in other petroliferous regions, deeper and more ancient reservoirs hold, as a rule,
lighter and more paraffinic crudes than do younger and shallower reservoirs. This
is, in essence, the statement of a "depth rule", which had earlier been hypothesized
by some European geologists and geochemists (HÖFER, 1922; KREJCI-GRAF, 1929,
1930a, b, 1932), and of a somewhat similar "age rule". BARTON (1934) postulated
that all crude oils start, in the reservoir, as heavy bitumen-like petroleums, which
slowly evolve with the concurring effects of temperature, pressure and catalysis,
through progressively lighter and more paraffinic oils, to the volatile end-members
of the paraffinic series, and eventually to methane, which he considered as the
final product of this natural process.

Since the publication of the paper by Barton, the "depth rule" has been shown to apply to many oil provinces of the world, which favored the general acceptance of the evolutionary hypothesis proposed by Barton. However, there have been reports on notable exceptions to this rule, even in such important petroliferous regions as Kuwait, the Apsheron peninsula, and Moldavia, and it has been suggested by K. Krejci-Graf (personal communication, 1964) that while the rule applies to naphthenic and asphaltic oils, it should not be used with paraffinic oils, the gravity of which tends to increase "*coeteris paribus*" with depth.

The above considerations are in substantial agreement with the conclusion of ROOF (1959), based essentially on theoretical evidence, that no generally valid relationship between oil character and reservoir depth is likely to be possible.

The validity of the "age rule", on the basis of available statistical data, seems to be quite questionable.

An important contribution to the problem of the evolution of petroleum was given by McNAB et al. (1952), who considered in their study several hundred crude oils from the United States and Venezuela. These authors concluded that the origin and evolution of petroleum embodies three distinct steps or phases:

(*1*) Accumulation of organic matter in marine or brackish water sediments.

(*2*) Transformation of the organic matter, or of part of it, to a heavy, bitumen-like material or embryonic petroleum.

(*3*) Maturing of the primary petroleum.

The first and second steps cover the process up to the genesis of petroleum in the source rock environment, where the transformation of a fraction of the organic matter into petroleum is assumed to take place by cracking or depoly-merization-type chemical reactions.

Between steps *2* and *3*, the heavy bituminous oil originally formed must migrate to favorable reservoir positions where it will undergo progressive evolution during geologic time under the influence of moderate temperature and pressure, as well as of catalysis.

According to McNAB et al. (1952), an indirect confirmation that petroleum does evolve even after its accumulation in the reservoir lies in the fact that appreciable quantities of oxygen- and of nitrogen-containing molecules are present in the oils found in younger sedimentary formations, while oils found in older formations contain lower amounts of such non-hydrocarbon components. This might well indicate a genetic relationship between the younger oils and the original organic source materials rich in oxygen- and nitrogen-bearing compounds.

The relationship existing between the A.P.I. gravities of American crude oils and the depths of their reservoirs, based on the data by McNab et al., is illustrated in Fig.14. It is evident that the producing depth, which reflects somehow the temperature to which the crude oils have been exposed, is statistically important in relation with the gravity of the oils. A similar diagram, illustrating the effect

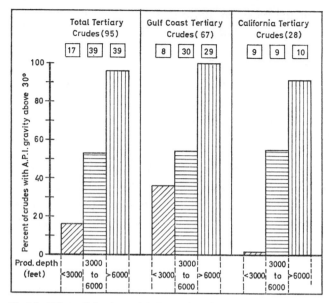

Fig.14. Effect of depth on A.P.I. gravity of American crude oils. (After McNab et al., 1952.)

of the age of the producing horizons on gravity, is presented in Fig.15, where the percentages of crude oils lighter and heavier than 30° A.P.I. are shown for petroleum of the three major geologic eras. The significance of this relationship is that, the degree of evolution for a given oil being necessarily a function of time, the direction of the metamorphic evolution must be from the heavier to the lighter oils. This is corroborated by thermodynamic considerations, since the values of the

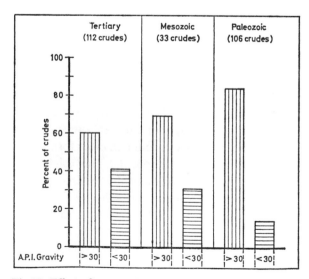

Fig.15. Effect of age on A.P.I. gravity of American crude oils. (After McNab et al., 1952.)

free energies of formation for all classes of hydrocarbons decrease going from higher to lower molecular weight compounds, the end-members being the lightest paraffins, which are characterized by negative values of their free energy of formation.

The work of McNab et al., besides confirming the evolutionary hypothesis previously proposed by BARTON (1934), has added quantitative data that indicated that a combination of thermal and catalytic reactions might account for the evolution of petroleum in the reservoirs. By experimental measurements, the above-mentioned authors have determined the value of the activation energy for thermal cracking for the "young" McMurray oil from the Athabaska tar deposit. Such value is in the order of 49,000 cal./mole, therefore showing that the thermal cracking of this oil would occur more easily than for an average gas oil, which has an activation energy of about 58,000 cal./mole. These results indicated that, over a geologic time of several hundred million years, this crude oil would be completely metamorphosed at 250°F by thermal cracking. This temperature might be lower with the concurrent effect of catalysis by suitable minerals.

These conclusions are in substantial agreement with those reached by KARTSEV (1964), who attributes the differences found in the hydrocarbon-type composition among crude oils of different ages from many petroliferous regions of the world to a thermo-catalytic metamorphism. The results of this metamorphism are shown in Fig.16, which indicates an overall shift towards paraffinic structures going from the younger to the older petroleums.

In laboratory experiments at relatively low pressures, Kartsev observed, among other reactions, the following processes: decarboxylation of fatty acids, decyclization of naphthenes, and formation of straight-chain paraffins from branched paraffins. The net result was the formation of light ends or, the equivalent, an increase in A.P.I. gravity.

This thermo-catalytic metamorphism is, according to Kartsev, the primary

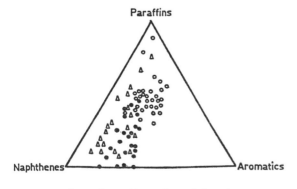

Fig.16. Hydrocarbon composition of crude oils. (After KARTSEV, 1964.)

evolutionary process, the effects of which are, however, sometimes masked by secondary alteration reactions such as oxidation and sulfurization. Therefore, a given oil may be highly metamorphosed and also have a high sulfur content, thereby resulting in a much heavier and more cyclic product than would be obtained in the absence of the secondary alteration process.

The effects of different alteration agents, such as oxygen, sulfur and bacteria, have been investigated by LOUIS (1956), LOUIS and BIENNER (1953, 1959) and LOUIS et al. (1955). As an example of secondary sulfurization processes in crude oil, the triangular diagram of Fig.17, which illustrates the changes in petroleum composition brought about by sulfurization, is presented (M. Louis, personal communication, 1963). Another important alteration agent is radioactivity. This was recently investigated by COLOMBO et al. (1964a). These authors found that the action of ionizing radiations on crude oils leads to the production of resinous and asphaltic components, together with gaseous hydrocarbons.

A detailed scheme of petroleum evolution, in the same general framework as that suggested by Kartsev, has been proposed by DOBRYANSKY (1961). Such an evolutionary process is illustrated in Fig.18. The consecutive phases of evolution are presented along the ordinate, proceeding downward. To each of such phases corresponds a typical representative product. The chemical composition of each product can be read on the abscissa by summing up the contribution of each class of compounds. Dobryansky believes that the evolution of petroleum is essentially a bi-directional process, and indicates in a combination of reactions of condensa-

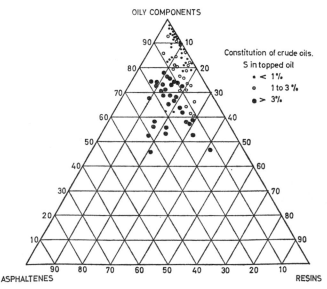

Fig.17. Evidence of secondary sulfurization in petroleum. Note that the more altered crudes (i.e., those which contain greater proportions of resins and asphaltenes) are characterized by higher sulfur contents. (Data from M. Louis.)

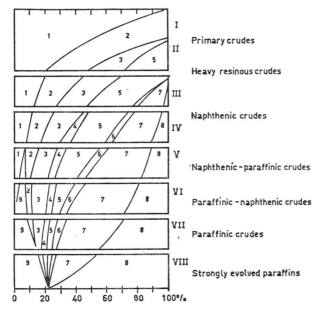

Primary crudes

Heavy resinous crudes

Naphthenic crudes

Naphthenic - paraffinic crudes

Paraffinic - naphthenic crudes

Paraffinic crudes

Strongly evolved paraffins

1) Originary hetero-atomic substances
2) Primary resins
3) Complex naphthenic -aromatic hydro carbons
4) Aromatic hydrocarbons
5) Heavier naphthenic hydrocarbons

6) Lighter naphthenic hydrocarbons
7) Heavier paraffinic hydrocarbons
8) Lighter paraffinic hydrocarbons
    (gas)
9) Secondary resinous substances
    (by - product).

Fig.18. Scheme of petroleum evolution. (After DOBRYANSKY, 1961.)

tion and molecular degradation the mechanism by which this evolution occurs.

The chemical evolution, after the accumulation of petroleum in the reservoirs, has sometimes been referred to as a "maturation" process. This is the case of McIVER's (1963) scheme presented in Fig.19. This picture is in substantial agreement with the ideas of Dobryansky, but the extreme positions of the process (methane and elementary carbon) are more clearly indicated.

HAEBERLE (1951) showed that the character of crude oils is not determined exclusively by their degree of evolution. He stressed the importance of the environment of deposition of source beds for the differentiation of the properties of Gulf Coast crudes. HUNT (1953) in a thorough study of crude oils from Wyoming, concluded that the major differences were dependent rather on source material and environment of deposition than on a possible evolution after accumulation. The more naphthenic and aromatic crudes were associated with the more saline environments of deposition, characterized by carbonates and sulfates rather than by sandstones and shales. For oils formed in clastic sediments, the more aromatic and naphthenic oils were associated with higher sand/shale ratios, or with the near-shore basin position.

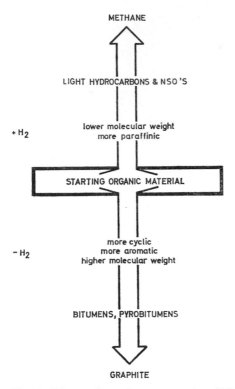

Fig.19. Scheme of petroleum maturation. (After McIVER, 1963.)

If it is assumed that differences in the environment of deposition may affect the chemistry of the formation of oil, it may be difficult to demonstrate that the oils now found have undergone metamorphic changes. Yet, there are some rather conclusive factors which confirm the occurrence of a metamorphic transformation of petroleum. One of these factors is the relative similarity of composition between virgin naphtha and thermally cracked naphtha, as shown by MARTIN et al. (1963b). While catalytic and hydrocracked naphthas were found to contain more branched than normal paraffins, both virgin and thermal naphthas contain large proportions of the normal paraffins. Other similarities of composition were found in the alkylbenzenes and in other components of such naphthas. Such similarities suggest that thermal cracking, rather than catalytic or hydrocracking, is the dominant process in the formation of the naphtha fraction of petroleum.

Another consideration in favor of a metamorphic evolution of petroleum is given by the results of the isotopic work by SILVERMAN (1964) who determined the $^{13}C/^{12}C$ ratio on a crude oil from the Murphy Coyote field in California, as well as from its distillation fractions. The results obtained by Silverman are shown in Fig.20, where the $^{13}C/^{12}C$ ratios are plotted against the boiling temperatures of the fractions. The isotopic ratio is lowest for methane and highest for the

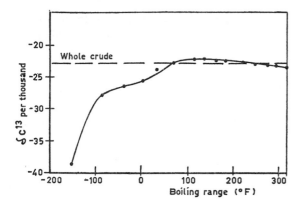

Fig.20. Carbon isotope ratios of petroleum and gas fractions. (Data from SILVERMAN, 1964a.)

fraction with boiling point around 230 °F. Silverman has explained this difference in the isotopic distribution by assuming that in the maturation of petroleum the lowest molecular weight hydrocarbons are formed by the decomposition of higher molecular weight components. If such lighter components are enriched in ^{12}C, then the residue which is left behind must be enriched in ^{13}C. This is illustrated by the scheme of Fig.21. As a matter of fact, data acquired in the thermal decomposition of simple organic compounds have indicated that the ^{12}C–^{12}C bonds are ruptured ca. 8 % more frequently than the ^{13}C–^{12}C bonds (STEVENSON et al., 1948; BRODSKII et al., 1959). This explains why the methane resulting from the maturation of petroleum is richer in the ^{12}C isotope. Furthermore, since the molecule which is left behind is necessarily less hydrogenated than the starting molecule, unsaturated products are formed, which will eventually lead to aromatics and to secondary asphalts through polymerization or condensation. Both these fractions of petroleum, as found by SILVERMAN and EPSTEIN (1958), have a remarkably high ^{13}C content.

At this point, it can be concluded that there is sufficient evidence for the

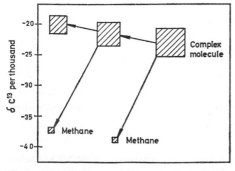

Fig.21. Petroleum maturation reactions. (Data from SILVERMAN, 1964a.)

existence of a thermal, and to a lesser degree of a catalytic transformation of petroleum. The mechanism of this evolutionary transformation is a combination of reactions of molecular degradation and condensation, the end-products of which are methane and carbon. It should also be recognized that differences in the environment of deposition of source sediments may result in chemical differences of the original oils. Furthermore, secondary alteration processes may overlap with the primary evolutionary process, thus giving rise to apparently abnormal trends.

MIGRATION AND ACCUMULATION

Of all phases of the geochemical history of petroleum, migration is probably the least understood, and the one on which geologists and geochemists are still much divided.

In recent years, many different ideas and mechanisms have been proposed, and the whole subject of migration is presently being investigated also with experimental laboratory work on simplified models and less complicated chemical systems.

In Chapter 7 of this volume some of the newer ideas have been thoroughly discussed, and a proposed mechanism of migration has been dealt with in a comprehensive way. In this section a short summary of pertinent ideas on the migration of petroleum will be presented, with no intention, however, to give a complete picture of the subject.

HOBSON (1954) has pointed out the main features which support the general belief that a phase of migration is an essential part of the process of forming a petroleum accumulation. They are: (a) The arrangement of gas, oil and water in the order of their densities; (b) the normal occurrence of the oil and gas in what is locally the highest accessible part of the reservoir rock; (c) the allegedly low concentration of newly formed oil or gas in the source rocks; (d) the fact that many reservoir rocks are considered to be improbable or impossible source rocks of petroleum.

Although in principle this distinction may not be necessary, yet for the purpose of discussion, migration can be considered as a two-step process, involving: (1) *primary migration* (the transfer of petroleum from the source to the reservoir rock); (2) *secondary migration* (the segregation of oil and gas within the reservoir rock, and their implacement in the highest available position).

Primary migration is the least understood, because it requires rather clear views on the genesis and on the time of formation of petroleum. It also involves a precise evaluation of the significance of source rocks, and a basic understanding of multi-component fluid flow during compaction of sediments and through their early lithification stage.

Some geologists (HOBSON, 1954; ROOF and RUTHERFORD, 1958; SILVERMAN, 1964b) assume, as a basis for their migration models, that oil is formed as discrete liquid globules within the source sediments, and that migration of petroleum takes place by movement of a separate oil phase through the pores of water-wet mineral particles. Other scientists (E. G. BAKER, 1956, 1959, 1960, 1962; AL'TOVSKII et al., 1958; MEINSCHEIN, 1959, 1961, 1965; ROBERTS, 1960) assume that petroleum migrates in a much more intimately disseminated state, either as a molecular solution or as a micellar dispersion within the water medium. This latter view-point has been clearly presented in Chapter 7 of this volume.

The migration of oil as discrete globules through a water-saturated medium has been criticized by DVALI (1962). HILL (1959) has pointed out that relatively high saturation of hydrocarbons (i.e., 15–25% of pore volume) must exist to create the continuity of the oil phase necessary for migration by this mechanism. The relatively low residual hydrocarbon saturations observed in many shales that are considered as probable source beds suggest that this mechanism is not respon-sible for primary migration. The same author has suggested that the residual organic matter in shales might be the vehicle for the migration of hydrocarbons. If the volume of residual organic matter is referred to the pore volume, it can be seen that, when the shale porosity reaches values as low as 15–20%, the fraction of such pore volume, which is actually occupied by the organic matter, is rather important. Eventually, according to Hill, this organic matter may form a continu-ous network through the water-wet shale. This network could then function as a wick for the expulsion of the hydrocarbons, which would therefore move along the surface of the organic matter with a mechanism somewhat similar to partition chromatography.

SILVERMAN (1964b) pointed out that secondary migration may involve the movement of a discrete petroleum phase through a system of essentially water-wet rocks. As proposed by NAGY (1960), it is logical to assume that this type of migration causes the selective removal of certain petroleum components by solubi-lization in water or by adsorption at the interface of the water film with mineral grains.

Systematic chemical variations in the oil composition within petroliferous areas were regarded by many investigators (BONHAM, 1956; HODGSON and BAKER, 1959; VAN EGGELPOEL, 1959, 1960; COLOMBO and SIRONI, 1961; D. R. BAKER, 1962; RIECKER, 1962; SOKOLOV et al., 1963) as clues of "chromatographic" effects in the course of petroleum migration. The effective possibility of chromatographic-type effects was shown by THOMPSON (1961) in laboratory experiments where petroleum was percolated through columns of dry and water-wet mineral sediments.

Chromatographic effects were believed to be responsible for carbon isotope fractionation in the methane from Italian natural gases (COLOMBO et al., 1964b, 1965). It was found that, as a rule, the $^{13}C/^{12}C$ ratio in methane decreases with increasing ratios of methane to total hydrocarbon in the gases (see Fig.22). Laboratory experiments showed small but nevertheless detectable carbon isotope fractionations occurring during the flow of methane through columns of

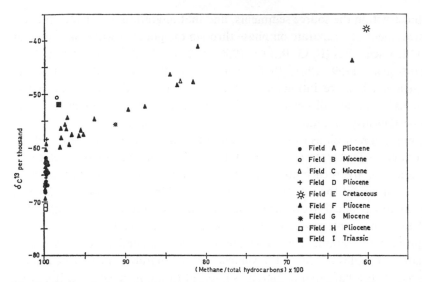

Fig.22. Carbon isotopic distribution of methane in Italian natural gases. Note that the methane of those gases which contain high amounts of ethane and higher hydrocarbons is enriched in the ^{13}C isotope (δ values referred to P.D.B. standard). (After COLOMBO et al., 1965.)

clay and carbonate sediments. These authors concluded that migration should be regarded as a complex process, which on one hand causes the segregation of each hydrocarbon component of the gas according to its mobility, and on the other hand gives rise, within each molecular species, to an isotopic fractionation, the extent of which depends on the molecular mass of the component itself.

SILVERMAN (1964a) has found, in the chemical and isotopic analysis of the crude oils from the Quiriquire field in Venezuela, some regular variations which suggest that migration took place in the updip direction of the basin. As expected for high molecular weight compounds, the $^{13}C/^{12}C$ ratios varied only very slightly from one crude oil to the other, while certain chemical properties, such as the sulphur and porphyrin concentrations, exhibited wider variations throughout the field.

In the same work, Silverman has pointed out that, in contrast to the relatively small chemical differences attributed to secondary migration of a whole petroleum, certain petroleums, produced from distinct horizons within a limited geographical area, are markedly different in chemical composition, in spite of the fact that other chemical characteristics of these oils suggest that they were derived from a common source. He suggested that such oils may have experienced physical separations of major petroleum fractions prior to or during the migration process. This mechanism has been named "separation–migration", to distinguish it from the typical secondary migration phenomenon, which gives rise only to minor chemical and physical changes. The "separation–migration" mechanism of Silverman requires the existence of two phases (liquid and vapor). If the original petroleum accumulation exists in a single-phase fluid state, then pressure reduction must first be experienced to convert the deposit into a two-phase system before the separation stage can occur. Such pressure reduction can take place as a result of faulting, or by an increase in the permeability of the cap-rock by erosional unloading. A schematic picture of the "separation–migration" model is presented in Fig.23.

Under fortunate conditions, detailed geochemical studies of oils may supply information on the history of migration and accumulation of hydrocarbons in a given basin. For example, GEDENK (1964) has concluded, on the basis of the hydrocarbon analysis of the gases in the Hardesse oil field of Germany, that the accumulation in the field took place through a dual migration mechanism. This hypothesis is based on the fact that some of the gases exhibit a remarkable anomaly in the ethane content, which was found to be much lower than expected (Fig.24). The suggestion was made that the reservoir, which contained initially a low gas/oil ratio crude, at a certain moment experienced a secondary gas influx.

An attempt to describe in a unitary way the complex processes which take place during migration and accumulation of petroleum was made by SOKOLOV et al. (1963). They have listed the following main types of migration of petroleum in sedimentary basins:

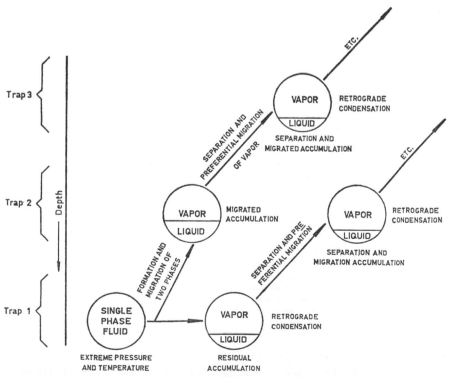

Fig.23. Scheme of the "separation–migration" model proposed by SILVERMAN (1964b).

(*1*) The filtration of gas and oil due to pressure differences within the inter-connected pores and fractures in rocks.

(*2*) The buoyancy of gas and oil in the water contained in porous and fractured rocks.

(*3*) The transfer of free and dissolved gas and oil by underground waters.

(*4*) The squeezing-out of gas and oil along with the water from sediments.

(*5*) The diffusion of gas and oil.

These authors regard each of the above mechanisms as being of particular importance in a given stage of the geochemical history of petroleum. For example, in the early stages of the diagenesis of sediments, the solution of liquid hydro-carbons in gaseous hydrocarbons, as well as the solution of both liquid and gaseous hydrocarbons in water, takes place. The water is then transferred to suitable reservoirs where both gaseous and liquid hydrocarbons are released by a decrease in pressure or by other mechanisms. Later on, the effect of buoyancy will enable gas and oil to accumulate in the highest accessible part of the beds. In this stage, such processes as the "differential entrapment" suggested by GUSSOW (1954) may take place.

The importance of diffusion of hydrocarbons has been clearly pointed out by Sokolov and his co-workers. Such diffusion is believed to give rise to the gas "anomalies" observed in surface layers above oil and gas pools, and is held responsible for the continuous dissipation of hydrocarbons from oil and gas deposits. The same authors measured the diffusion coefficients (D) of various sedimentary rocks, and found them to be in the range of 10^{-4}–10^{-9} cm^2/sec. When D is in the order of 10^{-6} cm^2/sec, the dissipation of gas pools by diffusion

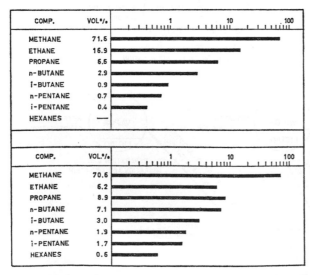

Fig.24. Hydrocarbon analysis of two liberated gases from the Hardesse oil field in Germany. Note the anomaly of the ethane content in the lower analysis. (After GEDENK, 1964.)

alone would be so great that, in order to explain the preservation of such pools throughout geologic times, it is required to assume that the gas lost is continuously being replaced by a gas influx from adjacent beds.

More recently, diffusion coefficients of hydrocarbons in water were determined experimentally by WITHERSPOON and SARAF (1964). They found that molecular size is the controlling factor of hydrocarbon diffusion.

The comprehensive model of migration proposed by Sokolov and his co-workers does actually include both "oil phase" and "solution" migrations. Concerning this latter type of migration, it should be recognized that, although a number of convincing mechanisms have been formulated by which hydrocarbons and other petroleum components can be entrained in the aqueous vehicle, there is up to now no entirely satisfactory explanation of how the large quantities of hydrocarbons that form important petroleum deposits are actually released from solution in the water. HOBSON (1961) has criticized in a general way the release mechanisms based on changes in pressure, temperature or in dilution. It seems probable that no single mechanism is responsible for the disassociation of the hydrocarbons from the water vehicle, but that, rather, several different mechanisms concur to give this overall effect. This very important problem can perhaps find clarification through carefully planned laboratory work.

The dynamic picture of the formation and preservation of oil deposits suggested by Sokolov is in essential agreement with the views of ROBERTS (1960, 1966). This author, mainly on the basis of hydrologic considerations, believes that the three classical requirements for having petroleum "traps", i.e., structure, reservoir and cover, define rather poorly the geometry only of the framework in which a trap for fluids may exist; indeed, also the fluid energy situation in and around the trap should be considered. The dynamic equilibrium representing a trap can be stable only in the position of minimum energy acting on fluids. According to ROBERTS (1966), the concept of a trap as a passive receiver and container of segregated fluid is not valid, nor is the idea of a trap being either completely open or shut. Indeed, most traps, when carefully observed, are partly open and partly shut. If a trap were shut, it is doubtful that displacement of water by petroleum could occur simply by gravity. On the other hand, if it were open, petroleum could not possibly remain entrapped. The physical and chemical differences among petroleums in the different traps of a petroliferous area, may, therefore, be assumed to be controlled principally by the ability of each trap to retain the more or less mobile individual components of petroleum. This is the essence of Robert's "trap competence" concept. The competence of the trap is a function of the physical and physico-chemical properties of the reservoir and surrounding rocks, of the hydrodynamic accessibility, and of the focusing power of the trap geometry in its geological framework.

The fact that, in general, deeper and older traps contain lighter and more paraffinic oils than do shallower and younger ones, may well be related, as the "transformationists" believe, to a progressive chemical metamorphism of crude oils within the traps; but could have an alternative explanation if one considers that older and deeper traps, owing to diagenesis and deeper burial, are in general more "competent", and therefore are capable of retaining the lighter and more mobile components of petroleum. In this picture of migration and accumulation of hydrocarbons, non-reservoir rocks are considered as membranes, which limit the transmissibility of fluids and are capable of causing, with more or less complex mechanisms, the physical and chemical differentiation of migrating fluids. Clays, which are colloidal electrolytes, are regarded as the principal membranes of sedimentary basins, excluding the basement and the atmosphere, which are considered the geometrical limits of the system.

It thus appears that together with the classical concept of "evolution of petroleum" one should consider also that of "evolution of petroleum assemblages", which latter reflects the ever changing conditions of entrapment in the geological and geochemical framework of the basin.

An interesting attempt to draw a geochemical cycle of hydrocarbons was recently made by HODGSON and HITCHON (1965). The schematic hydrocarbon cycle presented in Fig.25, is part of the major water cycle of the earth. The initial mobilization of hydrocarbons is accomplished by the waters, which may contain stabilizing agents such as natural surfactant molecules. Therefore, according to Hodgson and Hitchon and following E. G. BAKER's (1959, 1960, 1962) ideas, the amount of hydrocarbons that may actually be mobilized is, in general, largely independent of the amount of hydrocarbons available in the system, in the sense that an

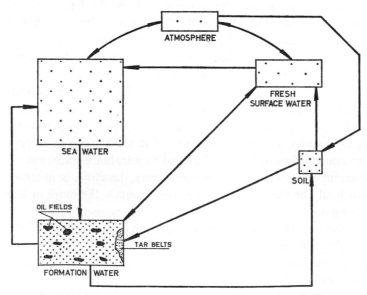

Fig.25. The role of hydrocarbons in the geochemical cycle of water. (After HODGSON and HITCHON, 1965.)

increase in their availability could not force the water system to take up an additional amount of hydrocarbons. Once mobilized by waters, the hydrocarbons would move in a dispersed state until they are unloaded by any of several mechanisms (variations in pressure, temperature, salinity, pH, redox potential, adsorption or destruction of solubilizing agents). When a discrete petroleum phase is formed, migration may continue as a two-phase flow until a position of minimum energy is reached. Thus an oil accumulation may be formed. It should be kept in mind, however, that oil fields are geologically transient features, and that while some oil fields form, others are undoubtedly being dissipated.

Research in this new area is in progress, and although it is most difficult even to formulate properly the phenomena envisaged and to define adequately the problems under investigation, it is believed that the next decade will lead to a great progress in the understanding of this fundamental aspect of petroleum geochemistry.

REFERENCES

ABELSON, P. H., 1959. Paleobiochemistry and organic geochemistry. *Fortschr. Chem. Org. Natur-stoffe*, 17: 379–403.

ABELSON, P. H., 1963. Organic geochemistry and the formation of petroleum. *World Petrol. Congr., Proc., 6th, Frankfurt, 1963*, 1: A397–407.

ABELSON, P. H. and HOERING, T. C., 1961. Carbon isotope fractionation in formation of amino acids by photosynthetic organisms: *Proc. Natl. Acad. Sci.*, 47: 623–632.

ABELSON, P. H. and PARKER, P. L., 1962. Annual Report of the Director of the Geophysical Laboratory for the year 1961–1962. *Carnegie Inst. Wash., Year Book*, 61: 181–184.

AL'TOVSKII, M. E., KUZNETSOVA, Z. I. and SHEVTS, V. M., 1958. *Origin of Oil and Oil Deposits*. Gostoptekhizdat, Moscow, 107 pp.

AMERICAN GEOLOGICAL INSTITUTE, 1960. *Glossary of Geology and Related Sciences with Supplement*, 2nd ed. A.G.I., Washington, D.C., 325 + 72 pp.

BAKER, D. R., 1962. Organic geochemistry of Cherokee groups in Southeastern Kansas and Northeastern Oklahoma. *Bull. Am. Assoc. Petrol. Geologists*, 46: 1621–1642.

BAKER, E. G., 1956. Oil migration in aqueous solution—a study of the solubility of *n*-octadecane. In: *A Symposium on Chemistry in the Exploration and Production of Petroleum*. Div. Petrol. Chem., Am. Chem. Soc., Dallas, Texas, pp. 5–17.

BAKER, E. G., 1959. Origin and migration of oil. *Science*, 129: 871–874.

BAKER, E. G., 1960. A hypothesis concerning the accumulation of sediment hydrocarbons to form crude oil. *Geochim. Cosmochim. Acta*, 19: 309–317.

BAKER, E. G., 1962. Distribution of hydrocarbons in petroleum. *Bull. Am. Assoc. Petrol. Geologist*, 46: 76–84.

BARTON, D. C., 1934. Natural history of the Gulf Coast crude oil. In: W. E. WRATHER and F. H. LAHEE (Editors), *Problems of Petroleum Geology*. Am. Assoc. Petrol. Geologists, Tulsa, Okla., pp. 109–155.

BENDORAITIS, J. G., BROWN, B. L. and HEPNER, L. S., 1963. Isolation and identification of isoprenoids in petroleum. *World Petrol. Congr., Proc., 6th, Frankfurt, 1963*, 5: 13–29.

BONHAM, L. C., 1956. Geochemical investigations of crude oils. *Bull. Am. Assoc. Petrol. Geologists*, 40: 897–908.

BRAY, E. E. and EVANS, E. D., 1965. Hydrocarbons in non-reservoir-rock source beds. *Bull. Am. Assoc. Petrol. Geologists*, 49: 248–257.

BREGER, I. A., 1960. Diagenesis of metabolites and a discussion of the origin of petroleum hydrocarbons. *Geochim. Cosmochim. Acta*, 19: 297–308.

BREGER, I. A. and WHITEHEAD, W. L., 1951. Radioactivity and the origin of petroleum. *World Petrol. Congr., Proc., 3rd, The Hague, 1951*, 1: 421–427.

BREGER, I. A. and BROWN, A., 1962. Kerogen in the Chattanooga shale. *Science*, 137: 221–224.

BREGER, I. A. and BROWN, A., 1963. Distribution and types of organic matter in a barred marine basin. *Trans. N.Y. Acad. Sci.*, 25: 741–753.

BRENNEMAN, M. C. and SMITH JR., P. V., 1958. The chemical relationships between crude oils and their source rocks. In: L. G. WEEKS (Editor), *Habitat of Oil*. Am. Assoc. Petrol. Geologists, Tulsa, Okla., pp. 818–849.

BRODSKII, A. M., KALINENKO, R. A. and LAVROVSKII, K. P., 1959. On the kinetic isotope effect in cracking: *Intern. J. Appl. Radiation Isotopes*, 7: 118.

BROOKS, B. T., 1948. Role of active-surface catalysis in the formation of petroleum, 1. *Bull. Am. Assoc. Petrol. Geologists*, 15: 611.

BROOKS, B. T., 1949. Active-surface catalysts in formation of petroleum, 2. *Bull. Am. Assoc. Petrol. Geologists*, 33: 1600–1612.

BROOKS, B. T., 1952. Evidence of catalytic action in petroleum formation. *Ind. Eng. Chem.*, 44: 2570.

BROOKS, B. T., 1959. Some open questions regarding petroleum origin. *J. Inst. Petrol.*, 45: 42–46.

COLOMBO, U., 1965. Aspetti geochimici dell'evoluzione del petrolio. *Riv. Combust.*, 19 (1): 1–15.

COLOMBO, U. and SIRONI, G., 1961. Geochemical analysis of Italian oils and asphalts. *Geochim. Cosmochim. Acta*, 25: 24–51.

COLOMBO, U., DENTI, E. and SIRONI, G., 1964a. A geochemical investigation upon the effects of ionizing radiation on hydrocarbons. *J. Inst. Petrol.*, 50: 228–237.

COLOMBO, U., GAZZARRINI, G., GONFIANTINI, R., SIRONI, G. and TONGIORGI, E., 1964b. Isotopic measurements of C^{13}/C^{12} ratio on Italian natural gases and their geochemical interpretation. *Intern. Geochem. Meeting, Paris, Sept. 1964, Paper*, in press.

COLOMBO, U., GAZZARRINI, F., SIRONI, G., CONFIANTINI, R. and TONGIORGI, E., 1965. Carbon isotope composition of individual hydrocarbons from Italian natural gases. *Nature*, 205: 1303–1304.

COOPER, J. E., 1962. Fatty acids in recent and ancient sediments and petroleum reservoir waters. *Nature*, 193: 744–746.

COOPER, J. E. and BRAY, E. E., 1963. A postulated role of fatty acids in petroleum formation. *Geochim. Cosmochim. Acta*, 27: 1113–1127.

COX, B. B., 1946. Transformation of organic material into petroleum under geological conditions, "the geological fence". *Bull. Am. Assoc. Petrol. Geologists*, 30: 645–659.

CUNNINGHAM-CRAIG, E. H., 1914. *Oil Finding*. Arnold, London, 286 pp.

CUNNINGHAM-CRAIG, E. H., 1923. Recent researches bearing upon the origin of petroleum. *J. Inst. Petrol.*, 9: 344–367.

DOBRYANSKII, A. F., 1961. *Chemistry of Petroleum*. Gostoptekhizdat, Leningrad, 450 pp.

DUNTON, M. L. and HUNT, J. M., 1962. Distribution of low molecular weight hydrocarbons in recent and ancient sediments. *Bull. Am. Assoc. Petrol. Geologists*, 46: 2246–2258.

DVALI, M. F., 1962. Trends in theoretical studies on the geology of oil and gas. *Sov. Geol.* 1962 (6); *Intern. Geol. Rev.*, 1964 (6): 68–74.

ENGLERS, C., 1888. Zur Bildung des Erdöls. *Chem. Ber.*, 21: 1816.

ERDMAN, J. G., 1962. Oxygen, nitrogen and sulfur in asphalts. *Proc. Am. Petrol. Inst., Sect. VIII*, 42: 33.

ERDMAN, J. G., MARLETT, E. M. and HANSON, W. E., 1958. The occurrence and distribution of low molecular weight aromatic hydrocarbons in recent and ancient carbonaceous sediments. *Am. Chem. Soc., 134th Meeting, Chicago, Preprints*, 1958, C-39–C-49.

GEDENK, R., 1964. Evidence of a dual hydrocarbon migration and its general meaning. *Intern. Geol. Meeting, Paris, Sept. 1964, Paper*, in press.

GILLET, A. C., 1959. Geochemical studies and experimental research on the possible formation of natural oil from cellulose. *Proc. Gen. Petrol. Geochem. Symp., Fordham Univ., 1959*, pp.89–96.

GOGUEL, R., 1963. Die chemische Zusammensetzung der in den Mineralen einiger Granite und ihrer Pegmatite eingeschlossenen Gase und Flüssigkeiten. *Geochim. Cosmochim. Acta*, 27: 155–181.

GUSSOW, W. C., 1954. Differential entrapment of oil and gas; a fundamental principle. *Bull. Am. Petrol. Geologists*, 38: 816–853.

HAEBERLE, F. R., 1951, Relationship of hydrocarbon gravities to facies in Gulf Coast. *Bull. Am. Assoc. Petrol. Geologists*, 35: 2238–2248.

HEDBERG, H. D., 1964. Geological aspects of origin of petroleum. *Bull. Am. Assoc. Petrol. Geologists*, 48: 1755–1803.

HILL, G. A., 1959. Oil migration. *Am. Assoc. Petrol. Geologists, Ann. Meeting, 1959.*

HOBSON, G. D., 1954. *Some Fundamentals of Petroleum Geology.* Oxford Univ. Press, London, 139 pp.

HOBSON, G. D., 1961. Problems associated with the migration of oil in "solution". *J. Inst. Petrol.*, 47: 170–173.

HODGSON, G. W. and BAKER, B. L., 1959. Geochemical aspects of petroleum migration in Pembina, Redwater, Joffre and Lloydminster oil fields of Alberta and Saskatchewan, Canada. *Bull. Am. Assoc. Petrol. Geologists*, 43: 311–328.

HODGSON, G. W. and HITCHON, B., 1965. Research trends in petroleum genesis. *Commonwealth Mining Met. Congr., 8th, Australia New Zealand, 1965, Paper,* 33 pp.

HÖFER, H., 1922. *Das Erdöl und seine Verwandten.* Vieweg, Braunschweig, 43 pp.

HULME, R. E., 1938. Optical activity in Pennsylvania oil. *St. Bonaventure Sci. Studies*, 6 (3): 125–132.

HUNT, J. M., 1953. Composition of crude oil and its relation to stratigraphy in Wyoming. *Bull. Am. Assoc. Petrol. Geologists*, 37: 1837–1872.

KARTSEV, A. A., 1964. Geochemical transformation of petroleum. In: U. COLOMBO and G. D. HOBSON (Editors), *Advances in Organic Geochemistry.* Pergamon Press, Oxford, pp.11–14.

KHALIFEH, Y. and LOUIS, M., 1961. Étude de la matière organique dans les roches sédimentaires. *Geochim. Cosmochim. Acta*, 22: 50–57.

KNEBEL, G. M. and RODRIGUEZ-ERASO, G., 1956. Habitat of some oil. *Bull. Am. Assoc. Petrol. Geologists*, 40: 547–561.

KREJCI-GRAF, K., 1929. Die rumänischen Erdöllagerstätten. *Schr. Brennstoffgeol.*, 1: 125.

KREJCI-GRAF, K., 1930a. Grundlagen der Ölgeologie. *Schr. Brennstoffgeol.*, 4: 32–114.

KREJCI-GRAF, K., 1930b. Geochemie der Erdöllagerstätten. *Abhandl. Prakt. Geol.*, 20: 10–11.

KREJCI-GRAF, K., 1932. Rule of density of oils. *Bull. Am. Assoc. Petrol. Geologists*, 16: 1038.

KREJCI-GRAF, K., 1963. Origin of oil. *Geophys. Prospecting*, 11: 244–275.

KUZNETSOV, S. I., 1950. Investigation of the possibility of contemporaneous formation of methane in gas-petroleum formations in the Saratov and Buguruslan regions. *Mikrobiologiya*, 19: 193–202.

KVENVOLDEN, K. A., 1962. Normal paraffin hydrocarbons in sediments from San Francisco Bay, California. *Bull. Am. Assoc. Petrol. Geologists*, 46: 1643–1652.

LIND, S. C. and BARDWELL, D. C., 1926. The chemical action of gaseous ions produced by alpha particles, IX. Saturated hydrocarbons. *J. Am. Chem. Soc.*, 48: 2335–2351.

LOUIS, M., 1956. Notes sur la géochimie du pétrole. *Geol. Rundschau*, 45: 56–62.

LOUIS, M., 1966. Reconnaissance des roches mères du pétrole. In: *Enciclopedia del Petrolio e del Gas Naturale.* Ente Nazionale Idrocarburi, Rome (in press).

LOUIS, M. et BIENNER, F., 1953. Étude géochimique de pétroles du Fossé Rhénan. *Rev. Inst. Franç. Pétrole Am. Combust. Liquides*, 8: 239–247.

LOUIS, M. et BIENNER, F., 1959. Étude géochimique des huiles et indices de pétrole du bassin de Paris. *Bull. Assoc. Franç. Techniciens Pétrole*, 1959 (137): 14 pp.

LOUIS, M., BIENNER, F., BONNARD, E., BURGER, J.J., GAYRAL, R., LÉVY, R., METROT, R., SALLÉ, C. et PÉCHELBRONN, STÉ., 1955. Contribution de la géochimie à l'étude de l'évolution des huiles brutes dans les bassins sédimentaires. *World Petrol. Congr., Proc., 4th, Rome, 1955*, 1: 337–357.

MAIR, B. J., 1960. Composition of petroleum and petroleum products. In: W. A. GRUSE and D. R. STEVENS (Editors), *Chemical Technology of Petroleum.* McGraw-Hill, New York, N.Y., pp.38–91.

MAIR, B. J., 1964. Hydrocarbons isolated from petroleum. *Oil Gas J.*, 62: 130–134.

MAIR, B. J. (Director), 1965. Annual report for the year ending June 30, 1965. *Am. Petrol. Inst. Res. Project 6, Carnegie Inst. Technol., Pittsburgh, Pennsylvania.* 18 pp.

MAIR, B. J., WILLINGHAM, C. B. and STREIFF, A. J., 1938. Chemical constitution of the "extract" portion of the lubrificant fraction from a mid-continent problem. *J. Res. Natl. Bur. Std.*, 21:581.

MARTIN, R. L., WINTERS, J. C. and WILLIAMS, J. A., 1963a. Distributions of *n*-paraffins in crude oils and their implications to origin of petroleum. *Nature*, 199: 110–113.

MARTIN, R. L., WINTERS, J. C. and WILLIAMS, J. A., 1963b. Composition of crude oils by gas chromatography: geological significance of hydrocarbon distribution. *World Petrol. Congr., Proc., 6th, Frankfurt, 1963*, 5: 231–260.

MCIVER, R. D., 1963. Maturation of oil, an important natural process. *Geol. Soc. Am., Ann. Meeting, 1963, Paper.*

MCNAB, J. G., SMITH, P. V. and BETTS, R. L., 1952. The evolution of petroleum. *Ind. Eng. Chem.*, 44: 2556–2563.

MEINSCHEIN, W. G., 1959. Origin of petroleum. *Bull. Am. Assoc. Petrol. Geologists*, 43: 925–943.

MEINSCHEIN, W. G., 1961. Significance of hydrocarbons in sediments and petroleum. *Geochim. Cosmochim. Acta*, 22: 58–64.

MEINSCHEIN, W. G., 1966. Origin of Petroleum. In: *Enciclopedia del Petrolio e del Gas Naturale.* Ente Nazionale Idrocarburi, Rome (in press).

MOODY, J. D., 1959. Comments on "Relation of primary evaporites to oil accumulation", by L. L. Sloss. *World Petrol. Congr., Proc., 5th, N.Y., 1959*, 1: 134–137.

MUELLER, G., 1963. Properties of extraterrestrial hydrocarbons and theory of their genesis. *World Petrol. Congr., Proc., 6th, Frankfurt, 1963*, 1: 383–396.

NAGY, B., 1960. Review of the chromatographic "plate" theory with reference to fluid flow in rocks and sediments. *Geochim. Cosmochim. Acta*, 19: 289–296.

PHILIPPI, G. T., 1957. Identification of oil source beds by chemical means. *Intern. Geol. Congr., 20th, Mexico, 1956, Proc.*, 3: 25–38.

RIECKER, R. E., 1962. Hydrocarbon fluorescence and migration of petroleum. *Bull. Am. Assoc. Petrol. Geologists*, 46: 60–75.

ROBERTS, W. H., III, 1960. The fluid environment of petroleum (some elementary reasoning). *Proc, Hydrogeol. Group, Am. Soc., Denver.*

ROBERTS, W. H., III, 1966. Hydrodynamic analysis in petroleum exploration. In: *Enciclopedia del petrolio e del gas naturale.* Ente Nazionale Idrocarburi, Rome (in press).

ROBINSON, R., 1963. Duplex origins of petroleum. *Nature*, 199: 113–114.

ROGERS, H. D., 1860. On the distribution and probable origin of the petroleum or rock oil of Pennsylvania, New York and Ohio. *Proc. Phil. Soc. (Glasgow)*, 4: 355–359.

ROOF, J. G., 1959. Variation of fluid properties with elevation in high relief oil reservoirs. *J. Inst. Petrol.*, 45: 373.

ROOF, J. G. and RUTHERFORD, W. H., 1958. Rate of migration of petroleum by proposed mechanisms. *Bull. Am. Assoc. Petrol. Geologists*, 42: 963–980.

RUSSELL, A., 1948. Interpretation of lignin-I. The synthesis of gymnosperm lignin. *J. Am. Chem. Soc.*, 70: 1060–1064.

SEYER, W. F., 1933. Pyrolysis of waxes and the origin of petroleum. *Bull. Am. Assoc. Petrol. Geologists*, 17: 1251.

SHEPPARD, C. W. and WHITEHEAD, W. L., 1946. Formation of hydrocarbons from fatty acids by alpha-particle bombardment. *Bull. Am. Assoc. Petrol. Geologists*, 30: 32–51.

SILVERMAN, S. R., 1964a. Investigations of petroleum origin and evolution mechanisms by carbon isotope studies. In: H. CRAIG, S. L. MILLER and C. J. WASSERBURG (Editors), *Isotopic and Cosmic Chemistry.* North-Holland, Amsterdam, pp.92–102.

SILVERMAN, S. R., 1964b. The migration and segregation of oil and gas. *Geol. Fluids Symp., Midland, Texas, Paper*, 36 pp.

SILVERMAN, S. R. and EPSTEIN, S., 1958. Carbon isotopic compositions of petroleums and other sedimentary organic materials. *Bull. Am. Assoc. Petrol. Geologists*, 42: 998–1012.

SMITH JR., P. V., 1954. Studies on origin of petroleum: Occurrence of hydrocarbons in recent sediments. *Bull. Am. Assoc. Petrol. Geologists*, 38: 377–404.

SOKOLOV, V. A., 1937. The origin of oil and radioactivity. *Intern. Geol. Congr., 17th, 1937*, 4: 5–6.

SOKOLOV, V. A., ZHUSE, T. P., VASSOJEVICH, N. B., ANTONOV, P. L., GRIGORIYEV, G. G. and KOZLOV, V. P., 1963. Migration processes of gas and oil, their intensity and directionality. *World Petrol. Congr., Proc., 6th, Frankfurt, 1963*, 1: 493–505.

STEVENSON, D. P., WAGNER, C. D., BEEK, O. and OTVOS, J. W., 1948. Isotope effect in the thermal cracking of propane-1-^{13}C. *J. Chem. Phys.*, 16: 993.

SYLVESTER-BRADLEY, P. C. and KING, R. J., 1963. Evidence for abiogenic hydrocarbons. *Nature*, 198: 728–731.

TAZIEFF, H., 1963. Dissolved gases in East African lakes. *Nature*, 200: 1308.

THOM JR., W. T., 1934. Present status of the carbon-ratio theory. In: W. E. WRATHER and F. H. LAHEE (Editors), *Problems of Petroleum Geology*. Am. Assoc. Petrol. Geologists, Tulsa, Okla., pp.109–155.

THOMPSON, R. R., 1961. Chromatographic effects of sedimentary minerals in regard to certain petroleum constituents. *Proc. Geochem. Soc., Ann. Meeting, 6th, Geochem. Soc., 1961.*

TIRATSOO, E. N., 1941. Radioactivity and petroleum. *Petroleum (London)*, 4: 58–63.

TRASK, P. D., 1932. *Origin and Environment of Source Sediments of Petroleum*. Gulf Publishing Co., Houston, Texas, 324 pp.

TRASK, P. D. and PATNODE, H. W., 1942. *Source beds of petroleum*. Am. Assoc. Petrol. Geologists, Tulsa, Okla., 566 pp.

VAN EGGELPOEL, A., 1959/1960. Étude sur l'évolution des huiles au cours des migrations et application à la détermination graphique des migrations. *Rév. Inst. Franç. Pétrole Ann. Combust. Liquides*, 14: 1595–1614; 15: 1–92.

VASSOJEVICH, N. B., 1962. The origin of petroleum. *Vestn. Mosk. Univ., Ser. IV: Geol.*, 1962 (3): 10–30.

WHITE, D., 1915. Some relations in origin between coal and petroleum. *J. Wash. Acad. Sci.*, 5: 189–212.

WHITEHEAD, W. L. and BREGER, I. A., 1963. Geochemistry of petroleum. In: I. A. BREGER (Editor), *Organic Geochemistry*. Pergamon, London, pp. 248–332.

WHITMORE, F. C., 1943. *Fundamental Research on Occurrence and Recovery of Petroleum*. Am. Petrol. Inst., New York, N.Y., 124 pp.

WITHERSPOON, P. A. and SARAF, D. N., 1964. Diffusion of methane, ethane, propane, and n-butane in water. *Intern. Geochem. Meeting, Paris, Sept. 1964.*

ZOBELL, C. E., 1943. Influence of bacterial activity on source sediments. *Oil Weekly*, 109 (8): 15.

ZOBELL, C. E., 1945. The role of bacteria in the formation and transformation of petroleum hydrocarbons. *Science*, 102: 364–369.

SUBJECT INDEX

Albertite, 31, 32

n-Alkanes, 77, 80, 82, 96

Amino acids, 101

Anthracene, 90

Arkoses, clay mineral content, 58, 62

—, composition of, 58

—, definition of, 58

Aromatic hydrocarbons, 77, 80, 88, 98

Asphalt (fraction), definition of, 261, 263

—, electron microscopy, 281, 282, 283

—, — spin and nuclear magnetic resonance spectroscopy of, 277, 278

—, electrophoretic mobility, 290, 291

—, elementary composition of, 265, 266

—, infrared spectra of, 272, 273, 274

—, isolation of, 263

—, molecular weight, 264

—, oxidation of, 267, 269, 270

—, peptization, 288, 289

—, precipitation of, 263

—, rheology of, 288

— thermal diffusion, 276, 277

— ultracentrifugation, 283, 284, 285, 286

Asphaltenes, 93, 101, 102, 103

—, acid content of, 149

—, association of their particles, 291, 292, 293

—, chemical reactions of, 271, 272

—, clusters of, 287

—, definition of, 264

—, electrical character of, 291

—, electron spin and nuclear magnetic resonance spectroscopy of, 277, 278

—, elementary composition of, 267

—, hydrogenation, 271

—, infrared spectra of, 272, 273, 274

—, mass spectrometry of, 275, 276

—, metal content of, 165

—, molecular weight, 267, 269, 271

—, peptization, 289

—, rheology of, 286, 287

—, structural model of, 275, 276, 279, 280, 281, 289

—, thixotropy of, 287

—, ultraviolet spectra of, 274

—, vanadium content of, 250

—, X-ray diffraction analysis of, 274, 275

Asphaltic deposits, asphalt lakes, 27

— —, — veins, 27

— —, impregnations in sedimentary rocks, 27

— substances, definition of, 26

— —, elemental composition of, 6, 27

— —, precipitation of asphalthenes, 27

— —, physical and chemical properties, 28, 30

— —, rheological properties, 30

Asphaltite, see gilsonite

Attapulgite, 39, 55, 63, 64, 66

Bacterial attack of hydrocarbons, 341

Bacteriochlorophyll, 223, 224, 225, 226, 235, 239

Bacteriopheophytin, 185, 186

Beidellite, 69

Bentonite, 64

Benzofluorene, 90

Bicyclononane, 88

Bicyclooctane, 88

Bile acids, 97, 309

Bitumens, acids in, 149

—, vanadium content of, 250

"Black oil rings", 26

Branched-chain alkanes, 77, 80, 83, 97

Brucite, 39

Calcite, 58

Cap rocks, definition of, 2

— —, types: clays, shales, limestones, salt, gypsum, anhydrite, 2, 3

Capillary pressures, 299, 304

Carbazoles, 101, 158, 160, 161

Carbenes, 264

Carbohydrates, 16, 97, 342

Carbon isotope ratios of carbonaceous substances, 335

— — — — methane, 359, 360

— — — — — after chromatographic flow, 360

— — — — organic matter in Recent sediments, 16

— — — — — — sedimentary rocks, 16

— — — — petroleum, 16, 310, 334, 356

— — — — distillate fractions, 356, 357

— — — — plant lipids, 16

β-Carotene, 150, 151

Ceresin, 83, 88

Chlorins, 169, 180, 181, 182

—, spectra of, 185, 188

Chlorite, 43, 45, 47, 51, 52, 53, 54, 55, 62, 65, 66

Chlorophyll, 102, 169, 218, 219, 220, 221, 222, 223

Cholestane, 97

REFERENCES INDEX

AASMUNDRUD, O., 220, 253
ABELSON, P. H., 341, 346, 365
ABRAHAM, H., 28, 30, 34, 263, 293
ADAMS, N. G., 89, 90, 104, 127, 129, 133, 170
ADAMSON, A. W., 314, 327
AGAZZI, E. J., 163, 169
ALBERDING, H., 27, 36
ALEXANIAN, C., 274, 293
ALLEN, M. B., 221, 227
ALLPHIN, N. L., 156, 174
ALLSUP, J. R., 16, 36
AL'TOVSKII, M. E., 341, 359, 365
ANDERSON, L. J., 241, 242, 253
ANDERSON, S., 242, 251
ANDREW, P. F., 77, 104
ANTONOV, P. L., 359, 361, 368
ARICH, G., 164, 165, 166, 169, 171
ARNOLD, R. C., 129, 169
ARNOLD, W., 219, 225, 258
ARONOFF, S., 194, 218, 229, 251, 258
AXE, N., 160, 169, 170
AYER, W. A., 221, 259
AZAD, J., 33, 36

BADER, R. G., 38, 74
BAGLI, J. F., 204, 211, 212, 252
BAIBUROVA, M. K., 90, 107
BAILEY, J. R., 160, 170, 171, 172, 173, 174, 175
BAK, B., 251
BAKER, B. L., 25, 35, 202, 203, 204, 210, 212, 213, 214, 217, 239, 241, 242, 243, 245, 246, 250, 251, 254, 359, 367
BAKER, D. R., 299, 317, 318, 320, 322, 359, 327, 365
BAKER, E. G., 8, 21, 34, 249, 251, 263, 293, 301, 305, 306, 307, 312, 315, 327, 359, 364, 365
BAKER, E. W., 209, 211, 252
BALDESCHWIELER, E. L., 156, 172
BALL, J. S., 81, 84, 94, 102, 104, 107, 111, 118, 119, 129, 143, 154, 157, 160, 162, 169, 170, 172, 173, 175
BARDWELL, D. C., 346, 367
BARGHORN, E. S., 310, 328
BARKER, M. G., 119, 172
BARNARD, J. R., 181, 251
BARNES, J. W., 194, 203, 251
BARNETT, B., 271, 295
BARNEWALL, J. M., 89, 106
BARR, K. W., 29, 34
BARTELL, F. E., 287, 293

BARTH, E. J., 263, 271, 272, 274, 287, 293
BARTON, A. D., 160, 173
BARTON, D. C., 24, 34, 263, 293, 346, 350, 353, 365
BARTON, D. H. R., 155, 170
BASSI, B. S., 290, 294
BATTI, P., 209, 251, 252
BEACH, L. K., 165, 168, 170
BEAN, R. M., 165, 175, 210, 258
BEARD, J. W., 285, 296
BEARD, D., 285, 296
BEATON, J. M., 221, 259
BEEK, O., 357, 369
BEITCHMAN, B. D., 272, 293
BELL, A. H., 70, 74
BELSKY, T., 310, 327
BENDORAITIS, J. G., 83, 86, 90, 97, 104, 107, 309, 327, 333, 335, 365
BENSON, A., 191, 253
BENTHER, H., 267, 271, 278, 294
BERSOHN, M., 279, 280, 281, 297
BERTRAND, D., 244, 251
BERUEFFY, R. R., 220, 254
BESTOUGEFF, M. A., 77, 78, 79, 81, 82, 83, 91, 99, 100, 103, 104, 124, 170, 271, 293
BETTS, R. L., 94, 106, 263, 296, 346, 351, 352, 353, 368
BEW, K., 282, 294, 295
BICKELHAUPT, F., 221, 259
BIEBER, H., 102, 104, 209, 210, 214, 252
BIENNER, F., 264, 293, 354, 367
BIGG, B., 160, 170
BIRCH, S. F., 89, 104, 119, 127, 128, 129, 133, 135, 136, 137, 138, 139, 170
BLAKEY, B. C., 288, 293
BLUMER, M., 168, 170, 182, 192, 193, 206, 215, 216, 217, 220, 251, 258
BLYTH, C. R., 324, 325, 327
BOGOMOLOV, A. I., 77, 84, 95, 96, 97, 98, 104
BOGORAD, L., 220, 251
BOLEN, R. J., 168, 171, 284, 294
BOLSHAKOVA, T. A., 82, 104
BONHAM, L. C., 249, 252, 359, 365
BONNARD, E., 264, 293, 354, 367
BONNETT, B., 15, 18, 35
BONNETT, R., 221, 259
BOULANGER, P., 101, 106
BOWMAN, P. B., 272, 294
BOYER, P. D., 227, 252
BRADLEY, W. E., 127, 174
BRADLEY, W. F., 37, 54, 73